CLASSICAL PROBLEMS
IN NUMBER THEORY

POLSKA AKADEMIA NAUK, INSTYTUT MATEMATYCZNY

MONOGRAFIE MATEMATYCZNE

TOM 62

PWN – POLISH SCIENTIFIC PUBLISHERS

WŁADYSŁAW NARKIEWICZ

CLASSICAL PROBLEMS IN NUMBER THEORY

WARSZAWA 1986

MATH
SEP/AE

ISBN 83-01-05931-1   ISSN 0077-0507

PRINTED IN POLAND

W R O C Ł A W S K A   D R U K A R N I A   N A U K O W A

Page, line	Instead of	Read
23_{-9}	interate	iterate
24_{-9}	$(-1)(-3)\ldots(-p)-$ $-3\cdot 5\cdot\ldots\cdot p\,((-1)^{(p+1)/2}-1)$	$3\cdot 5\cdot 7\cdot\ldots\cdot p\big((-1)^{(p+1)/2}-1\big)$
44_{+14}	$\dfrac{(2k-1)}{2^k}$	$\dfrac{(2k-1)}{2k}$
44_{-9}	a	the
55_{+9}	$C^{-1}bpk^4\log^4 k).$	$C_1bk^4\log^4 k)$ with a suitable C_1.
55_{-11}	$\times\,\log\log b^{-1}$	$\times\,(\log\log b)^{-1}$
62_{-10}	$\psi(-1)\,\tau(\psi)$	$\psi(-1)\,\overline{\tau(\psi)}$
65_{+5}	integrals	integral
66_{+5}	$(2r-h^{2r})$	$2rh^{2r}$
$68_{+10},$ $70_{-15}^{+9,\,+13}$	$|S|$	S
74_{+11}	However, numerical	Numerical
75_{+5}	$\big|\sum\limits_{n\leqslant x}\chi(n)\big|^k$	$\big|\sum\limits_{n\leqslant x}\chi(n)\big|^{2k}$
79_{-5}	$\varepsilon_{(p-1)/d}$	$\varepsilon_{(p-1)/\delta}$
93_{-8}	primes $q,\ q_1$	primes q_1
98_{+17}	$NP\in x$	$NP\leqslant x$
100_{-2}	$x^{1/2}+\log^6 x$	$x^{1/2}+O\,(\log^6 x)$
102_{+10}	$B(d)$	$B(D)$
119_{+1}	$y<C_3\log x$	$y>C_3\log x$
120_{+11}	$S\leqslant$	$S>$
121_{-12}	a_r	a_t
122_{+11}	it	il
$148_{-1,\,-3}$	$2n$	$3n$
151_{+22}	I_p	I_n
168_{+15}	A.6′	A.5′
177_{-12}	delete: "attempt"	

Page, line	Instead of	Read
190^{+1}	p^{d-k}	P^{d-k}
191^{+8}	$\dfrac{1}{3}\,^{2s(1+1/k)}$	$(1/3)\,2^{s(1+1/k)}$
196_{-14}	$2\log(2e/q)$	$2\log(eq/2)$
$199^{+8,\,14},$ $199^{+15,\,16}$	$P^{k(k+1)/2}$	$P^{(2k(k+1))}$
219^{+3}	0.008	0.009
219^{+4}	0.993	0.994
224^{+9}	power	powers
224_{-4}	ideed	indeed
234^{+18}	$D = ac$	$D = -ac$
234^{+19}	The first gives	The first corresponds to a form which is not properly primitive and the second gives
234^{+20}	are two such forms	is one such form
240^{+12}	$p \mid m$	$p \mid d$
$243^{+8},$ $243_{-1,\,-4}$	$\tau(X)$	$\tau(\chi)$
264_{-9}	where	with
265^{+10}	where	with
285_{-1}	$x^{1/2} < p$	$x^{1/2} < p$
290^{+12}	A.6′	A.5′
299_{-2}	Number.	Numer.
301^{+26}	Colloway	Calloway
316_{-27}	46	45
358^{+14}	insert: "Euler, J.A. 214"	
358^{+15}	delete: "214".	

Introduction

The development of the theory of numbers centres around certain old problems and this book is devoted to some of them. Our aim was to give a survey of the history of selected problems, presenting proofs of the major results concerning them and indicating the current state of research.

Necessarily a choice of problems had to be made and it was influenced by our wish to demonstrate various techniques. The reader will notice two major omissions: first, Fermat's Last Theorem is not even mentioned, and this is due to the existence of a beautiful survey covering this topic, P. Ribenboim's "Thirteen Lectures on Fermat's Last Theorem". The other omission concerns problems of distribution of prime numbers; however, the inclusion of this topic, which deserves a huge monograph in itself would burst the bounds of this book.

Our first chapter is devoted to elementary problems. We treat in it perfect numbers, Mersenne primes, two conjectures on Euler's phi-function and Egyptian fractions. In the second chapter primitive roots are studied. We begin with bounds for character sums and prove a relevant theorem of Burgess, applying it to the study of the least primitive root. Hooley's deduction of Artin's conjecture from the Extended Riemann Hypothesis is also included.

The main topics of the third chapter are: Tijdeman's proof of the finiteness of the set of solutions of Catalan's equation $a^x - b^y = 1$, the Erdös–Selfridge theorem concerning the product of consecutive integers and the current state of affairs in Grimm's conjecture, which was not formulated so long ago as the other problems dealt with in this book but which is undoubtedly very attractive.

The next chapter is devoted to the problem of Waring. We give Hilbert's proof as well as an analytical proof due to Heilbronn and based on the Hardy–Littlewood–Vinogradov approach. We evaluate all constants appearing in it to obtain an effective version of Waring's theorem, which permits us to obtain a proof of the Ideal Waring Theorem of Dickson, at least in its most important case.

In the last chapter we turn to binary quadratic forms, restricting our attention to positive definite forms. Apart from the classical results of Gauss, Dirichlet and Siegel we present Orde's elementary proof of Dirichlet's class number formulas and also give a determination of negative discriminants with class number one with the use of Baker's method, following Bundschuh and Hock.

All sections end up with a survey of the existing literature and each chapter with a list of open problems. We included also a choice of exercises, which are on various levels of difficulty.

In the Appendix we have put together various results used in the main text, with or without proof, and appropriate reference. We apologize to the reader for not including full proofs of all the results we use, but our aim was to indicate the ways of applying various methods which exist in number theory to concrete problems rather than to concentrate on the development of those methods. This may explain why neither the Riemann Hypothesis for curves nor Baker's theorem is proved here.

The book is partly based on courses given at the Université Bordeaux I and at Wrocław University and work on it started in the year 1975/76, when I enjoyed the hospitality of the U.E.R. Mathématiques et Informatique of the Bordeaux University at Talence.

I would like to thank innumerable friends and colleagues, whose comments helped me in my task and who suggested several improvements both in the selection of the material and in its presentation. My heartest thanks go to Mrs. Janina Smólska who made the correction of the language. I also want to offer my thanks to Miss Teresa Bochynek, who patiently typed and retyped my manuscript and, last but not least, to my family, who allowed me to devote my free time to the writing of this book.

Wrocław, June 1982

Władysław Narkiewicz

Contents

Notation

In the text we use the symbols commonly applied in number theory. In particular $a\,|\,b$ stands for the divisibility of b by a, $a\,\|\,b$ means that a divides b and a, b/a are co-prime. The greatest common divisor of a, b is denoted by (a, b) and the least common multiple by $[a, b]$. For any set X we denote its cardinality by $|X|$. We use Landau's symbol $f = o(g)$ to indicate $\lim f/g = 0$ and $f = O(g)$ stands for the boundedness of $|f/g|$. Instead of $f = O(g)$ we also use alternatively the symbol of Vinogradov $f \ll g$. Various arithmetical functions, like $\varphi(n)$, $\sigma(n)$, $\pi(x)$, $\pi(x; k, l)$, $\psi(x)$, $\psi(x; k, l)$, have their usual meaning (cf. [H–W]). From the two equally popular ways of denoting the number of divisors we choose $d(n)$.

References to the literature are of the following form: Gauss [01], where the number in parentheses is formed by the last two digits of the year of publication. Items from the same year are distinguished by letters a, b, c, ... Exceptionally we quote Dickson's "History of the Theory of Numbers" by Dickson [HTN] and [H–W] stands for "An Introduction to the Theory of Numbers" by G. H. Hardy and E. M. Wright.

I

Elementary problems

§ 1. PERFECT NUMBERS

1. A positive integer N is called *perfect* if it is equal to the sum of all its proper divisors, i.e., if $\sigma(N) = 2N$, where $\sigma(N)$ denotes the sum of all positive divisors of N. Such integers were considered already by Euclid, who proved in the ninth book of the *Elementa* that if the number $1 + 2 + \ldots + 2^n$ happens to be a prime then its product by 2^n is perfect. Euler was the first to prove that Euclid's method gives all even perfect numbers:

THEOREM 1.1 (L. Euler [49b]). *If N is an even perfect number, then it can be written in the form*

$$N = 2^{p-1}(2^p - 1)$$

where p and $2^p - 1$ are both primes. Conversely, if p and $2^p - 1$ are prime numbers, then the product $2^{p-1}(2^p - 1)$ is perfect.

Proof. We give a simple argument due to L. E. Dickson [11]. Let $N = 2^a Q$ (with Q odd and a positive) be an even perfect number. Then by the multiplicativity of σ

$$2^{a+1} Q = 2N = \sigma(N) = (2^{a+1} - 1)\sigma(Q);$$

hence $q = \sigma(Q)/2^{a+1}$ is an integer, $Q = (2^{a+1} - 1)q$ and $\sigma(Q) = 2^{a+1}q = Q + q$. This shows that Q can have only Q and q for divisors, and thus Q must be a prime, $q = 1$ and $1 + Q = \sigma(Q) = 2^{a+1}$. Clearly $a + 1$ must also be a prime since for every c dividing $1 + a$ the number $2^{a+1} - 1$ is divisible by $2^c - 1$.

The converse is easy: if p and $2^p - 1$ are primes, then for $N = 2^{p-1}(2^p - 1)$ we get $\sigma(N) = 2N$. □

Euler's original argument was similar; however, after arriving at the equality $Q = (2^{a+1} - 1)q$ he argued differently: if $\sigma(Q) = 2^{a+1}$ then $Q = 2^{a+1} - 1$

must be a prime because otherwise one would have $q > 1$ and $\sigma(Q) \geqslant Q + (2^{a+1} - 1) + q + 1$; hence

$$\frac{2^{a+1}}{2^{a+1}-1} = \frac{\sigma(Q)}{Q} \geqslant \frac{Q + 2^{a+1} + q}{Q} = \frac{2^{a+1}(1+q)}{Q} = \frac{2^{a+1}}{2^{a+1}-1} \cdot \frac{q+1}{q} > \frac{2^{a+1}}{2^{a+1}-1},$$

a contradiction.

Primes of the form $2^p - 1$ are called *Mersenne primes*. We shall deal with them in § 2 of this chapter.

Euler's theorem reduces the problem of describing even perfect numbers to the determination of all Mersenne primes. We do not know whether there are infinitely many even perfect numbers, but in any case examples are available, the smallest being 6 and the biggest known being $2^{86242}(2^{86243} - 1)$, (J. Brillhart, D. H. Lehmer, J. L. Selfridge, B. Tuckerman, S. S. Wagstaff, Jr. [83]).

2. Now we turn to odd perfect numbers. Here the situation is much worse since it is not known whether such numbers exist at all. This question forms one of the oldest problems in number theory.

It is not difficult to derive certain necessary conditions for an integer to be perfect. The next lemma states some of them:

LEMMA 1.1. *Let* $N = \prod_{p} p^{a_p}$ *be a perfect number. Then*

(i) $2N = \prod_{p|N}(1 + p + \ldots + p^{a_p}) = \prod_{p|N}(p^{a_p+1} - 1)/(p - 1),$

(ii) $\prod_{p|N}(1 + 1/p) \leqslant 2 < \prod_{p|N} p/(p - 1),$

(iii) *If* $p|N$ *then* $p^{a_p+1} - 1$ *is composed exclusively of primes dividing* $N \prod_{p|N}(p - 1),$

(iv) *If* $2 \nmid N$ *then there is a prime* $p_0|N$ *satisfying* $p_0 \equiv a_{p_0} \equiv 1 \pmod 4$ *and for the remaining prime divisors of* N *the corresponding exponents are even.*

Proof. The equalities in (i) follow immediately from the definition of a perfect number and the multiplicativity of $\sigma(n)$. The inequalities (ii) as well as (iii) follow from (i). To prove (iv) observe that in view of (i) exactly one factor $1 + p + \ldots + p^{a_p}$ is even and it is not divisible by 4. If a_p is odd, then the corresponding factor is even; hence there is exactly one such prime p, which is necessarily congruent to unity $\pmod 4$, since otherwise $1 + p + \ldots + p^{a_p}$ would be divisible by 4. For the same reason a_p cannot be congruent to $3 \pmod 4$. □

COROLLARY 1. *Every odd perfect number is of the form* pa^2 *where* $p \equiv 1 \pmod 4$ *is a prime.*

Proof. This follows from (iv). □

COROLLARY 2. *If $P(x)$ denotes the number of odd perfect numbers not exceeding x, then*

$$P(x) \ll x(\log\log x/\log x)^{1/2} = o(x).$$

Proof. Using the preceding corollary, we have

$$P(x) \leqslant \sum_{pa^2 \leqslant x} 1 = \sum_{p \leqslant x} \sum_{a^2 \leqslant x/p} 1 \leqslant \sum_{p \leqslant x} (x/p)^{1/2}$$

$$\leqslant x^{1/2} \pi(x)^{1/2} \Big(\sum_{p \leqslant x} 1/p \Big)^{1/2} \ll x(\log\log x/\log x)^{1/2}$$

by the Cauchy–Schwarz inequality and the Prime Number Theorem. □

(This corollary will be strengthened later (see Theorem 1.4 below).) Another type of conditions was found by J. J. Sylvester ([88a]):

PROPOSITION 1.1. *If N is an odd perfect number, then N is not divisible by $3 \cdot 5 \cdot 7$, and if, moreover, $3 \nmid N$ then N must have at least seven distinct prime divisors.*

Proof. The first assertion follows from the observation that if $3 \cdot 5 \cdot 7 | N$ then by Lemma 1.1 (iv) $3^2 \cdot 5 \cdot 7^2 | N$ and (ii) leads to

$$2 > (1 + 1/3 + 1/9)(1 + 1/5)(1 + 1/7 + 1/7^2) = 2.016\ldots > 2.$$

To obtain the second assertion it suffices to observe that if N has at most six prime divisors and is prime to 6 then by Lemma 1.1 (ii)

$$2 < \prod_{p|N} \frac{p}{p-1} \leqslant \frac{5 \cdot 7 \cdot 11 \cdot 13 \cdot 17 \cdot 19}{4 \cdot 6 \cdot 10 \cdot 12 \cdot 16 \cdot 18} = 1.949\ldots < 2. \quad □$$

Now we prove

THEOREM 1.2. *If N is an odd perfect number, then N has at least four distinct prime divisors.*

Our proof will make use of an auxiliary proposition on divisors of the binomial $a^n - b^n$, proved by A. S. Bang [86] for $b = 1$ and K. Zsigmondy [92] in the general case and rediscovered later several times. A divisor of $a^n - b^n$ is called *primitive* provided it does not divide $a^k - b^k$ for any positive $k < n$, and the result which we shall now prove asserts the existence of primitive prime divisors.

PROPOSITION 1.2. *If $a > b > 0$ are relatively prime integers then for every $n \geqslant 1$ there is at least one prime primitive divisor of $a^n - b^n$ except in the following cases*:

(a) $n = 1$, $a = b + 1$,

(b) $n = 2$, $a + b$ *equal to a power of* 2,

(c) $n = 6$, $a = 2$, $b = 1$.

Proof. There are several different proofs of this result and we have chosen an elementary argument due to A. Rotkiewicz [60].

We start with a simple lemma.

LEMMA 1.2. *Let $a > b > 0$ be coprime integers, $d \geq 1$, and let p be a primitive prime divisor of $a^d - b^d$. Define t by $p^t \| a^d - b^d$ and let $m \geq 1$ be an integer such that $p | a^m - b^m$. Then m is a multiple of d. Moreover, if u is defined by $p^u \| m/d$ and we assume that in the case $p = 2$ we have either $t \geq 2$ or $t = 1$ and $u = 0$, then*

$$p^{t+u} \| a^m - b^m.$$

Proof. Write $m = qd + r$ $(0 \leq r < d)$. Then

$$0 \equiv a^m - b^m \equiv a^{qd}(a^r - b^r) \pmod{p}$$

implying $a^r - b^r \equiv 0 \pmod{p}$ and $r = 0$, i.e., $d | m$. This establishes the first assertion. To prove the second observe that it suffices to prove the following two implications:

(i) If $p \nmid q$ then $a^d - b^d$ and $a^{dq} - b^{dq}$ are divisible by the same power of p, and

(ii) If either p is odd or $p = 2$ and $t \geq 2$ then $p^{t+1} \| a^{dp} - b^{dp}$.

Now, (i) results from

$$(a^{dq} - b^{dq})/(a^d - b^d) \equiv qa^d \not\equiv 0 \pmod{p},$$

and to prove (ii) assume first that p is odd. Then

$$a^{dp} - b^{dp} = \left(b^d + (a^d - b^d)\right)^p - b^{dp}$$

$$\equiv p(b^d)^{p-1}(a^d - b^d) + (a^d - b^d)^p \pmod{p(a^d - b^d)^2},$$

and since $p^t \| a^d - b^d$ and $p^{1+2t} | p^{tp}$ we get

$$a^{dp} - b^{dp} \equiv p^{1+t}(a^d - b^d) p^{-t} b^{d(p-1)} \pmod{p^{1+2t}};$$

thus $p^{1+t} \| a^{dp} - b^{dp}$. If $p = 2$, $2^t \| a^d - b^d$ and $t \geq 2$ then obviously $a^{2d} - b^{2d} = (a^d - b^d)(a^d + b^d)$ is divisible by 2^{t+1} but not by 2^{t+2} because $2 \| a^d + b^d$. □

COROLLARY. *If $(a, b) = 1$ and $m \geq 1$ then every prime primitive divisor p of $a^m - b^m$ satisfies $p \equiv 1 \pmod{m}$.*

Proof. The assertion being obvious for $m = 1$, assume $m \geq 2$. Then p must be odd, and since $a^{p-1} - b^{p-1} \equiv 0 \pmod{p}$ the first part of the lemma implies $m | p - 1$. □

Now we prove the proposition. The assertion is evident in the case $n = 1$ and if it failed for $n = 2$, then every prime divisor p of $a + b$ would also divide $a - b$; hence $p = 2$ and $a + b$ would be a power of 2. This leads to the exceptional case (b).

Turning to the case $n \geq 3$, assume that $a^n - b^n$ has no prime primitive divisors. We shall consider the product

$$(1.1) \qquad\qquad f_n(a, b) = \prod_{k | n} (a^k - b^k)^{\mu(n/k)}$$

and prove that under our assumptions it equals the maximal prime divisor p_n of n. Afterwards we shall evaluate $f_n(a, b)$ from below and prove that it exceeds p_n except for $n = 6$, $a = 2$ and $b = 1$.

As $f_n(a, b)$ is a rational number (it is in fact a rational integer, cf. Exercise 6), we may write

$$(1.2) \qquad\qquad f_n(a, b) = \prod_p p^{a_p}$$

with integral exponents a_p.

LEMMA 1.3. *The exponent a_2 in (1.2) vanishes, except for $n = 2^r$ with $r \geqslant 2$ and $2 \nmid ab$, in which case $a_2 = 1$.*

Proof. We assume that n has an odd prime divisor p and obtain $a_2 = 0$. Indeed, if $n = p^c N$ with $p \nmid N$ and $c \geqslant 1$ then

$$f_n(a, b) = \prod_{k | p^c N} (a^k - b^k)^{\mu(p^c N/k)}$$

$$= \prod_{d | N} \left(\prod_{k | p^c} (a^{dk} - b^{dk})^{\mu(p^c/k)} \right)^{\mu(N/d)} = \prod_{d | N} f_{p^c}(a^d, b^d)^{\mu(N/d)},$$

and since the equality

$$f_{p^c}(a^d, b^d) = \sum_{j=0}^{p-1} a^{jd p^{c-1}} b^{j p^{c-1}(p-1-j)}$$

implies that $f_{p^c}(a^d, b^d)$ is odd regardless of the parity of a, b (remember that $(a, b) = 1$), it follows that $f_n(a, b)$ is odd, i.e., $a_2 = 0$.

The case $n = 2$ being trivial, assume finally that $n = 2^r$ with $r \geqslant 2$. Then $f_n(a, b) = a^{2^{r-1}} + b^{2^{r-1}}$ and this number will be even if and only if ab is odd and in that case $f_n(a, b) \equiv 2 \pmod 4$. □

Let p be an arbitrary prime dividing $f_n(a, b)$. We shall show that it divides n. In the case $p = 2$ this results from the previous lemma, and so assume $p \neq 2$ and suppose that $p \nmid n$. Obviously p must be a primitive divisor of $a^d - b^d$ with a certain $d < n$. If t is defined by $p^t \| a^d - b^d$ and $v_p(x)$ denotes the exponent of p in the canonical factorization of a rational number x, then Lemma 1.2 gives

$$a_p = v_p(f_n(a, b)) = \sum_{k | n/d} \mu(n/kd) v_p(a^{kd} - b^{kd}) = t \sum_{k | n/d} \mu(n/kd) = 0,$$

a contradiction.

Our next step consists in showing that if p divides $f_n(a, b)$ then $a_p = 1$ and we have $p = p_n$, p_n being the maximal prime divisor of n. This will immediately imply the equality $f_n(a, b) = p_n$.

In the case $p = 2$ this assertion is contained in Lemma 1.3, and so we may assume $p \neq 2$. As p is a primitive divisor of $a^d - b^d$, d being a proper divisor of n, we may write $p^t \| a^d - b^d$ with $t \geqslant 1$ and $n = p^s dq$ with $p \nmid qd$

(because by the corollary to Lemma 1.2 we have $p \equiv 1 \pmod{d}$). Using Lemma 1.2, we deduce

$$a_p = v_p(f_n(a, b)) = \sum_{r\mid n/d} \mu(n/rd) v_p(a^{rd} - b^{rd})$$

$$= \sum_{r\mid n/d} (v_p(r) + t)\mu(n/rd) = \sum_{r\mid p^s q} v_p(r)\mu(p^s q/r)$$

$$= \sum_{r\mid p^s q} v_p(p^s q/r)\mu(r)$$

$$= \sum_{r\mid q} (s + v_p(q/r))\mu(r) - \sum_{k\mid q} v_p(p^{s-1} q/k)\mu(k)$$

$$= s\sum_{r\mid q} \mu(r) - (s-1)\sum_{k\mid q} \mu(k) = \begin{cases} 1 & \text{if } q = 1, \\ 0 & \text{if } q > 1. \end{cases}$$

Thus from $p \mid f_n(a, b)$ we get $q = 1$ and $a_p = 1$. It follows that $n = p^s d$ but $p \equiv 1 \pmod{d}$; thus $p > d$ and so $p = p_n$. As already remarked, this gives $f_n(a, b) = p_n$, and it remains to show that this is possible only in the case $n = 6$, $a = 2$, $b = 1$. Denote by P the set of all divisors d of n with $\mu(n/d) = 1$ and by M the set of all such divisors with $\mu(n/d) = -1$. Then

$$f_n(a, b) = \frac{\displaystyle\prod_{d\in P}(a^d - b^d)}{\displaystyle\prod_{d\in M}(a^d - b^d)} > \frac{\displaystyle\prod_{d\in P} a^{d-1}}{\displaystyle\prod_{d\in M} a^d} = a^T$$

where $T = \sum_{d\mid n} d\mu(n/d) - \sum_{d\in P} 1 = \varphi(n) - 2^{\omega(n)-1} \geqslant \frac{1}{2}\varphi(n)$.

If $n = p_n^s$ or $n = 2p_n^s$ with odd p_n then $\varphi(n) \geqslant p_n - 1$; thus $p_n = f_n(a, b) > 2^{(p_n - 1)/2}$ leads to a contradiction for $p_n \geqslant 7$. If $p_n = 3$ or 5 we again get a contradiction in the case $s \geqslant 2$ since then $T \geqslant p_n(p_n - 1)$. If $p_n = 2$ then $n = 2^k$; thus $f_n(a, b) \geqslant 2^{2^{k-1}} - 1 > 2$ for $k \geqslant 3$ and $f_4(a, b) = a^2 + b^2 \geqslant 5 > 2$. If $n = p_n^s q$ with odd p_n, not dividing q and $q \neq 1, 2$ then in view of $\varphi(q) \geqslant 2$ we obtain $\varphi(n) \geqslant 2(p_n - 1)$; thus $p_n = f_n(a, b) > 2^{p_n - 1}$, a contradiction. Hence we are left with the cases $n = 3, 5, 6, 10$, but they are easy in view of the following inequalities:

$$f_3(a, b) = a^2 + ab + b^2 \geqslant 7 > 3,$$

$$f_6(a, b) = (a - b)^2 + ab \geqslant 3 \quad \text{(except when } a = 2, b = 1),$$

$$f_{10}(a, b) = (a^3 + a^2)(a - b) + b^4 \geqslant 8 > 5$$

and

$$f_5(a, b) > 2^T = 8 > 5.$$

The proposition is thus established in all cases. $\square$

Defining a primitive divisor of $a^n + b^n$ in an obvious way, we have

COROLLARY. *If $a > b > 0$ are relatively prime integers then for every $n \geqslant 1$ there is at least one primitive prime divisor of $a^n + b^n$ except for $n = 3$, $a = 2$, $b = 1$.*

Proof. It suffices to observe that $a^n + b^n = (a^{2n} - b^{2n})/(a^n - b^n)$ and apply the proposition. □

We can now prove Theorem 1.2. Let N be an odd perfect number with at most three prime divisors. By Proposition 1.1 N must be divisible by 3. If $5 \nmid N$ then in view of Lemma 1.1 (ii)

$$2 < \prod_{p \mid N} \frac{p}{p-1} \leqslant \frac{3 \cdot 7 \cdot 11}{2 \cdot 6 \cdot 10} < 2;$$

thus $15 \mid N$. Note also that N must have three prime divisors since obviously no prime power can be perfect, and if $N = 3^a 5^b$ were perfect then again by the quoted lemma we would have

$$2 \leqslant \frac{3 \cdot 5}{2 \cdot 4} < 2.$$

Thus N must be of the form $3^a 5^b p^c$ and from (1.3) we infer that either $p = 11$ or $p = 13$. Consider first the case $p = 11$. Using Lemma 1.1 (iii) and (iv), we infer that $11^{1+c} - 1 = 2^A 5^B$ with suitable A, B, because c must be even and hence $11^{1+c} - 1$ cannot be divisible by 3. However, since $11^1 - 1 = 2 \cdot 5$, Proposition 1.2 implies that $11^{1+c} - 1$ must have a prime factor $\neq 2, 5$, and this gives a contradiction. In the case $p = 13$ we argue similarly. We can write $N = 3^a 5^b 13^c$ with an even a. As $5 \nmid 3^{1+a} - 1$, we must have $3^{1+a} - 1 = 2^A 13^B$. Since $3^3 - 1 = 2 \cdot 13$, Proposition 1.2 implies $1 + a \leqslant 3$; thus $a = 2$. However, by Lemma 1.1 (i)

$$2 \cdot 3^2 \cdot 5^b \cdot 13^c = \frac{3^3 - 1}{2} \cdot \frac{5^{b+1} - 1}{4} \cdot \frac{13^{c+1} - 1}{12},$$

and we obtain

$$65 > (5 - 5^{-b})(13 - 13^{-c}) = 18 \cdot 48/13 > 66,$$

a contradiction. □

The same procedure permits showing that there is no odd perfect number with 4 prime divisors (J. J. Sylvester [88b], whose proof, however, was inexact, L. E. Dickson [13], H. J. Kanold [49]). Later the existence of odd perfect numbers with five (I. S. Gradshtein [25], U. Kühnel [49] and G. C. Webber [51]) and six (C. Pomerance [74a] and N. Robbins in an unpublished Ph.D. thesis) prime divisors was also disproved. The best result up to date is that of P. Hagis, Jr., who proved in 1975 that an odd perfect number must have at least eight distinct prime divisors (P. Hagis, Jr. [80]). This was also obtained independently by E. Z. Chein [79a].

3. It seems that in this way it may be difficult to obtain essentially stronger results. However, even if we cannot decide whether there are any odd perfect integers with a given number of prime divisors we know that there can be only finitely many of them. This forms the content of the following theorem:

THEOREM 1.3 (L. E. Dickson [13]). *For every $k \geqslant 1$ there can be at most a finite number of odd perfect integers with k prime divisors.*

Proof. Let $k \geqslant 1$ and suppose there is an infinite sequence $N_1, N_2, \ldots$ of distinct odd perfect numbers having k prime divisors. Let

$$N_m = \prod_{i=1}^{k} p_{im}^{a_i(m)} \quad (m = 1, 2, \ldots)$$

be the canonical factorization of N_m into prime powers.

Replacing, if necessary, the sequence N_m by an infinite subsequence, we may assume that each of the sequences $\{p_{im}\}$, $\{a_i(m)\}$ is either constant or tends to infinity. Let I_1 be the set of all those indices i for which $p_{im} = p_i$ and $a_i(m) = a_i$ are constant sequences, let I_2 be the set of those i's for which $a_i(m)$ tends to infinity but $p_{im} = p_i$ is constant, and finally let I_3 be the set of those i's for which p_{im} tends to infinity. Then

(1.3)
$$2 = \sigma(N_m)/N_m$$
$$= \prod_{i \in I_1} \sigma(p_i^{a_i}) p_i^{-a_i} \prod_{i \in I_2} \sigma(p_i^{a_i(m)}) p_i^{-a_i(m)} \prod_{i \in I_3} \sigma(p_{im}^{a_i(m)}) p_{im}^{-a_i(m)}$$
$$= P_1(m) P_2(m) P_3(m).$$

Since

$$\lim_{m \to \infty} P_1(m) = \prod_{i \in I_1} \sigma(p_i^{a_i}) p_i^{-a_i},$$

$$\lim_{m \to \infty} P_2(m) = \lim_{m \to \infty} \prod_{i \in I_2} (1 + p_i^{-1} + \ldots + p_i^{-a_i(m)}) = \prod_{i \in I_2} \frac{p_i}{p_i - 1},$$

and

$$\lim_{m \to \infty} P_3(m) = 1,$$

we obtain the equality

$$2 = \prod_{i \in I_1} \frac{\sigma(p_i^{a_i})}{p_i^{a_i}} \prod_{i \in I_2} \frac{p_i}{p_i - 1}.$$

The biggest prime in the set $\{p_i : i \in I_2\}$ cannot cancel out in the fraction appearing here, and thus it should equal 2, but this is not possible since it divides a suitable N_m, an odd integer. This shows that I_2 must be empty; hence $2 = \prod_{i \in I_1} \sigma(p_i^{a_i}) \, p_i^{-a_i}$, and using (1.3) we arrive at

$$1 = \prod_{i \in I_3} \sigma(p_{im}^{a_i(m)}) \, p_{im}^{-a_i(m)} \geqslant \prod_{i \in I_3} (1 + p_{im}^{-1}),$$

which in turn shows that I_3 is also empty. Finally we are left with the set I_1 alone, and thus

$$N_m = \prod_{i \in I_1} p_i^{a_i},$$

a constant, giving a contradiction. □

4. Theorem 1.1 implies that the number of even perfect numbers not exceeding x is at most equal to

$$\sum_{\substack{p \\ 2^{p-1}(2^p - 1) \leqslant x}} 1 \leqslant \pi\big(\log(1 + x^{1/2})/\log 2\big) = O(\log x/\log\log x).$$

For the number $P(x)$ of odd perfect numbers $\leqslant x$ we do not have such a good bound. In Corollary 2 to Lemma 1.1 we have seen that $P(x) = O\big(x(\log\log x/\log x)^{1/2}\big)$ and now we present the best known bound for $P(x)$, due to E. Wirsing [59]:

THEOREM 1.4. $P(x) \ll \exp(c \log x/\log\log x)$ *with a certain constant* c.

Proof. We start with a lemma describing the possible form of a perfect number divisible by a given integer.

LEMMA 1.4. *Let* b *be a fixed odd integer. If* $(b, m) = 1$ *and the number* bm *is perfect, then for each* $k \geqslant 0$ *one of the following possibilities holds:*

(a) $m = 1$,

(b) $m = p_1^{a_1} \ldots p_j^{a_j}$ *with some* $j \leqslant k$, *where* p_1 *is a prime depending only on* b, *the exponents* $a_1, \ldots, a_j$ *are positive, and for* $i = 2, 3, \ldots, j$ *the prime* p_i *is uniquely determined by* b *and the exponents* $a_1, \ldots, a_{i-1}$,

(c) *The number* m *has a divisor* $b_k = p_1^{a_1} \ldots p_k^{a_k}$ *satisfying* $(b_k, m/b_k) = 1$ *with the primes* $p_1, \ldots, p_k$ *and the exponents* $a_1, \ldots, a_k$ *satisfying the same conditions as in case* (b) *for* $j = k$, *and finally* $\sigma(bb_k) < 2bb_k$.

Proof. In the case $k = 0$ observe that if $m \neq 1$ then $\sigma(b)/b < \sigma(mb)/mb = 2$ and after putting $b_0 = 1$ (c) will hold. Assume now the truth of the lemma for $k = K-1$ and apply it in this case to the perfect number bm. If (a) or (b) holds then our proof is complete. Assume thus that (c) is satisfied and b_{K-1} is that divisor of m which has all the properties listed in (c). As $bb_{K-1} < \sigma(bb_{K-1}) < 2bb_{K-1}$ holds, $\sigma(bb_{K-1})$ cannot divide $2bb_{K-1}$, and so there exist a prime p_K and integers $A > B$ such that $p_K^A \| \sigma(bb_{K-1})$ and $p_K^B \| 2bb_{K-1}$. Because of $2mb = \sigma(mb) = \sigma(mb/bb_{K-1}) \cdot \sigma(bb_{K-1})$ we infer that p_K divides m/b_{K-1}. Note also that p_K may be chosen as a function of b_{K-1} alone, i.e.,

p_K depends on $p_1, \ldots, p_{K-1}, a_1, \ldots, a_{K-1}, b$, and by the inductive assumption it follows that p_K depends only on $b, a_1, \ldots, a_{K-1}$.

Now define a_K by $p_K^{a_K} \| m/b_{K-1}$ and put $b_K = b_{K-1} p_K^{a_K}$. Clearly $\sigma(bb_K) \leqslant 2bb_K$, and if we had equality here, then $b_K = m$ would follow, showing that m satisfies condition (b) for $k = K$. In the remaining case (c) holds. $\square$

Let A_1, A_2, A_3 be the sets of all odd integers $\leqslant x$ having all their prime factors bigger than $\log x$, lying in the interval $(\log^{1/2} x, \log x)$, and not exceeding $\log^{1/2} x$, respectively. Using the previous lemma, we deduce

LEMMA 1.5. *If $b \geqslant 1$ then the number of odd perfect numbers of the form bm with $m \in A_1$ is bounded by* $\exp(\log 2 \, \log x / \log \log x)$.

Proof. If b is itself perfect then none of its proper multiples can be perfect and the lemma holds trivially. If b is not perfect then by Lemma 1.4 every $m \in A_1$ such that bm is perfect is of the form

$$m = p_1^{a_1} \ldots p_s^{a_s}$$

with a suitable s, and the sequence of exponents determines m uniquely. But $m \leqslant x$ and $p_i > \log x$; hence

$$\log \log x \sum_{i=1}^{s} a_i \leqslant \sum_{i=1}^{s} a_i \log p_i \leqslant \log x,$$

i.e.,

$$\sum_{i=1}^{s} a_i \leqslant \log x / \log \log x.$$

The lemma follows by noting that the number $A_0(T)$ of positive integral solutions of $x_1 + \ldots + x_s \leqslant T$ (with $s = 1, 2, \ldots$) equals $2^{[T]} - 1$. We now give a proof of this fact. Clearly it suffices to deal with an integral T. Noting that $A_0(1) = 1$, assume that the asserted equality holds for a certain T and observe that the map

$$F: \langle x_1, \ldots, x_s \rangle \mapsto \begin{cases} \langle x_1, \ldots, x_{s-1}, x_s - 1 \rangle & \text{if } x_s \geqslant 2, \\ \langle x_1, \ldots, x_{s-1} \rangle & \text{if } x_s = 1 \end{cases}$$

is well defined on the set of all solutions $[x_1, \ldots, x_s]$ of $x_1 + \ldots + x_s = T+1$ ($s \geqslant 1$, $x_i \geqslant 1$) and takes its values in the set of all solutions of $y_1 + \ldots + y_t = T$ ($t \geqslant 1$, $y_i \geqslant 1$). As the equation $F(X) = Y$ has for a given Y exactly two solutions, we infer that with the notation

$$A(T) = |\{x_1, \ldots, x_s: x_i \geqslant 1, s \geqslant 1, x_1 + \ldots + x_s = N\}|$$

we have $A(T+1) = 2A(T)$; thus $A(T) = 2^{T-1}$, which immediately implies $A_0(T) = 2^T - 1$. $\square$

Now we can complete the proof of the theorem. Let $A_i(x)$ denote the number of elements in A_i $(i = 2, 3)$. Writing a_i for a generic element of A_i $(i = 1, 2, 3)$ in the summations below and using the previous lemma, we obtain

(1.4)
$$P(x) = \sum_{\substack{a_1 a_2 a_3 \leqslant x \\ \text{perfect}}} 1 = \sum_{a_2 a_3 \leqslant x} \sum_{\substack{a_1 \leqslant x/a_2 a_3 \\ a_1 a_2 a_3 \text{ perfect}}} 1$$

$$\leqslant A_2(x) A_3(x) \exp \{\log 2 \log x (\log\log x)^{-1}\}.$$

To evaluate $A_2(x)$ write every $a \in A_2$ in the canonical form $a = \prod p^{a_p}$ and deduce $\log^{1/2} x \sum_{p|a} a_p \leqslant a_p \log p = \log a \leqslant \log x$; hence

(1.5)
$$\sum_{p|a} a_p \leqslant \log^{1/2} x.$$

Observe now that the number of non-negative integral solutions of the inequality $X_1 + \ldots + X_k \leqslant T$ does not exceed 2^{T+k} and, since $A_2(x)$ is bounded by the number of solutions of (1.5), we get

$$A_2(x) \leqslant \exp \{(\log 2)(1 + \pi(\log x) + \log^{1/2} x)\} \ll \exp \{B_1 \log x / \log\log x\}$$

for every constant B_1 exceeding $\log 2$. Since

$$A_3(x) \leqslant (1 + \log x / \log 2)^{\pi(\log^{1/2} x)} \ll \exp (B_2 \log^{1/2} x),$$

with a suitable constant B_2, our assertion results from (1.4). □

Notes and comments

1. The early history of the search for perfect numbers is exhaustively presented in L. E. Dickson [HTN] (vol. I, ch. I). Euler's proof of Theorem 1.1 (which, according to Dickson, was stated as early as A. D. 100 by Nicomachus) appears in a paper edited posthumously (L. Euler [49b]) in 1849; hence it is difficult to date it accurately. Other proofs were given by V. A. Lebesgue [44] and R. D. Carmichael [06]. (They are in fact two versions of the same argument.) In the main text we gave a proof found by L. E. Dickson [11], which seems to be the simplest.

Statement (iv) in Lemma 1.1 goes back to L. Euler [49b] and Corollary 1 to it was already asserted by R. Descartes [38] in a letter to Mersenne.

2. Theorem 1.2 was first proved by B. Peirce [32]. This result seems to have remained unnoticed for a long time, till C. Servais [87] and J. J. Sylvester [88b] published their proofs of it.

Proposition 1.2, although often called the *Birkhoff–Vandiver theorem*, was first established by A. S. Bang [86] (in the case $b = 1$) and K. Zsigmondy

[92]. Later it was rediscovered by R. D. Carmichael [09], G. Birkhoff and H. S. Vandiver [04]. For other proofs see: H. J. Kanold [50a], L. Rédei [58], A. Rotkiewicz [60] and H. W. Leopoldt [66]. The proof in the main text is that of Rotkiewicz. There are many applications of Proposition 1.2 in the elementary theory of numbers, one of them stating that for every $s \geqslant 1$ there is a prime p such that the decimal expansion of $1/p$ has period s. (See A. S. Bang [86], C. F. Osgood, R. J. Wisner [61]). A. Schinzel [62c] proved that in certain cases $a^n - b^n$ has at least two prime primitive divisors. To state his result more precisely, write $n = k_n m_n^2$ with square-free k_n and put $h = 1$ if k_{ab} is congruent to unity (mod 4) and $h = 2$ otherwise. If $a > b > 0$, $(a, b) = 1$ and the number n/hk_{ab} is odd, then $a^n - b^n$ has at least two primitive divisors for $n \geqslant 21$. In particular, one gets the existence of two prime primitive divisors for infinitely many values of n.

3. Questions about primitive divisors can also be stated for other sequences. Let a, b be roots of the polynomial $X^2 - PX - Q$, where P, Q are coprime integers such that $P^2 + 4Q$ is not a square, and a/b is not a root of unity. Then $u_n = (a^n - b^n)/(a - b)$ defines a sequence of rational integers called *Lucas numbers* (see É. Lucas [78c], R. D. Carmichael [13]). *Lehmer numbers* are defined by

$$u_n = \begin{cases} (a^n - b^n)/(a - b) & \text{if} \quad 2 \nmid n, \\ (a^n - b^n)/(a^2 - b^2) & \text{if} \quad 2 \mid n \end{cases}$$

where $a = (M^{1/2} + N^{1/2})/2$, $b = (M^{1/2} - N^{1/2})/2$ and M, N are co-prime non-zero rational integers of distinct absolute values and $M \equiv N \pmod 4$. (D. H. Lehmer [30].)

A prime p is called a *primitive divisor* of u_n provided it divides u_n and $p \nmid (P^2 + 4Q) u_2 u_3 \ldots u_{n-1}$ for Lucas numbers and $p \nmid M(M^2 + 4N) \times \times u_2 u_3 \ldots u_{n-1}$ for Lehmer numbers. Such primitive divisors were studied for Lucas sequences by R. D. Carmichael [13] (see also C. G. Lekkerkerker [53], L. K. Durst [61] and A. Rotkiewicz [62]) and for Lehmer numbers by M. Ward [55] (in the case where a, b are real) and A. Schinzel [62a]. Cf. also L. K. Durst [59], [62]. The question of the existence of more prime primitive divisors in these sequences was considered by A. Rotkiewicz [62] and A. Schinzel [62b], [68]. The problem of the existence of prime primitive divisors in Lucas and Lehmer sequences is subsumed in the following recent result of Stewart [77b]: there are only finitely many Lucas and Lehmer sequences with a, b generating co-prime ideals in a suitable extension of the rationals such that for a certain $n > 6$, $n \neq 8$, 10, 12 the nth term does not have a prime primitive divisor, and all such sequences can be effectively determined.

If a, b are integers in an algebraic number field then one can ask for prime ideals which divide $u_n = a^n - b^n$ without dividing $a^k - b^k$ for $1 \leqslant k \leqslant n-1$. Again one calls them *primitive divisors* and the natural question arises whether they exist, at least for all sufficiently large n. The first results on this subject are due to H. Sachs [56], who considered the case $b = 1$ and obtained certain sufficient conditions. (Cf. also L. Rédei [58]). L. P. Postnikova and A. Schinzel [68] proved that if a, b generate relatively prime ideals and a/b is not a root of unity then u_n has for $n > n_0(a, b)$ (an effective constant) a primitive prime ideal divisor. Later A. Schinzel [74] proved that one can take for n_0 a constant depending only on the degree of a/b. (Cf. also E. H. Grossman [74], who obtained by elementary methods a weaker result of the same kind.) The result of Schinzel was made completely explicit by C. L. Stewart [77b], who showed that one may take $n_0 = \max(2(2^d - 1), e^{452} d^{67})$, where d denotes the degree of a/b.

4. Our proof of Theorem 1.3 is that of H. N. Shapiro [49]. Dickson's original proof was rather complicated and made use of such heavy tools as Hilbert's basis theorem. Other proofs may be found in I. S. Gradshtein [25] and H. J. Kanold [56a]. For generalizations see H. N. Shapiro [49], M. M. Artyukhov [73], M. Beresin and E. Levine [72], M. Hausman and H. N. Shapiro [76].

The proof of Theorem 1.3 presented here does not give any effective bound for odd perfect integers with a prescribed number of prime divisors. A proof which is fully effective was recently given by C. Pomerance [77a]. He proved in fact a more general result, concerning those solutions of $\sigma(n) = an$ with fixed a which are not multiplies of an even perfect number. His proof is based on Baker's method; however, in the case $a = 2$, which corresponds to odd perfect numbers, the use of Baker's method can be avoided. His bound

$$n \leqslant (2k)^{2k^{2k^2}}$$

for an odd perfect number with k prime divisors has of course only theoretical significance.

5. The first improvement of Corollary 2 to Lemma 1.1 concerning the growth of $P(x)$, the number of odd perfect integers not exceeding x, was obtained by B. Volkmann [55], who proved $P(x) = O(x^{5/6})$. B. Hornfeck [55] got $P(x) = O(x^{1/2})$ and H. J. Kanold [56b] improved this to $P(x) = o(x^{1/2})$. His elegant argument relies on Theorem 1.3: let $\varepsilon > 0$ be fixed and let K be sufficiently large. Then we have at most $O(1)$ odd perfect numbers N with $\omega(N) \leqslant K$. For $N \leqslant x$ with $\omega(N) > K$ write

$$N = p^a q_1^{2a_1} \dots q_r^{2a_r} \qquad (q_1 < \dots < q_r, \ p \equiv a \equiv 1 \,(\mathrm{mod}\,4)).$$

One easily observes that for $N \leqslant x$ with $p^a > K$ the correspondence $N \to Np^{-a}$ is one-to-one and for $N \leqslant x$ with $p^a \leqslant K$ the same holds for the correspondence $N \to Np^{-a} q_r^{-2a_r}$. This leads to $P(x) \ll 1 + (x/K)^{1/2} + (x/K^2)^{1/2} < \varepsilon x^{1/2}$ for large x. In the same year P. Erdős [56a] proved $P(x) = O(x^\varepsilon)$

with a certain $c < 1/2$. In Kanold [57] a general method was given for the evaluation of the number of $n \leqslant x$ for which $f(n) = c$ where c is given and f is a multiplicative function. In the case of $f(n) = \sigma(n)/n$ this leads to $P(x) = O(x^{1/4} \log x (\log\log x)^{-1})$.

A major improvement was obtained by B. Hornfeck and E. Wirsing [57], who succeeded in proving $P(x) = O(x^\varepsilon)$ for every $\varepsilon > 0$. More exactly, they got the bound $P(x) = O(\exp(C \log x \log\log\log x / \log\log x))$ and a modification of their main idea led to Theorem 2.4. (E. Wirsing [59].)

6. An extensive numerical search was made in order to produce at least one odd perfect number. Today we know that there is no such number less than 10^{200} (M. Buxton and S. Elmore [76]). The previous records were held by B. Stubblefield [73] with 10^{100}, P. Hagis, Jr. [73], who got up to 10^{50} and B. Tuckerman [73], who had 10^{36}. It is also known that an odd perfect number must have a prime divisor exceeding 300000 (J. T. Condict [78]) and its second largest prime divisor exceeds 1000 (P. Hagis, Jr. [81]). (Previous records were held by P. Hagis, Jr., W. L. McDaniel [73]; [75a] and C. Pomerance [75a] with 100128, resp. 137.) Moreover, it has a prime power divisor exceeding 10^{12} (J. B. Muskat [66]). Lower bounds for a maximal prime divisor of the form $2^{2^k}+1$ (if such divisors exist) of an odd perfect number were given by N. Robbins [75].

7. There are many papers in which the non-existence of odd perfect numbers of a particular form is established. Let N be an integer satisfying the necessary condition for an odd perfect number given in Lemma 1.1 (iv), i.e., $N = p^a(q_1^{a_1} \dots q_s^{a_s})^2$ with $p \equiv a \equiv 1 \pmod 4$ and $q_1 \equiv \dots \equiv q_s \equiv 3 \pmod 4$. If one of the following conditions is satisfied then N cannot be perfect:

(i) $a_1 = \dots = a_{s-1} = 1$, $a_s = 1$, 2, 3, 4. (R. Steuerwald [37] − $a_s = 1$, H. J. Kanold [42] − $a_s = 2$, [50c] − $a_s = 3$, 4, cf. also H. J. Kanold [39] and A. Brauer [43].)

(ii) $a_1 = \dots = a_s = 2$, 3, 5, 12, 17, 24, 62. (H. J. Kanold [41] in the case $a_i = 2$, P. Hagis, Jr., W. L. McDaniel [72], [75b] in the remaining cases.)

(iii) The fourth power of the g.c.d. of the numbers $2a_i + 1$ does not divide N. (H. J. Kanold [41].)

(iv) $a_1 = \dots = a_{s-2} = 1$, $a_{s-1} = a_s = 2$. (H. J. Kanold [53].)

(v) $a = 5$, $a_1 \leqslant 2$. (H. J. Kanold [53].)

(vi) $a_1 \equiv \dots \equiv a_s \equiv 1 \pmod 3$. (W. L. McDaniel [70].)

Moreover, J. Touchard [53] showed that an odd perfect number must be congruent to 1, 9, 13, 25 (mod 36). (Cf. also M. Raghavachari [66], D. Rameswar Rao [72] for other proofs of this result.)

8. Already in 1888 C. Servais [88] showed that if N is odd perfect then its minimal prime divisor $m(N)$ is bounded by $\omega(N)$. This result was improved by O. Grün [52] to $3m(N)/2 - 3 \leqslant \omega(N)$, and K. K. Norton [61] obtained a still better result, namely

$$\omega(N) \geqslant \text{li}(m^2(N)) + O(n^2 \exp(-\log^c n))$$

where n is defined by $m(N) = p_n$, with p_n denoting the nth consecutive prime and the exponent c occurs in the prime number theorem:

$$\psi(x) = x + O(x \exp(-\log^c x)).$$

It is now known that one can take for c any number smaller than 3/5. (Norton had only 4/7 at his disposal.) Cf. D. Suryanarayana [66], [73].

Exercises

1 (T. Pepin [98]). Prove that no odd perfect number is congruent to 5 (mod 6).

2 (J. Touchard [53]). Prove that an odd perfect number is congruent either to 1 (mod 12) or to 9 (mod 36).

3 (L. Alpár [55]). Prove that if n has at most 3 distinct prime divisors and $n \mid \sigma(n)$ then either n is an even perfect number or $n = 120$ or finally $n = 672$.

4. Prove that if n is an odd perfect number then it has a prime factor less than $\omega(n)$.

5 (G. F. Cramer [41]). Show that the values of the ratio $\sigma(n)/n$ lie dense in the interval $[1, \infty)$.

6. Prove that if $f_n(a, b)$ is defined by (1.1) then

$$f_n(a, b) = b^{\varphi(n)} F_n(a/b)$$

where $F_n(x)$ is the nth cyclotomic polynomial.

7 (D. Suryanarayana [69]). A number n is called *super-perfect* if $\sigma(\sigma(n)) = 2n$. Prove that an even number n is super-perfect if and only if $n = 2^{p-1}$ where both p and $2^p - 1$ are primes.

8 (H. J. Kanold [69]). Prove that an odd super-perfect number must be a square.

9 (G. Lord [75]). Prove that if for a certain k and even n the kth interate of $\sigma(n)$ equals $2n$, then n is either perfect or super-perfect.

10 (P. Cattaneo [51]). Prove that if n is the sum of its proper divisors $\neq 1$, then n must be a square of an odd integer.

§ 2. MERSENNE NUMBERS

1. In connection with the problem of even perfect numbers M. Mersenne stated in 1644 that the numbers $M_p = 2^p - 1$ with $p = 2, 3, 5, 7, 13, 17, 19, 31, 67, 127$ and 257 are prime and for all other primes $p \leqslant 257$ the numbers M_p are composite. We know today that this list contains errors. In fact,

E. Fauquembergue [94] proved the compositeness of M_{67} and F. N. Cole [03] provided an explicit factorization into primes:

$$M_{67} = 193707721 \cdot 761838257287.$$

The number M_{257} is also composite.

On the other hand, the numbers M_{61}, M_{89} and M_{107}, not included in the list of Mersenne, are nevertheless prime. The primality of M_{61} was established independently by I. M. Pervushin [87] and P. Seelhoff [86], that of M_{89} by R. E. Powers [11] and that of M_{107} by the same author (R. E. Powers [14]).

Note that the number M_{127} (proved to be prime by E. Fauquembergue [94]) was for a long time the largest known prime, until it was surpassed in 1951 by $1 + 180 M_{127}^2$ (J. C. P. Miller [51]). Today the largest prime is M_{86243}, found by J. Brillhart et al. [83]. The previous record-holders were M_{19937} (B. Tuckerman [71]), M_{21701} (found by L. Nickel and C. Noll in 1978 (see C. Noll, L. Nickel [80])) and M_{44497} (D. Slowinski [79]).

The known Mersenne primes M_p correspond to the indices $p = 2, 3, 5, 7,$ 13, 17, 19, 31, 61, 89, 107, 127, 521, 607, 1279, 2203, 2281, 3217, 4253, 4423, 9689, 9941, 11213, 19937, 21701, 23209, 44497 and 86243. There is no other Mersenne prime with index $p < 50000$.

It is not known whether the set of Mersenne primes is infinite. Neither do we know whether there are infinitely many composite numbers M_p. However, for certain values of p one can easily show that M_p must be composite. The first result of this kind was stated by L. Euler [32] and proved by É. Lucas [77]:

PROPOSITION 1.3. *If $p \equiv 3 \pmod 4$ and $2p+1$ are both primes then M_p is divisible by $1 + 2p$.*

Proof. Easy induction leads to the identity

$$(2^n - 1) 3 \cdot 5 \cdot 7 \cdot \ldots \cdot n = (2n)(2n-2) \ldots (n+1) - 3 \cdot 5 \cdot 7 \cdot \ldots \cdot n$$

valid for odd n. If $n = p$ is a prime congruent to $3 \pmod 4$ then the right-hand side is congruent $(\mod(2p+1))$ to

$$(-1)(-3) \ldots (-p) - 3 \cdot 5 \cdot \ldots \cdot p \left((-1)^{(p+1)/2} - 1 \right),$$

which is divisible by $2p+1$ and since $2p+1$ is a prime it divides M_p. □

COROLLARY. *If $p \equiv 3 \pmod 4$ and $2p+1$ are primes and $p \neq 3$, then M_p is composite.*

Proof. It suffices to note that, for $p \geqslant 5$, M_p exceeds $2p+1$. □

2. If q is a prime dividing M_p then it must be congruent to unity $\pmod p$, and this implies that if $a(p)$ denotes the maximal prime divisor of M_p then $1 + p \leqslant a(p)$. P. Erdős and T. N. Shorey [76] improved upon this, proving the following result:

THEOREM 1.5. *There exists an effective constant C such that for all primes p one has $a(p) \geqslant C p \log p$.*

Proof. First we use Baker's method to deduce a lower bound for the number of prime factors of M_p in the case where $a(p)$ is not too large:

LEMMA 1.6. *If p is a prime such that $a(p) \leqslant p^2$, then one has*

$$\omega(M_p) \geqslant C_1 \log p / \log \log p$$

with an effective constant $C_1 > 0$.

Proof. We may assume that $p \geqslant 5$. Write $\omega(M_p) = t$ and let $M_p = q_1^{b_1} \dots q_t^{b_t}$ be the canonical factorization of M_p. By our assumption $q_j \leqslant p^2$ and clearly $b_j \leqslant p$ $(j = 1, 2, \dots, t)$. If now $L(x_1, \dots, x_t, u)$ denotes the linear form $\sum_{j=1}^{t} x_j \log q_j - u \log 2$, then in view of

$$|L(b_1, \dots, b_t, p)| = |\log(M_p/2^p)| = |\log(1 - 2^{-p})|$$

we obtain

(1.6) $$0 < |L(b_1, \dots, b_t, p)| < \exp(-p \log 2).$$

To get a lower bound for L we apply Theorem A.8 in the case $n = 1 + t$, $a_j = q_j$ $(j = 1, 2, \dots, t)$, $a_{t+1} = 2$, $A_i = p^2$ $(i = 1, 2, \dots, t)$, $A_{t+1} = 4$, $M = p$. This gives $D = \log 4 \cdot 2^t \cdot \log^t p$, $D' = (2 \log p)^t$, $\log D' = t(\log \log p + \log 2)$ and leads to

$$|L(b_1, \dots, b_t, p)| > \exp(-C_0 \log^{1+t} p (\log \log p + \log 2))$$

with $C_0 = C_0(t) = t \cdot 2^t \cdot \log 4 (16t + 16)^{200t + 200}$. By comparing this bound with (1.6) we obtain

$$p \log 2 \leqslant C_0 \log^{1+t} p (\log \log p + \log 2);$$

thus, with a certain effective and absolute constant M,

$$\log p \leqslant M(t \log t + t \log \log p).$$

If with a certain positive $\varepsilon < 1/2M$ one has $t < \varepsilon \log p / \log \log p$, then $\log p < 2 \varepsilon M \log p < \log p$, a contradiction. $\square$

Now it is easy to deduce the assertion of the theorem. If $a(p) \leqslant p \log p$, then for $p \geqslant 29$ one has $a(p) \leqslant p^2$, and so the lemma implies $t = \omega(M_p) \geqslant C_1 \log p / \log \log p$. Denote by P the tth consecutive prime congruent to $1 \pmod{p}$. As every prime dividing M_p satisfies this congruence, we obtain $a(p) \geqslant P$. Now by the Brun–Titchmarsh theorem (see Theorem A.2) we get

$$t = \pi(P, p, 1) \ll P/(p-1) \log(Pp^{-1}) \ll P/p \log \log p$$

since in view of $P \geqslant pt$ we have $\log(P/p) \geqslant \log\log p - \log\log\log p$, and so finally

$$P \geqslant tp \log\log p \geqslant p \log\log p \log p/\log\log p \geqslant p \log p. \quad \square$$

Our next theorem provides an evaluation of $b(p)$, the maximal prime power divisor of M_p:

THEOREM 1.6 (P. Erdös [76a]). *For every* $\varepsilon > 0$ *and every prime* p *one has* $b(p) > C(\varepsilon) p^{2-\varepsilon}$ *with a positive* $C(\varepsilon)$.

Proof. We start with a lemma concerning the number of primes with respect to which 2 has a given order.

LEMMA 1.7. *Denote by* $E(r)$ *the number of primes* q *with* $\mathrm{ord}_q(2) = r$. *Then*

$$E(r) < \left(\frac{\log 2}{2} + o(1) \right) r/\log r.$$

(It was conjectured (P. Erdös, loc.cit.) that for every $c > 0$ one has $E(r) = O(r^c)$ but this is still undecided.)

Proof. If $\mathrm{ord}_q(2) = r$, then $q \equiv 1 \pmod r$ and $q | 2^r - 1$. Let $q_1, \ldots, q_k$ ($k = E(r)$) be all such primes. Then $q_1 \ldots q_k < 2^r$ but for $j = 1, 2, \ldots, k$ we have $q_j > jr$, thus follows the inequality $k! \, r^k < 2^r$, which in view of $k < r$ and $\log(k!) = k \log k + O(k)$ implies $2k \log k + O(k) < r \log 2$ and our assertion follows immediately. $\square$

Now observe that if p, q are primes then $p = \mathrm{ord}_q(2)$ holds if and only if $q | 2^p - 1$; hence $E(p) = \omega(M_p)$ and thus the lemma implies

$$\omega(M_p) < \left(\frac{\log 2}{2} + o(1) \right) p/\log p.$$

If all prime powers dividing M_p are less than A, then for all positive δ and sufficiently large p we have

$$M_p \leqslant A^{\omega(M_p)} \leqslant \exp\left(\left(\frac{\log 2}{2} + \delta \right) \frac{p \log A}{\log p} \right);$$

thus for an arbitrary $c > 0$ and sufficiently large p

$$\left(\frac{\log 2}{2} + \delta \right) \frac{p \log A}{\log p} \geqslant p(\log 2 - c),$$

and this leads finally to $\log A \geqslant (2-\varepsilon) \log p$ for an arbitrary $\varepsilon > 0$ and sufficiently large p. $\square$

It has been conjectured (F. Jakóbczyk [51], J. Brillhart, G. D. Johnson [60]) that all numbers M_p are square-free. If this were true, then of course we would have $a(p) = b(p)$, and so Theorem 1.6 would improve the bound given in Theorem 1.5. A connection between this conjecture and the congruence $2^{p-1} \equiv 1 \pmod{p^2}$ is shown in Exercises 4 and 6.

3. To check the primality of M_p an algorithm has been invented which we present in the next theorem:

THEOREM 1.7 (The Lucas–Lehmer test). *Let S_k be the sequence defined by $S_1 = 4$, $S_k = S_{k-1}^2 - 2$ ($k \geqslant 2$). If p is an odd prime then the number M_p is prime if and only if it divides S_{p-1}.*

Proof. We present here a proof given by A. E. Western [32] and based on arithmetics in the field $Q(3^{1/2})$. An elementary proof was given by D. H. Lehmer [35] and reproduced by W. Sierpiński [64] (pp. 336-340).

Let us recall that the integers of the field $K = Q(3^{1/2})$ have the form $x + y3^{1/2}$ ($x, y \in Z$), the factorization in K is unique and the primes p factorize into irreducibles according to the following rule:

$$p = \begin{cases} \pi\hat{\pi} & \text{if} \quad p \equiv 1, \; 11 \,(\text{mod } 12) \\ p & \text{if} \quad p \equiv 5, \; 7 \,(\text{mod } 12), \end{cases}$$

$$3 = (3^{1/2})^2 \quad \text{and} \quad 2 = (2 - 3^{1/2})(1 + 3^{1/2})^2.$$

Here we denote by $\hat{a}$ the conjugate of a, i.e., for $a = x + y3^{1/2}$, $\hat{a} = x - y3^{1/2}$. Note also that $2 - 3^{1/2}$ is a unit.

LEMMA 1.8. (i) *If $p \equiv 1, \; 11 \,(\text{mod } 12)$ is a prime, π an irreducible factor of it and a an integer in K, not divisible by π, then $a^{p-1} \equiv 1 \,(\text{mod } \pi)$.*

(ii) *If $q \equiv 5, \; 7 \,(\text{mod } 12)$ is a prime and a an integer of K not divisible by q, then $a^q \equiv \hat{a} \,(\text{mod } q)$.*

Proof. Part (i) results from the observation that p is the norm of π and the analogue of Euler's theorem in algebraic number fields; to obtain (ii) write $a = x + y3^{1/2}$ ($x, y \in Z$). Then

$$a^q = (x + y3^{1/2})^q \equiv x^q + 3^{(q-1)/2} \, y^q \, 3^{1/2} \,(\text{mod } q)$$

but $x^q \equiv x \,(\text{mod } q)$, $y^q \equiv y \,(\text{mod } q)$ and since $q \equiv 5, \; 7 \,(\text{mod } 12)$ we obtain

$$3^{(q-1)/2} \equiv \left(\frac{3}{q}\right) \equiv \left(\frac{q}{3}\right)(-1)^{(q-1)/2} \equiv -1 \,(\text{mod } q);$$

thus finally $a^q \equiv x - y3^{1/2} \equiv \hat{a} \,(\text{mod } q)$. $\square$

If we put $u = -(2 + 3^{1/2})$ then $u\hat{u} = 1$, $u + \hat{u} = -4$, and for $n \geqslant 2$ we have the equality

$$u^{2^{n-1}} + \hat{u}^{2^{n-1}} = (u^{2^{n-2}} + \hat{u}^{2^{n-2}})^2 - 2,$$

implying

$$(1.7) \qquad\qquad S_n = u^{2^{n-1}} + \hat{u}^{2^{n-1}} \qquad \text{for } n \geqslant 1.$$

Assume now that $q = 2^p - 1$ is prime. As $q \equiv 7 \,(\text{mod } 12)$, the last lemma implies $u^q \equiv \hat{u} \,(\text{mod } q)$; hence

$$u^{q+1} - 1 \equiv u\hat{u} - 1 \equiv 0 \,(\text{mod } q),$$

and since q generates a prime ideal we get $u^{(q+1)/2} \equiv \pm 1 \pmod q$. To show that one should take the negative sign here observe that $u = v/\hat{v}$ with $v = 1 + 3^{1/2}$, and if we had $u^{(q+1)/2} \equiv 1 \pmod q$ then since $v\hat{v} = -2$ we would have

$$-2 \equiv v\hat{v} \equiv v^{q+1} \equiv (v\hat{v})^{(q+1)/2} \equiv (-2)^{(q+1)/2} \equiv -2\left(\frac{-2}{q}\right) \equiv 2 \pmod q,$$

a contradiction.

Hence $u^{2^{p-1}} \equiv -1 \pmod q$ and we obtain

$$S_{p-1} u^{2^{p-2}} = (u^{2^{p-2}} + \hat{u}^{2^{p-2}}) u^{2^{p-2}} = u^{2^{p-1}} + 1 \equiv 0 \pmod q.$$

Since u is a unit, this implies the divisibility of S_{p-1} by q as asserted.

To prove the sufficiency assume that p is an odd prime such that $M_p | S_{p-1}$. As $M_p \equiv 7 \pmod{12}$, M_p must have a prime factor q congruent to 5 or $7 \pmod{12}$. From (1.7) (with $n = p-1$) follows the congruence

$$(u/\hat{u})^{2^{p-2}} \equiv -1 \pmod q,$$

and since $u\hat{u} = 1$ this leads to $u^{2^{p-1}} \equiv -1 \pmod q$. Let k be the smallest positive integer with $u^k \equiv -1 \pmod q$. The preceding congruence shows that k divides 2^{p-1} and if $k = 2^j$ with $j \leqslant p-2$, then in view of

$$S_j u^{2^{j-1}} = (u^{2^{j-1}} + \hat{u}^{2^{j-1}}) u^{2^{j-1}} = u^{2^j} + 1 \equiv 0 \pmod q$$

we get $S_j \equiv 0 \pmod q$; thus $S_{j+1} \equiv -2 \pmod q$ and $2 \equiv S_{j+2} \equiv S_{j+3} \equiv \dots \pmod q$, contradicting $q | S_{p-1}$. Thus $k = 2^{p-1}$.

As $(v\hat{v})^{(q-1)/2} = (-2)^{(q-1)/2} \equiv \left(\frac{-2}{q}\right) \pmod q$, we have by Lemma 1.8

$$u^{(1+q)/2} = (v/\hat{v})^{(1+q)/2} = (v^2/v\hat{v})^{(q-1)/2} v/\hat{v} \equiv v^q \left(\frac{-2}{q}\right) \Big/ \hat{v} \equiv \left(\frac{-2}{q}\right) \pmod q.$$

If $q \equiv 5 \pmod{12}$ then $\left(\frac{-2}{q}\right) = 1$; hence $2^p = 2k | (1+q)/2$, i.e., $q \equiv 3 \pmod 4$, a contradiction. Thus $q \equiv 7 \pmod{12}$, $\left(\frac{-2}{q}\right) = -1$, showing that $u^{(1+q)/2} \equiv -1 \pmod q$ and this leads to $2^{p-1} = k | (1+q)/2$. By writing $q = 2^p t - 1$ with an integer t and using $q | 2^p - 1$ we obtain $t = 1$ and $M_p = 2^p - 1 = q$ is a prime. $\square$

4. It is well known, and a proof may be found in [H–W] (Theorem 323), that

$$\limsup_{N \to \infty} \sigma(N)/N \log\log N = \exp\gamma,$$

where γ is *Euler's constant*. In 1971 P. Erdös [71] observed that for Mersenne numbers M_n the sum of divisors attains smaller values:

THEOREM 1.8.

$$\limsup_{n \to \infty} \sigma(M_n)/M_n \log\log\log M_n > 0$$

and moreover

$$\sigma(M_n) \ll M_n \log\log\log M_n.$$

Proof. The first assertion is an easy consequence of the prime number theorem. Denote by $A_k = p_1 \cdots p_k$ ($p_1 < \ldots < p_k$) the product of the first k odd primes, recall that the prime number theorem gives $\log \varphi(A_k) = p_k + o(p_k)$, and put $N_k = M_{\varphi(A_k)}$. Then

$$\sigma(N_k)/N_k = \sum_{d \mid N_k} 1/d \geqslant \prod_{i=1}^{k} (1 + 1/p_i) \geqslant \exp\left\{\sum_{i=1}^{k} 1/p_i - \tfrac{1}{2} \sum_{i=1}^{k} 1/p_i^2\right\}$$

$$\gg \log p_k \gg \log\log \varphi(A_k) \gg \log\log\log N_k.$$

To prove the second assertion observe that it suffices to obtain the bound

(1.8)
$$\sum_{p \mid M_n} 1/p < \log\log\log n + O(1)$$

since then we would have

$$\frac{\sigma(M_n)}{M_n} = \sum_{d \mid M_n} \frac{1}{d} = \prod_{p \mid M_n} \left(1 + \frac{1}{p}\right) \prod_{p^\alpha p \| M_n} \frac{(1 + 1/p + \ldots + 1/p^{\alpha p})}{1 + 1/p}$$

$$\leqslant \exp\left\{\sum_{p \mid M_n} \frac{1}{p}\right\} \prod_{p^\alpha p \| M_n} \left(1 + \frac{1}{p^2} + \ldots + \frac{1}{p^{\alpha p}}\right) \ll \exp\left\{\sum_{p \mid M_n} \frac{1}{p}\right\} \ll \log\log n,$$

as needed.

Let $A(d)$ denote the set $\{p : \mathrm{ord}_p(2) = d\}$. We split the sum in (1.8) into three parts:

$$\sum_{p \mid M_n} 1/p = \sum_{d \mid n} \sum_{p \in A(d)} 1/p = \Sigma_1 + \Sigma_2 + \Sigma_3,$$

where

$$\Sigma_1 = \sum_{\substack{d \mid n \\ d \leqslant \log^{16} n}} \sum_{p \in A(d)} 1/p,$$

$$\Sigma_2 = \sum_{\substack{d \mid n \\ d > \log^{16} n}} \sum_{\substack{p < n \\ p \in A(d)}} 1/p,$$

$$\Sigma_3 = \sum_{\substack{d \mid n \\ d > \log^{16} n}} \sum_{\substack{p \geqslant n \\ p \in A(d)}} 1/p.$$

The sum Σ_3 is easily evaluated: one obviously has

$$\Sigma_3 \leqslant \sum_{\substack{p \geqslant n \\ p \mid 2^n - 1}} \frac{1}{p} \leqslant \frac{1}{n} \omega(2^n - 1) < 1.$$

To evaluate Σ_1 observe that for each fixed $d \leqslant \log^{16} n$ the inner sum contains at most

$$\omega(2^d - 1) < d \leqslant \log^{16} n$$

terms; so we have altogether at most $\log^{32} n$ distinct summands of the form $1/p$, and thus their sum cannot exceed the sum of inverses of the first $N = [\log^{32} n]$ primes.

Consequently

$$\Sigma_1 \leqslant \sum_{p \leqslant p_N} 1/p < \sum_{p \leqslant N^2} 1/p \ll \log\log N \ll \log\log\log n.$$

We now have to obtain a bound for Σ_2. It will turn out that Σ_2 is small; however, the proof of this fact will be rather delicate. We start with a lemma, which is of independent interest:

LEMMA 1.9. *If n is an integer and x satisfies $n \geqslant x > \log^{16} n$, then*

$$\prod_{p < x} (p-1, n) < \exp\left\{ C \frac{x}{\log x} \log\log n \right\},$$

where C is an absolute constant.

Proof. Reserving, during the proof, the letter q for primes, write

$$(p-1, n) = \prod_{q|n} q^{a_q(p)}$$

and observe that

$$\log \prod_{p<x} (p-1, n) = \log\left(\prod_{q|n} \prod_{p<x} q^{a_q(p)} \right) = \sum_{q|n} \log q \sum_{k=1}^{\infty} \pi(x, q^k, 1)$$

$$= \sum_{\substack{q^k < \log^{10} n \\ q|n}} \pi(x, q^k, 1) \log q + \sum_{\substack{q^k \geqslant \log^{10} n \\ q|n}} \pi(x, q^k, 1) \log q$$

$$= A_1 + A_2.$$

The Brun–Titchmarsh theorem (Theorem A.2) implies

$$A_1 \ll \sum_{q^k < \log^{10} n} \frac{\log q}{q^k} \cdot \frac{x}{\log x} \leqslant \frac{x \log\log n}{\log x}$$

and to evaluate A_2 we utilize the trivial bound $\pi(x, q^k, 1) \leqslant xq^{-k}$:

$$A_2 \ll x \sum_{\substack{q|n}} \sum_{\substack{k \\ q^k \geqslant \log^{10} n}} \frac{\log q}{q^k} \ll x \log n \sum_{\substack{q|n \\ q \geqslant \log^{10} n}} \frac{1}{q} \leqslant \frac{x\omega(n)}{\log^9 n} \ll \frac{x}{\log^8 n} \ll x \log^{-8} x;$$

hence finally

$$\prod_{p<x} (p-1, n) \leqslant \exp(A_1 + A_2) \leqslant \exp(Cx \log\log n / \log x)$$

with a suitable constant C as asserted. □

Now we can evaluate Σ_2. Since $A(d)$ contains at most d primes (the stronger bound given in Lemma 1.7 would not bring any improvement here) we get

$$\sum_{\substack{d|n \\ d>\log^{16}n}} \sum_{\substack{n>p \geqslant d^3 \\ p\in A(d)}} \frac{1}{d} \leqslant \sum_{\substack{d|n \\ d>\log^{16}n}} \frac{1}{d^3} \cdot d \ll 1,$$

and it remains to evaluate the sum

$$\sum_{\substack{d|n \\ d>\log^{16}n}} \sum_{\substack{p<n \\ p<d^3 \\ p\in A(d)}} 1/p = S.$$

To this end denote by X the set of those primes p from the interval $(\log^{16} n, n)$, for which $p^{1/3} < \operatorname{ord}_p(2)|n$ and, for $k = 4, 5, \ldots, M = [(\log\log n - \log\log\log n)/\log 2]$ put

$$Z_k = \{p \in ((\log n)^{2^k}, (\log n)^{2^{k+1}}]: \ p^{1/3} < \operatorname{ord}_p(2)|n\}.$$

Then

$$S \leqslant \sum_{p\in X} 1/p \leqslant \sum_{k=4}^{M} \sum_{p\in Z_k} 1/p.$$

For $4 \leqslant k \leqslant M-1$ denote by $f_k(y)$ the number of primes $\leqslant y$ belonging to Z_k. Since for these primes

$$(p-1, n) \geqslant \operatorname{ord}_p(2) > p^{1/3} > \log^{2^{k-2}} n,$$

we obtain

$$\prod_{p\leqslant y} (p-1, n) \geqslant \exp(f_k(y) 2^{k-2} \log\log n),$$

and by using the last lemma we obtain the bound

$$f_k(y) \ll y \log^{-1} y 2^{-k}.$$

By partial summation

$$\sum_{p\in Z_k} 1/p \ll \sum_{\log^{2^k} n < y \leqslant \log^{2^{k+1}} n} f_k(y) y^{-2} \ll 2^{-k},$$

and as $\sum_{p\in Z_M} 1/p$ is obviously bounded we finally get $\Sigma_2 = O(1)$. By putting together the resulting bounds for $\Sigma_1, \Sigma_2, \Sigma_3$, we obtain our assertion. ⌐

Notes and comments

1. Corollary 1 to Proposition 1.3 gives one of the many known sufficient conditions for a Mersenne number M_p to be composite (Cf. V. A. Golubev [58]). None of those conditions produced infinitely many such numbers. However, this can be deduced from this corollary by using an unproved hypothesis of L. E. Dickson [04], which implies that for any system of linear polynomials, whose product does not have a fixed divisor, there are infinitely many integers at which all those polynomials assume prime values. A generalization of this hypothesis was proposed by A. Schinzel and W. Sierpiński [58b].

2. P. Erdös asked in 1965 (P. Erdös [65]) whether $a(n)/n$ tends to infinity, where $a(n)$ denotes the maximal prime divisor of M_n. This conjecture is still open. Theorem 1.5 demonstrates that it will be true if we replace the sequence of all positive integers by the sequence of primes. Earlier C. L. Stewart [75] obtained $a(p) \geqslant \frac{1}{2}p(\log p)^{1/4}$, which also suffices for this purpose. Stewarts result is in fact more general, asserting that the maximal prime divisor of $a^p - b^p$ exceeds $\frac{1}{2}p(\log p)^{1/4}$ for all $a > b > 0$. He showed also that if X_c denotes the set of integers n with at most $c \log\log n$ distinct prime divisors and $c < 1/\log 2$ then the maximal prime divisor of $a^n - b^n$ has, for $n \in X_c$, an order essentially larger than n. Later (C. L. Stewart [77a]) this result was made more explicit: for $n \in X_c$ this prime divisor is $\gg n(\log n)^{1 - c\log 2}/\log\log\log n$, the implied constant depending on a, b and c. Moreover, for any function f tending to infinity and for almost all n the maximal prime divisor of $a^n - b^n$ exceeds $n \log^2 n/f(n) \log\log n$.

3. The *Lucas–Lehmer test* (Theorem 1.7) was found by E. Lucas [78c] and simplified later by D. H. Lehmer [30]. There is also another test with the same aim, stated by Lucas [77], which works for M_p with $p \equiv 3 \pmod 4$ and utilizes the same recurrence but starts with $S_1 = 3$. (Cf. A. E. Western [32] for a proof.) The Lucas–Lehmer test was generalized in many ways to allow the primality testing of a large class of integers. In this respect see I. Kaplansky [45], B. W. Brewer [51], H. Riesel [56], M. Ward [59], K. Inkeri, J. Sirkesalo [59], K. Inkeri [60], H. Riesel [69].

4. A sufficient and necessary condition for the primality of M_p in terms of Čebyšev polynomials was given by T. Bang [54]. J. P. Jones [79] constructed a polynomial in seven variables such that the set of its positive values at integral points coincides with the set of all Mersenne primes. This, however, does not show any practical way of finding new such primes.

5. The distribution of prime factors of M_n was studied by K. Szymiczek [69]. D. B. Gillies [64] conjectured that the number of prime divisors of M_p lying in the interval $[A, B]$ approaches the Poisson distribution as p and

B/A tend to infinity. J. R. Ehrmann [67] presented numerical evidence in support of this conjecture. Another conjecture was proposed by D. Shanks and S. Kravitz [67], who stated a conjectural asymptotical formula for the number $f_k(x)$ of primes $p \leqslant x$ for which M_p is divisible by $1 + 2kp$. Factors of Mersenne numbers can be found in J. Brillhart, G. D. Johnson [60], H. Riesel [62], J. Brillhart [64], S. Kravitz, M. Berg [64], S. Kravitz [66], J. Brillhart, J. L. Selfridge [67], J. Brillhart, D. H. Lehmer, J. L. Selfridge [75].

6. In Exercises 3 and 5 a connection between Mersenne numbers and primes q satisfying $2^{q-1} \equiv 1 \pmod{q^2}$ is pointed out. (Cf. A. Rotkiewicz [65], L. R. J. Warren and H. G. Bray [67].) These primes also play an important role in the study of the first case of *Fermat's Last Theorem*. The first number with this property, $q = 1093$, was discovered by W. Meissner [13] and the second, $q = 3511$, by N. G. W. H. Beeger [22a].

Since $\dfrac{2^{q-1}-1}{q} \equiv 1 + \dfrac{1}{3} + \dfrac{1}{5} + \ldots + \dfrac{1}{q-2} \pmod{q}$ (see e.g. P. Bachmann [10]) it follows that the congruence $2^{q-1} \equiv 1 \pmod{q^2}$ is equivalent to the divisibility of the sum $\dfrac{1}{3} + \dfrac{1}{5} + \ldots + \dfrac{1}{q-2}$ by q^2. (Cf. H. S. Vandiver [17].)

The current state of affairs in computing the solutions of $a^{q-1} \equiv 1 \pmod{q^2}$ is described in J. Brillhart, J. Tonascia, P. Weinberger [71]. Extending the previous computations of E. H. Pearson [63], H. Riesel [64] and K. E. Kloss [65], they tested in the case $a = 2$ the primes q up to $3 \cdot 10^9$. This test was extended up to $6 \cdot 10^9$ by D. H. Lehmer [81].

Certain conditions ensuring $a^{q-1} \not\equiv 1 \pmod{q^2}$ were given by W. Johnson [77], and in [78] the same author presented a simple algorithm to test this relation.

Exercises

1. (S. Kravitz [66]). Prove that if n is prime then every divisor of M_n is of the form $1 + 2kn$ with $k \not\equiv 2 \pmod 4$ and show that this may fail for n composite.

2. Show that if M_n is a prime power then it must be a prime.

3. (L. R. J. Warren and H. G. Bray [67]). Prove that if p, q are primes and $q^2 | M_p$ then $2^{(q-1)/2} \equiv 1 \pmod{q^2}$.

4. Show that, for $q = 1093$, 3511 (which are the only known primes satisfying $2^{q-1} \equiv 1 \pmod{q^2}$) and for all primes p, $q^2 \nmid M_p$.

5. (M. J. Deleon [78]). Let p be an odd prime and a a positive integer. Prove that if $a^p \equiv a \pmod{p^2}$ then for every m we have either $a^m \not\equiv 1 \pmod p$ or $a^m \equiv 1 \pmod{p^2}$.

6. Prove that if p is a prime then the binary expansions of $1/p$ and $1/p^2$ have the same period if and only if $2^{p-1} \equiv 1 \pmod{p^2}$.

§ 3. THE CONJECTURES OF CARMICHAEL AND LEHMER

1. In this short section we shall consider two conjectures concerning Euler's function $\varphi(n)$. The first goes back to R. D. Carmichael [07], who stated that there is no integer $m > 0$ for which the equation $\varphi(x) = m$ has exactly one solution, and gave an argument to support this assertion. However, he later recognized that his argument was insufficient (R. D. Carmichael [22]) and since then the statement in question is called *Carmichael's conjecture*.

The second problem is due to D. H. Lehmer [32], who asked whether there exist composed integers N with the property that $\varphi(N)$ divides $N-1$. Clearly every prime has this property.

We start with Carmichael's conjecture. Here not much is known except for numerical results, which are based on an observation made by R. D. Carmichael [22] and extended further by V. L. Klee, Jr. [47]. To state this observation recall that an integer d is a *unitary divisor of N* provided $d|N$ and $(d, N/d) = 1$. We shall call an integer D a *strong divisor of N* if $D|N$ and, moreover, the only unitary divisor of N dividing D equals 1. This means that if $D = \prod p^{a_p}$ and $N = \prod p^{b_p}$ then D is a strong divisor of N if and only if for all primes p dividing N one has $a_p < b_p$.

PROPOSITION 1.4. *Let N be a positive integer with the property that $\varphi(N) = \varphi(x)$ implies the equality $N = x$. If d is a strong divisor of N, m a unitary divisor of N, $(m, d) = 1$ and the number $p = 1 + \varphi(m)d$ happens to be prime, then p divides N.*

Proof. If $p \nmid N$ write

$$N = \prod_{i=1}^{s} p_i^{\alpha_i}, \qquad m = \prod_{i=1}^{t} p_i^{\alpha_i}, \qquad d = \prod_{i=1+t}^{s} p_i^{\beta_i} \qquad (0 \leqslant \beta_i < \alpha_i).$$

Then

$$\varphi\left(\frac{pN}{dm}\right) = (p-1)\varphi\left(\frac{N}{md}\right) = (p-1) \prod_{\substack{p_i | N \\ p_i \nmid m}} p_i^{\alpha_i - \beta_i - 1}(p_i - 1)$$

$$= \frac{(p-1)}{d}\varphi(N/m) = (p-1)\frac{\varphi(N)}{\varphi(m)d} = \varphi(N)$$

and thus $pN/dm = N$, which is impossible since p does not divide N. □

This simple proposition permits us to produce a huge quantity of prime numbers which must divide any integer, violating Carmichael's conjecture.

Denote the set of those integers by X. We now prove an old result of Carmichael, which can easily be extended by using Proposition 1.4 and a good table of prime numbers.

THEOREM 1.9. *If N belongs to the set X then N is divisible by $(2 \cdot 3 \cdot 7 \cdot 43)^2$.*

Proof. Divisibility by 2^2 follows from the observation that for odd N we have $\varphi(2N) = \varphi(N)$ and for $N \equiv 2 \pmod 4$ we have $\varphi(N/2) = \varphi(N)$. The divisibility of N by 3 follows now from Proposition 1.4, which we apply with $m = 1$, $d = 2$.

To proceed further we need a simple observation

If an integer $N \in X$ is divisible by p and $p-1$ where p is a prime, then $p^2 \mid N$.

If $p \mid N$ but $p^2 \nmid N$, then, making use of the easy observation that if δ divides N then $\varphi(\delta N) = \delta \varphi(N)$, we obtain

$$\varphi\left(\frac{(p-1)N}{p}\right) = \varphi(N).$$

This immediately implies that $3^2 \mid N$. Applying alternatively Proposition 1.4 and the above fact we obtain our assertion in view of the equalities $2 \cdot 3 + 1 = 7$, $2 \cdot 3 \cdot 7 + 1 = 43$. □

In the above argument only the case $m = 1$ of Proposition 1.4 was used. Considering other values of m, one can extend much further the list of primes which have to divide any member of X.

2. Lehmer's question about composite integers n for which $\varphi(n)$ divides $n-1$ is, like Carmichael's, still unanswered; however, we have here much more information at our disposal.

We start with a result which is analogous to Dickson's Theorem 1.3.

THEOREM 1.10 (C. Pomerance [77b]). *For any given integer $M \geqslant 2$ there can be only finitely many integers n with M distinct prime divisors for which $\varphi(n) \mid n-1$ and there is an effective bound for the largest of them.*

Proof. Assume that $\varphi(n) \mid n-1$ and let $k = (n-1)/\varphi(n)$. Observe first that n is square-free because $p^2 \mid n$ implies $p \mid (n, \varphi(n))$ and in our case we have $(n, \varphi(n)) = 1$. Note also that if m is a proper divisor of n then $m/\varphi(m) < k$, since otherwise we would have

$$k \leqslant \frac{m}{\varphi(m)} < \frac{n}{\varphi(n)} = k + \frac{1}{\varphi(n)};$$

thus in view of $\varphi(m) \mid \varphi(n)$ the equality $k = m/\varphi(m) = (n-1)/\varphi(n)$ would follow and so m would divide both n and $n-1$, which is possible only for $m = 1$. However, in this case $k = 1$ and $M = 1$.

Now we can establish an upper bound for the minimal prime divisor of n:

LEMMA 1.10. *If $\varphi(n) \mid n-1$ and n has M distinct prime divisors, then for the minimal prime p_0 dividing n we have $p_0 \leqslant cM^{1/2} \log^{1/2} M$, with a certain constant c.*

Proof. Let P be the maximal prime divisor of n and consider $N = qn$, where q is any prime larger than P. In view of

$$(1.9) \qquad \frac{\varphi(N)}{N} = (1 - 1/q)\frac{\varphi(n)}{n} = (1 - 1/q)(1 - 1/n)/k < 1/k \leqslant \tfrac{1}{2}$$

with $k = (n-1)/\varphi(n)$ we obtain

$$\frac{1}{2} > \frac{\varphi(N)}{N} = \prod_{p|N}\left(1 - \frac{1}{p}\right) = \exp\left\{\sum_{p|N}\log\left(1 - \frac{1}{p}\right)\right\} \geqslant \exp\left\{\sum_{p_0 \leqslant p \leqslant p_1}\log\left(1 - \frac{1}{p}\right)\right\}$$

where p_1 is the Mth consecutive prime number larger than p_0. Since the prime number theorem implies

$$-\sum_{p \leqslant x}\log\left(1 - \frac{1}{p}\right) = \log\log x + c + O(\exp\{-\log^{1/2} x\}),$$

we get

$$\log 2 \leqslant \log\log p_1 - \log\log p_0 + O(\exp\{-\log^{1/2} p_0\}),$$

and if we had $p_1 < p_0^{2-\varepsilon}$ with $\varepsilon = C\exp(-\log^{1/2} p_0)$ and a large C, then

$$\log 2 \leqslant \log(2-\varepsilon) + B\exp(-\log^{1/2} p_0)$$

with a certain constant B; thus for large p_0 we would get

$$\varepsilon/4 < \varepsilon/(2-\varepsilon) - \varepsilon^2/(2-\varepsilon)^2 < \log(1 + \varepsilon/(2-\varepsilon)) < B\exp(-\log^{1/2} p_0),$$

which is not possible for sufficiently large C.

Hence $p_1 \gg p_0^{2-\varepsilon}$ must hold and this implies that

$$M = \pi(p_1) - \pi(p_0) \gg p_1/\log p_1 \gg p_0^{2-\varepsilon}/\log p_0 \gg p_0^2/\log p_0$$

because p_0^ε is bounded. Now the assertion results immediately. $\square$

The next lemma permits us to evaluate the largest prime divisor of n from above:

LEMMA 1.11. *If* $\varphi(n)|n-1$ *and* $n = p_1 p_2 \cdots p_M$ *where* $p_1 > p_2 > \cdots > p_M$, *then for* $i = 1, 2, \ldots, M-1$ *we have*

$$p_i \leqslant (1+i)(1 + p_{i+1} p_{i+2} \cdots p_M) \leqslant 2Mp_{i+1} \cdots p_M.$$

Proof. Let $m = p_{i+1} p_{i+2} \cdots p_M$. Since $m|n$, we get $m/\varphi(m) < k$ and for $N = nq$, where q is any prime larger than p_1, we get $N/\varphi(N) > k$ by (1.9). This gives

$$k < \frac{N}{\varphi(N)} \leqslant \frac{m}{\varphi(m)}\left(\frac{p_i}{p_i - 1}\right)^{1+i},$$

and we arrive at

$$m/k\varphi(m) > (1 - 1/p_i)^{1+i} > 1 - (1+i)/p_i$$

. and

$$p_i < \frac{(i+1)\,k\varphi(m)}{k\varphi(m)-m} \leqslant (1+i)(1+m). \quad \square$$

The theorem follows immediately. In fact, if $\varphi(n) = M$ and $\varphi(n)$ divides $n-1$, then, as we already noted, n is square-free; thus $n = p_1 \ldots p_M$ $(p_1 > p_2 > \ldots > p_M)$. It follows by induction that for $k = 1, 2, \ldots, M-1$ the bound $p_{M-k} \leqslant (2Mp_M)^{2^{k-1}}$ holds and hence, using Lemma 1.10, we get

$$n \leqslant (2Mp_M)^{2^M}/2M < (BM^{3/2}\log M)^{2^M}$$

with a certain constant B, and it turns out that we can have only finitely many possibilities for n if M is fixed. $\square$

Finally we shall prove a bound for the number $\Phi(x)$ of composite integers $n \leqslant x$ satisfying $\varphi(n)\,|\,n-1$.

THEOREM 1.11 (C. Pomerance [77b]). *For x tending to infinity one has*

$$\Phi(x) \ll \Delta(x)$$

where $\Delta(x) = x^{1/2}(\log x)^{3/4}(\log\log x)^{-1/2}$.

Proof. Denote by A the set $\{n:\ \Delta(x) < n \leqslant x,\ \varphi(n)\,|\,n-1\}$. We shall first show that every $n \in A$ has a divisor m in the interval $(\Delta(x)/2Kp,\ \Delta(x))$ where $K = \omega(n)$ and p is the smallest prime factor of n. For this purpose write $n = p_1 p_2 \ldots p_K$ with $p_1 > p_2 > \ldots > p_K = p$. If $p \geqslant \Delta(x)$, then we can take $m = 1$; assume thus that

(1.10) $n > \Delta(x) > p.$

We now prove that if there is no such m then for $i = 1, 2, \ldots$ we can find an integer $d_{i-1} = p_{s_1} \ldots p_{s_{i-1}}$ dividing n which satisfies the inequalities

(1.11) $d_{i-1}\,p \leqslant \Delta(x)$

and

(1.12) $d_{i-1} \prod_{j > s_{i-1}} p_j > \Delta(x).$

From (1.10) we infer that for $i = 1$ we may take $d_0 = 1$. If the integers $d_0, \ldots, d_{i-1}$ are already chosen, consider the maximal integer s_i satisfying

(1.13) $d_{i-1} \prod_{j \geqslant s_i} p_j > \Delta(x)$

and put $d_i = d_{i-1}\,p_{s_i}$. If

$$d_{i-1} \prod_{j > s_i} p_j > \Delta(x)/2p,$$

we can put $m = d_i \prod_{j>s_i} p_j$. Otherwise, however, Lemma 1.11 leads to

$$d_i p \leqslant 2d_{i-1} pK \prod_{j>s_i} p_j \leqslant \Delta(x);$$

hence from this and from (1.13) we infer that (1.11) and (1.12) are valid with i replaced by $i+1$. Since this procedure cannot be continued indefinitely, the existence of a divisor of n in the interval $(\Delta(x)/2Kp, \Delta(x))$ follows.

Since $n \leqslant x$, Lemma 1.10 implies $p \ll K^{1/2} \log^{1/2} K$, and in view of $K = \omega(n) \ll \log n/\log\log n \ll \log x/\log\log x$ it follows that every integer $n \in A$ has a divisor m in the interval

$$I = \left(cx^{1/2}(\log\log x)^{1/2}(\log x)^{-3/4}, \Delta(x)\right)$$

with a certain positive constant c. Moreover, since n is square-free, $\varphi(m)$ divides $\varphi(n)$ and thus $(m, \varphi(m)) = 1$. Denoting by B the set of all integers $m \in I$ satisfying $(m, \varphi(m)) = 1$, we finally obtain

$$\Phi(x) \leqslant \Delta(x) + |A| \leqslant \Delta(x) + \sum_{m \in B} \sum_{\substack{n \leqslant x \\ m \mid n \\ n \equiv 1 \,(\mathrm{mod}\, \varphi(m))}} 1$$

and, writing $a(x) = c(x\log\log x)^{1/2} \log^{-3/4} x$, we arrive at

$$\Phi(x) \leqslant \Delta(x) + \sum_{m \in B}\left(1 + \frac{x}{m\varphi(m)}\right) \leqslant 2\Delta(x) + x\sum_{m \geqslant a(x)} \frac{1}{m\varphi(m)} \ll \Delta(x). \quad \square$$

Notes and comments

1. Carmichael's conjecture appeared first in Carmichael [07], where it was stated as a theorem and a supposed proof of it was presented. It was also given as an exercise in Carmichael [14] and this led to the discovery that the proof given is not fully adequate. R. D. Carmichael [22] explained this and presented the assertion as a conjecture. He noted also that every N in the set X must be divisible by 4 and that no Fermat prime $2^{2^k} + 1$ can divide N in the first power.

Proposition 1.4 was proved by V. L. Klee [47], who deduced Theorem 1.9 from it. He also made some further improvements on it and showed in particular that if $N \in X$ and $3^3 \nmid N$ then N must be divisible by the product of squares of the following primes: 13, 79, 157, 547, 1093, 3319, 3613, 6163, 6637, 6709, 36979, 39829, 40507, 42667, 45949, 46957, 74419, 81013, 85333, 91813 and 24 other primes exceeding 150000.

In the case where $3^3 \mid N$ he obtained the divisibility of $N \in X$ by the product of squares of the following primes: 19, 127, 2287, 4903, 5419, 13723, 82399, 98229, 101347, 304039, 617761, 688087, and another five primes exceeding 10^6. Moreover, if N is not divisible by 3^4, then the following primes may be added to this list: 37, 223, 1549, 4219, 4663, 4789, 9547, 10837, 25309, 27883, 29527, and other 28 primes exceeding 150 000. However, if 3^4 divides N, then the following primes may be added: 379, 6823, 15919, 40939, 43207, 123499, 130483, 143263, and another 13 primes exceeding 150 000.

From this result it can be immediately deduced that the smallest integer contained in X must exceed 10^{400}. Theorem 1.9 was later rediscovered by H. Donnelly [73], who noted in addition that the smallest integer N_0 in X cannot be divisible by 8, which led him to the discovery of new obligatory prime factors for N_0. Although he proved only $N_0 > 10^{77}$, which is weaker than the result of Klee, one can use his result to improve Klee's bound to $N_0 > 10^{468}$. All this makes Carmichael's conjecture highly plausible although we certainly cannot hope to work out its proof along these lines.

(Added in proof: P. Masai and A. Valette (Boll. Un. Mat. Ital., A, (6), 1 (1982), 313–316) got $N_0 > 10^{10^4}$.)

2. A large number of papers were concerned with the solvability and the number of solutions of the equation $\varphi(x) = m$ for a given m. R. D. Carmichael [08] tabulated all solutions for $m \leqslant 1000$; however, his table contains errors, which were noted by K. W. Wegner and S. R. Savitzky [70], who provided an extension of that table up to $m \leqslant 1978$. The case of $m \equiv 2 \pmod 4$ was settled by V. L. Klee, Jr. [46], who proved that the number of solutions equals 0, 2 or 4. The same result was obtained by E. Grosswald [73], who also gave formulas for the number of solutions in the cases $m \equiv 4 \pmod{24}$ and $m \equiv 12 \pmod{24}$. He noted that his method leads to similar formulas for $m \equiv 8 \pmod{16}$ and $m \equiv 16 \pmod{32}$.

The case where m is a product of powers of 2 and 3 was considered by J. Meffroy [72], [75], [77]. Cf. also R. Desq [78]. For other particular cases see N. S. Mendelsohn [76], L. L. Stepanova, E. L. Flikop [72].

S. S. Pillai [29] proved that the equation $\varphi(x) = m$ can have arbitrarily many solutions. A simple proof of this fact was given by A. Schinzel [56b], and P. Erdös [36a] showed that we can restrict x in this result, assuming that it is a product of three distinct primes. W. Sierpiński conjectured that for every $k \geqslant 2$ one can find an integer m_k such that $\varphi(x) = m_k$ has exactly k solutions. This is known to be true for $k = 2$, 3, 4 (V. L. Klee [46], A. Schinzel [56d]) but the general case is still unresolved although A. Schinzel [61] deduced the existence of m_k for all k from the hypothesis H (A. Schinzel and W. Sierpiński [58b]). It was proved by P. Erdös [58] that if such an integer m_k exists then there are infinitely many of them. Earlier he showed (P. Erdös [35]) that there exists a positive c such that for infinitely many integers m the number of solutions of $\varphi(x) = m$ exceeds m^c. K. Wooldridge [79] proved that one can take for c any number smaller than $3 - 2^{3/2} = 0.171\ldots$, and C. Pomerance [80] showed that one can take

$c = 0.5509\ldots$ and stated that even $c = 0.55655$ is admissible. P. Erdös conjectured that it is possible to take $c = 1 - \varepsilon$ for every $\varepsilon > 0$.

In [80] C. Pomerance proved also that the number of solutions of $\varphi(x) = m$ is bounded from above by

$$m\exp\bigl(-(1 + o(1))\log m\,(\log\log\log m)/(\log\log m)\bigr)$$

and in [81] he gave a more precise form of the $o(1)$ term.

3. Lehmer's question was stated in Lehmer [32], where it was shown that if n is a composite integer satisfying $\varphi(n) \mid n - 1$ then $\omega(n) \geqslant 7$. This was later improved by E. Lieuwens [70], who proved $\omega(n) \geqslant 11$ and by M. Kishore [77], who got $\omega(n) \geqslant 13$. (Cf. J.-M. Deshouillers [76], who refuted a conjecture of Lieuwens.)

Theorem 1.10, as well as the bound in Theorem 1.11, are due to C. Pomerance [77b]. Previously (Pomerance [76]) he had obtained the bound $\ll x^{2/3}(\log\log x)^{1/3}$.

Numbers n satisfying $n \equiv a\,(\mathrm{mod}\,\varphi(n))$ were studied by C. Pomerance [75b], [76], [77a]. The results are analogous to those in the case $a = 1$.

If n is composite and for all a prime to n one has $a^{n-1} \equiv 1\,(\mathrm{mod}\,n)$, then n is called a *Carmichael number*. Those numbers were first considered by R. D. Carmichael [12], who showed that they must all be square-free. Clearly every integer n with $n - 1$ divisible by $\varphi(n)$ is a Carmichael number. Bounds for the number of Carmichael numbers not exceeding x were given by W. Knödel [53a], [53b] and the best result is due to P. Erdös [56b], who proved the evaluation

$$\ll x\exp(-C\log x\,\log\log\log x\,\log\log^{-1}x)$$

with a positive constant C.

Carmichael numbers were studied by J. Chernick [39]. For generalizations see H. C. Williams [77] and D. H. Lehmer [76].

Composite integers n satisfying $2^n \equiv 2\,(\mathrm{mod}\,n)$ are called *pseudo-primes* and there is a vast literature about them. The reader should consult A. Rotkiewicz [72] for a survey.

4. Denote by $V(x)$ the number of integers $m \leqslant x$ for which the equation $\varphi(y) = m$ is solvable. S. S. Pillai [29] showed that

$$V(x) \ll x(\log x)^{-t} \qquad \text{for } t = e^{-1}\log 2$$

and P. Erdös [35] obtained

$$V(x) \ll x\log^{\varepsilon - 1} x \qquad \text{for all } \varepsilon > 0.$$

P. Erdös [45b] supplied the lower bound

$$V(x) \gg x \log\log x \log^{-1} x$$

and stated that one can get

$$V(x) \gg x (\log\log x)^k \log^{-1} x \quad \text{for every } k.$$

Later P. Erdös and R. R. Hall [73], [76] sharpened these bounds to

$$\frac{x}{\log x} \exp\big(A (\log\log\log x)^2\big) \ll V(x) \ll \frac{x}{\log x} \exp\big(B (\log\log x)^{1/2}\big)$$

with a suitable positive A and an arbitrary $B > 2^{3/2} \log^{-1/2} 2 = 3.3972\ldots$ (A similar upper bound for the number of $n \leqslant x$ for which $\varphi(\varphi(y)) = n$ is solvable was given by P. Erdös and R. R. Hall [77]). The exact behaviour of $V(x)$ is still unknown, however, for the related function $A(x)$ counting the number of integers n for which $\varphi(n) \leqslant x$ the analogous question is much easier. In fact, P. Erdös and P. Turán (see P. Erdös [45b]) showed that the limit $c = \lim\limits_{x \to \infty} A(x) x^{-1}$ exists and is positive and it is not difficult to establish that $c = \zeta(2) \zeta(3) \zeta^{-1}(6)$ (see R. E. Dressler [70]). P. T. Bateman [72] supplied the error term by proving

$$A(x) = cx + O\big(x \exp(-B(\log x \log\log x)^{1/2})\big)$$

where B is any constant less than $2^{-1/2}$.

Finally let us mention that if

$$E(x) = \sum_{n \leqslant x} \varphi(n) - (3/\pi^2) x^2,$$

then

$$E(x) \ll x \log^{2/3} x (\log\log x)^{1 + \varepsilon}$$

holds for every positive ε. (A. I. Saltykov [60], cf. A. Walfisz [53a], [53b].)

On the other hand, S. S. Pillai and S. Chowla [30] proved that $E(x) \neq o(x \log\log\log x)$ (cf. P. Erdös and H. N. Shapiro [51]) and D. Suryanarayana and R. Sitaramachandra Rao [72] obtained

$$\sum_{n \leqslant x} E(n) = \frac{3}{2\pi^2} x^2 + O\big(x^2 \exp(-C \log^{3/5} x (\log\log x)^{-1/5})\big)$$

for a certain positive C.

5. The question how often $(n, \varphi(n)) = 1$ holds was considered by P. Erdös [48], who proved that this happens for $(e^{-C} + o(1)) x (\log\log\log x)^{-1}$ integers $n \leqslant x$, where C is Euler's constant. This result was generalized in M. R. Murty and V. K. Murty [79], who showed that $(n, \varphi(n)) = k \geqslant 2$ holds for $(e^{-C}/k! + o(1)) x (\log\log\log\log x)^k (\log\log\log x)^{-1}$ integers $n \leqslant x$.

E. J. Scourfield [76] showed how to extend the result of Erdős to a large class of functions and proved that, if $f(n)$ is multiplicative and there exists a non-constant polynomial $V \in Z[X]$ with a non-zero constant term such that for all primes p one has $f(p) = V(p)$, then the condition $(n, f(n)) = 1$ holds for $(C + o(1)) x (\log\log\log x)^{-\lambda}$ integers $n \leqslant x$, where C is a positive constant and $\lambda \in (0, 1]$ denotes the density of the set of primes p for which the congruence $V(y) \equiv 0 \pmod{p}$ is solvable.

Exercises

1 (V. L. Klee [46]). Prove that if m is an odd integer then the equation $\varphi(x) = 2m$ can have 0, 2 or 4 solutions, and show that the first case occurs infinitely often.

2 (S. S. Pillai [29], A. Schinzel [56b]). Show that for suitable m the equation $\varphi(x) = m$ may have arbitrarily many solutions.

3 (C. Pomerance [74b]). Show that if an integer N has the property that, for every prime p, $p - 1 | \varphi(N)$ implies $p^2 | N$, then the equation $\varphi(x) = N$ has exactly one solution.

4 (A. Schinzel [56d]). Prove that the equation $\varphi(x) = 2 \cdot 7^k$ has $k = 0$, $x = 3, 4$ or 6 as its only solutions.

5 (P. Erdős [46]). Prove that for all k the equation $\varphi(x) = k!$ is solvable.

6. Prove that for every prime $p \geqslant 5$ the values of Euler's function are asymptotically uniformly distributed in the non-zero residue classes $\pmod{p}$.

7 (S. S. Pillai [29]). Denote by $\varphi_k(n)$ the kth iterate of $\varphi(n)$ and denote by $C(n)$ the smallest integer k such that $\varphi_k(n) = 2$. Prove that

$$(\log n - \log 2)/\log 3 \leqslant C(n) < \log n/\log 2.$$

8 (A. Schinzel [56d]). Prove that for any given d there are infinitely many integers m, divisible by d, such that the equation $\varphi(x) = m$ has no solutions.

§ 4. EGYPTIAN FRACTIONS

1. The only way of representing rational numbers known to ancient Egyptians was their representation as sums of unit fractions. The Rhind papyrus (see A. B. Chace et al. [27]) preserved in the British Museum contains a table for such representations of ratios $2/n$ for odd n not exceeding 101. We always have of course the trivial formula $m/n = 1/n + \ldots + 1/n$; however, the ancients considered only expansions with distinct denominators. For this reason unit fractions $1/n$ (with n integral and positive) are called *Egyptian fractions*. There are several interesting questions concerning them, which we shall now consider. The first question coming to mind is the following: let a/b be a given rational number from the interval $(0, 1)$. Denote by $N(a, b)$ the smallest integer s for which the equation

(1.14) $m/n = 1/x_1 + \ldots + 1/x_s$

is solvable and by $N^*(a, b)$ the minimal s for which it is solvable with distinct $x_1, \ldots, x_s$. Further put

$$N(b) = \max \{N(a, b): 1 \leqslant a \leqslant b-1\}$$

and

$$N^*(b) = \max \{N^*(a, b): 1 \leqslant a \leqslant b-1\}.$$

How large are $N(b)$ and $N^*(b)$?

The following result of P. Erdös [50] gives the best known lower bound for $N(b)$:

THEOREM 1.12. *For every positive ε and $n \geqslant n_0(\varepsilon)$ we have*

$$N^*(b) \geqslant N(b) \geqslant \left(\frac{1}{\log 2} - \varepsilon\right) \log \log b.$$

Proof. We need a very simple lemma:

LEMMA 1.12. *For every fixed n the equation*

$$1 = 1/x_1 + \ldots + 1/x_n$$

has only a finite number of solutions in positive integers $x_1, \ldots, x_n$, and if $x_1 \leqslant x_2 \leqslant \ldots \leqslant x_n$ is one of these solutions, then for $k = 1, 2, \ldots, n$ one has

(1.15)
$$x_k \leqslant n^{2^{k-1}}.$$

Proof. Since $1 = \sum_{i=1}^{n} 1/x_i \leqslant n/x_1$, inequality (1.15) holds for $k = 1$. Assuming that it holds for $k = 1, 2, \ldots, r-1$ (with a certain $r \leqslant n$), we can write

$$0 < 1 - \sum_{i=1}^{r-1} \frac{1}{x_i} = \sum_{i=r}^{n} \frac{1}{x_i} \leqslant \frac{n-r+1}{x_r} \leqslant \frac{n}{x_r};$$

thus

$$x_r \leqslant n\left(1 - \sum_{i=1}^{r-1} \frac{1}{x_i}\right)^{-1} \leqslant nx_1 \ldots x_{r-1} \leqslant n^{2^{r-1}},$$

proving (1.15). The first assertion follows immediately. □

For the proof of the theorem it suffices now to observe that, by the lemma,

$$(b-1)/b = 1/x_1 + \ldots + 1/x_t$$

implies $b \leqslant (1+t)^{2^t}$ and thus $t \geqslant \left(\frac{1}{\log 2} - \varepsilon\right) \log \log b$ results. □

It is not known whether this bound can be improved. P. Erdös (loc.cit.) conjectured that it is the best possible and that in fact one has $N(b) = O(\log \log b)$. The best result in this respect is again due to P. Erdös [50]:

THEOREM 1.13. *For* $b \geqslant 8$ *we have*

$$N^*(b) \leqslant 8 \log b / \log \log b. (*)$$

Proof. We need two easy lemmas:

LEMMA 1.13. *If* $0 < x < n!$ *is an integer, then* x *can be written as a sum of at most* n *distinct divisors of* $n!$.

Proof. The assertion is true for $n = 2$; so assume that it holds for $n = N-1$ where $N \geqslant 3$. If $0 < x < N!$ write $x = Ny+d$ with $0 \leqslant d < N$. If $y = 0$ then $x = d$ is the required representation. However, if y is positive then, since $y < (N-1)!$, we may write by the inductive assumption $y = c_1 + \ldots + c_s$, where $c_1, \ldots, c_s$ are divisors of $(N-1)!$ and $s \leqslant N-1$, but then $x = \sum_{i=1}^{s} Nc_i + d$ meets our demands. $\square$

LEMMA 1.14. *For* $n \geqslant 8$ *we have* $(n-1)! > n^{n/2}$.

Proof. If $n = 2k$ is even, then for $k \geqslant 6$

$$\frac{(n-1)!}{n^{n/2}} = (k-1)! \frac{k}{2k} \cdot \frac{k+1}{2k} \cdots \frac{(2k-1)}{2^k} \geqslant \frac{(k-1)!}{2^k} \geqslant \frac{1}{2} \frac{1 \cdot 2 \cdot 3 \cdot 4 \cdot 5}{2 \cdot 2 \cdot 2 \cdot 2 \cdot 2} = \frac{15}{8} > 1$$

thus our assertion holds for even $n \geqslant 12$. However, if $n = 2k+1$ is odd, then for $k \geqslant 5$

$$\frac{(n-1)!}{n^{n/2}} = \frac{k!}{(1+2k)^{1/2}} \cdot \frac{k+1}{2k+1} \cdot \frac{k+2}{2k+1} \cdots \frac{2k}{2k+1} \geqslant \frac{k!}{2^k(1+2k)^{1/2}}$$

$$= \frac{1}{2} \cdot \frac{2}{2} \cdot \frac{3}{2} \cdots \frac{(k-1)}{2} \cdot \frac{k}{2(1+2k)^{1/2}} > \frac{1}{2} \cdot \frac{2}{2} \cdot \frac{3}{2} \cdot \frac{4}{2} \cdot \frac{k}{2(1+2k)^{1/2}}$$

$$= \frac{3k}{4(1+2k)^{1/2}} > 1;$$

hence our assertion holds for odd $n \geqslant 11$. Since for $n = 8, 9, 10$ it is also true, our proof is complete. $\square$

Now let a/b be a rational number from $(0, 1)$, define n by $(n-1)! < b \leqslant n!$ and let x be a unique non-negative integer satisfying $x/n! \leqslant a/b < (x+1)/n!$. Since $x < n!$, Lemma 1.13 allows us to write $x = d_1 + \ldots + d_r$ where the d_i's are distinct positive divisors of $n!$ and $r \leqslant n$. Let us assume $d_1 < d_2 < \ldots < d_r$. Using the same lemma, we write $an! - bx = c_1 + \ldots + c_s$, where $0 < c_1 < \ldots < c_s$ are divisors of $n!$ and $s \leqslant n$. If we now put $u_i = n!/d_i$ $(i = 1, 2, \ldots, r)$ and $v_j = bn!/c_j$ $(j = 1, 2, \ldots, s)$, then

$$a/b = 1/u_1 + \ldots + 1/u_r + 1/v_1 + \ldots + 1/v_s.$$

(*) (Added in proof: M. D. Vose (Bull. London Math. Soc. 17 (1985), 21–24) obtained $N^*(b) \ll \log^{1/2} b$.)

Since $c_s \leqslant an! - bx < b$, we get $v_s > n!$ and in view of $u_1 = n!/d_1 \leqslant n!$ we arrive at $v_s > u_1$, proving that all denominators $u_1, \ldots, u_r, v_1, \ldots, v_s$ are distinct. This shows that $N^*(a, b) \leqslant r + s \leqslant 2n$ and it remains to bound n, but the choice of n and Lemma 1.14 imply for $n \geqslant 8$ the inequalities

$$(n \log n)/2 < \log(n-1)! < \log b \leqslant \log n! < n \log n,$$

from which we get $\log\log b < \log n + \log\log n < 2\log n$, giving finally

$$n < 2 \log b/\log n < 4 \log b/\log\log b$$

and

$$N^*(a, b) < 8 \log b/\log\log b. \quad \square$$

2. Another problem concerning Egyptian fractions was proposed by P. Erdös and E. G. Straus. They asked whether for all $n \geqslant 2$ the inequality $N(4, n) \leqslant 3$ holds, i.e., whether for all $n \geqslant 2$ the equation

(1.16)
$$\frac{4}{n} = \frac{1}{x} + \frac{1}{y} + \frac{1}{z}$$

is solvable in positive integers x, y, z.

It was checked by R. Obláth [49], L. A. Rosati [54], E. Kiss [59], K. Yamamoto [65] and R. W. Jollenstein [76] that this is indeed true for all $n \leqslant 11 \cdot 10^6$. R. Obláth [49] noted that if $n+1$ has a prime divisor congruent to $3 \pmod 4$ then (1.16) is solvable; hence for the number $A_4(x)$ of integers $n \leqslant x$ for which (1.16) has no solutions we obtain the bound $A_4(x) \ll x(\log x)^{-1/2}$. Using Selberg's sieve, W. A. Webb [70] improved this to obtain $A_4(x) \ll x(\log x)^{-7/4}$.

W. Sierpiński [57] asked whether $N(5, n) \leqslant 3$ holds for all $n \geqslant 2$ and A. Schinzel extended these conjectures to the following:

If a is a given positive integer, then there exists a constant $C(a)$ such that for all $n \geqslant C(a)$ the equation

(1.17)
$$a/n = 1/x + 1/y + 1/z$$

is solvable.

Denote by $A_a(x)$ the number of integers $n \leqslant x$ for which (1.17) has no solutions. The best known bound for $A_a(x)$ is due to R. C. Vaughan [70a], who obtained the following result:

THEOREM 1.14. *For any given positive integer a there exists a positive constant $B(a)$ such that for x tending to infinity*

$$A_a(x) \ll x \exp(-B(a) \log^{2/3} x).$$

Proof. After a short elementary preparation we shall use the large sieve and Bombieri's theorem (see Theorem A.1 and Theorem A.4). We start with a very simple auxiliary result, which will be used to produce a large quantity of integers n for which (1.17) is solvable.

LEMMA 1.15. *If one can find integers r, s, t such that $arst - 1$ divides $rn + s$, then* (1.17) *is solvable.*

Proof. Denoting the ratio $(rn + s)/(arst - 1)$ by q, we can take $x = stq$, $y = nrtq$ and $z = nrst$. □

Using this lemma, we may now find for every prime p a set of residue classes (mod p) which contain only those integers n for which (1.17) is solvable:

LEMMA 1.16. *For prime p put*

$$f_1(p) = \tfrac{1}{2} \sum_{m|(p+1)/a} \mu^2(m) \, d\big((p+1)/am\big)$$

if a divides $p+1$ and $f_1(p) = 0$ otherwise. Further, let $f(p) = [f_1(p)]$. Then there are at least $f(p)$ distinct residue classes (mod p) for all elements n of which equation (1.17) *is solvable.*

Proof. If $a \nmid (p+1)$ there is nothing to prove; so let a be a divisor of $p+1$ and put $p+1 = aU$. For every factorization $U = rst$, if we determine n from the congruence $rn + s \equiv 0 \pmod{p}$ then by Lemma 1.15 equation (1.17) is solvable. It remains thus to count the residue classes (mod p) arising in this way. The assertion of the lemma will be established if we show that if $U = rst = r_1 s_1 t_1$ are two distinct factorizations of U satisfying $\mu^2(t) = \mu^2(t_1) \neq 0$, $s \leqslant (U/t)^{1/2}$, $s_1 \leqslant (U/t_1)^{1/2}$ then the residue classes X, Y (mod p), defined as the solutions of $rX + s \equiv 0 \pmod{p}$ and $r_1 Y + s_1 \equiv 0 \pmod{p}$, are distinct. To prove this observe that $X = Y$ implies $sr_1 \equiv s_1 r \pmod{p}$, but $rst = r_1 s_1 t_1$; hence $s_1^2 r_1 t_1 \equiv s^2 tr_1 \pmod{p}$ and $s_1^2 t_1 \equiv s^2 t \pmod{p}$; however, because of $0 < s_1^2 t_1$, $s^2 t < p$, this implies $s_1^2 t_1 = s^2 t$, and since t, t_1 are square-free we must have $s = s_1$, $t = t_1$ and $r = r_1$. □

In view of Theorem A.1 and Proposition A.2 it suffices to establish the following evaluation:

LEMMA 1.17. *For x tending to infinity we have*

$$\sum_{p \leqslant x} f(p)/p \gg \log^2 x$$

with the implied constant depending only on a.

Proof. We shall prove the inequality

$$\sum_{p \leqslant x} f(p) \log p \geqslant C(a) \, x \log^2 x$$

with a positive $C(a)$, since an application of partial summation formula immediately gives the assertion of the lemma. Denoting the sum $\displaystyle\sum_{\substack{p \leqslant x \\ p \equiv r(\mathrm{mod}\, k)}} \log p$

by $A(x, k, r)$ and using the Prime Number Theorem, we can write

$$2 \sum_{p \leqslant x} f(p) \log p = 2 \sum_{\substack{p \leqslant x \\ p \equiv -1 (\mathrm{mod}\, a)}} f_1(p) \log p + O(x)$$

$$= \sum_{\substack{p \leqslant x \\ p \equiv -1 (\mathrm{mod}\, a)}} \log p \sum_{t | ((1+p)/a)} \mu^2(t)\, d\left(\frac{p+1}{at}\right) + O(x)$$

$$\geqslant \sum_{t \leqslant x^{1/3}/a} \mu^2(t) \sum_{\substack{p \leqslant x \\ p \equiv -1 (\mathrm{mod}\, a)}} \sum_{r | ((1+p)/at)} \log p + O(x)$$

$$\geqslant \sum_{t \leqslant x^{1/3}/a} \mu^2(t) \sum_{r \leqslant x^{1/3}/at} A(x, art, -1) + O(x).$$

If we write

$$R(x, k, r) = |A(x, k, r) - x/\varphi(k)|,$$

then

$$2 \sum_{p \leqslant x} f(p) \log p \geqslant x \sum_{t \leqslant x^{1/3}/a} \mu^2(t) \sum_{r \leqslant x^{1/3}/a} \varphi(art)^{-1} +$$

$$+ O\Big(\sum_{t \leqslant x^{1/3}/a} \sum_{r \leqslant x^{1/3}/at} R(x, art, -1) \Big) + O(x)$$

$$= A(x)\, x + O(B(x)) + O(x).$$

The main term $A(x)$ we shall evaluate in a straightforward manner and then our efforts will concentrate on bounding $B(x)$ from above. Since for all x, y we have $\varphi(xy) \leqslant x\varphi(y)$, it follows that

$$A(x) = \frac{x}{a} \sum_{r \leqslant x^{1/3}/a} \frac{1}{r} \sum_{t \leqslant x^{1/3}/ar} \mu^2(t)/\varphi(t),$$

and using

$$\sum_{t \leqslant T} \mu^2(t)/\varphi(t) \geqslant \sum_{t \leqslant T} \mu^2(t)\, t^{-1} \gg \log T$$

we are led to

$$A(x) \gg \frac{x}{a} \sum_{r \leqslant x^{1/3}/a} \frac{1}{r} \log(x^{1/3}/ar)$$

$$= \frac{x}{a} \log(x^{1/3}/a) \sum_{r \leqslant x^{1/3}/a} \frac{1}{r} - \frac{x}{a} \sum_{r \leqslant x^{1/3}/a} \frac{\log r}{r}$$

$$= \frac{x}{3a} \log x \left\{ \frac{1}{3} \log x - \log a + O(1) \right\} - \frac{x \log a}{a} \left\{ \frac{1}{3} \log x - \log a + O(1) \right\} -$$

$$- \frac{x}{2a} \left\{ \frac{1}{3} \log x - \log a \right\}^2 + O(x \log x) \gg x \log^2 x.$$

To evaluate the error term $B(x)$ a more sophisticated argument is necessary. Write

$$B(x) = \sum_{m \leqslant x^{1/3}/a} d(m) R(x, am, -1) = B_1 + B_2$$

where B_1 is that part of the sum above which corresponds to $m \leqslant x^{1/3}/a$ satisfying $R(x, am, -1) \leqslant x/m \log x$, and $B_2 = B(x) - B_1$. The first term is easy to evaluate since it does not exceed $x(\log x)^{-1} \sum_{m \leqslant x^{1/3}} d(m) m^{-1}$, and in view of $\sum_{m \leqslant x} d(m) = x \log x + O(x)$ we obtain by partial summation $\sum_{m \leqslant x} d(m) m^{-1} = O(\log^2 x)$, leading to $B_1 = O(x \log x)$.

To bound B_2 observe first that

$$R(x, am, -1) \leqslant |A(x, am, -1)| + x/\varphi(am)$$

$$\leqslant \sum_{\substack{k \leqslant x \\ k \equiv -1 \,(\mathrm{mod}\,am)}} \log k + \frac{x \log\log(am)}{am} \ll \frac{x \log x}{am};$$

hence, using Cauchy's inequality, we get

(1.18) $$B_2 \leqslant \frac{1}{d} \sum_{\substack{m \leqslant x^{1/3} \\ R(x, am, -1) > x/m \log x}} \frac{d(m)}{m^{1/2}} \cdot \frac{x \log x}{m^{1/2}}$$

$$\leqslant \frac{x \log x}{a} \left(\sum_{m \leqslant x^{1/3}} \frac{d^2(m)}{m} \right)^{1/2} \left(\sum_{\substack{m \leqslant x^{1/3} \\ R(x, am, -1) > x/m \log x}} \frac{1}{m} \right)^{1/2}.$$

To bound the middle factor observe that $d(mn)$ does not exceed $d(m) d(n)$ and thus

$$\sum_{m \leqslant T} d^2(m) = \sum_{m \leqslant T} d(m) \sum_{t \mid m} 1 = \sum_{t \leqslant T} \sum_{k \leqslant T/t} d(kt)$$

$$\leqslant \sum_{t \leqslant T} d(t) \sum_{k \leqslant T/t} d(k) \ll \sum_{t \leqslant T} d(t) T t^{-1} \log T \ll T \log^3 T,$$

which leads, by partial summation, to

(1.19) $$\sum_{m \leqslant T} d^2(m)/m \ll \log^4 T.$$

It remains to bound the last factor on the right-hand side of (1.18). Denote by $T(r, x)$ the number of integers $q \leqslant r$ for which $R(x, q, -1) > xq^{-1} \log^{-1} x$; let $\sum_1$ denote the sum over those integers $m \leqslant x^{1/3}$ for which $R(x, am, -1) > xm^{-1} \log^{-1} x$ and let $\sum_2$ denote the sum over those integers $m \leqslant ax^{1/3}$ for which $R(x, am, -1)$ exceeds $xm^{-1} \log^{-1} x$. Using partial summation, we get

(1.20) $$\sum_1 \frac{1}{m} \ll \sum_2 \frac{1}{m} \ll \sum_{m \leqslant ax^{1/3}} T(m, x) m^{-2},$$

and this shows that we need a good bound for $T(m, x)$. Such a bound is provided by the theorem of Bombieri (Theorem A.4), which we apply with $A = 6$ and x sufficiently large, so that $x^{1/6} > \log^{B(6)} x$, i.e., $x^{1/3} < x^{1/2} \log^{-B(6)} x$. This gives

$$T(m, x) \ll \sum_{q \leqslant m} \frac{q \log x}{x} R(x, q, -1) \ll \frac{m \log x}{x} \cdot \frac{x}{\log^6 x} = m \log^{-5} x;$$

by substituting the above in (1.20), we arrive at

$$\sum_1 \frac{1}{m} \ll \log^{-4} x.$$

Applying this bound and (1.19) to (1.18), we finally obtain $B_2 = O(x \log x)$; taking into account the previously obtained bound for B_1 and the lower bound for $A(x)$, we arrive at our assertion. □

As already indicated, the theorem is an immediate consequence of the last lemma and the large sieve inequality. □

3. Now we turn our attention to the magnitude of the denominators in expansion (1.14). If $1 \leqslant a < b$ are given integers, then by $D(a, b)$ we shall denote the minimal value of x_k which may occur in an expansion

$$a/b = 1/x_1 + \ldots + 1/x_k \qquad (x_1 < x_2 < \ldots < x_k)$$

of the number a/b into a sum of distinct Egyptian fractions. Furthermore, let $D(b)$ be the maximal value of $D(a, b)$ for $a = 1, 2, \ldots, b-1$. An obvious question which now arises is the magnitude of $D(b)$. A partial answer to it was obtained by M. N. Bleicher and P. Erdős [76a], [76b], and we shall now prove two of their results. We start with a lower bound for $D(b)$ in the case of prime b:

THEOREM 1.15. *If p is a prime, then*

$$D(p) \geqslant \frac{1}{\log 2} p \log p.$$

Proof. For every integer $a \in [1, p-1]$ consider the expansion

(1.21) $$a/p = 1/n_1(a) + \ldots + 1/n_k(a)$$

$(n_1(a) < n_2(a) < \ldots < n_k(a) = D(a, p); \ k = k(a))$.

If among the denominators $n_i(a)$ there were one divisible by p^2, then obviously $D(p) \geqslant p^2$ and the proof would be complete. Hence we may assume that no $n_i(a)$ is divisible by p^2. On the other hand, for every a at least one denominator $n_i(a)$ must be divisible by p. Let $X = \{x_1 < x_2 < \ldots < x_t\}$ be the set of all numbers $n_i(a)/p$, where $1 \leqslant a \leqslant p-1$, and $1 \leqslant i \leqslant k(a)$ are such that $p | n_i(a)$. By the previous remarks X is non-void and none of its elements is divisible by p. Also it is clear that

$$D(p) \geqslant p x_t.$$

It now suffices to obtain a good lower bound for x_t. Write the expansion (1.21) in the form

$$\frac{a}{p} = \frac{1}{px_{i_1}} + \ldots + \frac{1}{px_{i_r}} + \frac{1}{y_1} + \ldots + \frac{1}{y_s},$$

where r, s, $x_{i_1}, \ldots, x_{i_r}, y_1, \ldots, y_s$ depend on a and p does not divide $y_1 \ldots y_s$. The number

$$\frac{1}{p} \{a - \sum_{j=1}^{r} 1/x_{i_j}\}$$

brought to its reduced form cannot have a denominator divisible by p and hence

$$a x_{i_1} \ldots x_{i_r} \equiv \sum_{k=1}^{r} (x_{i_1} \ldots x_{i_r}) x_{i_k}^{-1} (\bmod p).$$

This congruence implies that a is uniquely determined by the choice of indices $i_1, \ldots, i_r$; thus the map $a \to \{x_{i_1}, \ldots, x_{i_r}\}$ of $\{1, 2, \ldots, p-1\}$ into 2^X is injective and since its value is never an empty set we obtain $p-1 \leqslant 2^t - 1$ and thus $x_t \geqslant t \geqslant \log p/\log 2$, implying in turn $D(p) \geqslant p \log p/\log 2$. □

The next theorem gives an upper bound for $D(b)$, which is not very far from the lower bound just obtained.

THEOREM 1.16. *For $b \geqslant 2$ we have $D(b) = O(b \log^4 b)$.*

Proof. Let $2 = p_1 < p_2 < \ldots$ be the sequence of all primes and denote by P_k the product $p_1 p_2 \ldots p_k$. We shall first show by direct construction that every integer $q \leqslant P_k$ can be written as a sum of distinct divisors of P_k, and hence the ratio q/P_k is a sum of distinct Egyptian fractions with denominators not exceeding P_k. (Lemma 1.18 below.) In a more complicated way we shall also show that for large k every number m lying between $(1-1/k) P_k$ and $(2-1/k) P_k$ is a sum of distinct divisors of P_k exceeding $C P_{k-4}$ with a suitable constant $C > 0$; hence m/P_k will be a sum of distinct Egyptian fractions with denominators $< P_k/P_{k-4}$ (corollary to Lemma 1.20). If $2 \leqslant a < b$ are given, we shall define k by means of $P_{k-1} < b \leqslant P_k$ and choose r and q in such a way that

$$(1-1/k) P_k \leqslant r = aP_k - bq \leqslant (2-1/k) P_k.$$

This will lead to $a/b = a/P_k + r/bP_k$ and we shall try to bound the obtained denominators in terms of b. Here the Prime Number Theorem will be used to show that in fact they are $O(b \log^4 b)$.

Now we provide the necessary details.

LEMMA 1.18. *Every positive integer not exceeding* $\sigma(P_k) = \prod_{i=1}^{k}(1+p_i)$ *can be written as a sum of distinct divisors of* P_k.

Proof. We use induction in k. For $k = 1, 2$ the assertion can easily be checked by hand. Thus, let $N \geqslant 3$ and assume that our assertion holds for all $k < N$. Let m be a positive integer not exceeding $\sigma(P_N)$. If $m \leqslant \sigma(P_{N-1})$ then we may apply the inductive assumption; so let us assume that $\sigma(P_{N-1}) < m \leqslant \sigma(P_N)$. In this case we have

$$0 < m - \sigma(P_{N-1}) \leqslant \sigma(P_N) - \sigma(P_{N-1}) = p_N \sigma(P_{N-1}).$$

Let t be the smallest positive integer such that

$$0 < m - \sigma(P_{N-1}) \leqslant t p_N.$$

Then

(1.22)
$$0 < t \leqslant \sigma(P_{N-1})$$

and

$$m - t p_N \leqslant \sigma(P_{N-1}).$$

If $m - t p_N$ is negative, then by Bertrand's postulate (see the corollary to Proposition A.4 or the corollary to Theorem 3.5) we get

$$m - (t-1) p_N \leqslant p_N \leqslant 2 p_{N-1} \leqslant \sigma(P_{N-1})$$

and thus

$$m - \sigma(P_{N-1}) \leqslant (t-1) p_N,$$

contrary to the choice of t. This shows that $0 < m - t p_N \leqslant \sigma(P_{N-1})$; hence by the inductive assumption we may write

$$m - t p_N = d_1 + \ldots + d_k,$$

where $d_1, \ldots, d_k$ are distinct divisors of P_{N-1}. Moreover, in view of (1.22) we have $t = \delta_1 + \ldots + \delta_l$, where $\delta_1, \ldots, \delta_l$ are distinct divisors of P_{N-1}. This leads to

$$m = d_1 + \ldots + d_k + p_N \delta_1 + \ldots + p_N \delta_l,$$

all summands being distinct divisors of P_N, as asserted. ☐

For the next step a little lemma concerning addition (mod p) is needed:

LEMMA 1.19. *Let p be a prime, $0 \leqslant r < p$, and let $x_1, \ldots, x_r$ be integers not divisible by p. Then the sums*

$$\sum_{i=1}^{r} \varepsilon_i x_i \quad (\varepsilon_i = 0, 1)$$

represent at least $1 + r$ distinct residue classes (mod p).

For $r = 1$ the assertion is obvious. Assume that it holds for all $r < N$ and let $x_1, \ldots, x_N$ be given integers not divisible by p. Denoting by $\bar{x}$ the residue class (mod p) represented by x, let

$$S = \left\{ \sum_{i=1}^{N-1} \varepsilon_i \bar{x}_i \colon \varepsilon_i = 0, 1\ (i = 1, \ldots, N-1) \right\}.$$

If $|S| \geqslant 1 + N$ the proof is complete. Otherwise we use the inductive assumption to obtain $|S| = N < p$. Obviously $\bar{x}_N \in S$ and $S + \bar{x}_N \subset S$, but this implies that $\bar{x}_N, 2\bar{x}_N, \ldots, (p-1)\bar{x}_N, p\bar{x}_N$ all lie in S; thus S necessarily contains all residue classes (mod p), i.e., $N = |S| = p$, a contradiction. $\square$

This lemma will be used in the proof of the next step, which is the main point in the proof of Theorem 1.16.

LEMMA 1.20. *Let k be a sufficiently large integer and let*

$$(1 - 1/k) P_k \leqslant m \leqslant (2 - 1/k) P_k.$$

Then $m = m_1 + d_1 + \ldots + d_r$ where $d_1, \ldots, d_r$ are distinct divisors of P_{k-1}, all $\geqslant P_{k-4}$, m_1 is a multiple of p_k and finally

$$\left(1 - 1/(k-1)\right) P_k \leqslant m_1 \leqslant \left(2 - 1/(k-1)\right) P_k.$$

Proof. We shall choose the numbers d_i from the set

$$D = \{d \colon d = P_{k-1}/p_a p_b p_c,\ [k/2] < a < b < c < k\},$$

which contains

$$\binom{k - [k/2]}{3} \gg k^3$$

elements, all of them being $\geqslant P_{k-1}/p_{k-1} p_{k-2} p_{k-3} = P_{k-4}$.

Since for sufficiently large k we have $p_k < k^2$, we may select $r = p_k - 1$ distinct elements $d_1, d_2, \ldots, d_r$ from D and apply Lemma 1.19 in the case $p = p_k$, $\{x_1, \ldots, x_r\} = \{d_1, \ldots, d_r\}$ to obtain a representation $m = m_1 + d_{i_1} + \ldots + d_{i_s}$ $(1 \leqslant i_j \leqslant r)$ with m_1 divisible by p_k.

Now we prove the inequality

(1.23) $$m_1 \geqslant \left(1 - \frac{1}{k-1}\right) P_k.$$

To do this observe that

$$m_1 = m - (d_{i_1} + \ldots + d_{i_s}) \geqslant \left(1 - \frac{1}{k}\right) P_k - (d_{i_1} + \ldots + d_{i_s}),$$

and writing $q = p_{[k/2]}$ we get

$$d_{i_1} + \ldots + d_{i_s} \leqslant (p_k - 1) P_{k-1}/q^3 < P_k/q^3.$$

Since $q^3 \geqslant c_1 (k \log k)^3$ with a positive c_1, it follows that

$$m_1 \geqslant \left(1 - \frac{1}{k} - \frac{c_1}{k^3 \log^3 k}\right) P_k > \left(1 - \frac{1}{k-1}\right) P_k$$

provided k is sufficiently large, proving (1.23). If $m_1 \leqslant \left(2 - \frac{1}{k-1}\right) P_k$, the proof is complete. If however this inequality does not hold, some further arguments become necessary. Write

(1.24) $$m_1 = m_2 + d_{r_1} + \ldots + d_{r_T}$$

with m_2 divisible by p_k, $d_{r_1}, \ldots, d_{r_T} \in D$ and

$$\left(1 - 1/(k-1)\right) P_k \leqslant m_2 \leqslant \left(2 - 1/(k-1)\right) P_k.$$

Observe that the lower bound here is always satisfied because with a suitable c_2

$$\sum_{d \in D} d \leqslant |D| P_{k-1}/q^3 \leqslant c_2 \frac{P_{k-1}}{\log^3 k},$$

and hence with any choice of $d_{r_1}, \ldots, d_{r_T}$ in (1.24) we have

$$m_2 = m_1 - \sum_{j=1}^{T} d_{r_j} \geqslant m_1 - c_2 P_{k-1}/\log^3 k$$

$$\geqslant \left\{\left(2 - \frac{1}{k-1}\right) p_k - \frac{c_2}{\log^3 k}\right\} P_{k-1} > \left(1 - \frac{1}{k-1}\right) p_k P_{k-1} = \left(1 - \frac{1}{k-1}\right) P_k$$

for k sufficiently large.

It suffices hence to find $d_{r_1}, \ldots, d_{r_T} \in D$ which satisfy

$$\sum_{j=1}^{T} d_{r_j} \equiv 0 (\bmod p_k) \quad \text{and} \quad \sum_{j=1}^{T} d_{r_j} \geqslant P_k/k(k-1)$$

as in this case

$$m_2 = m_1 - \sum_{j=1}^{T} d_{r_j} \leqslant \left(2 - \frac{1}{k} - \frac{1}{k(k-1)}\right) P_k = \left(2 - \frac{1}{k-1}\right) P_k.$$

Since Lemma 1.19 implies that from every sequence of at least p_k elements of D one can extract a subsequence whose sum is divisible by p_k, our aim is now reduced to show that there exists a sequence of at least p_k elements of D such that the sum of the remaining elements of D exceeds $P_k/k(k-1)$. But for every choice of p_k elements of D the sum of the remaining elements of D exceeds $(|D| - p_k) P_{k-4} \gg k^3 P_{k-4} \gg P_k/k \log^4 k$ and so, for sufficiently large k, exceeds $P_k/k(k-1)$. □

Corollary. *Every integer* m *satisfying*

$$(1-1/k)\,P_k \leqslant m \leqslant (2-1/k)\,P_k$$

is a sum of distinct divisors of P_k *which all exceed* CP_{k-4} *with a suitable positive constant* $C < 1$.

Proof. We use induction on k, choosing C in such a way that the assertion becomes true for all integers up to k_0 where k_0 is an integer with the property that, for $k \geqslant k_0$, Lemma 1.20 holds. This procedure is permitted in view of Lemma 1.18.

Assume now that our assertion is true for all $k < N$ (where $N > k_0$) and let

$$(1-1/N)\,P_N \leqslant m \leqslant (2-1/N)\,P_N.$$

Using Lemma 1.20, we can write $m = m_1 + d_1 + \ldots + d_r$, where $d_1, \ldots, d_r$ are distinct divisors of P_{N-1}, $d_i \geqslant P_{N-4}$ for $i = 1, \ldots, r$ and m_1 is a multiple of p_N satisfying

$$\big(1-1/(N-1)\big)\,P_N \leqslant m_1 \leqslant \big(2-1/(N-1)\big)\,P_N.$$

Applying the inductive assumption to m_1/p_N, we can write $m_1 = p_N(\delta_1 + \ldots + \delta_s)$ where $\delta_1, \ldots, \delta_s$ are distinct divisors of P_{N-1}, which are $\geqslant CP_{N-5}$. In view of $\delta_i\, p_N | P_N$, $\delta_i\, p_N \geqslant CP_{N-5}\, p_N > CP_{N-4}$ we obtain

$$m = p_N \delta_1 + \ldots + p_N \delta_s + d_1 + \ldots + d_r$$

and, as the summands here are distinct and $d_i \geqslant P_{N-4} > CP_{N-4}$, our proof is complete. □

Now we can prove the theorem. The case $a = 1$ being trivial, let $2 \leqslant a < b$, and choose k such that $P_{k-1} < b \leqslant P_k$ and an integer q such that in the case $P_k \nmid b$ the number $r = aP_k - bq$ lies in the interval $[(1-1/k)\,P_k, (2-1/k)\,P_k]$. As the length of this interval exceeds b, such a choice is always possible. Finally, in the case $P_k|b$, put $q = a$, $r = 0$. Note that q cannot be negative. In fact, if it were such, then $r = aP_k - bq \geqslant aP_k + b > 2P_k$, a contradiction.

Clearly we have $a/b = q/P_k + r/bP_k$ and now, using the preceding lemmas, we shall write both summands as sums of Egyptian fractions. Because of $bq < aP_k$ we have

$$q < aP_k/b < ap_k \leqslant bp_k < P_k;$$

thus we may apply Lemma 1.18 to the number q and obtain $q = d_1 + \ldots + d_s$ where $d_1, \ldots, d_s$ are distinct divisors of P_k, which leads to a representation

(1.25) $$q/P_k = 1/x_1 + \ldots + 1/x_s$$

with $x_1, \ldots, x_s < P_k$ distinct. In the case $r = 0$ this proves the theorem;

however, if $r > 0$ we use the corollary to Lemma 1.20 to write $r = \delta_1 + \ldots + \delta_s$ where $\delta_1, \ldots, \delta_s$ are distinct divisors of P_k all exceeding CP_{k-4} and so

(1.26) $$r/bP_k = 1/by_1 + \ldots + 1/by_s$$

with $y_i | P_k$ distinct and satisfying

$$by_i \leqslant bP_k/CP_{k-4} \leqslant C^{-1} bp_k p_{k-1} p_{k-2} p_{k-3} \ll bk^4 \log^4 k.$$

By adding (1.25) and (1.26) we get a representation of a/b as a sum of distinct Egyptian fractions with denominators not exceeding $\max(P_k, C^{-1} bpk^4 \log^4 k)$. But $P_k = p_k P_{k-1} \leqslant p_k b \ll bk \log k$ and by the Prime Number Theorem one easily concludes that $P_{k-1} \leqslant b \leqslant P_k$ implies $k \ll \log b/\log\log b$; thus the bound for the denominators is $O(b \log^4 b)$ as asserted. $\square$

Notes and comments

1. Several algorithms are known to produce a decomposition of the form (1.14) of a given rational number. The simplest goes back to Fibonacci and was later considered by J. J. Sylvester [80a]. The idea is very simple: if a/b is a given rational number from the interval $(0, 1)$, then choose x_1 to be the integer defined by $1/x_1 \leqslant a/b < 1/(x_1 - 1)$, write $a_1/b_1 = a/b - 1/x_1$ and apply the same method to a_1/b_1. Since clearly $a > a_1 > \ldots$, this algorithm terminates in at most a steps. The denominators occurring here rise exponentially.

The algorithm given by P. Erdös [50], which we used in the proof of Theorem 1.13, gives a smaller number of terms than any other known algorithm. The denominators obtained here do not grow too rapidly and it can be shown that the largest denominator is $\ll b^2 \log b (\log\log b)^{-1}$.

M. N. Bleicher [72] introduced another algorithm, which is based on continued fractions and gives a very good bound for the denominators, namely $b^2 - b$ $(b \geqslant 3)$. It leads to an expansion with at most $2 \log^2 b \times \log\log b^{-1}$ terms. Another algorithm of Bleicher (see A. Beck, M. N. Bleicher and D. W. Crowe [69]) is based on the Farey series and gives an expansion with at most $a - 1$ terms while the denominators are bounded by $b^2 - b$ (see M. N. Bleicher [72], Theorem 1 and Theorem 2). Another algorithm may be found in S. W. Golomb [62].

Lemma 1.12 is far from being the best possible. O. D. Kellogg [21] gave a heuristic argument implying that one can replace in it the inequality $x_n \leqslant n^{2^{n-1}}$ by $x_n \leqslant u_n$, where u_n is defined by recurrence: $u_1 = 1$, $u_{n+1} = u_n(1 + u_n)$. A proof was provided by R. D. Curtiss [22] (cf. also T. Takenouchi [21]). This, however, does not lead to an essential improvement of Theorem 1.12.

2. The conjecture of Schinzel was considered by W. A. Webb who, as we already noted, proved $A_4(x) \ll x(\log x)^{-7/4}$ (W. A. Webb [70]) and showed later (W. A. Webb [76]) that in any case the constant $C(a)$ occurring in this conjecture must exceed $\exp(B \log a \log\log a)$ for sufficiently large a, with a constant $B > 0$. See also W. A. Webb [74].

C. Viola [73] generalized Theorem 1.14 to the following form: if a, k are given, then the number of positive integers $N \leqslant x$ such that the equation $a/N = 1/x_1 + \ldots + 1/x_k$ has no positive integral solutions is $O(x \exp(-B(\log x)^{1-1/k})$ with $B = B(a, k)$.

A connection between the Erdös–Straus conjecture and covering congruences was established by L. Bernstein [62].

3. Theorems 1.15 and 1.16 were proved by M. N. Bleicher and P. Erdös ([76a]) and in fact they obtained in Theorem 1.16 a better bound $O(b \log^3 b)$. These results were subsequently improved by M. N. Bleicher and P. Erdös [76b], who showed by more subtle arguments that for prime p one has

$$D(p) \geqslant p \log p \, \log\log p \, (\log_3 p \log_4 p \, \ldots \, \log_{r+1} p)^{-1}$$

provided $\log_{2r} p \geqslant 1$ and $\log_m x$ denotes the mth iterate of the logarithm. The proof of this result is based on a careful investigation of the number $S(N)$ of distinct values of

$$\sum_{k=1}^{N} \varepsilon_k/k \qquad (\varepsilon_k = 0, 1).$$

It is first shown that $S(N)$ exceeds $\exp\left(\dfrac{1}{e} \cdot \dfrac{N}{\log N} \prod_{k=3}^{r+1} \log_k N\right)$ where r is any integer such that $\log_{2r} N \geqslant 1$ (cf. also M. N. Bleicher, P. Erdös [75]) and, as the reasoning used in the proof of Theorem 1.15 leads to $S(x_t) \geqslant p$, one gets the needed lower bound.

M. N. Bleicher and P. Erdös also proved $D(b) \leqslant Cb \log^2 b$ with $C = (2/\log 2)^3$ for $b \geqslant 2$ and $D(b) \leqslant (1+\varepsilon) b \log^2 b$ for sufficiently large b and $\varepsilon > 0$. Their method is essentially the same as in the proof of Theorem 1.16 but the interval in Lemma 1.20 has to be chosen differently.

The equation $a/n = 1/x \pm 1/y \pm 1/z$ was first considered by W. Sierpiński [56]. W. Sierpiński [57], J. Sédlacek [59], G. Palamá [59], B. M. Stewart, W. A. Webb [66] and E. G. Straus and M. V. Subbarao [78] showed that for fixed a and sufficiently large n it is solvable for $a < 19$, $a < 21$, $a < 24$, $a < 36$ and $a < 40$ respectively.

The question of representing rational numbers with odd denominators as sums of distinct Egyptian fractions with odd denominators was also considered and the possibility of such representations was established by R. Breusch [54] and B. M. Stewart [54]. See also W. Sierpiński [57]. It is not known whether the analogue of the Fibonacci–Sylvester algorithm ends in a finite number of steps, and this is the substance of a problem proposed by S. K. Stein.

Exercises

1 (M. Nakayama [39]). Prove that $N(3, b) = 3$ if and only if every prime dividing b is congruent to unity (mod 3).

2. Prove that if $(a, b) = 1$ then $N(a, b) \leqslant 2$ if and only if $b = mn(ra - n)$ with suitable positive integers m, n, r.

3. Obtain an analogue of the preceding exercise in the case where $N(a, b) \leqslant 3$.

4 (K. Yamamoto [64]). Prove that if $p \leqslant 11$ is prime, then $N(p-1, p) \leqslant 4$.

5 (M. N. Bleicher–P. Erdős [76a]). Prove that if b is either a power of 2 or the product of the first k primes or finally equal to $k!$, then $D(b) = b$.

6 (ibidem). Prove that $D(3^n) = 2 \cdot 3^n$ for $n = 1, 2, \ldots$

7 (ibidem). Prove that if $b = p^n$ is a prime power then $D(b) \leqslant 2p^{n-1} D(p)$.

8 (A. Schinzel [56c]). Prove that the equation $3/(2n+1) = 1/x_1 + 1/x_2 + 1/x_3$ is, for all positive $n > 3$, solvable in odd integers $x_1 < x_2 < x_3$.

OPEN PROBLEMS

1. Does there exist an odd perfect number?

2. Are there infinitely many Mersenne primes?

3. Are there infinitely many composite numbers M_p with prime p?

4 (F. Jakóbczyk [51]). Prove that all numbers M_p are square-free.

5 (P. Erdős [65]). Let $P(n)$ be the maximal prime divisor of n. Prove that $P(M_n)/n$ tends to infinity.

6 (P. Erdős [76a]). Prove that the number of primes p for which 2 has the order $r \pmod p$ is $O(r^\varepsilon)$ for every positive ε.

7 (A. Schinzel [62c]). Let $u_n = a^n - b^n$, where $a > b > 0$ are integers. Prove that there is an index n such that u_n has at least three prime primitive divisors.

8. (a) Are there infinitely many primes p with $2^{p-1} \equiv 1 \pmod{p^2}$?

(b) Is there any such prime $p \neq 1093, 3511$?

(c) Are there infinitely many primes p with $2^{p-1} \not\equiv 1 \pmod{p^2}$?

9 (R. D. Carmichael [22]). Prove that for a positive integer m the equation $\varphi(x) = m$ cannot have a unique solution.

10 (D. H. Lehmer [32]). Does there exist a composite integer N with $\varphi(N)$ dividing $N - 1$?

11 (W. Sierpiński). Prove that for every $k \geqslant 2$ one can find an integer m_k such that the equation $\varphi(x) = m_k$ has exactly k solutions.

12. Prove that there exist infinitely many Carmichael numbers.

13. (a) Obtain the asymptotics for $V(x)$, the number of integer $m \leqslant x$, for which the equation $\varphi(y) = m$ is solvable.

(b) (P. Erdős, R. R. Hall [76]). Prove that for all $c \geqslant 1$ one has $\lim\limits_{x \to \infty} V(cx)/V(x) = c$.

14 (P. Erdős). Prove that for every $\varepsilon > 0$ and infinitely many integers m the equation $\varphi(x) = m$ has at least $m^{1-\varepsilon}$ solutions.

15 (M. N. Bleicher and P. Erdös [76a]). Define $D(b)$ as in § 4. Prove that if $(a, b) = 1$ one has $D(ab) \leqslant D(a) D(b)$.

16 (ibidem). Prove that for every positive ε one has $D(b) = O(b \log^{1+\varepsilon} b)$.

17 (P. Erdös [50]). Define $N(b)$ as in § 4. Prove that $N(b) = O(\log\log b)$.

18 (P. Erdös, E. G. Straus). Prove that for $n \geqslant 2$ the equation $4/n = 1/x + 1/y + 1/z$ is solvable in positive integers x, y, z.

19 (W. Sierpiński [57]). Prove the same for the equation $5/n = 1/x + 1/y + 1/z$.

20 (A. Schinzel). Prove that there exists a constant $C(a)$ such that for all $n \geqslant C(a)$ the equation

$$a/n = 1/x + 1/y + 1/z$$

is solvable in positive integers x, y, z.

21 (S. K. Stein). Let b be odd and $1 \leqslant a \leqslant b-1$. Define x_1 as the minimal odd number such that $a/b \geqslant 1/x_1$ and if $x_1, \ldots, x_r$ are already defined and

$$A_r = a/b - (1/x_1 + \ldots + 1/x_r) > 0$$

then let x_{r+1} be the minimal odd integer with $A_r \geqslant 1/x_{r+1}$. Prove that this algorithm terminates in a finite number of steps.

II

Primitive
roots

---

§ 1. CHARACTER SUMS

1. In the study of the distribution of primitive roots an important role is played by various sums involving characters. This is the reason for studying such sums before developing the story of primitive roots, which is the main topic of this chapter.

The importance of character sums to number theory was already noted by C. F. Gauss, who in his study of cyclotomy (Gauss [01], art. 356) was led to the definition, in a particular case, of what is nowadays known as a *Gaussian sum*.

We shall now define Gaussian sums, develop their fundamental properties and use them to obtain the Pólya–Vinogradov bound for the sum of the values of a character in an interval.

Let n be a given positive integer and let χ be a character $(\bmod\, n)$. If a is a given integer and ζ_n a fixed nth primitive root of unity, which we shall take to be equal to $\exp(2\pi i/n)$, then the corresponding *Gaussian sum* $\tau_a(\chi)$ is defined by the formula

$$\tau_a(\chi) = \sum_{x=1}^{n} \chi(x)\, \zeta_n^{ax}.$$

In the case $a = 1$ we shall omit the subscript and write simply $\tau(\chi)$ for $\tau_1(\chi)$.

Gauss himself considered the case where n is an odd prime and χ the corresponding quadratic character.

The following proposition establishes the principal properties of Gaussian sums:

PROPOSITION 2.1. (i) *If* $(a, n) = 1$ *then for all* b *one has* $\tau_{ab}(\chi) = \overline{\chi(a)}\, \tau_b(\chi)$. *If, moreover,* χ *is a primitive character then this equality holds for all* a.

In particular, if either $(a, n) = 1$ or χ is primitive, then

$$\tau_a(\chi) = \bar{\chi}(a) \cdot \tau(\chi).$$

(ii) If $n = n_1 n_2 \ldots n_r$ is a factorization of n into pairwise coprime factors and $\chi = \chi_1 \ldots \chi_r$ is the corresponding factorization of a character $\chi \,(\mathrm{mod}\, n)$ into characters $\chi_i \,(\mathrm{mod}\, n_i)$, then

$$\tau(\chi) = \prod_{i=1}^{r} \chi_i (n/n_i) \tau(\chi_i).$$

(iii) If χ is a primitive character $(\mathrm{mod}\, n)$, then $|\tau(\chi)| = n^{1/2}$.

(iv) If χ_0 is the principal character $(\mathrm{mod}\, n)$, then $\tau(\chi_0) = \mu(n)$.

Proof. If $(a, n) = 1$ and x runs over a complete set of residues $(\mathrm{mod}\, n)$ then ax does the same; hence

$$\tau_{ab}(\chi) = \sum_{x(\mathrm{mod}\, n)} \chi(x) \zeta_n^{abx} = \bar{\chi}(a) \sum_{x(\mathrm{mod}\, n)} \chi(ax) \zeta_n^{abx} = \bar{\chi}(a) \tau_b(\chi).$$

If $(a, n) > 1$ and χ is primitive, then it suffices to prove $\tau_a(\chi) = 0$. Writing $(a, n) = d$, $a = a_1 d$, $n = n_1 d$ with $(a_1, n_1) = 1$, we get

$$\tau_a(\chi) = \sum_{x(\mathrm{mod}\, n)} \chi(x) \zeta_{n_1}^{a_1 x} = \sum_{r=0}^{n_1-1} \left(\sum_{q=0}^{d-1} \chi(qn_1 + r) \right) \zeta_{n_1}^{a_1 r}.$$

We shall prove that the inner sum vanishes for $r = 0, 1, \ldots, n_1 - 1$. If we put for $r = 1, 2, \ldots$,

$$X_r = \{x(\mathrm{mod}\, n) : x \equiv r (\mathrm{mod}\, n_1), (x, n) = 1\},$$

then the inner sum equals $\sum_{x \in X_r} \chi(x)$. Now X_r is a coset in the group $G(n)$ $= (Z/nZ)^*$ with respect to the subgroup X_1, and if u_r is a fixed element of X_r then

$$\sum_{x \in X_r} \chi(x) = \chi(u_r) \sum_{u \in X_1} \chi(u).$$

Since χ is primitive, it is not identically equal to 1 on X_1 and, X_1 being a subgroup, the sum $\sum_{u \in X_1} \chi(u)$ vanishes.

To prove (ii) observe that in the case $r = 2$, after choosing integers A, B with $An_1 + Bn_2 = 1$ and denoting by x_i the residue $x(\mathrm{mod}\, n_i)$ for $i = 1, 2$, we get

$$\tau(\chi) = \sum_{x(\mathrm{mod}\, n)} \chi(x) \zeta_n^x = \sum_{x(\mathrm{mod}\, n)} \chi_1(x_1) \chi_2(x_2) \exp\left\{\frac{2\pi i}{n} x(An_1 + Bn_2)\right\}$$

$$= \sum_{x(\mathrm{mod}\, n)} \chi_1(x_1) \chi_2(x_2) \exp\left\{\frac{2\pi i x A}{n_2}\right\} \exp\left\{\frac{2\pi i x B}{n_1}\right\}$$

$$= \sum_{x(\mathrm{mod}\, n)} \chi_1(x_1) \chi_2(x_2) \exp\left\{\frac{2\pi i x_2 A}{n_2}\right\} \exp\left\{\frac{2\pi i x_1 B}{n_1}\right\} = \tau_B(\chi_1) \tau_A(\chi_2)$$

by the Chinese Remainder Theorem and it now suffices to apply (i).

In the general case we use induction. By applying the inductive assumption to $n_0 = n_1 \ldots n_{r-1}$ and making use of the case $r = 2$ just proved, we get our assertion.

To prove (iii) we write, using (i),

$$\varphi(n)|\tau(\chi)|^2 = \sum_{a(\mathrm{mod}\,n)} \tau_a(\chi)\overline{\tau_a(\chi)}$$

$$= \sum_{x(\mathrm{mod}\,n)} \sum_{y(\mathrm{mod}\,n)} \chi(x)\overline{\chi(y)} \sum_{a(\mathrm{mod}\,n)} \zeta_n^{a(x-y)} = n \sum_{x(\mathrm{mod}\,n)} \chi(x)\overline{\chi(x)}$$

$$= n \cdot \varphi(n),$$

and this readily implies our assertion.

Finally, to prove (iv) observe that $\tau(\chi_0) = \sum\limits_{(k,n)=1} \zeta_n^k = A_n$, say, and since for $d \geqslant 2$

$$\sum_{d\mid n} A_d = \sum_{d\mid n} \sum_{\substack{1\leqslant k \leqslant d \\ (k,d)=n}} \zeta_d^k = \sum_{k=1}^{n} \zeta_n^k = 0$$

and $\sum\limits_{d\mid n} A_d = 1$ for $n = 1$, the Möbius inversion formula gives $A_n = \mu(n)$. □

2. Proposition 2.1 does not shed any light on the argument of $\tau(\chi)$. In the case of a quadratic character and prime n its value was determined by C. F. Gauss [11], and by using this it is easy to obtain a simple formula valid for all primitive real characters.

THEOREM 2.1. *If χ is a real primitive character* (mod n) *then*

$$\tau(\chi) = \begin{cases} n^{1/2} & \text{if} \quad \chi(-1) = 1, \\ in^{1/2} & \text{if} \quad \chi(-1) = -1. \end{cases}$$

Proof. We first prove this formula for the case of $n = p$, where p is a prime, following the argument of W. C. Waterhouse [70].

We shall construct a linear mapping in a $(p-1)$-dimensional linear complex space and compute the discriminant of its matrix in two bases. The comparison of the results obtained will give us the desired equality.

The space in question will be the space L of all complex-valued functions defined on $G(p)$, the group of non-zero residue classes (mod p). In this space we have two obvious choices for a basis: one formed by the characteristic functions $\varepsilon_1, \ldots, \varepsilon_{p-1}$ of points in $G(p)$ and the other by all distinct characters $\chi_1, \ldots, \chi_{p-1}$ mod p. For $g \in L$ we define

$$T_g(n) = \sum_{k=1}^{p-1} g(k)\zeta_p^{kn} \quad \text{for} \quad n = 1, 2, \ldots, p-1.$$

Clearly the map $T\colon g \to T_g$ is linear. We now compute the discriminant Δ of T.

One can easily see that the matrix of T^2 in the basis $\varepsilon_1, \ldots, \varepsilon_{p-1}$ equals

$$\begin{bmatrix} p & 0 & \cdots & 0 \\ 0 & 0 & \cdots & p \\ \cdot & \cdot & \cdots & \cdot \\ 0 & p & \cdots & 0 \end{bmatrix};$$

hence $\Delta^2 = (-1)^{p(p-1)/2} p^{p-1}$ and it follows that

(2.1) $$\Delta = \pm i^{p(p-1)/2} p^{(p-1)/2}.$$

The sign is readily obtained as follows: put $\exp(i\pi/p) = x$ and write, with indices k, j satisfying $0 \leqslant k, j \leqslant p-1$,

$$\Delta = \det(\zeta_p^{kn}) = \prod_{k<j} (\zeta_p^j - \zeta_p^k) = \prod_{k<j} x^{k+j}(x^{j-k} - x^{k-j})$$

$$= \prod_{k<j} x^{k+j} \cdot \prod_{k<j} (2i\sin\{(j-k)\pi/p\}).$$

The first factor here equals 1 and the second $i^{p(p-1)/2} A$ with positive A, since $0 < (j-k)\pi/p < \pi$. This shows that the sign in (2.1) is positive, i.e.,

(2.2) $$\Delta = i^{p(p-1)/2} p^{(p-1)/2}.$$

To find Δ via the basis composed of characters observe first that for any character χ we have $T_\chi = \tau(\chi)\bar\chi$ and thus the matrix of T in this basis consists of blocks

$$\begin{bmatrix} 0 & \tau(\chi_i) \\ \tau(\bar\chi_i) & 0 \end{bmatrix}$$

corresponding to pairs of conjugate non-real characters χ_i, $\bar\chi_i$ and has moreover two diagonal entries: -1, corresponding to the trivial character, and $\tau(\chi)$, corresponding to the quadratic character χ. By using Proposition 2.1 (iii) and (iv) and the obvious fact that for any character ψ one has $\tau(\bar\psi) = \psi(-1)\tau(\psi)$ we obtain

$$\Delta = -\tau(\chi) \prod_{\psi \neq 1, \chi} (-\tau(\psi)\tau(\bar\psi)) = -\tau(\chi)(-1)^{(p-3)/2} p^{(p-3)/2} \prod_{\psi \neq 1, \chi} \psi(-1)$$

$$= (-1)^{(p-1)/2} \tau(\chi) p^{(p-3)/2} (-1)^N,$$

where N denotes the number of characters $\psi \neq 1$, χ for which $\psi(-1) = -1$, counting only one character from every pair of conjugates. Now there are $(p-1)/2$ characters with this property. If $p \equiv 1 \pmod 4$ they are all non-real; thus in this case $N = (p-1)/4$, and if $p \equiv 3 \pmod 4$ then the quadratic character also shares this property and $N = (p-3)/4$.

Using (2.2), we now get

$$\tau(\chi) = i^{p(p-1)/2} (-1)^{N + (p-1)/2} p^{1/2},$$

and considering separately the cases $p \equiv 1 \pmod 4$ and $p \equiv 3 \pmod 4$ we obtain our assertion for prime n.

Now we turn to the general case. Proposition A.7 implies that if χ is a primitive real character $\pmod n$ then $n = 2^a p_1 \ldots p_r$, where $p_1, \ldots, p_r$ are distinct odd primes and $a = 0, 2, 3$. This shows that we can write $\chi = \prod_{i=0}^{r} \chi_i$, where $\chi_i(x) = (x/p_i)$ for $i \neq 0$ and $\chi_0(x)$ is a primitive real character $\pmod{2^a}$. Proposition 2.1 (ii) shows that

$$\tau(\chi) = \prod_{i=1}^{r} \chi_0(p_i) \chi_i(p_0) \prod_{1 \leqslant j < k \leqslant r} \left(\frac{p_j}{p_k}\right)\left(\frac{p_k}{p_j}\right) \cdot \prod_{s=0}^{r} \tau(\chi_s).$$

If we denote by t_k the number of prime divisors of n congruent to $k \pmod 8$ and put $K = \binom{t_3 + t_7}{2}$, then

$$\prod_{i=1}^{r} \chi_0(p_i) = \begin{cases} 1 & \text{if} \quad a = 0, \\ (-1)^{t_3 + t_7} & \text{if} \quad a = 2, \\ (-1)^{t_3 + t_5} & \text{if} \quad a = 3, \quad \chi_0(-1) = 1, \\ (-1)^{t_5 + t_7} & \text{if} \quad a = 3, \quad \chi_0(-1) = -1, \end{cases}$$

$$\prod_{i=1}^{r} \chi_i(p_0) = \begin{cases} 1 & \text{if} \quad a = 0, 2, \\ \prod_{i=1}^{r} \left(\frac{2}{p_i}\right) = (-1)^{t_3 + t_5} & \text{if} \quad a = 3, \end{cases}$$

and

$$\prod_{1 \leqslant j < k \leqslant r} \left(\frac{p_j}{p_k}\right)\left(\frac{p_k}{p_j}\right) = (-1)^K.$$

By using the already proved part of the theorem and directly computing the value of $\tau(\chi_0)$, we get

$$\tau(\chi_s) = \begin{cases} p_s^{1/2} & \text{if} \quad p_s \equiv 1 \pmod 4, \\ i p_s^{1/2} & \text{if} \quad p_s \equiv 3 \pmod 4, \\ 1 & \text{if} \quad s = 0, \quad a = 1, \\ 2i & \text{if} \quad s = 0, \quad a = 2, \\ 2^{3/2} i & \text{if} \quad s = 0, \quad a = 3, \quad \chi_0(-1) = -1, \\ 2^{3/2} & \text{if} \quad s = 0, \quad a = 3, \quad \chi_0(-1) = 1. \end{cases}$$

By multiplying all the resulting equalities we obtain our assertion. □

COROLLARY. *If n is a positive, odd and square-free integer, then in the case of $n \equiv 1 \pmod 4$ the n-th cyclotomic field $Q(\zeta_n)$ contains $n^{1/2}$ whereas in the case of $n \equiv 3 \pmod 4$ it contains $i n^{1/2}$.* □

3. By using the properties of Gaussian sums developed above we prove a result of G. Pólya [18a] and I. M. Vinogradov [18] giving the first nontrivial bound for the sum of values of a primitive character (mod N) in an interval. Our proof is that given by I. Schur [18].

THEOREM 2.2. *If $N \geqslant 3$ and χ is a primitive character (mod N) then for all $x \geqslant 1$ one has*

$$\left| \sum_{n \leqslant x} \chi(n) \right| \leqslant N^{1/2} \log N.$$

Proof. By using Proposition 2.1 (i) we obtain

$$\tau(\bar{\chi}) \sum_{n \leqslant x} \chi(n) = \sum_{m=1}^{N-1} \overline{\chi(m)} \sum_{n \leqslant x} \zeta_N^{mn},$$

and thus in view of part (iii) of that proposition we may write

$$\left| \sum_{n \leqslant x} \chi(n) \right| \leqslant N^{-1/2} \sum_{m=1}^{N-1} \left| \sum_{n \leqslant x} \zeta_N^{mn} \right|$$

$$\leqslant N^{-1/2} \sum_{m=1}^{N-1} \frac{1}{\left| \sin\left(\dfrac{\pi m}{N}\right) \right|} = 2N^{-1/2} \sum_{1 \leqslant m \leqslant (N-1)/2} \frac{1}{\left| \sin\left(\dfrac{\pi m}{N}\right) \right|}$$

$$\leqslant N^{1/2} \sum_{m \leqslant (N-1)/2} \frac{1}{m}$$

because $0 < \alpha < \pi/2$ implies $1/\sin\alpha < \pi/2\alpha$.

Since for $t \geqslant 5$ one has $\sum_{m \leqslant t/2} 1/m \leqslant \log t$ our assertion follows for $N \geqslant 6$, and for $N = 3, 4, 5$ one easily checks its truth directly. $\square$

4. If p is an odd prime and the length of the interval over which we add the values of a character $\chi \pmod{p}$ is small in comparison with p, e.g., is of the order $O(p^t)$ with t smaller than $1/2$, then a better bound than that resulting from Theorem 2.2 is available, due to D. A. Burgess [62a]. He was able to apply the Riemann conjecture for function fields (proved by A. Weil [48]) to obtain a bound leading to many interesting applications.

THEOREM 2.3. *If p is an odd prime and χ a non-principal character* (mod p) *then for all positive integers N, h, r the following inequality holds:*

$$|S_h(N)| = \left| \sum_{m=1+N}^{h+N} \chi(m) \right| \leqslant Ch^{1-1/(r+1)} p^{1/4r} \log p,$$

C being an absolute constant.

Proof. The idea of the proof is to use Weil's result to obtain a good bound for

$$S_{h,r} = \sum_{x=0}^{p-1} |S_h(x)|^{2r}$$

(Lemma 2.1 below) and then evaluate $|S_h(n)|$ in terms of $S_{H,r}$ with a suitably chosen $H = H(h, n)$.

Since $S_h(N)$ is a periodic function of h with period p, we shall henceforth assume $h < p$.

LEMMA 2.1. *For all positive integrals h and r we have*

$$S_{h,r} < (4r)^r ph^r + 2r h^{2r} p^{1/2}.$$

Proof. We may assume $h \geqslant 4r$ since otherwise

$$S_{h,r} \leqslant ph^{2r} < p(4r)^r h^r.$$

To see how the proof works consider first the case $r = 1$. In this case we have

$$S_{h,1} = \sum_{x=0}^{p-1} |S_h(x)|^2 = \sum_{x=0}^{p-1} \sum_{k_1=1}^{h} \sum_{k_2=1}^{h} \chi(x+k_1) \overline{\chi(x+k_2)},$$

and since for all m we have the equality $\overline{\chi(m)} = \chi(m)^{n-1}$ with n equal to the order of χ, it follows that

$$S_{h,1} = \sum_{k_1=1}^{h} \sum_{k_2=1}^{h} \sum_{x=0}^{p-1} \chi((x+k_1)(x+k_2)^{n-1}).$$

To the inner sum we can apply Weil's theorem (Theorem A.9), provided the polynomial $(x+k_1)(x+k_2)^{n-1}$ does not differ by a constant factor from an nth power (mod p). This will occur if and only if $k_1 \not\equiv k_2 \pmod{p}$, and by applying in the case $k_1 \equiv k_2 \pmod{p}$ the trivial bound we arrive at

$$S_{h,1} \leqslant \sum_{k_1=1}^{h} \sum_{\substack{1 \leqslant k_2 \leqslant h \\ k_2 \neq k_1}} p^{1/2} + \sum_{k=1}^{h} p \leqslant h^2 p^{1/2} + hp,$$

which is even slightly better than our assertion.

In the general case the principal idea is the same; however, we have to count in a delicate way the polynomials which differ merely by a constant from a dth power with $d > 1$, $d | n$. We start as before:

$$S_{h,r} = \sum_{x=0}^{p-1} |S_h(x)|^{2r}$$

$$= \sum_{x=0}^{p-1} \sum_{k_1,\ldots,k_{2r}=1}^{h} \chi(\prod_{j=1}^{r} (x+k_j)) \overline{\chi(\prod_{j=1+r}^{2r} (x+k_j))}$$

$$= \sum_{k_1,\ldots,k_{2r}=1}^{h} \sum_{x=0}^{p-1} \chi(\prod_{j=1}^{r} (x+k_j)(x+k_{j+r})^{n-1}),$$

and if T denotes the number of polynomials

(2.3) $$\prod_{j=1}^{r} (x+k_j)(x+k_{j+r})^{n-1}   (1 \leqslant k_1, \ldots, k_{2r} \leqslant h)$$

which are dth powers (mod p) with $d > 1$, $d|n$, then by using Theorem A.9 we arrive at

$$S_{h,r} \leqslant (2r - h^{2r}) p^{1/2} + p \cdot T.$$

We thus need a bound for T. To obtain it observe that if a polynomial of the form (2.3) is a dth power (mod p) with $d > 1$, then none of the residues $k_1 \,(\text{mod } p), \ldots, k_{2r} \,(\text{mod } p)$ can appear once. If we now denote by T_0 the number of $2r$-tuples $(k_1, \ldots, k_{2r})$ where $1 \leqslant k_i \leqslant h$ $(i = 1, 2, \ldots, 2r)$ such that no k_i appears only once, then $T \leqslant T_0$.

To evaluate T_0 let us first fix the number q of distinct k_i's and the indices $1 = j_1 < j_2 < \ldots < j_q$ of their first appearances. We get h^q possibilities for the numbers $k_{j_1}, \ldots, k_{j_q}$, and since for the remaining $2r - q$ positions we can choose numbers only from the set $\{k_{j_1}, \ldots, k_{j_q}\}$, we get altogether $q^{2r-q} h^q$ $2r$-tuples.

By using $h > r$ we now get

$$T_0 \leqslant \sum_{q=1}^{r} \binom{2r-1}{q-1} q^{2r-q} h^q \leqslant \sum_{q=2}^{r} \binom{2r-1}{q-1} \left(\frac{h}{q}\right)^r \left(\frac{q^2}{hr}\right)^r (hr)^r$$

$$= \sum_{q=2}^{r} \binom{2r-1}{q-1} \left(\frac{q}{r}\right)^r (hr)^r \leqslant (hr)^r \sum_{j=0}^{2r-1} \binom{2r-1}{j} = (hr)^r \cdot 2^{2r-1} < (4hr)^r$$

and the lemma follows. □

To obtain an upper bound for $S_h(N)$ in terms of $S_{H,r}$ with a suitably chosen H we need a sequence of lemmas, which we shall now outline.

Let h and N be fixed and denote, for short, $|S_h(N)|$ by S. With every prime $q < p$ and any integer $0 \leqslant t < q$ we shall associate an interval $I(q, t)$ with the property that

$$S \leqslant \sum_{t=0}^{q-1} \left| \sum_{m \in I(q,t)} \chi(m) \right|.$$

Selecting a set A of M primes $q < p$, we deduce

$$M \cdot S \leqslant \sum_{q \in A} \sum_{t=0}^{q-1} \left| \sum_{m \in I(q,t)} \chi(m) \right|$$

and afterwards a technical lemma will show that one can select a set J of disjoint intervals $I(q, t)$ such that this inequality will be preserved up to a constant factor if we restrict the summation to those q, t for which $I(q, t) \in J$.

By applying an elementary sum transformation (Lemma 2.4) we shall obtain with a suitable T the evaluation

$$\left| \sum_{m \in I(q,t)} \chi(m) \right| \leq \frac{1}{T} \sum_{m \in I(q,t)} |S_T(m)| + 2T$$

and finally by choosing the parameters M and T according to S in an appropriate way and applying Hölder's inequality to the last formula we shall arrive at our assertion.

Now we perform the program outlined above. Consider a positive integer $q < p$ and observe that the numbers $0, -p, -2p, \ldots, -(q-1)p$ form a complete set of residues $(\bmod\, q)$; thus

$$S = \left| \sum_{t=0}^{q-1} \sum_{\substack{N+1 \leq n \leq N+h \\ n \equiv -tp(\bmod q)}} \chi(n) \right| \leq \sum_{t=0}^{q-1} \left| \sum_{\substack{N+1 \leq n \leq N+h \\ n \equiv -tp(\bmod q)}} \chi(n) \right|.$$

Denoting by $I(q, t)$ the interval $[(N+tp+1)/q, (N+h+tp)/q]$ (whose length is less than h/q) and putting $m = (n+tp)/q$, we get from the above inequality

(2,4) $$S \leq \sum_{t=0}^{q-1} \left| \sum_{m \in I(q,t)} \chi(qm) \right| = \sum_{t=0}^{q-1} \left| \sum_{m \in I(q,t)} \chi(m) \right|.$$

We shall need a large set of pairs (q, t) with disjoint sets $I(q, t)$ and this can be accomplished with the aid of the following lemma:

LEMMA 2.2. *Let A be a set of M coprime integers contained in an interval $[Q_1, Q_2]$ with $Q_1 > M$ and $Q_2 < p/2h$. Then for every $q \in A$ one can find a set $T(q)$ of integers contained in $[0, q)$ which has $q - M$ elements and has the property that all intervals $I(q, t)$ with $q \in A$, $t \in T(q)$ are disjoint.*

Proof. If for a certain q the intervals $I(q, t)$ and $I(q, t')$ have a common point, then the inequality $h < p$ implies $t = t'$. Assume now that $q \neq q'$ and the intervals $I(q, t)$ and $I(q', t')$ have a non-empty intersection. Since the sum of the lengths of two overlapping intervals must be at least equal to the diameter of their union, we must have (interchanging if necessary the pairs (t, q) and (t', q')) the inequality

$$\frac{p}{qq'} > \frac{h(q+q')}{qq'} > (h-1)(1/q + 1/q')$$

$$\geq \frac{1}{qq'}(Nq' + hq' + Nq + p(tq' - t'q)) > 0,$$

which implies

$$p > p(tq' - t'q) + (Nq' + hq' - Nq) > 0;$$

hence there is only one possible value of $tq' - t'q$. Since $0 \leq t < q$, $0 \leq t' < q'$ and $(q, q') = 1$, it follows that for given q and q' there is only one possible pair t, t' such that $I(q, t)$ and $I(q', t')$ have a non-empty intersection. For each $q \in A$ remove from $[0, q)$ all values of t which can appear here for any q'. The remaining set will contain at least $(q-1)-(M-1) = q-M$ elements and if we select $q-M$ of them to form the set $T(q)$, then all the assertions of the lemma will be satisfied. $\square$

In the following lemma we show that without any substantial loss one can carry out the summation in (2.4) over a set of mutually disjoint intervals $I(q, t)$.

LEMMA 2.3. *Let* $0 < v < 1$ *be a fixed constant. Choose a positive integer* $M < v|S|$, *select* Q_1 *so that* $\pi(2Q_1) - \pi(Q_1) \geqslant M$ *and* $p/2 > Q_1 > hM/(vS-M)$ *and finally define* $Q_2 = 2Q_1$. *If* A *is a set of* M *primes contained in* $[Q_1, Q_2]$ *and the sets* $T(q)$ *are defined for* $q \in A$ *in accordance with Lemma 2.2, then for* $J = \{I(q, t): q \in A, t \in T(q)\}$ *we shall have*

$$MS \leqslant \frac{1}{1-v} \sum_{I(q,t) \in J} \Big| \sum_{m \in I(q,t)} \chi(m) \Big|.$$

Proof. In view of (2.4) we need an upper bound for

$$X = \sum_{q \in A} \sum_{\substack{0 \leqslant t < q \\ t \notin T(q)}} \Big| \sum_{m \in I(q,t)} \chi(m) \Big|$$

but, evaluating the inner sum trivially and remembering that $I(q, t)$ is of length $\leqslant h/Q_1$ and $|T(q)| = q-M$, we obtain

$$X \leqslant \sum_{q \in A} M\left(1 + \frac{h}{Q_1}\right) = M^2\left(1 + \frac{h}{Q_1}\right) < vSM$$

and the lemma follows. $\square$

Now we bound the sum $\sum_{m \in I(q,t)} \chi(m)$ in terms of $S_{H,r}$ with a suitably chosen H and for this purpose we need a simple lemma:

LEMMA 2.4. *Let* $f(n)$ *be any function satisfying* $|f(x)| \leqslant 1$ *and let* I *be a given interval. Then for every positive and integral* H *we have*

$$\Big| \sum_{n \in I} f(n) \Big| \leqslant 2H + \frac{1}{H} \sum_{n \in I} \Big| \sum_{m=n+1}^{n+H} f(m) \Big|.$$

Proof. We have

$$\sum_{n \in I} \Big| \sum_{m=n+1}^{n+H} f(m) \Big| \geqslant \Big| \sum_{n \in I} \sum_{k=1}^{H} f(n+k) \Big|$$

$$= \Big| \sum_{k=1}^{H} \Big\{ \sum_{n \in I} f(n) + \sum_{\substack{n \notin I \\ n-k \in I}} f(n) - \sum_{\substack{n \in I \\ n-k \notin I}} f(n) \Big\} \Big|$$

$$\geqslant \Big| \sum_{k=1}^{H} \sum_{n \in I} f(n) \Big| - 2 \sum_{k=1}^{H} k \geqslant H \Big| \sum_{n \in I} f(n) \Big| - 2H^2,$$

which is equivalent to our assertion. $\square$

COROLLARY 1. *For every* q, t *and* H *we have*

$$\left| \sum_{n \in I(q,t)} \chi(n) \right| \leqslant 2H + \frac{1}{H} \sum_{n \in I(q,t)} |S_H(n)|. \ \square$$

COROLLARY 2. *Using the notation of Lemma 2.3, assume that* H *is a positive integer such that* $H < (\frac{1}{2} - \varepsilon)(S/Q_2)$ *for a certain* $\varepsilon > v/2$. *Then*

$$MS \leqslant \frac{1}{(2\varepsilon - v) H} \sum_{I \in J} \sum_{n \in I} |S_H(n)|.$$

Proof. By Lemma 2.3 and the previous corollary we obtain

$$MS \leqslant \frac{1}{1-v} \sum_{I \in J} \left(2H + \frac{1}{H} \sum_{n \in I} |S_H(n)| \right),$$

but in view of

(2.5) $$\sum_{I \in J} 1 \leqslant \sum_{q \in A} q \leqslant MQ_2$$

this leads to

$$MS \leqslant \frac{2HQ_2}{1-v} M + \frac{1}{(1-v)H} \sum_{I \in J} \sum_{n \in I} |S_H(n)| \leqslant \frac{1-2\varepsilon}{1-v} MS + \frac{1}{(1-v)H} \sum_{I \in J} \sum_{n \in I} |S_H(n)|,$$

and since $1 - \dfrac{1-2\varepsilon}{1-v} = \dfrac{2\varepsilon - v}{1-v} > 0$ our assertion follows. $\square$

Now we have all tools prepared for the proof of the theorem. Retaining the notation of Lemma 2.3 and Corollary 2 to Lemma 2.4, we apply Hölder's inequality to the right-hand side of the inequality of that corollary and obtain

$$MS \leqslant \frac{1}{(2\varepsilon - v) H} \left(\sum_{I \in J} \sum_{n \in I} 1 \right)^{1-1/2r} \left(\sum_{I \in J} \sum_{n \in I} |S_H(n)|^{2r} \right)^{1/2r}.$$

But by (2.5) $\sum_{I \in J} \sum_{n \in I} 1 \leqslant \left(1 + \dfrac{h}{Q_1} \right) MQ_2$ and, since the intervals $I \in J$ are mutually disjoint and contained in the interval

$$[(N+1)/Q_2, \ (N+h+Q_1 p - p)/Q_1]$$

of length

$$\frac{2(N+h+Q_1 p - p) - N - 1}{2Q_1} = p + \frac{N + 2(h-p) - 1}{2Q_1} < 2p,$$

we have in view of $S_H(n+p) = S_H(n)$

$$\sum_{I \in J} \sum_{n \in I} |S_H(n)|^{2r} \leqslant \sum_{n=0}^{2p-1} |S_H(n)|^{2r} \leqslant 2 \sum_{n=0}^{p-1} |S_H(n)|^{2r} = 2S_{H,r}.$$

Finally we get

$$(2.6) \qquad HMS \leqslant \frac{1}{2\varepsilon - v}\left(1 + \frac{h}{Q_1}\right)^{1-1/2r}(MQ_2)^{1-1/2r}2^{1/2r}S_{H,r}^{1/2r}.$$

Now it is time to make a choice of the parameters Q_1, Q_2, M and H, but before doing that we shall quickly deal with certain cases in which our assertion either becomes trivial or is a consequence of Theorem 2.2. They are the following:

(a) In the case $h \leqslant p^{1/4 + 1/4r}\log^{r+1}p$ our assertion holds with $C = 1$ since otherwise we would have

$$h \geqslant |S| \geqslant h^{1 - 1/(r+1)}p^{1/4r}\log p$$

and thus h would exceed $p^{1/4 + 1/4r}\log p$.

(b) In the case $h \geqslant \frac{1}{2}p^{1/2 + 1/4r}$ if our assertion with $C = 1$ is false, then by Theorem 2.2

$$h^{1 - 1/(r+1)}p^{1/4r}\log p < |S| \leqslant p^{1/2}\log p,$$

giving for $p \geqslant 17$

$$h < p^{1/2 + 1/4r - 1/4r^2} \leqslant \tfrac{1}{2}p^{1/2 + 1/4r},$$

but for $p < 17$ the theorem is true in any case.

(c) In the case $r \geqslant \log p$ the assertion holds with $C = 1$, since otherwise

$$h \geqslant |S| > h^{1 - 1/(r+1)}p^{1/4r}\log p,$$

and thus

$$h^{1/(r+1)} > p^{1/4r}\log p > \log p;$$

however, $h^{1/(r+1)} = \exp(\log h/(r+1)) < \exp(\log h/\log p) \leqslant e$ and we would have $\log p \leqslant e$, $p < 16$.

We may hence assume in the sequel that following inequalities are satisfied:

$$(2.7) \qquad p^{1/4 + 1/4r}\log^{r+1}p < h < \tfrac{1}{2}p^{1/2 + 1/4r},$$

$$(2.8) \qquad 1 \leqslant r < \log p$$

and we may also assume

$$(2.9) \qquad S > h^{1 - 1/(r+1)}p^{1/4r}\log p.$$

We make the following choice:

$$H = [rp^{1/2r}], \qquad Q_1 = S/16H, \qquad Q_2 = 2Q_1 = S/8H,$$

$$M = [S^2/2^7\,hH\log p], \qquad \varepsilon = 87/340, \qquad v = 1/85.$$

We have to check that the conditions of Lemmas 2.2, 2.3 and the Corollary 2 to Lemma 2.4 are satisfied by this choice of parameters. In Lemma 2.2 we had to assume $M < Q_1 < Q_2 < p/2h$. Since $M/Q_1 \leqslant S/8h\log p < 1/8\log p < 1$ the first inequality follows and as regards the second observe that if $Q_2 \geqslant p/2h$ then $S \geqslant 4pH/h$; hence $h^2 \geqslant 4pH \geqslant 4p(p^{1/2r}-1)$, but this in view of (2.7) leads to $p^{1/2r} \leqslant 16/15$; however (2.8) implies that $p^{1/2r} > e^{1/2} > 3/2 > 16/15$, which is a contradiction.

Checking the conditions of Lemma 2.3 is more complicated. We have to show that $M < vS$, $\pi(2Q_1)-\pi(Q_1) \geqslant M$ and $p/2 > Q_1 > hM/(vS-M)$.

The ratio M/S is bounded by

$$\frac{S}{2^7\,hH\log p} \leqslant \frac{1}{2^7\,H\log p} < \frac{1}{2^7\,\log p} < \frac{1}{2^7\,\log 2} < \frac{1}{85},$$

which proves the first inequality. To obtain the second we have to assume that p is sufficiently large (this does not restrict the generality), so that for $u \geqslant \log p/16$ we have the inequality $\pi(2u)-\pi(u) > u/2\log u$. But in view of (2.7), (2.8) and (2.9) we have

$$Q_1 = \frac{S}{16H} \geqslant \frac{S}{16rp^{1/2r}} \geqslant \frac{1}{16r}h^{1-1/(r+1)}\,p^{-1/4r}\log p$$

$$\geqslant \frac{\log^{r+1}p}{16r}\,p^{1/4-(1/4(r+1))-(1/4r(r+1))} \geqslant \frac{\log^2 p}{16r} > \frac{\log p}{16};$$

hence

$$\pi(Q_2)-\pi(Q_1) \geqslant \frac{Q_1}{2\log Q_1} \geqslant \frac{S}{32H\log S},$$

and if this were less than M, then

$$\frac{S^2}{2^7\,hH\log p} > \frac{S}{2^5\,H\log S}$$

and

$$4h\log p < S\log S \leqslant h\log h < h\log p,$$

a contradiction.

We have seen above that $Q_1 < p/2h$; thus the second condition is satisfied and to prove the third observe that if $Q_1 \leqslant hM/(S-M)$ we obtain

$$\left(\frac{S}{85}-\frac{S^2}{2^7\,hH\log p}\right)\frac{S}{16H} \leqslant \left(\frac{S}{85}-M\right)Q_1 \leqslant hM \leqslant \frac{hS^2}{2^7\,hH\log p},$$

which leads to

$$\frac{1}{85}-\frac{S}{2^7\,hH\log p} \leqslant \frac{1}{8}\log p,$$

and finally

$$\frac{8\log p}{85} \leqslant 1+\frac{S}{2^4\,hH} \leqslant 1+\frac{1}{16H} < 2$$

gives $\log p \leqslant 170/8$ showing $p < 10^{10}$. Thus for sufficiently large p the conditions of Lemma 2.3 are satisfied. The last condition to be checked is that of Corollary 2 to Lemma 2.4, stating that $H < (1/2-\varepsilon)S/Q_2$, $\varepsilon > v/2 = 1/170$. But from the definition of Q_2 it follows immediately that with every ε from the interval $(1/170, 7/16)$ this inequality holds. Our choice of ε has this advantage that the coefficient in (2.6) equals 2.

Having checked all the conditions we may apply (2.6) to get a lower bound for $S_{H,r}$. As $1+h/Q_1 < 2h/Q_1$ (due to $Q_1 = S/16H < h/16$), we obtain

$$HMS \leqslant 2\left(\frac{2h}{Q_1}\,MQ_2\right)^{1-1/2r} 2^{1/2r}\,S_{H,r}^{1/2r} = 2(4hM)^{1-1/2r}\,2^{1/2r}\,S_{H,r}^{1/2r}$$

and

$$S_{H,r} \geqslant \frac{(HMS)^{2r}}{2^{1+2r}}(4hM)^{1-2r} = H^{2r}\,Mh^{1-2r}\,S^{2r}\,2^{-6r+1}$$

$$\geqslant 2^{-6r-7}\,h^{-2r}\,H^{2r-1}\,S^{2+2r}\,\log^{-1}p.$$

Now we apply Lemma 2.1 and, using $H^r \leqslant r^r\,p^{1/2}$ as well as $(r/H)^{1/2} \ll p^{-1/4r}$, arrive at our assertion via the following chain of inequalities:

$$S^{2+2r} \leqslant 2^{6r+7}\,h^{2r}\,H^{1-2r}\,\log p\,\{H^r\,p(4r)^r + 2rH^{2r}\,p^{1/2}\}$$

$$= 2^{6r+7}\,h^{2r}\,H^{1-r}\,p^{1/2}\,\log p\,\{(4r)^r\,p^{1/2} + 2rH^r\}$$

$$\leqslant 2^{6r+7}\,h^{2r}\,H^{1-r}\,p^{1/2}\,\log p\,\{2\cdot 4^r\,r^r\,p^{1/2}\}$$

$$= 2^{8(r+1)}\,h^{2r}\,Hp\log p\,(r/H)^r;$$

hence

$$S \leqslant 16h^{1-1/(1+r)}\,H^{1/2(1+r)}\,(p\log p)^{1/2(1+r)}\,(r/H)^{1/2}$$

$$\ll h^{1-1/(1+r)}\,(rp^{1/2r})^{1/2(1+r)}\,(p\log p)^{1/2(1+r)}\,p^{-1/4r}$$

$$\ll h^{1-1/(1+r)}\,p^{1/4(r+1)}\,(\log p)^{1/(1+r)}$$

contradicting (2.9) for sufficiently large p. □

Notes and comments

1. As already noted, the first character sums considered were Gaussian sums. They originated in art. 356 of Gauss [01], where the periods of length $(p-1)/2$, p being an odd prime, were studied. In modern terminology these periods are equal to

$$P_+ = \sum_r \exp(2\pi i r/p) \quad \text{and} \quad P_- = \sum_n \exp(2\pi i n/p),$$

where r runs through quadratic residues and n through non-residues (mod p). The difference between those periods obviously equals the Gaussian sum $\tau(\chi)$ where χ is the quadratic character. In the quoted section of "Disquisitiones Arithmeticae" Gauss computed this difference up to the sign and devoted his paper [11] to the determination of this sign (our Theorem 2.11 for prime n). His proof was rather complicated but later much simpler ones were found. A. Cauchy [40a], [40b] and G. Dirichlet [37a] gave proofs which are both connected with theta-functions. As pointed out by L. Kronecker [80], they are not essentially different. Kronecker himself produced two proofs. One (Kronecker [56]) is very simple and based on the identity

$$\prod_{k=1}^{(p-1)/2} (\zeta_p^{2k-1} - \zeta_p^{-(2k-1)}) = \begin{cases} p^{1/2} & \text{if} \quad p \equiv 1\,(\text{mod }4), \\ ip^{1/2} & \text{if} \quad p \equiv 3\,(\text{mod }4). \end{cases}$$

The second (Kronecker [89]) works for arbitrary moduli and is based on Cauchy's integral theorem. This proof is reproduced in Bachmann [94], Landau [27a]. A simplification of it was given by L. J. Mordell [18b]. The proof presented here was found by W. C. Waterhouse [70]. Various other proofs of Theorem 2.11 are known, some of them applying to the period P_+ rather than to $\tau(\chi)$; however, one can easily see that the problems of determining the values of these sums are equivalent. J. G. van der Corput [21] and R. P. Bambah and S. Chowla [47] gave proofs based on an approximation to P_+ by a suitable integral. L. Carlitz [56a], [68], T. Estermann [45], H. Hasse [50] and L. J. Mordell [62a] employed more elementary considerations. In Borevich and Shafarevich [72] a proof due to I. Schur [21] is presented. For other proofs see the excellent survey of B. C. Berndt and R. Evans [81]. We only note a recent new proof given by D. M. Bressoud [81].

Gaussian sums and their various generalizations play an important role in number theory. In Chapter V we shall see at work an analogue, for arbitrary polynomials in place of x^2, of the sum $\sum_{x=0}^{p-1} \exp(2\pi i x^2/p)$, which for odd primes p equals $2P_+$. Gaussian sums occur in a natural way in the study of Dirichlet's L-functions, appearing in their functional equations. The generalization of Gaussian sums to algebraic number fields (see E. Hecke [19], H. Hasse [51], [52b]) play a similar role in the theory of higher L-functions. Another field of application of Gaussian sums was pointed out by H. W. Leopoldt [59], [62], who used them to build a systematic theory of the abelian extensions of the rationals.

A general theory of Gaussian sums in finite rings was developed by E. Lamprecht [53], [57]. All multiplicative relations between ideals generated by Gaussian sums belonging to characters (mod p) of a given order were determined by K. Yamamoto [66], who confirmed a conjecture of H. Hasse [50].

2. There is no analogue of Theorem 2.1 for characters (mod p) of higher order. In fact, S. Chowla [62a], [62b] and L. J. Mordell [62b] proved that, if for a primitive character $\chi \pmod p$ the ratio $\tau(\chi) p^{-1/2}$ is a root of unity, then χ must be the quadratic character. For a simple proof and a generalization of this result, see R. J. Evans [77] (see also A. Yokoyama [64]). In Cavior [64] one can find a full description of integers $a \in Q(\zeta_p)$ with $|a| = p^{1/2}$. Theorem 2.1 can be deduced from that description in the case $p \equiv 1 \pmod 4$.

The distribution of the ratios $\tau(\chi) p^{-1/2}$ where $p \equiv 1 \pmod 6$ and χ is a cubic character (mod p) was the substance of an old conjecture of E. E. Kummer [42], [46], whose truth would imply that those ratios are non-uniformly distributed on the unit circle. However, numerical investigations of this conjecture (J. v. Neumann, H. H. Goldstine [53], E. Lehmer [56], C.-E. Fröberg [74]) lead however to the belief that it is at least not precise. In fact, it has finally turned out to be false and the ratios in question have been found to have a uniform distribution on the unit circle (D. R. Heath-Brown, S. J. Patterson [79]). Earlier C. J. Moreno [74] proved a uniform distribution of the cubes of these ratios and S. J. Patterson [78] showed that the arguments of $\tau(\chi)$ where χ is the cubic residue symbol (mod k) are uniformly distributed as k tends to infinity through all integers $k \equiv 1 \pmod 3$.

For previous study of cubic Gaussian sums see J. W. S. Cassels [69], [70], J. H. Loxton [74], [78], I. V. Reshetukha [70], [75].

Although the result of S. Chowla and L. J. Mordell quoted above shows that for higher order characters there is no analogue of Theorem 2.1, it is possible to obtain explicit formulas for Gaussian sums in special cases. R. Odoni [73] found such a formula for all primitive characters (mod p^N) where p is a prime and $N \geqslant 2$. For cubic characters (mod p) a formula for $\tau(\chi)$ was conjectured by J. W. S. Cassels [70] and proved by C. R. Matthews [79a] with the aid of elliptic functions. In Matthews [79b] such a formula was obtained for quartic characters, confirming a conjecture of J. H. Loxton [78]. Cf. also A. D. McGettrick [72]. A survey of these questions was given by J. H. Loxton [76].

3. The last equality in Proposition 2.1(i) characterizes primitive characters. This was proved by T. M. Apostol [70] and another proof was given by H. Joris [77].

Although the proof of Theorem 2.2 is rather simple, it provides a remarkably good bound, which does not differ much from the lower bound deduced from Parseval's inequality by A. Rényi [47]:

$$\max_{x} \left| \sum_{n \leqslant x} \chi(n) \right| \gg N^{1/2}$$

(χ — a primitive character (mod N)). A. Sárközy [77] noted that the implied constant may be taken to be $1/\pi\sqrt{2}$ (the slightly better constant given by Rényi seems to be erroneous). For $N = p$, Sárközy gave a better bound

$$\max_x \left| \sum_{n \leq x} \chi(n) \right| \geq \pi^{-1/2}(p^{1/2} - p^{-1/2}).$$

H. L. Montgomery and R. C. Vaughan [79] proved the evaluation

$$\sum_{\substack{\chi \neq \chi_0 \\ \chi(\mathrm{mod}\, N)}} \max_x \left| \sum_{n \leq x} \chi(n) \right|^k \ll_k \varphi(N)\, N^k$$

and deduced that for most characters (mod N) the bound is

$$\left| \sum_{n \leq x} \chi(n) \right| \ll N^{1/2}.$$

Assuming the Extended Riemann Hypothesis, the same authors (H. L. Montgomery and R. C. Vaughan [77]) showed that

$$\left| \sum_{n \leq x} \chi(n) \right| \ll N^{1/2} \log\log N;$$

however, no unconditional proof of this result is known. This bound is the best possible since R. E. A. C. Paley [32] constructed an infinite sequence of distinct quadratic characters $\chi_i (\mathrm{mod}\, N_i)$ with

$$\max_x \left| \sum_{n \leq x} \chi_i(n) \right| \geq \tfrac{1}{7} N_i^{1/2} \log\log N_i.$$

(See also P. T. Bateman and S. Chowla [50], where a stronger form of this result was obtained.) In the case where $N = p^k$ is a prime power and χ a primitive character (mod N) A. Fujii, P. X. Gallagher and H. L. Montgomery [74] proved

$$\left| \sum_{n \leq x} \chi(n) \right| < C_p\, x^{1/2}\, N^{1/6}$$

and A. Fujii [73] evaluated the constant C_p explicitly.

4. The *method of Burgess* made its first appearance in D. A. Burgess [57], where one can already find all the essential ingredients of his later papers on this subject, although he only dealt there with quadratic characters. As a corollary of his main result he got for $n_2(p)$, the least quadratic non-residue (mod p), the bound $n_2(p) \ll p^{t+\varepsilon}$ with $t = \tfrac{1}{4} e^{-1/2} = 0.1516\ldots$ and an arbitrary positive ε, improving the result of I. M. Vinogradov [26], [27a], [27b], who had $n_2(p) \ll p^{2t} \log^2 p$.

Note that N. C. Ankeny [52] showed the bound $n_2(p) = O(\log^2 p)$ to be a consequence of the Extended Riemann Hypothesis. This bound should be very close to the optimal bound because the lower bound $n_2(p) \gg \log p$ for infinitely many primes p was established independently by V. R. Fridlender [49], H. Salié [49] and P. Turán [50] (see the Theorem 2.6 in the next section). An analogue of this lower bound for higher powers was obtained by P. D. T. A. Elliott [68].

Without any unproved hypotheses Yu. V. Linnik [42] showed that the inequality $n_2(p) \leqslant C(\varepsilon) p^\varepsilon$ holds for all primes $p \leqslant x$ with the exception of at most $O(x^\varepsilon)$ of them.

For elementary evaluations of $n_2(p)$ as well as of $n_2'(p)$, the smallest odd prime quadratic non-residue (mod p), see A. Brauer [31], T. Nagell [50], [52], H. J. Kanold [50b], B. Stolt [54], L. Rédei [53], R. H. Hudson and K. S. Williams [80]. From the results of Nagell and Rédei it follows that for all primes $p \neq 3$, 5, 7, 11, 13, 59, 109 and 131 we have the inequality $n_2'(p) < p^{1/2}$.

The mean value of $n_2(p)$ was found by P. Erdős [61] and an analogous result for higher powers was proved by P. D. T. A. Elliott [67b]. (Cf. also P. D. T. A. Elliott [68], [70a], K. K. Norton [71].)

I. M. Vinogradov conjectured that the least prime quadratic residue mod p is $O(p^\varepsilon)$ for all positive ε and the best result in this respect is due to Yu. V. Linnik and A. I. Vinogradov [66], who obtained the bound $\ll p^{1/4+\varepsilon}$ using Burgess's evaluations of character sums. Later P. D. T. A. Elliott [67a] showed that Vinogradov's conjecture is a consequence of the Extended Riemann Hypothesis. See also D. Wolke [69] and J. Pintz [77a, b, c].

5. In Burgess [57] it is shown that there can be at most $\ll p^{1/4} \log^{3/2} p$ consecutive quadratic residues (or non-residues) mod p and this bound was later reduced to $p^{1/4} \log p$ (D. A. Burgess [63b]). The first result concerning consecutive quadratic residues seems to be due to H. S. Vandiver [25], who proved the existence of three consecutive quadratic residues (mod p) for certain classes of primes p. In the same year A. A. Bennett [25] gave the following simple proof of this assertion for all primes $p \geqslant 19$: the form $f(u, v) = uv(u^2 - v^2)$ attains for (u, v) equal to $(5, 4)$, $(3, 1)$ or $(5, 1)$ the values $5 \cdot 6^2$, $2^2 \cdot 6$ and $2^2 \cdot 30$ respectively. Since at least one of the numbers 5, 6, 30 is a quadratic residue (mod p) for any prime $p \geqslant 7$, we can find u, v such that $f(u, v)$ is a quadratic residue (mod p). Putting $x = (u^2 + v^2)^2$, $y = 4uv(u^2 - v^2)$, we find that x, y, $x+y$ and $x-y$ are proportional (mod p) to squares (mod p), and thus $(x/y) - 1$, x/y, $(x/y) + 1$ (where the division is to be understood (mod p)) are three consecutive squares (mod p) and one easily sees that for $p \geqslant 19$ they are non-zero. Later (Bennett [26a]) the same author conjectured that for every integer n there exists a constant $N(n)$ such that there are n consecutive quadratic residues (mod p) for every prime $p > N(n)$ and noted that $N(2) = 5$, $N(3) = 17$, $N(4) = 53$. Later he stated (Bennett [26b]) that $N(5) = 193$ but did not publish the proof in view of its laboriousness. Bennett's conjecture was established by A. Brauer [28], who also proved an analogous result on consecutive quadratic non-residues. Later he obtained (in Brauer [32]) the upper bound $p^{1/2}$ for the length of a sequence of consecutive non-residues provided $p \equiv 3 \pmod 4$. I. Schur conjectured that the same holds for all large primes $p \equiv 1 \pmod 4$. This weaker assertion follows of course from Burgess's result but an elementary proof of it seemed desirable. It was achieved by R. H. Hudson [71], [77], who also obtained in Hudson [72] an analogous result for higher powers. His conjecture that for all primes $p \neq 13$ one can have at most $p^{1/2}$ consecutive quadratic non-residues is still unresolved, although Burgess's result reduces it to a check of finitely many primes. See also R. H. Hudson [73a], where the question of lower bounds is considered.

P. D. T. A. Elliott [70b] observed that the minimal pair n, $n+1$ of consecutive quadratic non-residues $\pmod p$ satisfies $n \ll p^{1/4+\varepsilon}$ (for all $\varepsilon > 0$) and this result was modified in Elliott [72] to $n \ll p^{1/4-c}$, where c is any number smaller than $e^{-10}/8$. See also R. H. Hudson [73b], where the case of three consecutive integers with equal Legendre symbols is considered.

6. Theorem 2.3 was obtained independently by D. A. Burgess [62a] and Wang Yuan [59a]. Our proof is that of Burgess.

The same method can also be adapted to deal with composite moduli and this has been done in Burgess [62b], where for primitive characters $\pmod k$ the bound

$$\left| \sum_{x=1+N}^{h+N} \chi(x) \right| \ll h^{1-1/(r+1)} k^{1/4r+\varepsilon} \qquad (\varepsilon > 0, \text{ arbitrary})$$

has been proved for $r = 1, 2, \ldots$ in the case of square-free k and for $r = 2$ in the case of other k.

In a subsequent paper (D. A. Burgess [63a]) some additional improvements were introduced, which made it possible to obtain in Theorem 2.3 the bound

$$\ll h^{1-1/r} p^{(r+1)/4r^2} \log p.$$

Similar improvements apply also to the case of composite k.

Exercises

1 (T. M. Apostol [70]). Prove that, if for a character $\chi \pmod k$ one has the equality

$$\tau_a(\chi) = \overline{\chi(a)} \tau(\chi)$$

for all a, then χ is a primitive character $\pmod k$.

2 (L. Rédei [47], L. Carlitz [60]). Let p be an odd prime; and let $B = \sum_{m=1}^{p-1} c_m \zeta_p^m$ with $c_m = 1$ or -1 for $m = 1, 2, \ldots, p-1$. Show that, if B is divisible by $(1-\zeta_p)^{(p-1)/2}$ in the ring of integers of the pth cyclotomic field, then either c_m or $-c_m$ equals $\left(\dfrac{m}{p}\right)$ for $m = 1, 2, \ldots, p-1$, i.e., B can differ from the Gaussian sum with the real primitive character $\pmod p$ only in sign.

(Hint: prove first that for $j = 1, 2, ..., (p-1)/2$ the sum $\sum_{j=1}^{p-1} m^j c_m$ is divisible by p, then consider the polynomial $f(x)$ over $GF[p]$ which satisfies $f(0) = 0$, $f(m) = c_m$ for $m = 1, 2, ..., p-1$ and show that $f^2(x) = x^{p-1}$.)

3 (D. A. Burgess [62a]). Show that if p is a sufficiently large prime and χ a non-principal character (mod p) then to every $\varepsilon > 0$ one can find a $\delta > 0$ such that if h exceeds $p^{1/4+\varepsilon}$ then for all n we have $|S_h(n)| < hp^{-\delta}$.

4 (D. A. Burgess [57]). Deduce from the previous exercise that for large p one can have at most $O(p^{1/4+\varepsilon})$ consecutive quadratic residues (or non-residues) (mod p) for every $\varepsilon > 0$.

5 (D. A. Burgess [57]). Prove that the least quadratic non-residue (mod p) is $O(p^{t+\varepsilon})$, where $t = e^{-1/2}/4$ and $\varepsilon > 0$ is arbitrary.

6. Let p be a prime, $x < p$ and k a divisor of $p-1$. Denote by $f_k(x)$ the number of kth power residues (mod p) belonging to the interval $(0, x)$. Prove that

$$f_k(x) = x/k + O(p^{1/2} \log p),$$

the implied constant being $\leqslant 1$.

7 (H. Davenport [33]). Let $\chi_1, ..., \chi_t$ be non-principal characters (mod p) of orders $N_1, ..., N_t$ respectively, and let $z_1, ..., z_t$ be given roots of unity of orders $N_1, ..., N_t$ respectively. Prove that there exist

$$(1 + o(1)) \frac{p}{N_1 ... N_t}$$

distinct residues x(mod p) such that for $j = 1, 2, ..., t$ one has $\chi_j(x+j) = z_j$.

8. Give an evaluation of the error term in the previous exercise.

9 (B. Segal [41]). Obtain an upper bound for the smallest integer x satisfying the conditions of exercise 7.

10 (D. A. Buell and K. S. Williams [78]). Prove that if $p \equiv 1 \pmod 4$ is a prime and $m(p)$ denotes the maximal number of quadratic residues (mod p) such that all their non-zero differences are also quadratic residues, then we have

$$m(p) < \frac{1+\varepsilon}{4 \log 2} p^{1/2} \log p$$

for all $\varepsilon > 0$ and sufficiently large p.

11. Give a numerical value for the constant C in Theorem 2.3.

§ 2. THE LEAST PRIMITIVE ROOT

1. Let p be a prime. The existence of a *primitive root* (mod p), i.e., of a number g such that all powers $g, g^2, ..., g^{p-1} \equiv 1 \pmod p$ are incongruent (mod p), was asserted first by J. H. Lambert in 1769 (see e.g. L. E. Dickson [HNT], vol. I, p. 181). Four years later Euler tried to prove the existence of such a number. His proof, however, was shown to be incomplete by Gauss, who in Gauss [01] gave two different proofs of his own.

Nowadays we have at our disposal a large number of proofs of the existence of primitive roots, the simplest being the following: since Z/pZ is a field, the equation $x^k = 1$ has in its multiplicative group $G(p)$ at most k solutions. If $G(p)$ were noncyclic, it would contain for a certain prime q the group $C_q \oplus C_q$ as a subgroup, and hence the equation $x^q = 1$ would have at least $q^2 > q$ solutions, a contradiction. Thus $G(p)$ must be cyclic and any of its generators is a primitive root (mod p).

The main problem in the theory of primitive roots is their distribution among the residues (mod p) and the first question arising here is the following:

Let $g(p)$ be the least positive primitive root (mod p). What can be said about its magnitude?

If p has a particular form it is possible sometimes to give an explicit value for $g(p)$. So F. J. Richelot [32] noted that if $p = 2^{2^k} + 1$ is a Fermat prime then $g(p) = 2$ for $k = 0, 1$ and $g(p) = 3$ for $k \geqslant 2$. (See Exercise 12.) However, we do not know whether for infinitely many k we get here a prime, and so this result possibly applies only to finitely many primes.

Another result of this type states that, if $p \equiv 3 \pmod 8$ is a prime and the number $(p-1)/2$ is also prime, then $g(p) = 2$. This and other similar theorems were already obtained in 1830 by M. A. Stern [30]. The reader may consult G. Wertheim [97a] and R. Fueter [46] for other criteria of a similar type.

The first general result was obtained in 1918 by I. M. Vinogradov [18], who showed that $g(p) \leqslant 4^{\omega(p-1)} p^{1/2} \log p$, $\omega(m)$ denoting the number of distinct factors of m. Before proving this and other results on $g(p)$, we shall first obtain a result which is the basis for all known evaluation of $g(p)$ and is also applicable to other problems.

PROPOSITION 2.2. *Let p be a prime and d a divisor of $p-1$. Denote by $\varepsilon_d(x)$ the characteristic function of d-th power residues (mod p) and by $\eta_d(x)$ the characteristic function of the set of integers whose order (mod p) equals d. Then the following identities hold*:

(i) $\varepsilon_d(a) = \dfrac{1}{d} \sum\limits_{\substack{\chi \\ \chi^d = 1}} \chi(a),$

(ii) $\sum\limits_{\delta | d} \eta_\delta(a) = \varepsilon_{(p-1)/d}(a),$

(iii) $\eta_d(a) = \sum\limits_{\delta | d} \varepsilon_{(p-1)/d}(a) \mu(d/\delta),$

(iv) $\dfrac{\varphi(p-1)}{p-1} \sum\limits_{d | p-1} \dfrac{\mu(d)}{\varphi(d)} \sum\limits_{\substack{\chi \\ \operatorname{ord} \chi = d}} \chi(t) = \eta_{p-1}(t)$

$$= \begin{cases} 1 & \text{if } t \text{ is a primitive root (mod } p), \\ 0 & \text{otherwise.} \end{cases}$$

Proof. Let $H_d \subset \hat{G}(p)$ be the group of all characters χ (mod p) satisfying

$\chi^d = 1$. Since the subgroup of $G(p)$ annihilated by H_d equals $G(p)^d$, we obtain

$$\frac{1}{d} \sum_{\chi \in H_d} \chi(a) = \begin{cases} 1, & a \in G(p)^d, \\ 0, & a \notin G(p)^d \end{cases}$$

proving (i).

To prove (ii) it suffices to observe that a is a $(p-1)/d$th power (mod p) if and only if the order of a divides d, and (iii) then follows by the Möbius inversion principle. The proof of (iv) is more complicated. If t is divisible by p then both sides of (iv) vanish and the proof is complete. If t is not divisible by p then $f_t(d) = \sum\limits_{\substack{\chi \\ \operatorname{ord}\chi = d}} \chi(t)$ is a multiplicative function of d; thus we may write

$$S(t) = \sum_{d \mid p-1} \frac{\mu(d)}{\varphi(d)} f_t(d) = \prod_{\substack{q \mid p-1 \\ q\,\text{prime}}} \left(1 - \frac{f_t(q)}{\varphi(q)}\right).$$

If t is not a primitive root (mod p), then it must be a qth power (mod p) for a certain prime divisor q of $p-1$, thus for all characters χ of order q we have $\chi(t) = 1$, which implies $f_t(q) = \varphi(q)$ and $S(t) = 0$.

If t is a primitive root (mod p) and we denote by χ_q a generator of the cyclic group H_q (for $q \mid p-1$, prime), then

$$f_t(q) = \sum_{j=1}^{q-1} \chi_q^j(t) = -1$$

and

$$S(t) = \prod_{\substack{q \mid p-1 \\ q\,\text{prime}}} \left(1 + \frac{1}{q-1}\right) = \frac{p-1}{\varphi(p-1)}. \quad \Box$$

COROLLARY 1. *An integer t is a primitive root (mod p) if and only if* $\sum\limits_{d \mid p-1} \mu(d)\varepsilon_d(t) = 1$.

Proof. Apply (iii) in the case $d = p-1$. $\Box$

COROLLARY 2. *Let $x \geqslant 2$ be an integer. If*

$$M = M(p, x) \geqslant \max_{\substack{\chi \neq \chi_0 \\ \chi \bmod p}} \left| \sum_{n \leqslant x} \chi(n) \right|,$$

and moreover $x > M \cdot 2^{\omega(p-1)}$, then $g(p) \leqslant x$.

Proof. If $g(p) \geqslant 1 + x$, then by (iv) we get

$$0 = x + \sum_{\substack{d \mid p-1 \\ d > 1}} \frac{\mu(d)}{\varphi(d)} \sum_{\substack{\chi \\ \operatorname{ord}\chi = d}} \sum_{t \leqslant x} \chi(t);$$

thus

$$x \leqslant M \sum_{\substack{d|p-1 \\ d>1}} \mu^2(d) < 2^{\omega(p-1)} \cdot M.$$

Using the Pólya–Vinogradov inequality, one obtains

COROLLARY 3. *For all odd primes p one has* $g(p) \leqslant 2^{\omega(p-1)} p^{1/2} \log p$.

Proof. Theorem 2.2 shows that in Corollary 2 one can put $M = p^{1/2} \log p$. □

COROLLARY 4. *The number* $T_p(x)$ *of positive integers* $n \leqslant x$ *which are primitive roots* (mod p) *equals*

$$\frac{\varphi(p-1)}{p-1} x + O(2^{\omega(p-1)} p^{1/2} \log p),$$

where the implied constant is bounded by 1.

Proof. Using (iv), we arrive at

$$T_p(x) = \frac{\varphi(p-1)}{p-1} x + \sum_{\substack{d|p-1 \\ d>1}} \frac{\mu(d)}{\varphi(d)} \sum_{\text{ord}\chi=d} \sum_{n \leqslant x} \chi(n)$$

and now, using Theorem 2.2, we obtain

$$\left| T_p(x) - \frac{\varphi(p-1)}{p-1} x \right| \leqslant \sum_{d|p-1} \mu^2(d) p^{1/2} \log p = 2^{\omega(p-1)} p^{1/2} \log p. \quad □$$

In Vinogradov [18] Corollary 4 was derived first and then Corollary 3 was deduced. In this way the factor $4^{\omega(p-1)}$ arose in place of $2^{\omega(p-1)}$.

2. Subsequently the factor $\log p$ in Corollary 3 was replaced by $\log\log p$ (I. M. Vinogradov [30]) and later L. K. Hua [42b] was able to remove the logarithmical factor completely. We now give a simple proof of his result, due to P. Erdös and H. N. Shapiro [57].

THEOREM 2.4. *If p is an odd prime, then*

$$g(p) < 2^{1+\omega(p-1)} p^{1/2}.$$

Proof. We use the following simple lemma:

LEMMA 2.5. *If A, B are subsets of the set of residue classes* (mod p) *such that* $a+b \not\equiv 0 \pmod{p}$ *for* $a \in A$, $b \in B$ *and* χ *is a non-principal character* (mod p), *then*

$$\left| \sum_{\substack{a \in A \\ b \in B}} \chi(a+b) \right| \leqslant (p|A||B|)^{1/2}.$$

Proof. Using Proposition 2.1 (i), we obtain

$$\tau(\bar{\chi}) \sum_{\substack{a \in A \\ b \in B}} \chi(a+b) = \sum_{\substack{a \in A \\ b \in B}} \sum_{h=1}^{p} \bar{\chi}(h) \exp\left\{ \frac{2\pi i h(a+b)}{p} \right\};$$

and now part (iii) of that proposition and Cauchy's inequality give

$$p^{1/2}\left|\sum_{\substack{a\in A\\b\in B}}\chi(a+b)\right|\leqslant\sum_{h=1}^{p}\left|\sum_{a\in A}\exp\left\{\frac{2\pi iah}{p}\right\}\right|\left|\sum_{b\in B}\exp\left\{\frac{2\pi ibh}{p}\right\}\right|$$

$$\leqslant p|A|^{1/2}|B|^{1/2}.\quad\square$$

To prove the theorem put $x = g(p)-1$ and $A = B = \{1, 2, \ldots, [x/2]\}$. As $x < p-1$, the set $A+B$ does not contain zero. Proposition 2.2 (iv) permits us to write

$$0 = \left[\frac{x}{2}\right]^2 + \sum_{\substack{d\mid p-1\\d>1}}\frac{\mu(d)}{\varphi(d)}\sum_{\operatorname{ord}\chi=d}\sum_{a,b\in A}\chi(a+b);$$

hence Lemma 2.5 implies

$$\left[\frac{x}{2}\right]^2\leqslant\sum_{\substack{d\mid p-1\\d>1}}\frac{\mu^2(d)}{\varphi(d)}\sum_{\operatorname{ord}\chi=d}\left|\sum_{a,b\in A}\chi(a+b)\right|$$

$$\leqslant p^{1/2}\left[\frac{x}{2}\right]\sum_{\substack{d\mid p-1\\d\neq1}}\mu^2(d) = (2^{\omega(p-1)}-1)p^{1/2}\left[\frac{x}{2}\right];$$

thus $[x/2]\leqslant(2^{\omega(p-1)}-1)p^{1/2}$ and finally

$$g(p) = 1+x\leqslant 2+2\left[\frac{x}{2}\right]\leqslant 2^{1+\omega(p-1)}p^{1/2}-2p^{1/2}+2 < 2^{1+\omega(p-1)}p^{1/2}.\quad\square$$

It is obvious that any improvement in bounding character sums results in a new bound for $g(p)$. Thus the Burgess bound implies the following evaluation, which is at present the best known bound for $g(p)$:

THEOREM 2.5 (D. A. Burgess [62a], Wang Yuan [59a]). *If p is an odd prime, then for every positive ε one has*

$$g(p) = O(p^{1/4+\varepsilon}).$$

Proof. Apply Corollary 2 to Proposition 2.2 with $M(p, x) = x^{1-1/(r+1)}p^{1/4r}\log p$, where r is an arbitrary positive integer. Then

$$g(p)\ll p^{1/4+1/4r}\log^{r+1}p\cdot 2^{(r+1)\omega(p-1)}$$

and if r is sufficiently large then due to $\omega(p-1)\ll\log p/\log\log p$ the desired bound results. $\square$

Not much is known about lower bounds for $g(p)$. Here V. R. Fridlender [49], H. Sàlié [49] and P. Turán [50] obtained the following result:

THEOREM 2.6. *Let B denote the Linnik constant, i.e., such a number that every arithmetic progression $nk+r$ with coprime k and r contains a prime not* *exceeding Ck^B where C is independent of k and r. Then for every $\varepsilon > 0$ one can find infinitely many primes p such that*

$$g(p) \geqslant \frac{1-\varepsilon}{B} \log p.$$

Proof. Let $p_1 = 2, \ldots, p_m$ be the first m primes and for each of them choose a quadratic residue, say a_i $(i = 1, \ldots, m)$. If c is a solution of the system

$$x \equiv 1 \,(\mathrm{mod}\, 8),$$

$$x \equiv a_i \,(\mathrm{mod}\, p_i) \quad (i = 2, \ldots, m),$$

then c is prime to $8p_2 \ldots p_m$ and thus there exists a prime p, congruent to $c \,(\mathrm{mod}\, 8p_2 \ldots p_m)$, which does not exceed $C(8p_2 \ldots p_m)^B$. Because of

$$\left(\frac{p}{p_j}\right) = \left(\frac{a_j}{p_j}\right) = +1 \quad (j = 2, \ldots, m)$$

we have

$$\left(\frac{p_j}{p}\right) = \left(\frac{p}{p_j}\right)\left(\frac{p_j}{p}\right) = (-1)^{(p-1)(p_j-1)/4} = 1,$$

and since $p \equiv 1 \,(\mathrm{mod}\, 8)$ we also have $\left(\frac{2}{p}\right) = 1$. Thus all integers composed of the first m primes are quadratic residues mod p and we must have $g(p) > p_m$. But the Prime Number Theorem implies that for sufficiently large m we have $p_2 \ldots p_m < (e + 2\varepsilon)^{p_m}$; hence

$$p \leqslant 8^B C (e + 2\varepsilon)^{Bp_m}$$

and

$$g(p) > p_m \geqslant \frac{\log p}{B\log(e+2\varepsilon)} - \frac{\log 8^B C}{B\log(e+2\varepsilon)}$$

$$\geqslant \frac{1-2\varepsilon}{B} (\log p - \log(8^B C)) \geqslant \frac{1-\varepsilon}{B} \log p$$

provided p is sufficiently large. □

As the Extended Riemann Hypothesis implies that for B we may take any number exceeding 2, we see that under this hypothesis we have $g(p) \geqslant (1/2 - \varepsilon) \log p$ for all $\varepsilon > 0$ and infinitely many primes p. It is known that one can take for B any number exceeding 17 (J. J. Chen [79b]); hence without any hypotheses we have

$$g(p) \geqslant (1-\varepsilon)\frac{\log p}{17}$$

infinitely often.

3. From Dirichlet's theorem on primes in progressions it follows that for every prime p one can find primitive roots which are primes themselves. One can thus consider the minimal prime primitive root (mod p), which we shall denote by $g'(p)$. Clearly Linnik's theorem implies the estimate

$$g'(p) < Cp^B$$

where C and B are absolute constants.

Unfortunately no better bound is known and thus one is led to consider possible improvements at least for infinitely many primes. The best result in this respect is due to P. D. T. A. Elliott [69a], who got for infinitely many primes p the inequality

$$g'(p) < 475 \log^{8/5} p.$$

We shall now give a proof of a less precise result, based on the same ideas but avoiding certain technical complications.

THEOREM 2.7. *For every positive ε there are infinitely many primes p such that $g'(p) < \log^{2+\varepsilon} p$. The number of primes $p \leqslant x$ which do not satisfy this inequality is $O(x/\log^2 x)$.*

Proof. The main tool in the proof is the following lemma, which we shall state in a slightly more general form than actually needed, to permit its use also in the proof of the next theorem. To state it we have to introduce a character sum depending on certain parameters which is similar to that appearing in the Proposition 2.2 (iv). We define it as follows: for every prime p and a divisor d of $p-1$ choose a real number $\beta_{d,p}$ subject to the condition $0 \leqslant \beta_{d,p} \leqslant \varphi^{-1}(d)$. Let $H \geqslant 2$ and put

$$(2.10) \qquad\qquad T_p = T_p(H) = \sum_{\substack{d>1 \\ d\,|\,p-1}} \beta_{d,p} \sum_{\substack{\chi \bmod p \\ o(\chi)=d}} \Big| \sum_{q \leqslant H} \chi(q) \Big|,$$

where in the innermost sum the summation index q is restricted to primes and $o(\chi)$ denotes the order of the character χ.

Denote by $\varrho(p)$ the number of those divisors d of $p-1$ for which $\beta_{d,p}$ does not vanish.

LEMMA 2.6. *Let $x \geqslant 2$ and $e < H < x^a$ for a certain fixed a. Let $\lambda > 1$, $R > 1$ and denote by S the set of all primes $p \leqslant x$ for which $\varrho(p) \leqslant R$ and $T_p \geqslant \pi(H)/\lambda$. Then for the cardinality of S we have the bound*

$$|S| \ll \left(\frac{\log x}{\log H} \right)^{1/2} \exp\big(\log(x^2 H) \log(\lambda^2 R^2 \log x) \log^{-1} H\big),$$

where the implied constant depends only on a and, in particular, is independent of the choice of $\beta_{d,p}$.

Proof. Using Hölder's inequality, we get for $r = 1, 2, \ldots$ the bound

$$T_p^{2r} \leqslant (T_p')^{2r-1} \sum_{\substack{d > 1 \\ d \mid p-1}} \sum_{\substack{\chi \bmod p \\ o(\chi)=d}} \Big| \sum_{\substack{q \leqslant H \\ q \text{ prime}}} \chi(q) \Big|^{2r},$$

where

$$T_p' = \sum_{\substack{d > 1 \\ d \mid p-1}} \beta_{d,p}^{2r/(2r-1)} \sum_{\substack{\chi \bmod p \\ o(\chi)=d}} 1 \leqslant \varrho(p).$$

For $p \in S$ we have $\varrho(p) \leqslant R$; thus

$$\sum_{p \in S} T_p^{2r} \ll R^{2r} \sum_{p \leqslant x} \sum_{\substack{\chi \bmod p \\ \chi \neq \chi_0}} \Big| \sum_{\substack{q \leqslant H \\ q \text{ prime}}} \chi(q) \Big|^{2r},$$

and to bound the right-hand side of the last inequality write

$$\Big(\sum_{\substack{q \leqslant H \\ q \text{ prime}}} \chi(q) \Big)^r = \sum_{n \leqslant H^r} a_n \chi(n),$$

where $|a_n| \leqslant r!$, and apply the prime number theorem and the corollary to Theorem A.1 to obtain

$$H^{2r} |S| (\lambda \log H)^{-2r} \leqslant \sum_{p \in S} T_p^{2r} \ll r! \, R^{2r} (x^2 + H^r)(1+\varepsilon)^r (H \log^{-1} H)^r$$

for every positive ε and sufficiently large H. Choosing $r = [\log(x^2 H)/\log H]$ and observing that $x^2 H^{-r} \ll \exp\{2 \log x - \log(x^2 H) + \log H\} \leqslant 1$, we get for $|S|$ the bound

$$|S| \ll R^{2r} r! \, \lambda^{2r} \cdot \log^r H (1+\varepsilon)^r.$$

Choosing ε from the interval $(0, e]$ and using Stirling's formula, we are led to

$$|S| \ll r^{1/2} \exp\big(r \log(R^2 \lambda^2 \log H) + r \log r\big),$$

and since $\log H = O(\log x)$ and $r = O(\log x / \log H)$ our assertion follows. $\square$

For the proof of our theorem we shall apply this lemma in the particular case $\beta_{d,p} = \mu^2(d) \varphi^{-1}(d)$. For this purpose observe first that, by Proposition 2.2 (iv), $g'(p) > H$ implies $T_p \geqslant \pi(H)$ with this particular choice of $\beta_{d,p}$. In fact, from $g'(p) > H$ it follows that

$$\sum_{d \mid p-1} \frac{\mu(d)}{\varphi(d)} \sum_{\substack{\chi \\ o(\chi)=d}} \sum_{q \leqslant H} \chi(q) = 0;$$

thus

$$\pi(H) = \Big| \sum_{\substack{d \mid p-1 \\ d \neq 1}} \frac{\mu(d)}{\varphi(d)} \sum_{\substack{\chi \\ o(\chi)=d}} \sum_{q \leqslant H} \chi(q) \Big| \leqslant T_p.$$

To apply the last lemma we first have to find a large set of primes p with small $\omega(p-1)$, which will be done in the next lemma:

LEMMA 2.7. *There are at most* $O(x \log^{-2} x)$ *primes* $p \leqslant x$ *such that* $p-1$ *has more than* $3 \log\log x$ *distinct prime divisors.*

Proof. The corollary to Theorem A.4 implies that, if $A(x)$ is the number of primes $p \leqslant x$ for which $d(p-1) > \log^2 x$, then $A(x)\log^2 x = O(x)$; thus $A(x) = O(x/\log^2 x)$. But if $\omega(p-1) > 3\log\log x$ then in view of $d(p-1) \geqslant 2^{\omega(p-1)}$ we get $d(p-1) \geqslant (\log x)^{3\log 2} > \log^2 x$. $\square$

Now we make our choice of the parameters. Take $\lambda = 2$, $R = 3\log\log x$ and $H = C_1 \log^C x$, where $C > 2$, $C_1 > 0$ are constants. Denote by S_0 the set of all primes $p \leqslant x$ for which $p-1$ has at most $3\log\log x$ distinct prime divisors and which also satisfy $g'(p) > C_1 \log^C x$. Obviously S_0 is contained in the set S constructed as in Lemma 2.6 with the aid of our choice of parameters; hence its cardinality in view of Lemma 2.6 satisfies for all $\delta > 0$ and sufficiently large x the inequality

$$|S_0| \ll \log x \cdot \exp\left\{ \frac{(2+\delta)\log x \cdot (1+\delta)\log\log x}{C\log\log x + O(1)} \right\}$$

$$\ll \log x \cdot \exp\left\{ \frac{(2+\delta)(1+\delta)}{C} \log x \right\}.$$

Choosing δ so that $(2+\delta)(1+\delta)/C < 1$ we finally get $|S_0| \ll x^{1-\varepsilon}$ for a certain positive ε.

This bound shows that, if S_1 is the set of all primes $p \leqslant x$ for which $\omega(p-1) \leqslant 3\log\log x$ and $g'(p) > \log^C p$, then

$$|S_1| \leqslant \pi(x^{1/2}) + |\{p \leqslant x: \omega(p-1) \leqslant 3\log\log x, g'(p) > 2^{-C}\log^C x\}|$$

$$\ll x^{1/2} + x^{1-\varepsilon} \ll x\log^{-2} x.$$

By Lemma 2.7 there are at least $x/\log x + O(x/\log^2 x)$ primes $p \leqslant x$ with $\omega(p-1) \leqslant 3\log\log x$ and we finally conclude that there are at most $O(x\log^{-2} x)$ primes $p \leqslant x$ with $g'(p) > \log^C x$ for any C exceeding 2. $\square$

4. Lemma 2.6 can also be used to get a bound for the mean value of $g(p)$. The best up-to-date result is due to D. A. Burgess and P. D. T. A. Elliott [68], who proved

$$\sum_{p \leqslant x} g(p) \ll x\log x (\log\log x)^4.$$

Using their ideas, we present here the proof of the following weaker theorem:

THEOREM 2.8. *There exists a positive constant B such that*

$$\sum_{p \leqslant x} g(p) \ll x \log^B x.$$

(Our proof will give for B the value 47.4.)

Proof. We shall again base our arguments on Lemma 2.6; however, the implication $T_p > \pi(H) \Rightarrow g'(p) < H$ for one particular choice of $\beta_{d,p}$ used here will be insufficient for our purpose and we shall instead rely on a lemma relating a bound for $g'(p)$ to the behaviour of T_p for two choices of the parameters $\beta_{d,p}$.

To make these choices fix a number $V \geqslant 2$, denote by P_p the product of all primes $\leqslant V$ dividing $p-1$ and put

$$\beta_{d,p}^{(1)} = \begin{cases} \mu^2(d)/\varphi(d) & \text{if} \quad d \mid P_p, \, d > 1, \\ 0 & \text{otherwise,} \end{cases}$$

$$\beta_{d,p}^{(2)} = \begin{cases} 1/d & \text{if } d \text{ is a prime dividing } p-1 \text{ and } d > V, \\ 0 & \text{otherwise.} \end{cases}$$

As in the previous case we denote by $\varrho_i(p)$ the number of d's for which $\beta_{d,p}^{(i)}$ is positive and by $T_p^{(1)}(H)$, $T_p^{(2)}(H)$ the corresponding sums (2.10). Now we prove

LEMMA 2.8. *Let $H \geqslant 2$ be given. If $\omega(p-1) < (\varphi(P_p)/P_p) \cdot V$ and*

$$\pi(H) > \frac{T_p^{(1)}(H) + (P_p/\varphi(P_p)) \cdot T_p^{(2)}(H) + 1}{W}$$

where $W = 1 - (\omega(p-1)/V) \cdot (P_p/\varphi(P_p))$, then $g'(p) \leqslant H$.

Proof. We use an elementary sieve to obtain a lower bound for the number of prime primitive roots (mod p) not exceeding H which will be similar to that obtained by direct application of Proposition 2.2 (iv) but will have fewer terms.

Fix a primitive root (mod p) and, for any n not divisible by p, denote the index of n with respect to it by $i(p)$. Then obviously

(2.11) $\left| \{q \leqslant H : q \text{ prime primitive root (mod } p) \} \right|$

$$= \left| \{q \leqslant H : q \text{ prime, } (i(q), p-1) = 1 \} \right| \geqslant \sum_{\substack{q \leqslant H \\ q \text{ prime} \\ (i(q), P_p) = 1}} 1 - \sum_{\substack{r > V \\ r \text{ prime} \\ r \mid p-1}} \sum_{\substack{q \leqslant H \\ q \text{ prime} \\ q \mid i(r)}} 1.$$

The first sum in (2.11) can be transformed as follows:

$$\sum_{\substack{q \leqslant H \\ q \, \text{prime} \\ (i(q), P_p) = 1}} 1 = \sum_{\substack{q \leqslant H \\ q \, \text{prime}}} \sum_{d | (i(q), P_p)} \mu(d)$$

$$= \sum_{\substack{q \leqslant H \\ q \, \text{prime}}} \sum_{d | P_p} \frac{\mu(d)}{d} \sum_{\substack{\chi(\text{mod } p) \\ \chi^d = 1}} \chi(q)$$

$$= \sum_{\substack{\delta | P_p \\ o(\chi) = \delta}} \sum_{\substack{\chi(\text{mod } p) \\ o(\chi) = \delta}} \sum_{\substack{d | P_p \\ \delta | d}} \frac{\mu(d)}{d} \sum_{\substack{q \leqslant H \\ q \, \text{prime}}} \chi(q)$$

$$= \frac{\varphi(P_p)}{P_p} \sum_{\substack{\delta | P_p}} \sum_{\substack{\chi(\text{mod } p) \\ o(\chi) = \delta}} \frac{\mu(\delta)}{\varphi(\delta)} \sum_{\substack{q \leqslant H \\ q \, \text{prime}}} \chi(q).$$

Now observe that the term corresponding to $\delta = 1$ in the last sum is at least equal to

$$\frac{\varphi(P_p)}{P_p} (\pi(H) - 1)$$

and the sum of all the remaining terms does not exceed $(\varphi(P_p)/P_p) T_p^{(1)}$ in absolute value.

Moreover, the second sum in (2.11) equals

$$\sum_{\substack{r > V \\ r \, \text{prime} \\ r | p - 1}} \sum_{\substack{q \leqslant H \\ q \, \text{prime}}} \frac{1}{q} \sum_{\substack{\chi(\text{mod } p) \\ \chi^r = 1}} \chi(q),$$

and hence its absolute value is bounded by

$$\sum_{\substack{r > V \\ r \, \text{prime} \\ r | p - 1}} \frac{1}{r} \pi(H) + \sum_{\substack{r > V \\ r \, \text{prime}}} \frac{1}{r} \sum_{\substack{\chi(\text{mod } p) \\ o(\chi) = r}} \left| \sum_{\substack{q \leqslant H \\ q \, \text{prime}}} \chi(q) \right|$$

$$\leqslant \pi(H) \sum_{\substack{r > V \\ r \, \text{prime} \\ r | p - 1}} \frac{1}{r} + T_p^{(2)} \leqslant \frac{\pi(H)}{V} \omega(p - 1) + T_p^{(2)}.$$

Returning to (2.11) we finally conclude that the number of prime primitive roots $(\text{mod } p)$ not exceeding H is equal to at least

$$\frac{\varphi(P_p)}{P_p} (\pi(H) - 1) - \frac{\varphi(P_p)}{P_p} T_p^{(1)} - \frac{\pi(H)}{V} \omega(p - 1) - T_p^{(2)},$$

which is positive by our assumptions. $\square$

Using Lemmas 2.6 and 2.8, we can now establish the theorem. At first we divide the odd primes $p \leqslant x$ into disjoint classes $A_{k,m} (k \geqslant 1, m \geqslant 1)$ in the following way:

If $\varrho_2(p) \neq 0$ then with certain k, $m \geqslant 1$ we can write

$$2^{k-1} \leqslant \varrho_1(p) < 2^k, \qquad 2^{m-1} \leqslant \varrho_2(p) < 2^m$$

and we put $p \in A_{k,m}$. However, if $\varrho_2(p) = 0$, then define $k \geqslant 1$ by $2^{k-1} \leqslant \varrho_1(p) < 2^k$ and put $p \in A_{k,0}$. In this way the union of the sets $A_{k,m}$ contains all odd primes $\leqslant x$, because, in view of $V \geqslant 2$, $\varrho_1(p)$ never vanishes.

Now we take the parameter V to be equal to $\log^2 x$ and, fixing for a moment k and m, we define $H = H(k, m)$ by

$$H = (\log x)^C \cdot 4^{ND}$$

where $N = \max(k, m)$, and $C < 100$, $D > 0$ will be fixed later.

Finally, we divide the odd primes $p \leqslant x$ into two classes. A prime $p \in A_{k,m}$ will belong to class A if either

$$T_p^{(1)}(H) > \pi(H)/4 \quad \text{or} \quad T_p^{(2)}(H) > \pi(H)/\log x$$

holds for $H = H(k, m)$. Otherwise p will belong to class B.

To obtain the required bound for $\sum_{p \leqslant x} g(p)$ we shall deal separately with primes in A and B, applying Lemma 2.6 in the first case and Lemma 2.8 in the second.

Since for every positive δ we have $\varrho_i(p) \leqslant d(p-1) \underset{\delta}{\ll} x^\delta$, it follows that $2^N \underset{\delta}{\ll} x^\delta$ and so $H(k, m) \underset{\varepsilon}{\ll} x^\varepsilon$ for every $\varepsilon > 0$. We may thus apply Lemma 2.6 first with $R = 2^k$, $\lambda = 4$ and then with $R = 2^m$, $\lambda = \log x$, to obtain

$$|A \cap A_{k,m}| \leqslant |\{p \leqslant x : \varrho_1(p) \leqslant 2^k, T_p^{(1)} > \pi(H)/4\}| +$$
$$+ |\{p \leqslant x : \varrho_2(p) \leqslant 2^m, T_p^{(2)} > \pi(H)/\log x\}|$$
$$\ll \log^{1/2} x \exp((2\alpha + \varepsilon) \log x) \ll x^{2\alpha + \varepsilon'},$$

where α is any number satisfying $4^N \log^3 x \leqslant H^\alpha$ and $\varepsilon' > 0$ is arbitrary.

Since the number of non-empty sets $A_{k,m}$ is $O(x^\varepsilon)$ for every $\varepsilon > 0$ we get, using Theorem 2.5, the evaluation

(2.12)
$$\sum_{\substack{p \in A \\ p \leqslant x}} g(p) \underset{\varepsilon}{\ll} x^{2\alpha + 1/4 + \varepsilon}.$$

To deal with primes belonging to B we use Lemma 2.8, applying it to the set $A_{k,m} \cap B$. To check that the assumptions of that lemma are satisfied observe that for $p \leqslant x$ we have on the one hand $\omega(p-1) \ll \log p \leqslant \log x$ and on the other hand

$$\frac{\varphi(P_p)}{P_p} V \gg \frac{\log^2 x}{\log\log p} \geqslant \frac{\log^2 x}{\log\log x},$$

which shows that for sufficiently large x the first assumption is satisfied.

Moreover, the same argument gives

$$W = 1 - \frac{\omega(p-1)}{V} \frac{P_p}{\varphi(P_p)} > 1 - \frac{\log\log x}{\log x};$$

thus

$$\frac{T_p^{(1)}(H) + (P_p/\varphi(P_p)) T_p^{(2)}(H) + 1}{W} < \frac{\pi(H)\{\log x/4 + \log\log x\} + \log x}{\log x - \log\log x} < \pi(H)$$

provided that again x is sufficiently large. Lemma 2.8 now implies $g'(p) \leqslant H = \log^C x 4^{ND}$ for $p \in A_{k,m} \cap B$ and using $2^N \leqslant d(p-1)$ we are led to $g'(p) \leqslant d^{2D}(p-1)\log^C x$. This in turn implies that

$$\sum_{\substack{p \leqslant x \\ p \in B}} g(p) \leqslant \log^C x \sum_{p \leqslant x} d^{2D}(p-1) \leqslant \log^C x \sum_{n \leqslant x} d^{2D}(n)$$

and in view of the corollary to Proposition A.1 we finally obtain

(2.13)
$$\sum_{\substack{p \leqslant x \\ p \in B}} g(p) \ll x \log^{C+4^D-1} x.$$

Choosing $\alpha = 3/8 - \eta$ with an arbitrary positive η, $C = 3/\alpha$ and $D = 1/\alpha$, we obtain in view of (2.12) and (2.13) the evaluation

$$\sum_{p \leqslant x} g(p) \ll x \log^B x \quad \text{with} \quad B = C + 4^D - 1 < 47.4. \quad \square$$

Notes and comments

1. Tables giving the smallest primitive roots for all primes up to 5000 were given by G. Wertheim [93], [97b]. Certain errors in them were corrected by C. Posse [10], who also extended them up to 10000 (C. Posse [11b]), using a method of A. N. Korkin (see C. Posse [11a]). The tables of A. E. Western and J. C. P. Miller [68] give the smallest primitive roots for all primes up to 50021, for all primes congruent to 1 (mod 24) up to 100000 and for all primes congruent to 1 or 49 (mod 120) up to 250000. These tables provide also indices with respect to those primitive roots, extending thus the previous tables of C. G. J. Jacobi [39] and R. V. Andree [62]. All primitive roots for primes smaller than 1000 are given in R. Osborn [61] and for those smaller than 5000 in H. Hauptmann, E. Vegh and J. Fisher [70].

2. Hua's proof (L. K. Hua [42b]) of Theorem 2.4 is based on the bound

$$\left| \sum_{a=0}^{A} \sum_{n=-a}^{a} \chi(n) \right| \leqslant (1+A_0)k^{1/2},$$

valid for every non-principal character $\chi \pmod k$ where A_0 is the least positive residue of $A \pmod k$. (L. K. Hua [42a].) The proof of Theorem 2.4 given in Section 2 can be modified to yield $g(p) \ll \omega(p-1)^C p^{1/2}$ with a certain constant C. (P. Erdös and H. N. Shapiro [57].) Using Brun's sieve, P. Erdös [45a] obtained, for p sufficiently large, $g(p) \ll p^{1/2} \log^{17} p$, which in certain cases is better than the bound given in Theorem 2.4. (Cf. Exercises 1 and 2.)

The bound of Wang Yuan [59a], [59b], [61] and D. A. Burgess [62a] presented in Theorem 2.5 is the best known evaluation of $g(p)$. It is conjectured that for every positive ε one has $g(p) = O(p^\varepsilon)$. Using the Extended Riemann Hypothesis, one can, in fact, prove this conjecture. N. C. Ankeny [52] proved that under this assumption one has $g(p) = O(Y^2 \log^2 Y)$ with $Y = 2^{\omega(p-1)} \log p$. A simple proof of the slightly stronger evaluation $g(p) = O(Y^2)$ was given by H. L. Montgomery [71]. (Since $Y \ll \exp(B \log p / \log \log p)$, these results imply $g(p) = O(p^\varepsilon)$.) Wang Yuan [59b], [61] proved under this hypothesis the bound $g(p) \ll \omega(p-1)^6 \log^2 p$, which for large values of $\omega(p-1)$ is better.

3. Before the proof of Theorem 2.6 was found, S. S. Pillai [44b] showed that the inequality $g(p) \gg \log \log p$ holds for infinitely many primes p.

From the results of P. D. T. A. Elliott [69b] it follows that an overwhelming majority of primes satisfy the inequality $g'(p) \leqslant C p^\varepsilon$. In fact, with an appropriate choice of the constant C, the number of primes $p \leqslant x$ which do not satisfy this inequality is $\ll \log^t x$ with a certain constant t.

Theorem 2.8 was proved by D. A. Burgess and P. D. T. A. Elliott [68].

The proof of the stronger form of Theorem 2.9, giving the bound $O(x \log x \log \log^4 x)$ (D. A. Burgess, P. D. T. A. Elliott [68]), is based on the same idea as the proof we have given but involves one more application of the Lemmas 2.6 and 2.8.

R. Warlimont [78] used a similar idea to show that if $g(m)$ denotes the minimal positive integer of maximal order $\pmod m$ then we have $\sum_{m \leqslant x} g(m)$
$= O(x^{1+\varepsilon})$ for every positive ε. A numerical investigation of these integers was made by C. Brenner and J. L. Brenner [62].

Using still the same method, S. D. Cohen, R. W. K. Odoni and W. W. Stothers [74] studied the least primitive root $h(p) \pmod{p^2}$ and got

$$\sum_{p \leqslant x} h(p) \ll x \log x \log \log^4 x,$$

i.e., the same evaluation as for $g(p)$. This is not very surprising since numerical evidence suggests that the equality $g(p) = h(p)$ holds in most cases. Among the primes smaller than $1\,001\,321$ only one, viz. $p = 40487$, does not satisfy this condition (E. L. Litver and G. E. Yudina [71]).

Earlier D. A. Burgess [71] obtained the bound

$$\sum_{p \leqslant x} h(p) \ll x \log^4 x \log \log^6 x.$$

The paper of S. D. Cohen et al. quoted above brings also the bound $h(p)$ $\ll p^{1/4+\varepsilon}$ for all positive ε.

4. The question of the existence of consecutive primitive roots was first answered by B. Segal [41], who proved, using the evaluation of character sums given by H. Davenport [39a], that the number of integers $x < p$ for which all numbers $x, x+1, \ldots, x+k-1$ are primitive roots (mod p) is equal to $(\varphi(p-1)/(p-1))^k + O(2^{k\omega(p-1)} k p^{1-t})$ with certain positive constants $t = t(k)$. (Now we know, owing to A. Weil [48], that one can take $t = \frac{1}{2}$ for all k.) Segal's result implies in particular that for sufficiently large primes p one can find arbitrary long sequences of primitive roots (mod p).

Segal's paper was not given the attention it deserved and his result was later rediscovered independently by M. Szalay [70] and J. Johnsen [71]. Previous results on this topic belong to E. Vegh [69], [70a], [70b], who considered certain special cases. E. Vegh [72] deals with a similar problem for primitive roots (mod p^m).

In the simplest case, $k = 2$, E. Vegh [68] supplied a very elegant elementary argument ensuring the existence of a pair of consecutive primitive roots (mod p), provided $p \geqslant 5$ and the ratio $\varphi(p-1)/(p-1)$ exceeds $1/3$. (Note that a result of J.-M. Deshouillers [70a], [70b] shows that this set of primes has positive density.) We cannot resist the temptation to present it here: observe that if t is a primitive root (mod p) then t^{p-2} also is a primitive root and since $p \geqslant 5$ they are different. Because of $t(t^{p-2}+1) \equiv t+1 \pmod{p}$ we get $\left(\dfrac{t+1}{p}\right) = -1$ if and only if $\left(\dfrac{t^{p-2}+1}{p}\right) = -1$, and thus exactly one of the numbers t, t^{p-2} is followed by a quadratic non-residue (mod p). Now, if $u \neq t$, t^{p-2} is a primitive root then $u^{p-2} \neq t, t^{p-2}$, and we finally conclude that exactly half of the primitive roots (mod p) are followed by quadratic non-residues. This observation implies that if the assertion were false we would have at least $3\varphi(p-1)/2$ quadratic non-residues (mod p); thus $3\varphi(p-1)/2 \leqslant (p-1)/2$, contradicting the assumption.

In Szalay [75] pairs of primitive roots with a given difference g were considered and it was shown that their number equals

$$(p-2)(\varphi(p-1)/(p-1))^2 + O\left(p^{1/2} 4^{\omega(p-1)} \cdot (\varphi(p-1)/(p-1))^2\right),$$

where the implied constant does not exceed 1. This implies in particular that for all $p > 10^{19}$ there is at least one pair of primitive roots with a given difference. For a weaker earlier result see Vegh [71].

(Added in proof: Cf. S. D. Cohen, Proc. Amer. Math. Soc. 93 (1985), 189–197; 94 (1985), 605–611.)

5. Primitive roots in recurrence sequences u_n of order k were studied by

N. M. Korobov [53], who proved that if T is its period (mod p) (which is less than p^k) then u_n contains

$$\frac{\varphi(p-1)}{p-1} T + O(p^{(k+1)/2+\varepsilon})$$

primitive roots (mod p) for every positive ε. This result follows from the estimate

$$\left| \sum_{k=1}^{T} \exp(2\pi i u_k/p) \right| \leqslant p^{k/2}.$$

V. I. Nechaev and L. L. Stepanova [65] generalized this result to algebraic number fields, which amounts to dealing with primitive roots in $GF(p^N)$ in place of $GF(p)$. The error terms in the results of Korobov, Nechaev and Stepanova were improved by I. E. Shparlinskij [78].

Primitive roots in more complicated sequences were considered in Nechaev, Polosuev [64].

6. In certain cases one can obtain upper bounds for $g(p)$ by elementary methods; however, they are much worse than those obtained with the use of character sums. So A. Brauer [54] proved elementarily that for $p \equiv 1 \pmod 4$ one has $g(p) < p^{1-1/r}$, where $r = \omega(p-1)$. Cf. also C. T. Whyburn [73].

Exercises

1. Let $f_k(x)$ denote the number of kth power residues (mod p) in the interval $(0, x)$. Prove that the number $F(x)$ of primitive roots (mod p) in this interval equals $\sum_{d|p-1} \mu(d) f_d(x)$.

2 (P. Erdös [45a]). (a) Let

$$S_1 = \sum_{\substack{q|p-1 \\ q\,\text{prime} \\ q>\log^3 p}} f_q(x).$$

Prove that $S_1 = O(x/\log^2 p)$.
   (b) Let

$$S_2 = x - \sideset{}{'}\sum_{q_1|p-1} f_{q_1}(x) + \sideset{}{'}\sum_{q_1 \cdot q_2|p-1} f_{q_1 q_2}(x) + \ldots + (-1)^r \sideset{}{'}\sum_{q_1 \ldots q_r|p-1} f_{q_1 \ldots q_r}(x) + \ldots,$$

where the dash indicates that we are summing over those primes $q, q_1, q_2, \ldots$ dividing $p-1$ which do not exceed $\log^3 p$. Using a sieve method prove that

$$S_2 > C_1 \frac{x}{\log\log p} - C_2 p^{1/2} \log^{17} p.$$

(c) Deduce $g(p) < p^{1/2} \log^{17} p$ for large p.
   3. Let $d|p-1$ and let $g_d(p)$ be the minimal positive integer of order (mod p) equal to d. Obtain an upper bound for $g_d(p)$.
   4. Prove that for p sufficiently large there are at least $p^{1/4}$ primitive roots (mod p) not exceeding $p^{1/4+\varepsilon}$.

5 (S. D. Cohen, R. W. K. Odoni, W. W. Stothers [74]).

(a) Prove that if x, y are positive integers smaller than p^2 which are congruent (mod p) and are both pth powers, then $x = y$.

(b) Prove that if $\varepsilon > 0$ is given then for sufficiently large primes p there are at most $p^{1/2+\varepsilon}$ integers smaller than p which are pth power residues (mod p^2).

(c) Prove that for sufficiently large p there are at most $p^{1/2+\varepsilon}$ primitive roots (mod p) which are not primitive roots (mod p^2).

(d) Prove that the least primitive root (mod p^2) is smaller than $p^{1/4+\varepsilon}$ for sufficiently large p.

6 (J. D. Baum [65], A. Wilansky [76]). Prove that if q is an odd prime and $p = 2q+1$ is also a prime, then in the case $q \equiv 1 \pmod 4$ the number $1+q$ is a primitive root (mod p) whereas in the case $p \equiv 3 \pmod 4$ q is a primitive root (mod p).

7 (M. Hausman [76]). Prove that if p is a sufficiently large prime then there is a primitive root (mod p) prime to $p-1$.

8 (M. G. Monzingo [76]). Show that if all primitive roots (mod p) are consecutive then $p \leqslant 5$.

9 (D. Shanks [72]). Prove that if there exists a primitive root $g \pmod p$ which satisfies $g^2 \equiv 1+g \pmod p$ then either $p = 5$ or $p \equiv \pm 1 \pmod{10}$.

10 (B. Segal [41], M. Szalay [70], J. Johnsen [71]). Prove that if $p \geqslant p_0(n)$ then there are at least n consecutive primitive roots (mod p).

11 (L. Carlitz [56b]). Let $f_1, \ldots, f_r$ be square-free and pairwise co-prime polynomials (mod p). Prove that the number of $x \pmod p$ for which all values $f_i(x)$ $(i = 1, 2, \ldots, r)$ are primitive roots (mod p) is asymptotically equal to $\varphi(p-1)^r/p^{r-1}$.

12 (F. J. Richelot [32], G. Wertheim [97a]). Prove that if $p = 2^{2^m}+1$ is a Fermat prime then $g(p) = 2$ for $m = 0, 1$ and $g(p) = 3$ for $m \geqslant 2$.

13 (C. G. J. Jacobi [39]). Prove that if g is a primitive root (mod p^2) then it is also a primitive root (mod p^k) for $k \geqslant 3$.

14 (V. A. Lebesgue [67]). Prove that if g is a primitive root (mod p) and $gg' \equiv 1 \pmod p$, $1 < g$, $g' < p$ then either g or g' is a primitive root (mod p^k) for $k = 1, 2, 3, \ldots$

15 (G. Wertheim [97a]). Show that if q is a prime and $p = 2^m q+1$ is again a prime then every quadratic non-residue $a \pmod p$ for which $a^{2^m} \not\equiv 1 \pmod p$ is a primitive root (mod p).

16 (G. Wertheim [97a]). Deduce from Exercise 15 sufficient conditions for the numbers 2, 5, 6, 7, 10, 11 and 13 to be primitive roots (mod p).

17. Let p be a prime and A a number not divisible by p. Obtain a bound for the minimal primitive root (mod p) belonging to a given residue class (mod A).

§ 3. ARTIN'S CONJECTURE

1. In the previous section we were concerned with numbers which are primitive roots for a given prime. Now we invert the problem and look for those primes for which a given integer a is a primitive root. Of course certain integers a must be excluded here because neither -1 nor a perfect square can be a primitive root (mod p) for an odd prime p. For other integers there are no evident reasons why they could not be primitive roots for suitable primes, and so the question arises whether every integer a which is neither equal to -1 nor to a perfect square (which excludes also the cases $a = 0$ and

$a = 1$) is a primitive root for infinitely many primes, or at least for one prime.

For certain particular values of a this question was already considered in the previous century (cf. C. F. Gauss [01] art. 72, 315 (for $a = 10$)), but without any conclusive results. The general question was asked first in 1927 by E. Artin, who also gave a conjectural asymptotic formula for the number of primes $p \leqslant x$ for which a is a primitive root. This formula was later readjusted by H. Heilbronn as it did not fit the numerical evidence supplied by D. H. Lehmer and E. Lehmer [62]. For forty years there was no progress as regards this question until C. Hooley [67] deduced the asymptotical formula in Heilbronn's version from the Extended Riemann Hypothesis.

We are going to give the proof of Hooley's result; however, to avoid the use of the theory of Dedekind zeta-functions we shall deduce Artin's conjecture not directly from the Extended Riemann Hypothesis but from one of its arithmetical consequences, which we state as follows:

(A) For any positive integer k and its divisor d the number $\pi_K(x)$ of prime ideals in the field $K = Q(\zeta_k, b^{1/d})$ (where b is a given rational integer) with norms bounded by x equals $\operatorname{li} x + O(x^{1/2} n \log(kx))$, where the implied constant is absolute and n denotes the degree of K/Q.

THEOREM 2.9 (C. Hooley [67], cf. also [76]). *If a is a rational integer which is neither -1 nor a full square and (A) is satisfied for $b = a$, for any square-free number k and $d = k/(k, h)$ where h is the largest positive integer such that a is a perfect h-th power, then for the number $N_a(x)$ of primes $p \leqslant x$ for which a is a primitive root the following asymptotic formula holds:*

$$N_a(x) = c(a) x/\log x + O(x \log\log x/\log^2 x).$$

Here $c(a)$ is a positive constant defined in the following way: write $a = a_1 a_2^2$ with a_1 square-free. If $a_1 \not\equiv 1 \pmod 4$ then

$$c(a) = \prod_{q|h}\left(1 - \frac{1}{q-1}\right)\prod_{q \nmid h}\left(1 - \frac{1}{q(q-1)}\right),$$

and if $a \equiv 1 \pmod 4$, then

$$c(a) = \prod_{q|h}\left(1 - \frac{1}{q-1}\right)\prod_{q \nmid h}\left(1 - \frac{1}{q(q-1)}\right)(1 - \mu(|a_1|)) \prod_{q|(h,a_1)}\frac{1}{q-2}\prod_{\substack{q|a_1 \\ q \nmid h}}\frac{1}{q^2-q-1}$$

where q runs over primes in both formulas (as well as in the following proof).

Proof. We shall first write $N_a(x)$ as a sum of four summands, each of which is a sum over primes $\leqslant x$ satisfying certain power residue conditions. One of those summands will constitute the main term and the others will form the remainder. Two of those summands we shall easily evaluate by using nothing but the Brun–Titchmarsh theorem, whereas the main term and the remaining part of the error term will be expressed in terms of $\pi_K(x)$ with various fields K. At this stage condition (A) will be invoked and then, in the final step, we shall put together the resulting evaluations to obtain the assertion.

For given ξ denote by $N_a(x, \xi)$ the number of primes $p \leqslant x$, with the property that a is not a qth power residue (mod p) for any prime $q \leqslant \xi$ which divides $p-1$. Moreover, for given $\eta_1 < \eta_2$, $M_a(x, \eta_1, \eta_2)$ will denote the number of primes $p \leqslant x$ such that for a certain prime divisor q of $p-1$, lying in the interval $(\eta_1, \eta_2]$ a is a qth power residue (mod p). Using these notations we now prove:

LEMMA 2.9. *If* $2 < \xi_1 < \xi_2 < \xi_3 < x-1$, *then*

$$N_a(x, \xi_1)$$
$$\geqslant N_a(x) \geqslant N_a(x, \xi_1) - M_a(x, \xi_1, \xi_2) - M_a(x, \xi_2, \xi_3) - M_a(x, \xi_3, x-1).$$

Proof. Since a is a primitive root (mod p) if and only if it is not a qth power residue (mod p) for any prime divisor q of $p-1$, we have $N_a(x) = N_a(x, x-1)$ and the first inequality results immediately. Moreover, we obviously have

$$N_a(x, x-1) \geqslant N_a(x, \xi_1) - M_a(x, \xi_1, x-1),$$

and it suffices to observe that for trivial reasons

$$M_a(x, \xi_1, x-1) \leqslant M_a(x, \xi_1, \xi_2) + M_a(x, \xi_2, \xi_3) + M_a(x, \xi_3, x-1). \quad \square$$

Now we evaluate the terms $M_a(x, \xi_2, \xi_3)$ and $M_a(x, \xi_3, x-1)$. The first of them is at most equal to $\sum_{\xi_2 < q \leqslant \xi_3} \pi(x, q, 1)$, the letter q here and below being reserved for primes, and so by the Brun–Titchmarsh theorem (Theorem A.2) we get

$$M_a(x, \xi_2, \xi_3) \ll \frac{x}{\log(x/\xi_3)} \sum_{\xi_2 < q \leqslant \xi_3} \frac{1}{q}$$
$$\ll \frac{x}{\log(x/\xi_3)} \left\{ \log\log\xi_3 - \log\log\xi_2 + O\left(\frac{1}{\log\xi_2}\right) \right\}.$$

To bound $M_a(x, \xi_3, x-1)$ observe first that if a is a qth power residue (mod p) for a certain prime q dividing $p-1$ and contained in $(\xi_3, x-1]$ then $a^{(p-1)/q} \equiv 1 \pmod{p}$; hence p divides $a^k - 1$ with $k = (p-1)/q \leqslant x/\xi_3$. This shows that the product D of all such primes divides $\prod_{m \leqslant x/\xi_3} (a^m - 1)$ and we obtain

$$2^{M_a(x, \xi_3, x-1)} \leqslant D \leqslant \prod_{m \leqslant x/\xi_3} a^m,$$

which leads to

$$M_a(x, \xi_3, x-1) \ll \sum_{m \leqslant x/\xi_3} m \ll (x/\xi_3)^2.$$

Now we choose ξ_2, ξ_3, putting $\xi_2 = x^{1/2}/\log^2 x$ and $\xi_3 = x^{1/2} \log x$. With this choice

(2.14) $M_a(x, \xi_3, x-1) \ll x/\log^2 x$

and

(2.14)′ $M_a(x, \xi_2, \xi_3)$

$$\ll \frac{x}{\log x} \left\{ \log \left(1 + O\left(\frac{\log \log x}{\log x} \right) \right) + O\left(\frac{1}{\log x} \right) \right\} \ll \frac{x \log \log x}{\log^2 x}.$$

We end this preparatory step by expressing the remaining terms occurring in Lemma 2.9 through functions $P_a(x, k)$ defined as the number of primes $p \leqslant x$ with the property that every prime divisor q of k divides also $p-1$ and moreover a is a qth power residue mod p.

Observe first that the inequality

(2.15) $M_a(x, \xi_1, \xi_2) \leqslant \sum_{\xi_1 < q \leqslant \xi_2} P_a(x, q)$

follows immediately from the definition and then turn to the proof of the equality

(2.16) $N_a(x, \xi_1) = \sum_{k \in X} \mu(k) P_a(x, k),$

where X denotes the set of all integers whose prime factors do not exceed ξ_1.

If $A(p)$ denotes the set of those primes q dividing $p-1$ for which a is a qth power residue (mod p) and $D_p = \prod_{\substack{q \leqslant \xi_1 \\ q \in A(p)}} q$, then the expression on the right of (2.16) equals

$$\sum_{k \in X} \mu(k) \sum_{\substack{p \leqslant x \\ q|k \Rightarrow q \in A(p)}} 1 = \sum_{p \leqslant x} \sum_{\substack{k|p-1 \\ k \in X \\ q|k \Rightarrow q \in A(p)}} \mu(k) = \sum_{p \leqslant x} \sum_{k|D_p} \mu(k) = \sum_{\substack{p \leqslant x \\ D_p = 1}} 1 = N_a(x, \xi_1),$$

giving (2.16).

Putting together (2.14), (2.14)′, (2.15), (2.16) and using Lemma 2.9, we obtain

(2.17) $N_a(x)$

$$= \sum_{k \in X} \mu(k) P_a(x, k) + O\left(\sum_{\xi_1 < q \leqslant \xi_2} P_a(x, q) \right) + O(x \log \log x/\log^2 x),$$

which forces us to obtain an evaluation of $P_a(x, k)$. We shall achieve this with the aid of the following lemma.

LEMMA 2.10. *Let* k *be a square-free integer. If* L_k *denotes the field* $Q(\zeta_k, a^{1/k})$ *and* $n(k)$ *is its degree, then for* $x \geqslant 2$

$$P_a(x, k) = \pi_{L_k}(x)/n(k) + O(\omega(k)) + O(x^{1/2}),$$

where the implied constants depend on a *but not on* k *or* x.

Proof. If a is a perfect hth power and h is the maximal integer with this property, then a prime p is counted in $P_a(x, k)$ if and only if $p \nmid a$, $p \equiv 1 \pmod{k}$, $p \leqslant x$ and for every prime divisor q of $k_1 = k/(k, h)$ the congruence $X^{k_1} \equiv a \pmod{p}$ is solvable.

As $4 \nmid k_1$, the polynomial $X^{k_1} - a$ is irreducible over Q and L_k is its splitting field. Since the p's counted in $P(x, k)$ do not divide ak, we can infer from the Kummer–Dedekind theorem (Proposition A.9) that $P_a(x, k)$ is the number of all primes $p \leqslant x$ which do not divide ak and which split in the k_1-st cyclotomic field $Q(\zeta_{k_1})$ and in $Q(a^{1/k_1})$. But the primes in question are exactly those splitting primes in L_k/Q which do not divide ak. As L_k/Q is normal of degree $n(k)$, every splitting prime has $n(k)$ distinct prime ideal factors, all of norm p, thus the difference $|n(k) P_a(x, k) - \pi_{L_k}(x)|$ cannot exceed

$$\sum_{\substack{P \\ NP \leqslant x; \deg P \geqslant 2}} 1 + \sum_{\substack{P \\ NP \in x \\ P|ak}} 1 \ll x^{1/2} + n(k)\omega(k) + n(k)\omega(a)$$

(where P runs over prime ideals in L_K) and our proof is complete. □

COROLLARY. *Assumption* (A) *implies*

$$P_a(x, k) = \frac{\mathrm{li}\, x}{n(k)} + O(x^{1/2} \log(kx)).$$

Proof. It suffices to observe that $\omega(k) \ll \log k$. □

Before we substitute the resulting evaluation of $P(x, k)$ in (2.17) we need an explicit form for $n(k)$.

LEMMA 2.11. *If* $a = a_1 a_2^2$ *where* $a_1 \neq 1$ *is square-free, and we put*

$$\varepsilon(k) = \begin{cases} 2 & \text{if } a_1 \equiv 1 \pmod{4} \text{ and } 2a_1|k, \\ 1 & \text{otherwise} \end{cases}$$

then $n(k) = k_1 \varphi(k)/\varepsilon(k)$, *with* $k_1 = k/(k, h)$.

Proof. Let $M = Q(\zeta_k, a^{1/k_1})$, $L = Q(a^{1/k_1})$ and $Q_k = Q(\zeta_k)$. Since the extension Q_k/Q is normal and $[L:Q] = k_1$, we must have $m[M:Q_k] = k_1$ with a suitable integer m. If p is any prime divisor of m, then the degree of $Q_k(a^{1/p})/Q_k$ divides $[M:Q_k]$. But k_1 being square-free, we have $(m, [M:Q_k]) = 1$ and so p cannot divide $[M:Q_k]$. As the degree of $Q_k(a^{1/p})/Q_k$ equals either 1 or p, it must thus be equal to 1 and we obtain $a^{1/p} \in Q_k$. The latter field, being abelian over Q, cannot contain $a^{1/p}$ with p odd except when a is a pth power of a rational integer, but this cannot happen since it would imply $p|h$ and thus $p \nmid k_1$. It follows that $p = 2$ and we see that m equals 1 or 2. The latter case occurs if and only if $2|k_1$ and $a^{1/2} \in Q_k$, and we shall now prove that this happens exactly when $a_1 \equiv 1 \pmod 4$ and $2a_1|k$. Assume first that $a_1 \equiv 1 \pmod 4$ and $2a_1|k$. If k_1 were odd, then k/k_1 would be even, thus h would be even and a would be a square, which is excluded by our assumption. Thus $2|k_1$. The corollary to Theorem 2.1 shows now that if a_1 is positive then $a_1^{1/2} \in Q(\zeta_{a_1}) \subset Q(\zeta_k)$, and if a_1 is negative then $a^{1/2} \in Q(\zeta_{|a_1|}) \subset Q(\zeta_k)$ as asserted.

Now assume that k_1 is even and $a^{1/2} \in Q(\zeta_k)$. Then $Q(\zeta_k)$ contains $a_1^{1/2}$ and so $Q(a_1^{1/2}) \subset Q(\zeta_k)$.

We can now conclude the proof of the theorem. Using the corollary to Lemma 2.10 and putting $\xi_1 = (1/M)\log x$ $(M > 1)$, we get

$$\sum_{k \in X} \mu(k) P_a(x, k) = \operatorname{li} x \sum_{k \in X} \frac{\mu(k)}{n(k)} + O\left(x^{1/2} \sum_{k \in X} \mu^2(k) \log(kx)\right);$$

taking into account

$$|X| \leqslant 2^{\pi(\xi_1)} \leqslant \exp\left\{B_1 \frac{\xi_1}{\log \xi_1}\right\} \ll x^{1/4}$$

and

$$\max_{k \in X} k = \prod_{\substack{q \leqslant \xi_1 \\ q\,\text{prime}}} q \leqslant \xi_1^{\pi(\xi_1)}, \qquad \log \max_{k \in X} k \leqslant \pi(\xi_1)\log \xi_1 \ll \xi_1 \ll \log x,$$

we get for the error term the bound $O(x^{3/4}\log x)$.

Lemma 2.11 implies that the series

(2.18) $$\sum_{k=1}^{\infty} \frac{\mu(k)}{n(k)}$$

converges absolutely, being majorized by

$$2h \sum_{k=1}^{\infty} \frac{1}{k\varphi(k)}.$$

Moreover,

$$\sum_{k \in X} \frac{\mu(k)}{n(k)} = \sum_{k=1}^{\infty} \frac{\mu(k)}{n(k)} + O\left(\sum_{k \geqslant \xi_1} \frac{\mu^2(k)}{n(k)}\right),$$

and since the remainder term is bounded by

$$2h \sum_{k \geqslant \xi_1} \frac{1}{k\varphi(k)} \ll \sum_{k \geqslant \xi_2} \frac{\log\log k}{k^2} \ll \frac{\log\log \xi_1}{\xi_1} \ll \frac{\log\log\log x}{\log x},$$

we obtain for the first term in (2.17)

$$(2.19) \qquad \sum_{k \in X} \mu(k) P_a(x, k) = \mathrm{li}\, x \sum_{k=1}^{\infty} \frac{\mu(k)}{n(k)} + O\left(\frac{x \log\log\log x}{\log^2 x}\right).$$

Moreover, for the second term in (2.17), we get

$$\sum_{\xi_1 < q \leqslant \xi_2} P_a(x, q) = \mathrm{li}\, x \sum_{\xi_1 < q \leqslant \xi_2} \frac{1}{n(q)} + O\left(\log(\xi_2 x) x^{1/2} \pi(\xi_2)\right)$$

$$\ll \mathrm{li}\, x \sum_{\substack{\xi_1 < q \leqslant \xi_2 \\ q \text{ prime}}} \frac{1}{q^2} + \frac{x}{\log^2 x} \ll \frac{\mathrm{li}\, x}{\xi_1} + \frac{x}{\log^2 x} \ll \frac{x}{\log^2 x}.$$

The last inequality jointly with (2.17) and (2.19) gives now

$$P_a(x) = \mathrm{li}\, x \sum_{k=1}^{\infty} \frac{\mu(k)}{n(k)} + O\left(\frac{x \log\log x}{\log^2 x}\right),$$

and it remains to show that the sum of the series (2.18) equals $C(a)$. We use here Lemma 2.11. If $a_1 \not\equiv 1 \pmod 4$, then $n(k)$ is a multiplicative function; expanding (2.18) into Euler's product, we are ready. Otherwise, writing $A = |a_1|$,

$$\sum_{k=1}^{\infty} \frac{\mu(k)}{n(k)} = \sum_{k=1}^{\infty} \frac{\mu(k)(k, h)}{k\varphi(k)} + \sum_{2A|k} \frac{\mu(k)(k, h)}{k\varphi(k)}$$

$$= \sum_{k=1}^{\infty} \frac{\mu(k)(k, h)}{k\varphi(k)} + \frac{\mu(2A)(h, 2A)}{2A\varphi(2A)} \sum_{(k, 2A)=1} \frac{\mu(k)(k, h)}{k\varphi(k)}$$

and using again Euler's product formula, we obtain our goal. $\square$

2. Without using the Extended Riemann Hypothesis we cannot prove that there exist infinitely many primes for which a given integer is a primitive root. We cannot even do that for a single integer.(*) However, it is possible to prove that most integers are primitive roots for at least one prime. This was first shown by P. X. Gallagher [67] and his bound for the number of those integers smaller than x which are not primitive roots was later improved by R. C. Vaughan [73]. They both used the large sieve inequality. We now prove Gallagher's result:

_____

(*) Added in proof: R. Gupta and M. Ram Murty (Inv. math. 78 (1984), 127–130) proved the existence of infinitely many such integers. Moreover M. Ram Murty and S. Srinivasan (preprint 1985) showed that all integers having a prime divisor outside a possible exceptional set of at most six primes, have this property, in particular the number $2 \cdot 3 \cdot 5 \cdot 7 \cdot 11 \cdot 13 \cdot 17$. This shows that in Theorem 2.10 one has $F(x) = \sum_{m^2 \leqslant x} 1 + O(\log^6 x) = x^{1/2} + \log^6 x$, and implies that $g'(p) \leqslant 17$ holds for infinitely many primes.

THEOREM 2.10. *Let $F(x)$ be the number of integers $n \leqslant x$ which are not primitive roots for any prime $p \leqslant x^{1/2}$. Then*

$$F(x) \ll x^{1/2} \log x.$$

Proof. We shall apply the large sieve (Theorem A.1), observing that, since there are $\varphi(p-1)$ primitive roots (mod p), if a is not a primitive root (mod p) for $p \leqslant x^{1/2}$, then there are $\varphi(p-1)$ forbidden residue classes (mod p) for a . The large sieve inequality now gives $F(x) \ll x/S$ where

$$S = \sum_{q \leqslant x^{1/2}} \mu(q)^2 \prod_{p|q} \frac{\varphi(p-1)}{p - \varphi(p-1)} \geqslant \sum_{p \leqslant x^{1/2}} \frac{\varphi(p-1)}{p - \varphi(p-1)} \geqslant \sum_{p \leqslant x^{1/2}} \frac{\varphi(p-1)}{p-1},$$

p being as usual restricted to primes.

The sum on the right will be evaluated in the following lemma:

LEMMA 2.12. *For $T \geqslant 2$ one has*

$$\sum_{p \leqslant x} \frac{\varphi(p-1)}{p-1} = C \operatorname{li} x + O_D(x/\log^D x)$$

where $C = \sum_{n=1}^{\infty} \mu(n)/(n\varphi(n))$ and D is an arbitrarily large fixed number.

Proof. We have

$$\sum_{p \leqslant T} \frac{\varphi(p-1)}{p-1} = \sum_{p \leqslant T} \sum_{d|p-1} \frac{\mu(d)}{d} = \sum_{d \leqslant T} \frac{\mu(d)}{d} \pi(T; d, 1)$$

$$= \operatorname{li} T \sum_{d \leqslant T} \frac{\mu(d)}{d\varphi(d)} + O\left(\sum_{d \leqslant T} \frac{1}{d} \left| \pi(T; d, 1) - \frac{\operatorname{li} T}{\varphi(d)} \right| \right)$$

$$= C \operatorname{li} T + O\left(\operatorname{li} T \sum_{d > T} \frac{1}{d\varphi(d)} \right) + O(R(T))$$

where

$$R(T) = \sum_{d \leqslant T} \frac{1}{d} \left| \pi(T; d, 1) - \frac{\pi(T)}{\varphi(d)} \right|.$$

The first error term is $\ll T^{1/2}$ and to evaluate the second we use Theorem A.4 to obtain

$$R(T) \leqslant \sum_{d \leqslant T^{1/4}} \frac{1}{d} \left| \pi(T; d, 1) - \frac{\operatorname{li} T}{\varphi(d)} \right| + \sum_{T^{1/4} < d \leqslant T} \frac{1}{d} \left| \pi(T; d, 1) - \frac{\operatorname{li} T}{\varphi(d)} \right|$$

$$\ll_D T \log^{-D} T + T^{-1/4} \sum_{d \leqslant T} T d^{-1} + T^{-1/4} \sum_{d \leqslant T} \frac{T}{\varphi(d) \log T} \ll_D T \log^{-D} T. \quad \square$$

The theorem follows now immediately. $\square$

3. A similar but more involved procedure may be applied to prove that the asymptotic formula

(2.20) $$N_a(x) = C\operatorname{li}x + O\left(x(\log x)^{-D}\right)$$

holds for most numbers $a \leqslant y$ where $y = y(x) \leqslant x^2$, C has the meaning from Lemma 2.12 and coincides with the value of $C(a)$ if a is equal to $a_1 a_2^2$ with square-free a_1, not congruent to $1 \pmod 4$ and, moreover, a is not a full power. This formula does not of course imply that there is at least one a for which it holds for all x. It says only that there exists a constant $B(D)$, depending only on D such that for all x and most $a \leqslant y$ the difference $|N_a(x) - C\operatorname{li}x|$ does not exceed $B(d) x(\log x)^{-D}$; however, the set $S_{x,y}$ of exceptional a's depends on x and the intersection $\bigcap\limits^{x} S_{x,y}$ may be empty.

The best upper bound for the cardinality of that exceptional set $S_{x,y}$ was obtained by R. Warlimont [72], who strengthened a previous result of M. Goldfeld [68]. We now prove a special case of this result.

THEOREM 2.11 (R. Warlimont [72]). *To every $D > 1$ there corresponds a constant $B(D)$ with the property that for all but $O(x\log^{2D-1} x)$ numbers $a \leqslant x^2$ one has*

$$|N_a(x) - C\operatorname{li}x| \leqslant B(D) x \log^{-D} x,$$

where $C = \sum\limits_{n=1}^{x} \mu(n)/n\varphi(n) = \prod\limits_{p}(1 - 1/p(p-1))$ and the constant implied by the symbol O is absolute.

Proof. Observe that Proposition 2.2 (iv), Lemma 2.12 and the Prime Number Theorem imply that for $x \geqslant 2$ and $a \leqslant x^2$ one has for every $D > 1$ the equality

$$N_a(x) = C\operatorname{li}x + \sum_{p \leqslant x} \frac{\varphi(p-1)}{p-1} \sum_{\substack{d \mid p-1 \\ d > 1}} \mu(d)\varphi^{-1}(d) \sum_{\substack{\chi(\bmod p) \\ o(\chi) = d}} \chi(a) + O_D(x\log^{-D} x).$$

Denote the middle term in this expression by $W_a(x)$ and put

$$M = \{a \leqslant x^2 : |W_a(x)| > x\log^{-D} x\}, \qquad M(x) = |M|.$$

The theorem will be established if we show that $M(x) \ll x\log^{2D-1} x$, the implied constant being absolute. Writing

$$c_a(x) = \begin{cases} 0 & \text{if} \quad W_a(x) = 0, \\[2mm] \dfrac{|W_a(x)|}{W_a(x)} & \text{if} \quad W_a(x) \neq 0, \end{cases}$$

we obtain

$$\sum_{a \in M} |W_a(x)| = \sum_{a \in M} c_a(x) W_a(x) = \sum_{p \leqslant x} \frac{\varphi(p-1)}{p-1} \sum_{\substack{d \mid p-1 \\ d > 1}} \frac{\mu(d)}{\varphi(d)} \sum_{\substack{\chi(\bmod p) \\ o(\chi) = d}} \sum_{a \in M} c_a(x)\chi(a)$$

$$= \sum_{\substack{p \leqslant x \, d|p-1 \\ d>1}} \sum_{\substack{\chi(\bmod p) \\ o(\chi)=d}} \frac{\varphi(p-1)\,\mu(d)}{p-1} \frac{}{\varphi(d)} \sum_{a \in M} c_a(\chi)\chi(a)$$

$$\leqslant \left\{ \sum_{\substack{p \leqslant x \, d|p-1 \\ o(\chi)=d}} \sum_{\substack{\chi(\bmod p)}} \frac{\varphi^2(p-1)}{(p-1)^2\,\varphi^2(d)} \right\}^{1/2} \left\{ \sum_{\substack{p \leqslant x \, d|p-1 \\ d>1}} \sum_{\substack{\chi(\bmod p) \\ o(\chi)=d}} \sum_{a \in M} \left| \sum c_a(\chi)\chi(a) \right|^2 \right\}^{1/2}$$

$$= V_1^{1/2} \cdot V_2^{1/2}.$$

We evaluate the first factor with the aid of the Brun–Titchmarsh theorem (Theorem A.2):

$$V_1 \leqslant \sum_{d \leqslant x} \frac{\pi(x;d,1)}{\varphi(d)} = \sum_{d \leqslant x^{1/2}} \frac{\pi(x;d,1)}{\varphi(d)} + \sum_{x^{1/2}<d \leqslant x} \frac{\pi(x;d,1)}{\varphi(d)}$$

$$\ll \sum_{d \leqslant x^{1/2}} \frac{x}{\varphi^2(d)\log x} + \sum_{x^{1/2}<d \leqslant x} \frac{x}{d\varphi(d)} \ll \frac{x}{\log x}.$$

To get a bound for the second factor we use the corollary to Theorem A.1, which gives

$$V_2 \leqslant (x^2+\pi x) \sum_{a \in M} |c_a(\chi)|^2 \ll x^2 M(x),$$

and so we obtain the inequality

$$\sum_{a \in M} |W_a(x)| \ll \frac{x^{3/2} M^{1/2}(x)}{\log^{1/2} x}.$$

Since obviously

$$\sum_{a \in M} |W_a(x)| > xM(x)\log^{-D} x,$$

the asserted bound for $M(x)$ follows immediately. $\square$

Notes and comments

1. Originally Artin conjectured that the coefficient in the formula $N_a(x) = c(a)x/\log x + o(x/\log x)$ should be independent of a and equal to $c = \prod_p (1-1/p(p-1))$.

However, this was in disagreement with numerical experiments (D. H. Lehmer, E. Lehmer [62]) and H. Heilbronn suggested a modified form for $c(a)$ which appears in Theorem 2.9. Nevertheless, c gives for most integers a a good approximation for $c(a)$. Indeed, it is easy to show that the number of $a \leqslant x$ for which $|c(a)-c| > \log^{-1} x$ holds is $O(x^{1/2} \log^2 x)$. See L. J. Goldstein [71] for a heuristic explanation of the derivation of Artin's formula and its modification.

An upper bound for $N_a(x)$ differing from that given in Theorem 2.9 only in the error term can be obtained unconditionally. This was demonstrated by A. I. Vinogradov [71], who proved the inequality

$$N_a(x) \leqslant c(a)\, x/\log x + O(x \log \log^2 x \log^{-5/4} x)$$

by using Selberg's sieve in conjunction with the theory of L-functions. If one is satisfied with the bound

$$N_a(x) \leqslant (c(a) + o(1))\, x/\log x,$$

then one can proceed as follows (cf. L. J. Goldstein [70]): fix a positive ε and choose an integer $N(\varepsilon)$ with the property

$$\left| \sum_{k \geqslant N} \mu^2(k)/n(k) \right| \leqslant \varepsilon,$$

where $n(k)$ is defined in Lemma 2.10. By using Lemmas 2.9, 2.10, (2.16) and the fact that for any finite set of fields k we have by the prime ideal theorem (Theorem A.11)

$$|\pi_k(x) - x/\log x| \leqslant Bx/\log^2 x$$

with a certain constant B depending only on that set, we get

$$N_a(x) \leqslant c(a)\, x/\log x + \varepsilon x/\log x + Bx/\log^2 x,$$

and our assertion follows.

A. I. Vinogradov [71], [73] showed also that the assertion of Theorem 2.9 (with the error term of order $O(x (\log\log x)^2 \log^{-7/6} x)$) follows from a kind of density hypothesis for Artin's L-functions of the splitting fields of $X^q - a$, where q runs through all primes. Cf. R. W. van der Waall [75], P. D. T. A. Elliott [70a].

2. C. Hooley [67] remarked at the end of his paper that his method works also in the case where two integers a, b are given and we seek the primes for which both are primitive roots. This was established by K. R. Matthews [76], who considered, more generally, n given integers.

Another remark of Hooley, stating that his method provides asymptotics for the set of primes for which a given number a is the minimal primitive root, was never followed.

An analogue of Artin's conjecture for fields of algebraic functions in one variable over a finite field of constants was deduced from the Riemann Hypothesis for curves by H. Bilharz [37]. As in this case the Riemann Hypothesis is a theorem (A. Weil [48]) so is this instance of Artin's conjecture.

H. Hasse [52a] indicated a possible approach to Artin's conjecture showing that its truth would follow provided one could find an interval

$(1, X]$ with $X > 1$ in which the series

$$\sum_p \frac{1}{n_p} \frac{\log \zeta_{K_p}(s)}{\log \zeta(s)},$$

where $K_p = Q(\zeta_p, a^{1/p})$ and $n(p) = [K_p : Q]$, converges uniformly.

3. Artin's conjecture has been generalized in several directions. One interesting generalization, due to L. J. Goldstein [68], [70], [71], runs as follows: let P be a set of rational primes. For every prime p in P let L_p be a finite normal extension of the rationals and if k is a square-free integer, product of primes $p_1, \ldots, p_t \in P$, then we let L_k to be the composite of $L_{p_1}, \ldots, L_{p_t}$. Finally, let $L_1 = Q$ and put $n(k) = [L_k : Q]$. If the series $\sum_k 1/n(k)$ converges, Goldstein conjectures that the set of all primes q, such that for no prime p q splits in L_p/Q, has a natural density equal to $\sum_k \mu(k)/n(k)$. One can easily see (cf. the proof of Lemma 2.10) that if P consists of all primes and $L_p = Q(\zeta_p, a^{1/p})$ then we get Artin's conjecture.

In certain cases Goldstein's conjecture turned out to be true. The results of H. W. Knobloch [54] and L. Mirsky [49] show that it holds in the case where P is the set of all primes and L_p equals $Q(\zeta_{p^r})$ for some fixed $r \geqslant 2$. Moreover, L. J. Goldstein [68], [70] demonstrated its truth in the case where L_p contains $Q(\zeta_{p^2})$ with the exception of finitely many primes p. The Extended Riemann Hypothesis implies its truth if for a certain $a \in Z$ and all sufficiently large primes p one has $Q(\zeta_p, a^{1/p}) \subset L_p$. (This generalizes Theorem 2.9.) Finally L. J. Goldstein [73] showed that the Extended Riemann Hypothesis implies his conjecture if all extensions L_q/Q are abelian,

$$\sum_{q \geqslant T} n(q)^{-1} \ll \log^{-2} T,$$

for a suitable $\theta \geqslant 0$ one has $\log |d_k| = O(k^\theta n(k))$ (where d_k is the discriminant of L_k) and for sufficiently large primes q no prime $< q$ splits completely in L_q. This again generalizes Hooley's theorem.

In the general case Goldstein's conjecture fails, as shown by P. J. Weinberger [72] and J. P. Serre (unpublished).

4. Another generalization of Artin's conjecture was given by G. Cooke, P. J. Weinberger [75] and H. W. Lenstra, Jr. [77]. In its most general form it runs as follows: if L/K is a finite normal extension of an algebraic number field K and we are given a finitely generated infinite subgroup W of the multiplicative group of K, an integer k and a subset C of the Galois group of L/K which is a union of conjugacy classes, and X is the set of all prime ideals P of K such that

(i) the Artin symbol $\left(\dfrac{P}{L/K}\right)$ is contained in C,

(ii) $n_P(w) = 0$ for $w \in W$, where n_P is the canonical exponent associated with P,

(iii) if $F: W \to (Z_K/P)^*$ is the natural map, then the index of $F(W)$ in $(Z_K/P)^*$ divides k (where Z_K is the ring of integers of K),

then X has a density which is given by an explicit formula.

In the case $L = K$, $C = (1)$ this conjecture is a consequence of the General Riemann Hypothesis (GRH) (G. Cooke, P. J. Weinberger [75]) and the general case is easily reducible to it, as observed by H. W. Lenstra, Jr. [77]. It may happen that the conjectural density vanishes; all such cases have been described in H. W. Lenstra, Jr. [77].

5. H. Hasse [65], [66a] determined the density of those primes p for which $\mathrm{ord}_p(a)$ is divisible by a given prime q. An analogous question for prime powers q^r was solved by K. Wiertelak [78]. See R. W. K. Odoni [81] for a generalization of Hasse's result.

One of the theorems in Goldstein [73] implies that under GRH the set of primes p with a given value of $(p-1)/\mathrm{ord}_p a$ has a density. This was also proved by H. Möller [72] by Hooley's method.

6. The bound in Gallagher's Theorem 2.10 was improved by R. C. Vaughan [73] (cf. also R. Warlimont [72], where the same result is announced) to $F(x) = O(x^{1/2} \log^c x)$ with a certain $c < 2/5$. To obtain this improvement one has to evaluate S more precisely. If $f(n)$ is the completely multiplicative function whose value at primes p equals $\varphi(p-1)/(p-\varphi(p-1))$, then

$$S = \sum_{q \leqslant x^{1/2}} \mu^2(q) f(q).$$

One shows first that

$$\sum_{p \leqslant T} \frac{\varphi(p-1)}{p-\varphi(p-1)} = (C + o(1)) \frac{T}{\log T}$$

and then uses a result of E. Wirsing [61] (Satz 1) implying that, if f is a non-negative multiplicative function with $\sum_{p \leqslant T} f(p) \sim \tau(T/\log T)$, then

$$\sum_{n \leqslant T} \mu^2(n) f(n) = (C(\tau) + o(1)) \frac{T}{\log T} \prod_{p \leqslant T} \left(1 + \frac{f(p)}{p}\right).$$

Note that, since no square can be a primitive root, whence $F(x) \geqslant x^{1/2}$; thus Gallagher's bound is not far from the lower bound. Lemma 2.12

appears in P. J. Stephens [69]. Gallagher's proof did not make use of it and was based on a lower evaluation of S, which can be obtained elementarily.

7. Theorem 2.11 is a special case ($y = x^2$) of the result of R. Warlimont [72], who showed that if $\log^8 x \leqslant y \leqslant x^2$ then (2.20) holds for $n \leqslant y$ with at most $O(x^{1/k} k^2 \log^{2D + 1/k - 2} x T^{1 - 1/k})$ exceptions, where $k = [2\log x/\log y]$ and $T = \max \{d(n): n \leqslant x^2\}$. Previously D. M. Goldfeld [68] had the bound $O_D(y^{9/10}(5\log x + 1)^{g + D + 2})$, where $g = \log x/\log y$ and $1 < y \leqslant x$.

P. J. Stephens [69] proved that, in some sense, Artin's conjecture is true on the average by showing that if N exceeds $\exp(4(\log x \log\log x)^{1/2})$ then

$$\frac{1}{N} \sum_{a \leqslant N} N_a(x) = C\operatorname{li} x + O_D(x/\log^D x).$$

Exercises

1. Prove Theorem 2.10 without the use of Bombieri's theorem.

2 (P. J. Stephens [69]). Prove that if t is a positive constant and $N > x\log^t x$ then

$$\frac{1}{N} \sum_{a \leqslant N} N_a(x) = C\operatorname{li} x + O_D\left(\frac{x}{\log^D x}\right)$$

holds for all $D > 1$.

3. Prove the conjecture of Goldstein (see the Notes and Comments, Section 3) in the case where P is the set of all primes and L_q is, for all primes q, the field generated by the q^rth primitive root of unity. Here $r \geqslant 2$ is a fixed integer.

4 (R. Warlimont [72]). Prove that the inequality $|c - c(a)| \leqslant \log^{-1} x$ holds for all $a \leqslant x$ with at most $O(x^{1/2} \log^2 x)$ exceptions.

5 (K. R. Matthews [76]). Let $N(x)$ be the number of primes $p \leqslant x$ for which both 2 and 3 are primitive roots. Deduce from the Extended Riemann Hypothesis an asymptotic formula for $N(x)$.

OPEN PROBLEMS

1. Prove that for any non-principal character $\chi(\operatorname{mod} N)$ one has

$$\left|\sum_{n \leqslant x} \chi(n)\right| \ll N^{1/2} \log\log N.$$

2. Prove that for every positive ε one has $g(p) = O(p^\varepsilon)$.

3. Prove the same evaluation for $g'(p)$.

4. Prove that $\limsup g(p)/\log p$ is infinite.

5. Prove Theorem 2.9 without assuming the GRH.

6. Prove that the minimal kth power non-residue $(\operatorname{mod} p)$ is $O(p^\varepsilon)$. (This is weaker than problem 2.)

7 (P. D. T. A. Elliott [69a]). Prove that the minimal quadratic non-residue mod p is $O(\log^{1+\varepsilon} p)$ for every $\varepsilon > 0$.

8. Prove that $\sum_{p \leqslant x} g(p) \ll x$ and obtain a non-trivial lower bound for this sum.

9. Do the same for the sum $\sum_{p \leqslant x} h(p)$, where $h(p)$ denotes the least primitive root (mod p^2).

10. Obtain a bound for the number of primes $p \leqslant x$ for which $g(p) \neq h(p)$.

11. Find a sufficient and necessary condition for the truth of Goldstein's conjecture.

III

Problems on consecutive integers

§ 1. CATALAN'S CONJECTURE

1. In the first volume of Nouvelles Annales de Mathématiques published in 1842 one finds on pages 519–521 a list of problems and theorems stated without proofs. It includes, marked with number 48, the following theorem by E. Catalan: "*Deux nombres entiers consécutifs, autres que 8 et 9, ne peuvent pas être des puissances exactes*". He never published a proof of this assertion and in fact it is rather doubtful whether he had one. Even now there is no proof of this statement, but in 1976 R. Tijdeman [76] proved that the equation

$$(3.1) \qquad\qquad a^x - b^y = 1$$

has at most finitely many solutions $x, y \geqslant 2$, $a, b > 1$.

Although certain special cases of (3.1) were treated earlier (and a survey of the relevant literature can be found in L. E. Dickson's History [HTN], vol. II), it is customary to speak about *Catalan's equation* and *Catalan's conjecture*.

In some cases it is not very difficult to show the impossibility of (3.1). The first fairly general result of this type was obtained by V. A. Lebesgue [50]:

THEOREM 3.1. *Catalan's equation has no solutions in the case of an even exponent* y.

Proof. Obviously it suffices to consider the case $y = 2$. Suppose thus that $a^x = 1 + b^2$ with $x \geqslant 2$ and $b > 1$. One sees that x must be odd and b even, since if $2 \nmid b$ then $b^2 + 1 \equiv 2 \pmod 4$ could not be a proper power.

Write our equation in the form $a^x = (b+i)(b-i)$ and observe that since $b+i$ and $b-i$ are coprime in the Gaussian ring $Z[i]$ one must have

$$b+i = i^\alpha(u+iv)^x, \qquad b-i = (-i)^\alpha(u-iv)^x$$

with suitable integral u, v and $0 \leqslant \alpha \leqslant 3$. It follows that $u^2 + v^2 = a$ and in view of $2 \nmid a$ one of the numbers u, v has to be odd and the other even. We shall now show that the odd one equals 1 or -1. To achieve this write

$$2i = (b+i) - (b-i) = i^\alpha\left((u+iv)^x - (-1)^\alpha(u-iv)^x\right)$$

$$= i^\alpha \sum_{k=0}^{x}\binom{x}{k}(1-(-1)^{\alpha+k})v^k u^{x-k} i^k$$

and consider two cases according to the parity of α.

If α is even, $\alpha = 2\beta$ then

$$1 = (-1)^\beta \sum_{2\nmid k}\binom{x}{k}u^{x-k}(-1)^{(k-1)/2}v^k$$

and, since the right-hand side is divisible by v, we obtain the equality $v = \pm 1$, and if α is odd, $\alpha = 1 + 2\beta$, then

$$1 = (-1)^\beta \sum_{2|k}\binom{x}{k}u^{x-k}(-1)^{k/2}v^k,$$

and it follows similarly, that $u = \pm 1$.

Defining now

$$F(X, Y) = \sum_{\substack{2|k \\ 0 \leqslant k < x}}\binom{x}{k}(-1)^{k/2}X^{x-k}Y^k,$$

we can write the last two equalities as follows:

$$F(u, v) = (-1)^{(\alpha-1)/2} \qquad \text{if } \alpha \text{ is odd,}$$
$$F(v, u) = (-1)^{(\alpha+x-1)/2} \qquad \text{if } \alpha \text{ is even.}$$

Taking into account that in the first case $u = \pm 1$, $2|v$ and in the second $v = \pm 1$, $2|u$ and that

$$F(-1, v) = -F(1, v) \qquad \text{if } \alpha \text{ is odd,}$$
$$F(-1, u) = -F(1, u) \qquad \text{if } \alpha \text{ is even,}$$

we obtain the existence of a positive even integer Q with $F(1, Q) = 1$ or -1. This will lead to a contradiction. To obtain it observe first that $F(1, Q) = -1$ is impossible because of

$$F(1, Q) = \sum_{\substack{2|k \\ 0 \leqslant k < x}}\binom{x}{k}(-1)^{k/2}Q^k \equiv 1 \,(\text{mod } 4).$$

However, if $F(1, Q) = 1$ then

$$\sum_{\substack{2|k \\ 4 \leqslant k < x}} \binom{x}{k}(-1)^{(k-2)/2} Q^{k-2} + x(x-1)/2 = (1 - F(1, Q))/Q^2 = 0,$$

but this equality is inconsistent with the fact that for $k \geqslant 4$ each of the terms $\binom{x}{k} Q^{k-2}$ is divisible by a higher power of 2 than $x(x-1)/2$, which is a consequence of

$$\binom{x}{k} Q^{k-2} = \frac{x(x-1)}{2} \binom{x-2}{k-2} \frac{2Q^{k-2}}{k(k-1)},$$

$$2^{k-1} | 2Q^{k-2} \quad \text{and} \quad 2^{k-1} \nmid k(k-1). \quad \square$$

2. If the integers a, b in (3.1) are fixed, then (as shown by W. J. Leveque [52]) there is at most one solution of this equation (even if we admit the values x, $y = 1$) with the exception of the case $a = 3$, $b = 2$, which admits two solutions: $3^2 - 2^3 = 3^1 - 2^1 = 1$. J. W. S. Cassels [53] simplified the proof and succeeded in obtaining an explicit form of the possible solution. We now prove this result:

THEOREM 3.2. *Let a, $b \geqslant 2$ be given and denote by A and B the product of all distinct odd divisors of a and b, respectively. Let t, u be the least positive solutions of the congruences*

$$a^t \equiv 1 \pmod{B},$$

$$b^u \equiv -1 \pmod{A}.$$

If x, y are positive integers satisfying $a^x - b^y = 1$, then $x = t$, $y = u$ with the exception of the following cases:

(i) *$a = 3$, $b = 2$, in which case $x = 2$, $y = 3$ is a second solution,*
(ii) *$a = 2^N - 1$, $a \equiv 1 \pmod{B}$, $b \equiv -1 \pmod{A}$, in which case the solution $x = 2$, $y = 1$ may occur instead.*

Proof. We start with an old result of C. Gerono [70], for which a very simple proof was supplied by D. C. B. Marsh [57]:

LEMMA 3.1. *If a, x, y are positive integers and $2^x - a^y = 1$, then either $a = 1$ or $y = 1$.*

Proof. Assume that $2^x - a^y = 1$ and a, $y \geqslant 2$. Clearly a must be odd and, in view of Theorem 3.1, y is odd as well. Thus $(1 + a^y)/(1 + a) = a^{y-1} + \ldots \ldots + a + 1$ is odd and not equal to 1 or -1, and we see that $2^x = 1 + a^y$ $= (1 + a)\dfrac{1 + a^y}{1 + a}$ has an odd prime divisor, a contradiction. $\square$

Now let $a^x - b^y = 1$, x, $y \geqslant 1$, a, $b \geqslant 2$ and define t, u, A, B as in the statement of the theorem. By Theorem 3.1 $2 \nmid y$ and since $b^y \equiv -1 \pmod{A}$

we must have $u|y$. Assuming $u \neq y$, we infer the existence of a prime divisor p of y/u and we may thus write $y = py_1$ with $u|y_1$. Applying the corollary to Proposition 1.2, we find that with the exception of $b = 2$, $y = 3$ there exists an odd prime dividing $(b^y + 1)/(b^{y_1} + 1)$, hence A, but not $b^{y_1} + 1$, and this contradicts $b^{y_1} \equiv -1 \pmod A$. The exceptional case corresponds to $3^2 - 2^3 = 1$, and we see that apart of it $y = u$.

To prove the equality $x = t$ one proceeds similarly. Obviously $t|x$ and, if p is an odd prime divisor of x/t, then $x = px_1$ with $t|x_1$; thus we can again apply the corollary to Proposition 1.2 to obtain, except for $x = 6$ and $a = 2$, an odd prime divisor q of $(a^x - 1)/(a^{x_1} - 1)$, and hence of B, which does not divide $a^{x_1} - 1$, which contradicts $a^{x_1} \equiv 1 \pmod B$. Note that in the exceptional case $p = 3$ and $x_1 = 2$ and we may take $q = 7$ to obtain a contradiction in the same way.

It follows that x/t must be a power of 2; hence either $x = t$ or $x = 2x_0$ with $t|x_0$, giving $(a^{x_0} + 1)(a^{x_0} - 1) = b^y$. If a is even, the numbers $a^{x_0} + 1$, $a^{x_0} - 1$ would both be yth powers; thus $y = 1$, $a^x = b + 1$ and $x = t$. However, if a is odd and q is an odd prime divisor of $a^{x_0} + 1$, then $q|B|a^t - 1|a^{x_0} - 1$; hence $q = 2$, a contradiction. This shows that $a^{x_0} + 1$ is a power of 2 and Proposition 1.4 now implies $x_0 = 1$; hence $x = 2$, $t = 1$ and $a = 2^N - 1$ with a suitable N. To prove that this corresponds to the exceptional cases it remains to show that either $a = 3$ or $u = y = 1$. Since $(2^N - 1)^2 - b^y = 1$ we get $b^y = 2^{N+1}(2^{N-1} - 1)$, showing that $2^{N-1} - 1 = c^y$ with a certain integral c. Lemma 3.1 now implies $c = 1$ or $y = 1$. In the first case $N = 2$, $a = 3$, and in the second

$$1 + b = 2^{N+1}(2^{N-1} + 1) + 1 \equiv 0 \pmod{(2^N - 1)};$$

thus $b \equiv -1 \pmod A$ and $u = 1$. □

3. We now consider equation (3.1), regarding x, y as fixed, i.e., we look for integral solutions of the polynomial diophantine equation

(3.2) $$x^m - y^n = 1.$$

It follows from an old result of C. L. Siegel [29] that for $n \geqslant 3$ this equation has only a finite number of solutions; A. Baker [69a] gave a fresh proof of this result, which effectively evaluates the magnitude of the possible solutions.

We now present a proof of Siegel's theorem for our particular case and start with a preliminary result, proved by C. L. Siegel [21], which we shall deduce from the Roth–Leveque theorem (see Theorem A.6).

PROPOSITION 3.1. *Let K be an algebraic number field of degree m over the* *rationals, let A, B, C be non-zero elements of K and let n be an integer exceeding 2m. Then the equation*

(3.3) $Ax^n - By^n = C$

has at most a finite number of solutions in integers of K.

Proof. It suffices to consider the case where A, B, C are integers of K.

If $a_1, \ldots, a_n$ are roots of the polynomial $AX^n - B$, then our equation can be written in the form

(3.4) $Ay^n \prod_{j=1}^{n} (x/y - a_k) = C.$

Assume now that it has infinitely many solutions $\langle x_N, y_N \rangle$ ($N = 1, 2, \ldots$) in integers of K. Denote by $\lceil a \rceil$ the maximal modulus of the conjugates of an algebraic number a, and observe that without restricting generality we may assume

$$\lceil y_N \rceil = \max \{ \lceil x_N \rceil, \lceil y_N \rceil \}$$

for $N = 1, 2, \ldots$ By applying to (3.3) a suitable embedding of K into the complex field we may also ensure that $\lceil y_N \rceil = |y_N|$ holds for all N.

Let

$$\Delta_N = \inf_{j=1,\ldots,m} |x_N/y_N - a_j|.$$

If Δ_N does not tend to zero, say $|\Delta_N| \geq \varepsilon > 0$ holds for infinitely many N's, then (3.4) gives for those N's

$$|C| \geq |A| |y_N|^n \Delta_N^n \geq \varepsilon^n |A| |y_N|^n.$$

Hence $\lceil y_N \rceil = |y_N| = O(1)$, but y_N are algebraic integers and this evaluation can hold only for finitely many of them; thus (3.3) would have only finitely many solutions, contrary to our assumption.

Thus $\lim \Delta_N = 0$. Let us now fix $0 < \delta < 1/m$. By taking if necessary a subsequence and using the Roth–Leveque theorem (Theorem A.6) we may assume that with a fixed j_0 we have

$$\Delta_N = |x_N/y_N - a_{j_0}| \geq H_K(x_N/y_N)^{-1-\delta}$$

(where H_K denotes the height with respect to the field K, see Appendix, Section 5 for its definition), and also, with a suitable $\varepsilon > 0$,

$$|x_N y_N^{-1} - a_j| \geq \varepsilon \qquad (j \neq j_0).$$

Equality (3.4) implies

$$|C| \geqslant |Ay^n| \, \varepsilon^{n-1} \, H_K(x_N \, y_N^{-1})^{-2-\delta},$$

and as the height $H_K(x_N/y_N)$ does not exceed $(2|y_N|)^m$ we obtain

$$|y_N|^{n-(2+\delta)m} \ll C.$$

Since $|y_N|$ tends to infinity, we arrive at $n \leqslant (2+\delta)m \leqslant 2m+1$, contrary to our assumptions. $\square$

After these preliminaries we can prove

THEOREM 3.3. *If $n \geqslant 2$ and $f(X) \in Z[X]$ is a polynomial having at least three distinct roots with multiplicities prime to n, then the equation*

$$y^n = f(x)$$

has only finitely many solutions x, $y \in Z$.

(It should be noted that the argument below works also in the case where the coefficients of f and the solutions x, y are integers in a finite extension of the rationals; however, we shall not need this generalization.)

Proof. We write our equation in the form

$$(3.5) \qquad\qquad y^n = \alpha \prod_{j=1}^{m} (x - x_j)^{a_j},$$

where $x_1, \ldots, x_m$ are distinct roots of $f(X)$, $\alpha \in Z$ and $a_j \geqslant 1$ for $j = 1, 2, \ldots, m$. Assume that $(a_j, n) = 1$ holds for $j = 1, 2, \ldots, r$ with a certain $r \geqslant 3$, denote by N the degree of f and write $x_j = t_j/q$ where $t_1, \ldots, t_m$ are integers in the splitting field K of $f(X)$ over the rationals and q is a fixed rational positive integer. Then (3.5) takes the form

$$q^N y^n = \alpha \prod_{j=1}^{m} (qx - t_j)^{a_j}.$$

Let D be the product of all differences $t_i - t_j$ $(i \neq j)$ and denote by P the set of prime ideals of the ring Z_K of integers of K which divide the ideal generated by $Dq\alpha$. Assume further that (3.5) has infinitely many solutions x, $y \in Z$ and write I_j for the ideal of Z_K generated by $qx - t_j$ for any such solution. Here and in the sequel certain expressions will depend on x and y; however, wherever possible, we shall not write this explicitly to avoid overcrowding the formulas.

Observe that any prime ideal dividing I_i and I_j for $i \neq j$ must divide $t_i - t_j$ and thus lie in P. Write for $j = 1, 2, \ldots, m$

$$I_j = \prod_{\mathfrak{p} \in P} \mathfrak{p}^{b_{j,\mathfrak{p}}} \cdot J_j \quad \text{with} \ \Big(J_j, \prod_{\mathfrak{p} \in P} \mathfrak{p} \Big) = 1.$$

Now

$$q^N y^n Z_K = Z_K I_1^{a_1} \dots I_m^{a_m} = J_0 J_1^{a_1} \dots J_m^{a_m}$$

where all prime ideal divisors of J_0 lie in P, and thus, since the J_i's are pairwise coprime, we infer that $J_i^{a_i}$ must be an nth power for $i = 1, 2, \dots, m$. Since $(a_j, n) = 1$ holds for $j = 1, 2, 3$, we obtain

$$J_i = A_i^n \quad (i = 1, 2, 3)$$

with suitable ideals A_i, and by writing $b_{j_\mathfrak{p}} = d_{j_\mathfrak{p}} n + r_{j_\mathfrak{p}}$ $(0 \leqslant r_{j_\mathfrak{p}} \leqslant n-1$, $j = 1, 2, 3; \mathfrak{p} \in P$) we obtain

(3.6) $$I_j = B_j C_j^n \quad (j = 1, 2, 3)$$

with B_1, B_2, B_3 lying in a finite set which does not depend on x and y.

Let K_0 be a fixed extension of K in which all ideals of Z_K become principal. (There exist such extensions of K with degree not exceeding the class-number of K by Proposition A.11.) Equalities (3.6) imply that with suitable units ε_j of K_0 and integers α_j, $T_j \in K_0$ one has

$$qx - t_j = \varepsilon_j \alpha_j T_j^n \quad (j = 1, 2, 3),$$

where $\alpha_1, \alpha_2, \alpha_3$ lie in a finite set independent of x, y.

Since by Dirichlet's unit theorem (Theorem A.10) every unit ε in K_0 may be put in the form $\varepsilon = \eta_1 \eta_2^n$, where η_1, η_2 are both units in K_0 and η_1 belongs to a finite set, we obtain that for $j = 1, 2, 3$

$$qx - t_j = v_j u_j^n$$

where u_j, v_j are integers in K_0 and all v_j's belong to a finite set. Obviously u_j, v_j depend on x, y but by selecting if necessary an infinite subset of solutions of (3.5) we may assume that v_1, v_2, v_3 are fixed. (We shall make use of this procedure several times to ensure that certain parameters are constant.)

Subtracting we obtain (for $i \neq j$)

$$0 \neq t_i - t_j = v_j u_j^n - v_i u_i^n.$$

It is worth noting that in the case where $n \geqslant 2[K_0 : \mathbb{Q}]$ one may now apply Proposition 3.1 to prove that the numbers u_1, u_2, u_3 all lie in a finite set, which leads in a straightforward way to the finiteness of the set of solutions of (3.5). However, if n does not satisfy this inequality, further steps are necessary.

For $j = 1, 2, 3$, denote by θ_j any solution of $X^n = v_j$ and let $L = K_0(\zeta_n, \theta_1, \theta_2, \theta_3)$. Since for $i \neq j$ the integer $\theta_i u_i - \theta_j u_j$ divides $x_i - x_j$, it generates an ideal in Z_L which belongs to a finite set. We may assume that this ideal does not depend on x, y and thus for $i \neq j$

(3.7) $$0 \neq \theta_i u_i - \theta_j u_j = \varepsilon_{ij} A_{ij},$$

where A_{ij} are integers in L independent of x, y and $\varepsilon_{ij} = \varepsilon_{ij}(x, y)$ are units in L.

Our next step consists in showing that for every $i \neq j$ the set of units $\{\varepsilon_{ij}(x, y)\}$ is infinite for every infinite set of pairs $[x, y]$ satisfying (3.5). If for a certain pair i, j $(i \neq j)$ this set were finite, then we could assume that ε_{ij} is independent of x, y, and so the non-zero integer $A = \theta_i u_i - \theta_j u_j$ would also be independent of x, y. But in this case

$$(\theta_j u_j)^n + t_j - t_i = qx - t_i = (A + \theta_j u_j)^n = \sum_{k=0}^{n} \binom{n}{k} \theta_j^k A^{n-k} u_j^k,$$

and since the polynomial

$$\sum_{k=0}^{n-1} \binom{n}{k} \theta_j^k A^{n-k} t^k$$

is non-zero, we would have only finitely many possibilities for u_j and hence for x and y.

Having settled this, we may now conclude the proof. Let M be an arbitrary integer exceeding $2[L:Q]$ and, for $i \neq j$, write

$$\varepsilon_{ij}(x, y) = \Omega_{ij} \omega_{ij}^M,$$

where ω_{ij}, Ω_{ij} are units of L and Ω_{ij} all lie in a fixed finite set. We may assume that Ω_{ij} do not depend on x, y. From (3.7) we infer (and this is the only place where we use the condition $p \neq 2$)

$$\theta_0 u_0 - \theta_1 u_1 = \Omega_{01} A_{01} \omega_{01}^M,$$
$$\theta_1 u_1 - \theta_2 u_2 = \Omega_{12} A_{12} \omega_{12}^M,$$
$$\theta_2 u_2 - \theta_0 u_0 = -\Omega_{02} A_{02} \omega_{02}^M,$$

which leads us to

$$\Omega_{01} A_{01} (\omega_{01}/\omega_{02})^M + \Omega_{12} A_{12} (\omega_{12}/\omega_{02})^M = \Omega_{02} A_{02}.$$

By Proposition 3.1 the ratios ω_{01}/ω_{02}, ω_{12}/ω_{02} can assume only finitely many values, and hence the ratios

$$\frac{\theta_1 (u_1/u_0) - \theta_2 (u_2/u_0)}{\theta_2 (u_2/u_0) - \theta_0}, \quad \frac{\theta_0 - \theta_1 (u_1/u_0)}{\theta_2 (u_2/u_0) - \theta_0}$$

may be assumed to be independent of x, y. This shows that neither u_1/u_0 nor u_2/u_0 depends on x, y. If we now put $u_1 = \tau_1 u_0$, $u_2 = \tau_2 u_0$, we finally get

$$0 \neq t_2 - t_1 = v_1 u_1^n - v_2 u_2^n = (v_1 \tau_1^n - v_2 \tau_2^n) u_0^n,$$

and as v_1, v_2, τ_1, τ_2 are fixed this leaves only finitely many possibilities for u_0. As $x = 1 + v_0 u_0^n$, the same applies to x and also to y. However, this contradicts the assumed infiniteness of the set of solutions of (3.5). $\square$

COROLLARY. *If* m, $n \geqslant 2$, *then the equation* $x^m = y^n + 1$ *has only finitely many integral solutions* x, y.

Proof. If $\max(m, n) \geqslant 3$ this follows from the theorem, and if $m = n = 2$ the assertion becomes obvious. $\square$

4. We conclude this section with the proof of Tijdeman's theorem, which reduces Catalan's conjecture to finitely many numerical cases. Our proof will be based on Theorem 3.3, which we proved in a non-effective way, hence our proof of Tijdeman's result has the same disadvantage. However, A. Baker [69a] gave a fully effective proof of Theorem 3.3 and hence the theorem below also has such a proof. Unfortunately the number of integers which remain to be checked is extremely large, and so there is no hope of performing the computation. In any case one knows that (1.9) has no solutions with a, b less than 10^{11} (S. Hyyrö [64]), but this is still very far from the bound which can be obtained by Baker's method. A bound of this kind was published by M. Langevin [76a], viz. $a^x < \exp\exp\exp\exp 730$.

THEOREM 3.4 (R. Tijdeman [76]). *The number of integral solutions* a, b, x, $y \geqslant 2$ *of the equation* $a^x - b^y = 1$ *is finite.*

Proof. We follow Tijdeman's argument; however, we appeal to another form of Baker's theorem.

In view of Theorem 3.3 it suffices to show that the exponents x and y must be bounded by a constant. We may obviously assume that those exponents are prime numbers, and by interchanging, if necessary, the numbers a^x, b^y we can write our equation in the form

$$a^x - b^y = \varepsilon,$$

where $\varepsilon = 1$ or -1, $x > y \geqslant 2$ (thus $x \neq 2$); moreover, in the case $\varepsilon = 1$ we may assume that y is odd because of Theorem 3.1. Our assumptions imply in particular $a < b$.

LEMMA 3.2. *There are positive integers* A, B *and* r, $s \in \{-1, 0, 1\}$ *such that*

$$b + \varepsilon = y^r A^x \qquad and \qquad a - \varepsilon = x^s B^y.$$

Proof. Since

(3.8) $$b^y + \varepsilon = (b + \varepsilon)(b^{y-1} - \varepsilon b^{y-2} + \ldots + \varepsilon^{y-1}),$$

the greatest common divisor d of $b + \varepsilon$ and $(b^y + \varepsilon)/(b + \varepsilon)$ must divide y; hence either $d = 1$ or $d = y$. In the first case $b + \varepsilon$ must be an xth power and we may take $r = 0$. In the second case either $y(b + \varepsilon)$ or $(b + \varepsilon)/y$ is an xth power and we may take either $r = -1$ or $r = 1$.

If we replace in (3.8) b by a, y by x and ε by $-\varepsilon$, we obtain the second assertion. $\square$

Using this lemma we can now substantially improve the bound $y < x$ for the exponent y:

LEMMA 3.3. *There exists an absolute constant C_1 such that $y \leqslant C_1 \log^4 x$.*

(The exponent 4 here may be improved, but this would be of no avail to us.)

Proof. First, let $A = 1$. In this case $b + \varepsilon = y^r$ and so either $r = 0$, $b = 2$, $\varepsilon = -1$ and thus $a < 2$, a contradiction, or $r = 1$, $b = y - \varepsilon$, implying $a < b = y - \varepsilon \leqslant y + 1 \leqslant x < x^2$. Similarly, if $B = 1$ then $a - \varepsilon = x^s$, and so either $a = 0$, $\varepsilon = 1$, $a = 2 < x^2$ or $s = 1$ and $a = x + 1 < x^2$. Thus if either A or B equals 1 we have $a < x^2$. Now $0 < |x \log a - y \log b| = |\log(1 + \varepsilon b^{-y})| < \exp(-y \log b)$ and, since Baker's Theorem A.8 gives

$$|x \log a - y \log b| \geqslant \exp(-C_2 \log^2 a \log b \log x)$$

with an absolute constant C_2, one gets

$$y \leqslant C_2 \log^2 a \log x \ll \log^3 x$$

as asserted.

Now assume that both A and B exceed 1. We shall first obtain an upper bound for the linear form

$$L(X, Y, Z) = X \log x - Y \log y + Z \log(B/A)$$

in the case $X = sx$, $Y = ry$, $Z = xy$, and then use Baker's theorem to obtain a lower bound for L. The comparison of those bounds will lead to the asserted inequality.

Obviously $L(sx, ry, xy) = \log\left(\dfrac{a - \varepsilon}{b + \varepsilon}\right)$. First we look at the case $\varepsilon = 1$, where

$$1 > \frac{1 + b^y}{(1 + b)^y} = \frac{a^x}{(1 + b)^y} > \frac{(a - 1)^x}{(1 + b)^y};$$

thus $L(sx, ry, xy) \neq 0$ and

$$\frac{(a - 1)^x}{(b + 1)^y} = (x^s B^y)^x (y^r A^x)^{-y} = (1 + x^{-s} B^{-y})^{-x} \{(1 + y^{-r} A^{-x})^y + y^{-ry} A^{-xy}\}.$$

Observe now that since $A \geqslant 2$ we have $\xi = y^{-r} A^{-x} < 1/2$; hence

(3.9) $$\log\left((1 - \xi)^y + \xi^y\right) \leqslant -y \log(1 - \xi) \leqslant 2 \cdot \xi \cdot y$$

and

$$0 < |L(sx, ry, xy)| \leqslant \frac{x}{x^s B^y} + \frac{x}{y^r A^x} = \frac{x}{a - 1} + \frac{2y}{b + 1} \leqslant \frac{3x^2}{B^y}.$$

In the case $\varepsilon = -1$ we apply the reasoning above to $b^y - a^x = 1$ to obtain

$$0 < |L(sx, ry, xy)| \leqslant \frac{y}{y^r A^x} + \frac{2x}{x^s B^y} = \frac{y}{b - 1} + \frac{2x}{a + 1} \leqslant \frac{4x^2}{B^y}.$$

We may safely assume that $y < C_3 \log x$ with an arbitrary fixed C_3, and so $B^{y/2} \geqslant 4x^2$ provided C_3 is sufficiently large; thus the above inequalities imply

$$0 < |L(sx, ry, xy)| < \exp(-y \log B/2) < 1.$$

To apply Baker's theorem, which will provide a lower bound for L, we need an evaluation of the height of B/A, which equals of course $\max(A, B)$. Now the last inequality implies

$$|xy \log(B/A)| \leqslant 1 + x \log x + y \log y;$$

thus $|\log(B/A)| \leqslant 1 + (2\log x)/y \leqslant C_4$ with a certain constant $C_4 > 1$ and $\exp(-C_4)B \leqslant A \leqslant \exp(C_4 B)$, which shows that the height of B/A does not exceed $\exp(C_4 B)$. Applying now Baker's theorem (Theorem A.8), we get with an appropriate constant C_5

$$|L(sx, ry, rx)| > \exp(-C_5 \log^3 x \log\log x \log B),$$

and this together with the upper bound implies

$$y \leqslant 2C_5 \log^3 x \log\log x \ll \log^4 x$$

as asserted. □

To prove the theorem it remains to establish the boundedness of x. In the case $A = 1$ this is easy since, as we have already seen, in this case $b = y - \varepsilon \leqslant y + 1$; thus

$$x \log 2 \leqslant x \log a \leqslant y \log b + 1 \leqslant y \log y + 2,$$

implying $x \ll y^2$, and the last lemma shows $x \ll \log^8 x$, which immediately gives $x \ll 1$.

However, if $A \neq 1$ then we use Baker's theorem for the third time, this time to bound from below the expression

$$S = |ry \log y - x \log(aA^{-y})|.$$

Since $(aA^{-y})^x y^{-ry} = (b^y + \varepsilon)/(b + \varepsilon)^y \neq 1$, S is non-zero. Moreover

$$(aA^{-y})^x y^{-ry} = (1 - \varepsilon y^{-r} A^{-x})^y + \varepsilon(y^r A^x)^{-y};$$

thus $S = |\log f_\varepsilon(\xi)|$ where $f_\varepsilon(t) = (1 - \varepsilon t)^y + \varepsilon t^y$ and $\xi = (y^r A^x)^{-y}$. Observe that $A \neq 1$ implies $0 < \xi < 1/2$. To bound S from above we apply in the case $\varepsilon = 1$ inequality (3.9), which gives $|S| \leqslant 2 \cdot \xi \cdot y$, and in the case $\varepsilon = -1$ we write

$$|S| = |\log\{(1+\xi)^y - \xi^y\}| = \left|\log\left\{1 + \sum_{j=1}^{y-1} \binom{y}{j}\xi^j\right\}\right| \leqslant \sum_{j=1}^{y-1} \binom{y}{j}\xi^j \leqslant \sum_{j=1}^{y-1} (y\xi)^j,$$

and, since for large x

$$y\xi = \frac{y}{y^r A^x} \leqslant y^2 A^{-x} \leqslant y^2 2^{-x} \ll \frac{\log^8 x}{2^x} \ll 1,$$

we get

$$0 < S < y^2 \xi.$$

Consequently, in both cases we have

(3.10) $0 < S \leqslant y^2 \xi = \dfrac{y^2}{y' A^x} \ll y^3 A^{-x} \ll \exp\left\{-\dfrac{x}{2} \log A\right\}$

for sufficiently large x.

To make the final step observe first that

$$|x \log(a A^{-y})| \leqslant 1 + y \log y \leqslant 2 y \log y;$$

hence $|\log(a A^{-y})| \ll (\log^5 x)/x \ll 1$ and $a \leqslant C_6 A^y$ with a constant C_6 which we may assume to exceed unity. Applying the theorem of Baker, we obtain the bound

$$S \leqslant \exp(-C_7 \, y \log y \log\log y \log x \log A),$$

which, compared with (3.10), leads, at least for large x, to

$$x \log 2 \leqslant x \log A \ll y \log y \log\log y \log x;$$

now Lemma 3.3 implies $\log^7 x \ll x$, which in turn gives $x = O(1)$. ☐

Notes and comments

1. As we already pointed out, Catalan formulated his problem in 1842 and repeated it in the 27th volume of Crelles Journal. Before that only three special cases had been considered: according to L. E. Dickson [HTN], Levi ben Gerson in XIVth century proved the impossibility of $3^m - 2^n = \pm 1$ for $m \geqslant 3$. B. F. Frenicle [57] showed that for prime p the number $1 + p^n$ cannot be a square and finally L. Euler [38] demonstrated the impossibility of $x^3 + 1 = y^2$ for $x \neq 2$.

2. The first general result on Catalan's question was Theorem 3.1, proved by V. A. Lebesgue [50] in 1850. For the next step one had to wait twenty years until G. C. Gerono [70] showed that (3.1) has no solutions with a or b prime except $3^2 - 2^3 = 1$. (Cf. C. T. C. Wall [57] and W. Sierpiński [58] for very short proofs of this assertion.) It was shown by T. Nagell [21a] that (3.1) cannot hold in the case $x = 3$ or $y = 3$ and Chao Ko [65] settled in the negative the case $x = 2$. (For a simple proof see E. Z. Chein [76].)

J. W. S. Cassels [53], [60] proved that if in (3.1) x and y are prime then $x|b$ and $y|a$. Using this, A. Mąkowski [62] and S. Hyyrö [63] showed that three consecutive integers can never be powers. The impossibility of (3.1) in the case where a, b are consecutive integers was shown by W. J. Leveque [52] (in the case $a = b + 1$) and R. Hampel [56]. A. Schinzel [56a] gave a simple proof of that and A. Rotkiewicz [56] obtained a generalization. Certain necessary conditions for (3.1) were given by K. Inkeri [64].

3. Proposition 3.1 appears as a special case of one of the main results of Siegel's thesis (C. L. Siegel [21]) with a slightly worse bound for n and Theorem 3.3 was in the case $n = 2$ published by Siegel anonymously (C. L. Siegel [26]). The proof in the general case is the same. The theorem holds also when the polynomial f has two simple roots, but in this case one must assume that $n \geqslant 3$. (Cf. W. J. Leveque [64].) An effective proof was given by A. Baker [69a].

Later Siegel returned to the equation $ax^n - by^n = c$ and proved (C. L. Siegel [37]) that if a, b are large in comparison with c then this equation has at most one solution in positive coprime integers x, y.

A. Schinzel and R. Tijdeman [76] showed that if the polynomial f has at least two simple roots and the equation $y^m = f(x)$ is solvable with integral x, y and $y \neq 0, 1, -1$ then m does not exceed a constant depending only on f, which can be effectively determined. This shows that f can represent only a finite number of perfect powers. They conjectured that if f has at least three distinct roots then it can represent only a finite number of square-full integers, i.e., integers N with the property that if a prime p divides it, so does p^2. The truth of this conjecture would imply the existence of infinitely many primes p with $2^{p-1} \not\equiv 1 \pmod{p^2}$.

Irreducible polynomials $f(x, y) \in Z[x, y]$ for which the equation $f(x, y) = 0$ has an infinite set of rational solutions with bounded denominators were characterized by C. L. Siegel [29]. In the special case $f(x, y) = y^m - g(x)$, with $g \in Z[x]$ a more explicit necessary and sufficient condition was given by W. J. Leveque [64]. It is rather complicated, and so we state here only a necessary condition from his paper.

Write

$$g(x) = c(x - a_1)^{r_1} \ldots (x - a_t)^{r_t}$$

where $a_1, \ldots, a_r$ are distinct algebraic numbers and put $s_i = m/(m, r_i)$. Let $s_1 \leqslant s_2 \leqslant \ldots$ The condition states that either $s_2 = s_3 = \ldots = 1$ or $s_1 = s_2 = 2$, $s_3 = s_4 = \ldots = 1$.

Several results stated in this subsection hold also for polynomials with coefficients in an algebraic number field, the solutions of the corresponding equations being integers of this field.

Certain conditions under which the equation $f(x) = g(y)$ (with $f, g \in Z[x]$) has only finitely many solutions were given by H. Davenport, D. J. Lewis, A. Schinzel [61]. See also A. Schinzel [82] where a simple necessary and sufficient condition for the existence of infinitely many rational solutions with bounded denominators was given (Theorem 8).

4. S. S. Pillai [45] conjectured that if m is a given integer then the equation $a^x - b^y = m$ has only finitely many solutions $a, b > 1$, $x, y \geqslant 2$. For fixed a, b he proved this earlier (S. S. Pillai [31]). In fact, for sufficiently large x one has $|a^x - b^y| \geqslant a^{(1-\varepsilon)x}$ for every positive ε. This result was made effective by W. J. Ellison [70].

If m is sufficiently large with respect to a, b, then Pillai's equation can have at most one solution (S. S. Pillai [36c]). A. Herschfeld [36] proved this in the special case $a = 2$, $b = 3$.

5. The equation $y^2 = x^3 + k$ has a long history. In connection with a question of Diophantes P. Fermat wrote to Digby on 15 August 1657: "*Je lui avois écrit qu'il n'y a qu'un seul nombre quarré en entiers qui, joint au binaire, fasse un cube, et que ledit quarré est 25, auquel si vous ajoutez 2, it se fait 27, qui est cube.*" (P. Fermat [57].) Although in his comments to Diophantes he wrote that he could prove this assertion by a rigorous argument (P. Fermat [70], p. 333–334) he did not leave a proof. The first solution of the equation $y^2 = x^3 - 2$ was given by L. Euler [70], (art. 193), who used algebraic numbers in a rather informal way; however, his approach can now easily be justified.

The equation $y^2 - x^3 = k$ for various particular values of k was studied by many authors and in several cases the finiteness of the number of integral solutions was already established in the previous century. Using his work on diophantine approximations (A. Thue [08], [09]), A. Thue [17] proved that for all $k \neq 0$ this equation, and more generally the equation $dy^n = ax^2 + bx + c$, has for $n \geqslant 3$, only finitely many integral solutions, provided $ad \neq 0$ and the quadratic polynomial has a non-zero discriminant. The same result was obtained independently by E. Landau and A. Ostrowski [20]. L. J. Mordell [22], [23] obtained an analogous result for the equation $ex^2 = ax^3 + bx^2 + cx + d$ in the case where the cubic polynomial has only simple roots. This also implies the finiteness of the number of solutions of $y^2 = x^3 + k$ for $k \neq 0$.

An effective proof of the Thue–Landau–Ostrowski–Mordell theorem was given by A. Baker [68], who showed that for $x^3 \neq y^2$ we have

$$|x^3 - y^2| > 10^{-10} \log^{10^{-4}} |x|.$$

His later result (A. Baker [69a]) replaced the right-hand side by $10^{-9} \log^{1/4} |x|$ and H. M. Stark [73] got here $C(\varepsilon) \log^{1-\varepsilon} |x|$ with an effective positive constant $C(\varepsilon)$ and an arbitrary positive ε.

It was conjectured by M. Hall, Jr. (see B. J. Birch, S. Chowla, M. Hall, Jr., A. Schinzel [65], M. Hall, Jr. [71]) that the inequality $|x^3 - y^2| < x^{1/2}$ has only a finite number of integral solutions and that one cannot replace the exponent in it by any larger number. So far only the second of these conjectures has been proved. Namely, L. V. Danilov [82] showed that for infinitely many integers x, y we have $0 < |x^3 - y^2| < 433 \cdot \sqrt{2} \cdot |x|^{1/2}$. (Cf. the paper of B. J. Birch et al. quoted above as well as M. Nair [78].)

Baker's method gives rather exorbitant upper bounds for the solutions of $x^3 - y^2 = k$; however, as demonstrated on the example of $k = 28$ by W. J. Ellison, F. Ellison, J. Pesek, C. E. Stahl, D. S. Stall [72], it can nevertheless be used to provide a complete set of solutions. (This paper is sometimes quoted under the name Anne Arbor.)

For other methods of finding solutions or disproving their existence see L. J. Mordell [14], O. Hemer [52], [54], [56], J. W. S. Cassels [50], M. Hall, Jr. [53], W. Ljunggren [63], H. London [68], R. Finkelstein, H. London [70], [71], N. P. Herzberg [75], N. M. Stephens, F. B. Coghlan [71], see also M. Hall, Jr. [71]. A table for small values of k was given by M. Lal, M. F. Jones. W. J. Blundon [66].

J. Coates [70b] proved that the maximal prime divisor of $x^3 - y^2$ exceeds $10^{-3} (\log\log X)^{1/4}$, where $X = \max(|x|, |y|)$, provided $(x, y) = 1$. This is an effectivization of a particular case of a theorem of K. Mahler [53], who considered the maximal prime divisor of $ax^n + by^m$ ($a, b \neq 0, m \geqslant 3, n \geqslant 2$) and showed that for fixed m, n it tends to infinity with X. S. V. Kotov [76] showed that this prime divisor is $\geqslant (\log X \log\log X)^{1/2}$ with the implied constant being effective. (Cf. A. J. van der Poorten [77], T. N. Shorey [80].)

S. P. Mohanty [73] observed that for infinitely many positive k the equation $x^3 + k = y^2$ has at least 6 coprime solutions and N. M. Stephens [75] replaced 6 by 8 showing also that for negative k at least 12 solutions occur infinitely often. V. G. Sprindzhuk [63] bounded the number of solutions from above by

$$C(\varepsilon) k^\varepsilon \exp\big(t_3(k) \log 3\big),$$

where $t_3(k)$ denotes the number of classes C in the class-group of the field generated by $ik^{1/2}$ satisfying $C^3 = 1$.

R. Fueter [30] proved that the equation $x^3 - y^2 = k$ has either infinitely many or no rational solutions, except for $k = 1$ or $k = 432$, in which cases there is exactly one such solution. A simpler proof of this result was given by L. J. Mordell [66]. Various classes of integers k for which there are no rational solutions were described in K. L. Chang [48], H. M. Edgar [66], L. J. Mordell [47a] and E. S. Selmer [56].

The equation $x^3 - y^2 = k$ is the subject of the books of L. J. Mordell [47b] and H. London and R. Finkelstein [73].

6. S. S. Ramanujan [13] stated the following problem:

"$2^n - 7$ *is a perfect square for the values* 3, 4, 5, 7, 15 *of* n. *Find other values.*"

One usually attributes to him the conjecture that there are no other solutions. This was established by T. Nagell [48]. Other proofs were given by J. Browkin, A. Schinzel [56], T. Skolem, S. Chowla, D. J. Lewis [59],

L. J. Mordell [60a], S. Chowla, M. Dunton, D. J. Lewis [60]. Cf. also
H. Hasse [66b].

A more general equation was considered by R. Apéry [60b], who proved
that, if p is a given odd prime and A is a given positive integer not divisible
by p, then the equation $x^2 + A = p^n$ can have at most two solutions. If $A \neq 7$
then the same assertion holds for the equation $x^2 + A = 2^{n+2}$ (R. Apéry
[60a]). The last result was improved by J. Browkin and A. Schinzel [60],
who proved that if $A \not\equiv 0, 4, 7 \pmod 8$ then this equation can have at most
one solution. The conjecture posed by them and stating that for positive
$A \neq 7, 23, 2^k - 1$ $(k = 1, 2, \ldots)$ the equation $x^2 + A = 2^{n+2}$ has at most one
solution was confirmed by F. Beukers [79], [81b]. In the case of negative A,
F. Beukers showed in the same paper that the above equation can have at
most four solutions and this bound is attained infinitely often, e.g., by the
numbers $A = 3 \cdot 2^{k+1} - 4^k - 1$ $(k = 1, 2, \ldots)$.

A necessary and sufficient condition for the solvability of the equation

$$x^2 + A = p^n$$

(p being an odd prime not dividing A) was obtained in the case
$A \equiv 3 \pmod 4$, $A > 0$ and square-free by R. Alter and K. Kubota [73]: let
$d = d(A, p)$ be the order of that ideal class in the class-group of the field
generated by $ip^{1/2}$ which contains a prime ideal divisor of p. The equation is
solvable if and only if $(-A/p) = 1$ and either

(i) $4p^d - A$ is a square and $3p^d - A = \pm 2$,

or

(ii) $p^d - A$ is a square.

In the case (i) $n = 3d$ gives the only solution and in the case (ii) there can
be at most two solutions.

F. Beukers [79], [81b] showed that for negative A this equation has at
most 4 solutions; however, no case with four solutions is known.

The equation $x^2 + 11 = 3^n$ attracted particular attention. The first proofs
of its unsolvability were due to E. L. Cohen and W. Ljunggren (see E. L.
Cohen [72b]) and other proofs were given by R. Alter and K. Kubota [75]
(for a correction see MR 51 # 344), E. L. Cohen [76], [78] and K. Inkeri
[79].

E. L. Cohen [72a], [74] proved that if $d \equiv 3 \pmod 8$ and $p = (1+d)/4$
≥ 19 is a prime then $x^2 + d = p^n$ is insolvable. The equations $x^2 + 3 = y^n$
and $x^2 + 5 = y^n$ $(n \geq 3)$ were shown to be insolvable by T. Nagell [23].
Cf. also E. Brown [75], [76]. The equation $x^2 + 7 = y^n$ was considered by
D. J. Lewis [61], who showed that it has no solutions in the case where y is
odd and not a prime power.

7. The analogue of Catalan's equation in the field of rational functions
was studied by M. B. Nathanson [74] and V. S. Albis González [75].

Exercises

1 (C. T. C. Wall [57], W. Sierpiński [58]). Prove that, if n and $n+1$ are both prime powers, then either $n = 8$ or n is a Mersenne prime or finally $n+1$ is a Fermat prime, i.e., $n = 2^{2^k}$.

2 (M. B. Nathanson [74]). Prove that the equation $1 = a^m - b^n$ $(m, n \geqslant 2)$ cannot have non-constant solutions a, b in the polynomial ring in one variable over a field whose characteristic does not divide mn.

3 (ibidem). Prove that the equation $1 = a^m - b^n$ $(m, n \geqslant 3)$ does not have non-constant solutions a, b in the field of rational functions in one variable over a field with the characteristic not dividing mn.

4 (ibidem). Solve the equation $X^2 - Y^2 = 1$ in the field of rational functions in one variable over Q with X, Y non-constant.

5 (W. J. Leveque [52]). Prove that the equation $a^x + 1 = (a^y + 1)^z$ has no solutions with $z \geqslant 2$ if $a \geqslant 3$ and in the case $a = 2$ it has only the solution $z = 2$, $x = 3$, $y = 1$.

6 (ibidem). Show that if for all n there holds an identity of the form

$$\sum_{j=1}^{n} j^\alpha = \left(\sum_{j=1}^{n} j^\beta \right)^m$$

with $m \geqslant 2$ then $m = 2$, $\alpha = 3$ and $\beta = 1$.

7 (S. P. Mohanty [75]). Prove that there is no integer k for which there exist five consecutive integers $y_i = y + i$ $(i = 0, 1, ..., 4)$ and suitable integers $x_0, ..., x_4$ such that $y_i^2 - x_i^3 = k$.

§ 2. A PRODUCT OF CONSECUTIVE INTEGERS CANNOT BE A POWER

1. It is easy to observe that the product of two consecutive positive integers is never a complete power. Indeed, the integers $n+1$ and $n+2$ are coprime, and thus their product is a complete power only if n and $n+1$ are complete powers with the same exponent, which is absurd. Also the case of three consecutive integers is easy since the identity $(n+1)(n+2)(n+3) = (n+2)((n+2)^2 - 1)$ shows that if this product were a mth power then $n+2$ and $(n+2)^2 - 1$ would also be mth powers, which is impossible.

It was conjectured in the previous century that a product of $k \geqslant 2$ consecutive positive integers cannot be a square, and, more generally, an mth power of an integer with $m \geqslant 2$. It seems that the first explicit formulation of this conjecture appeared on p. 183 of the Nouvelles Annales de Mathématiques 16 (1857) in a footnote written by O. Terquem, one of the editors:

"*Le produit de tant des nombres consécutifs qu'on veut ne peut être une puissance parfaite d'aucun nombre*". This sounds more like an assertion but on p. 290 of the same volume E. Prouhet writes: "*Le produit de trois nombres consécutifs ne peut être aucune puissance parfaite d'un nombre et cela existe probablement pour le produit d'un nombre quelconque de nombres consécutifs*".

The first really difficult result concerning this conjecture was obtained by J. J. Sylvester [92], who proved the following theorem, rediscovered later by I. Schur [29a] and known nowadays as the *Sylvester–Schur theorem*:

THEOREM 3.5. *If* $n > k$ *then there is a prime* p *exceeding* k *which divides* $n(n+1) \dots (n+k-1)$.

This theorem establishes the conjecture in the case where $k < n < k^2 - k$ since then the prime occurring in the theorem must divide the product $n(n+1) \dots (n+k-1)$ in the first power.

Several proofs of this theorem are available. We shall present one due to D. Hanson [73], whose idea goes back to P. Erdős [34]. It is based on a good elementary bound for the least common multiple of all integers less than n. (Erdős in his paper used a weaker bound.) We begin with the proof of that bound:

PROPOSITION 3.2. *If* $B(n)$ *denotes the least common multiple of all integers* $\leq n$, *then for* $n \geq 1$ *one has* $B(n) < 3^n$.

Proof. Let $a_1, a_2, \dots$ be the infinite sequence defined recurrentially by $a_1 = 2$, $a_{n+1} = a_1 a_2 \dots a_n + 1$. Observe first that this implies

(3.11) $$a_{n+1} = a_n^2 - a_n + 1;$$

hence

(3.12) $$a_n^2 > a_{n+1} > (a_n - 1)^2$$

and an easy inductive argument gives

(3.13) $$1/a_1 + \dots + 1/a_n = 1 - 1/(a_{n+1} - 1) < 1$$

as well as

(3.14) $$a_{n+1} > 2^{2^{n-1}} + 1 \qquad (n = 2, 3, \dots).$$

For every fixed integer n denote by $r(n)$ the unique integer r with the property $a_r \leq n < a_{r+1}$ and finally denote by $C(n)$ the quotient

$$\frac{n!}{\prod\limits_{j=1}^{r(n)} [n/a_j]!} = \frac{n!}{\prod\limits_{j=1}^{\infty} [n/a_j]!}.$$

Since we can write

$$C(n) = \binom{n}{[n/a_1], \dots, [n/a_r], m} \cdot m!$$

where $m = n - \sum\limits_{i=1}^{r} \left[\dfrac{n}{a_i}\right] \geq 0$, the number $C(n)$ is an integer.

The proof of the proposition depends on two facts, which we are now going to establish:

(a) For all n, $B(n)$ divides $C(n)$, and

(b) for $n > 1300$ we have $C(n) < 3^n$.

Since for $n \leqslant 1300$ the inequality $B(n) < 3^n$ is easily verifiable by inspection, our proof will then be complete.

The proof of (a) relies on (3.13) and the following simple lemma:

LEMMA 3.4. *If $b_1, \ldots, b_n$ are positive integers such that the sum of their reciprocals is smaller than 1 and $1 \leqslant x < b_n$, then*

$$\sum_{i=1}^{n} [x/b_i] < [x].$$

Proof. Since $[[a]/b] = [a/b]$ and $[x/b_n] = 0$, one gets

$$\sum_{i=1}^{n} [x/b_i] = \sum_{i=1}^{n-1} [x/b_i] = \sum_{i=1}^{n-1} [[x]/b_i] \leqslant \sum_{i=1}^{n-1} [x]/b_i \leqslant [x](1 - 1/b_n) < [x]. \quad \square$$

To prove (a) write $C(n) = \prod_p p^{\alpha_p}$ and note that

$$\alpha_p = \sum_{j=1}^{t_p} ([n/p^j] - [n/a_1 \, p^j] - [n/a_2 \, p^j] - \ldots) \quad \text{where} \quad t_p = [\log n/\log p].$$

Applying Lemma 3.4 to the numbers $p^j, a_1 p^j, \ldots$, which is possible due to (3.13), we see that all the summands occurring here are positive; thus $\alpha_p \geqslant t_p$. This implies $p^{t_p} | C(n)$ but p^{t_p} is obviously the largest power of p not exceeding n, whence (a) follows.

Now again fix n and let $r = r(n)$. Write for short $[n/a_i] = \alpha_i$ ($i = 1, 2, \ldots, r$) and $m = \alpha_1 + \alpha_2 + \ldots + \alpha_r$. In view of the lemma we have $m < n$ and moreover

$$\alpha_1^{\alpha_1} \ldots \alpha_r^{\alpha_r} C(n) = n(n-1) \ldots (m+1) \frac{m!}{\alpha_1! \ldots \alpha_r!} \alpha_1^{\alpha_1} \ldots \alpha_r^{\alpha_r}$$

$$< n^{n-m}(\alpha_1 + \ldots + \alpha_r)^m = n^{n-m} m^m < n^n;$$

thus

(3.15) $$C(n) < n^n/\alpha_1^{\alpha_1} \ldots \alpha_r^{\alpha_r}.$$

We now need one more technical step, which will enable us to get rid of the square brackets occurring implicitly in the last inequality. Namely, we prove

LEMMA 3.5. *If $t = p/q > 1$ is a rational number and N is its integral part, then*

$$t^t < N^N (et)^{1 - 1/q}.$$

Proof. Since $t \leqslant N + (q-1)/q$, we have $N \geqslant t - 1 + 1/q$; thus

$$t^t / N^N \leqslant t^t / ((t - 1 + 1/q)^{t-1+1/q})$$

$$= \left(1 + \frac{1}{(p-q+1)/(q-1)}\right)^{((p-q+1)/(q-1))((q-1)/q)} \cdot t^{(q-1)/q} < (et)^{1-1/q}. \quad \square$$

By applying this lemma in the case $t = n/a_i$, $q = a_i$, $N = \alpha_i$ and using (3.15), we get

$$(3.16) \qquad C(n) < n^n \prod_{j=1}^{r} (en/a_j)^{1-1/a_j} \prod_{k=1}^{r} (n/a_k)^{-n/a_k}$$

$$< n^n \prod_{j=1}^{r} (en/a_j)^{1-1/a_j} \prod_{k=1}^{\infty} (n/a_k)^{-n/a_k},$$

the infinite product being convergent in view of (3.12) and (3.14). Since (3.12) implies that for $j = 3, 4, \ldots$ we have

$$\frac{a_j \log a_{j+1}}{a_{j+1} \log a_j} < \frac{2a_j \log a_j}{(a_j - 1)^2 \log a_j} < \frac{1}{2},$$

it follows that

$$\sum_{j=6}^{\infty} \frac{\log a_j}{a_j} < 2 \frac{\log a_6}{a_6},$$

and so

$$\sum_{j=1}^{\infty} \frac{\log a_j}{a_j} < 1.08240 + 10^{-5} < \log 2.952;$$

thus

$$c = \prod_{j=1}^{\infty} a_j^{1/a_j} < 2.952.$$

Using (3.13) and (3.16), we obtain

$$C(n) < (en)^{r-1+1/(a_r+1-1)} c^n \prod_{j=1}^{r} a_j^{1/a_j - 1}$$

and, since

$$\prod_{j=1}^{r} a_j^{1-1/a_j} \geqslant a_1^{r - \sum_{j=1}^{r} 1/a_j} = 2^{r-1+1/(a_{r+1}-1)},$$

we get for $r \geqslant 2$

$$C(n) < (en/2)^{r-1+1/(a_r+1-1)} c^n < (en/2)^{r-5/6} c^n.$$

Taking into account (3.14), we infer that

$$r < \frac{\log\log n - \log\log 2}{\log 2},$$

and on substituting this into the foregoing inequality we easily check that for $n \geqslant 1300$ one obtains the inequality $C(n) < 3^n$. This proves (b). $\square$

2. We find that it is easier to work with the binomial coefficient $\binom{n}{k}$ in place of the product $n(n+1) \dots (n+k-1)$. This is allowed in view of the following observation: if for $n > 2k$ there existed a prime $p > k$ dividing $\binom{n}{k}$, then Theorem 3.1 would follow, because due to

$$k!\binom{n+k-1}{k} = n(n+1) \dots (n+k-1)$$

and $n+k-1 > 2k$ the left-hand side has a prime divisor exceeding k and so has the right-hand side.

In view of that it suffices to prove the following result:

THEOREM 3.6. *If k, n are positive integers such that $n > 2k$, then there exists a prime $p > k$ which divides $\binom{n}{k}$.*

Proof. Assume that $n > 2k$ and that no prime factor of $\binom{n}{k}$ exceeds k.

We start with a simple lemma, bounding the prime power divisors of $\binom{n}{k}$:

LEMMA 3.6. *If p^m is a prime power dividing $\binom{n}{k}$ then $m \leqslant [\log n/\log p]$.*

Proof. If $p^a \| k!$, $p^b \| n!$ and $p^c \| (n-k)!$ then obviously

$$m \leqslant b - a - c$$

$$= \sum_{1 \leqslant j \leqslant \log n/\log p} \left(\left[\frac{n}{p^j}\right] - \left[\frac{k}{p^j}\right] - \left[\frac{n-k}{p^j}\right] \right) \leqslant \sum_{1 \leqslant j \leqslant \log n/\log p} 1 = \left[\frac{\log n}{\log p}\right]. \quad \square$$

By this lemma we see that our assumptions imply

$$\binom{n}{k} \leqslant \prod_{p \leqslant k} p^{\alpha_p}$$

where $\alpha_p = [\log n/\log p]$; thus

(3.17)
$$\left(\frac{n}{k}\right)^k \leqslant \binom{n}{k} \leqslant n^{\pi(k)}.$$

As for $k \geqslant 8$ we have $\pi(k) \leqslant k/2$, it follows that $\left(\dfrac{n}{k}\right)^k \leqslant n^{k/2}$ and $n^{1/2} \leqslant k$.

Thus in the case $8 \leqslant k < n^{1/2}$ the theorem is true. Moreover, one can easily see that for $k \geqslant 300$ the inequality $\pi(k) < 2k/9$ is true and so (3.17) leads to $n^{7/9} \leqslant k$, demonstrating the truth of the theorem in the range $300 \leqslant k < n^{7/9}$.

In the range $8 \leqslant k \leqslant 300$, $n^{1/2} \leqslant k$ the theorem could be proved by a tedious checking of all possible cases; however, this can be reduced to a fairly simple check using the observation that the theorem is certainly true if the interval $[n-k+1, n]$ contains at least one prime number and, in particular, if the maximal difference $p_{i+1} - p_i$ between primes with $p_i \leqslant n$ is less than $k+1$. Denote this maximal difference by D_n and use the table of the first occurrences of given differences of primes made up by L. J. Lander, T. R. Parkin [67]. Since in our range $n \leqslant 90000$ and $D_n \leqslant 72$, we can restrict ourselves to $k \leqslant 72$, $n \leqslant 72^2 = 5184$. But $D_{5184} = 34$, and thus $k \leqslant 34$, $n \leqslant 34^2 = 1156$. Proceeding further in the same manner, we get $D_{1156} = 22$, $k \leqslant 22$, $n \leqslant 22^2 = 484$; $D_{484} = 14$, $k \leqslant 14$ and $n \leqslant 14^2 = 196$, and so finally we have to check $\left(\dfrac{n}{k}\right)$ for $8 \leqslant k \leqslant 14$ and $2k < n < k^2$. This can be done by a simple inspection of the list of primes not exceeding 196, which shows that we always encounter a prime in $[n-k+1, n]$ except for $k = 13$ and $n = 126$. But in this case $n(n-1) \ldots (n-k+1)$ has a factor 31 and so does $\left(\dfrac{n}{k}\right)$.

In the range $2 \leqslant k \leqslant 7$ we apply (3.17) to get a bound for n, which never exceeds 100, and an easy check of the list of primes less than 100 concludes our task in this case.

It remains to consider the range $k \geqslant 300$, $k > n^{7/9}$. We shall consider three cases:

Case I. $n \geqslant 4k$, Case II. $3k \leqslant n < 4k$, Case III. $2k \leqslant n < 3k$. In all these cases our argument will be based on the following lemma, which is a simple consequence of Proposition 3.2:

LEMMA 3.7. *If* $k > n^{2/3}$ *and all prime factors of* $\left(\dfrac{n}{k}\right)$ *are* $\leqslant k$, *then*
$$\left(\frac{n}{k}\right) < 3^{k+n^{1/2}}.$$

Proof. By Lemma 3.6 we obtain
$$\left(\frac{n}{k}\right) \leqslant \prod_{p \leqslant k} p \prod_{p \leqslant n^{1/2}} p \prod_{p \leqslant n^{1/3}} p \cdots$$

and, since for $k > n^{2/3}$ and $r = 2, 3, \ldots$ we have $k^{1/r} > n^{1/(2r-1)}$, it follows that
$$\prod_{p \leqslant k} p \prod_{r=2}^{\infty} \prod_{p \leqslant n^{1/(2r-1)}} p \leqslant \prod_{p \leqslant k} p \prod_{p \leqslant k^{1/2}} p \prod_{p \leqslant k^{1/3}} p \cdots < 3^k$$

by Proposition 3.2. Since for the same reason

$$\prod_{p \leqslant n^{1/2}} p \prod_{p \leqslant n^{1/4}} p \ldots < 3^{n^{1/2}},$$

the asserted inequality follows. $\square$

In case I we use the bound

$$\binom{n}{k} > \binom{4k}{k} > \left(\frac{4^4}{3^3}\right)^k \frac{1}{4k},$$

which is easily provable by recurrence. Jointly with the last lemma this gives

$$3^{k+n^{1/2}} > \left(\frac{4^4}{3^3}\right)^k \frac{1}{4k} > 3^{2k}/4k,$$

and in view of $k > n^{7/9}$ we arrive at

$$3^{k-k^{9/14}} < 4k,$$

which for $k \geqslant 300$ is certainly false since then $k - k^{9/14} > k/2$; thus we would have $3^k < 16k^2$ and this fails already for $k \geqslant 6$.

In case II we proceed similarly, using the bound

$$\binom{n}{k} > \binom{3k}{k} > \left(\frac{27}{4}\right)^k \frac{1}{3k},$$

which together with Lemma 3.4 leads to

$$3^{k+2k^{1/2}} > \left(\frac{27}{4}\right)^k \frac{1}{3k} > \frac{6^k}{3k} \quad \text{and} \quad k3^{2k^{1/2}+1} > 2^k,$$

which is false for $k \geqslant 72$. Indeed, for those k we have $2k^{1/2}+1 < k/4$, and thus we would have

$$k\left(\log 2 - \frac{\log 3}{4}\right) < \log k;$$

however, $\log 2 - (\log 3)/4 > 0.41$ and the function $(\log x)/x$ attains its maximal value, equal to $e^{-1} < 0.37$, at $x = e$.

In case III we use $\binom{n}{k} \geqslant \binom{2k}{k} > 4^k/2k$, which with Lemma 3.4 leads to $4^k < (2k)3^{k+(3k)^{1/2}}$. However, for $k \geqslant 300$ we have $(3k)^{1/2} \leqslant k/10$, and thus the inequality $\log 2k > k\log(4 \cdot 3^{-1.1}) > 0.15k$ results, which is contradictory since for $k \geqslant 300$ we have $(\log 2k)/k \leqslant (\log 600)/300 < 0.03$.

All the cases thus being settled, our proof is complete. $\square$

COROLLARY (Bertrand's postulate). *For $x \geqslant 2$ there is always a prime between x and $2x$.*

Proof. By the theorem there must be a prime $p > k$ dividing

$$(k+1)(k+2) \ldots (2k-1) 2k$$

but such a prime is clearly less than $2k$. This establishes the corollary for integral x, and if x is not an integer then it suffices to take $k = [x]$. □

3. The next important step towards proving the conjecture was made independently by P. Erdős [39a] and O. Rigge [39], who proved that a product of consecutive integers is never a square. We shall now give Erdős's proof of this result with a simplification taken from P. Erdős and J. L. Selfridge [75].

THEOREM 3.7. *The product of $k \geqslant 2$ consecutive integers is never a square of an integer.*

Proof. Assume that the product $P_{n,k} = (n+1)(n+2) \ldots (n+k)$ equals a square of an integer. Observe first that $n \geqslant k$ since otherwise by Bertrand's postulate there would be a prime in $[[(n+k)/2], n+k]$ and it would divide $P_{n,k}$ in the first power. Thus we may apply Theorem 3.1 to obtain a prime divisor $p > k$ of $P_{n,k}$. This prime must divide $P_{n,k}$ in at least the second power, and since it can divide only one of the numbers $n+i$ ($i = 1, 2, \ldots, k$) we must have $(1+k)^2 \leqslant p^2 \leqslant n+k$, which implies

$$(3.18) \hspace{4cm} n > k^2.$$

Now write for $i = 1, 2, \ldots, k$, $n+i = a_i x_i^2$, where x_i^2 is the biggest square dividing $n+i$. Then obviously the numbers $a_1, \ldots, a_k$ are all square-free, and moreover they cannot have a prime factor $\geqslant k$ because such a factor would divide $P_{n,k}$ in an odd power.

Now note that the numbers $a_1, \ldots, a_k$ must be distinct. In fact, if $i > j$ and $a_i = a_j$ then we would have

$$k > i-j = a_i(x_i^2 - x_j^2) > 2a_i x_i \geqslant 2(a_i x_i^2)^{1/2} = 2(n+i)^{1/2} > 2n^{1/2} > n^{1/2},$$

contrary to (3.18).

From this we infer that the product $a_1 a_2 \ldots a_k$ is at least equal to the product of the first k square-free positive integers. Let $1 = b_1 < b_2 < \ldots$ be the sequence of all square-free integers and let $M(x)$ be the number of such integers $\leqslant x$. Since exactly 12 of the residue classes (mod 36) are divisible by either 4 or 9, it follows that for integral x, we have $M(36x) \leqslant 24x$. Writing, for an arbitrary integer N, $N = 36q + r$, $0 \leqslant r < 36$, we thus obtain ($f(r)$ being the number of integers $1 \leqslant j \leqslant r$ which are not divisible either by 4 or by 9)

$$M(N) \leqslant M(36q) + f(r) = \tfrac{2}{3}N - \tfrac{2}{3}r + f(r).$$

A direct check reveals that $f(r) - \tfrac{2}{3}r \leqslant \tfrac{4}{3}$, and thus we arrive at $M(N) \leqslant \tfrac{2}{3}N + \tfrac{4}{3}$. For $N \geqslant 50$ there are two additional not square-free numbers less than N, namely 5^2 and 7^2, and so finally for $N \geqslant 50$ we get

$M(N) < 2N/3$. Since 51 is the 32-nd square-free number, this shows that for $r \geqslant 32$ we have $b_r > 3r/2$. Thus for $k \geqslant r \geqslant 32$ we get

$$\prod_{j \leqslant k} b_j > \left(\frac{3}{2}\right)^{k-r} \frac{k!}{r!} \prod_{j \leqslant r} b_j = \left(\frac{3}{2}\right)^k k! \prod_{j \leqslant r} \left(\frac{2b_j}{3j}\right),$$

and in view of $\prod_{j \leqslant 63} (2b_j/3j) \geqslant 1$ we arrive at the inequality

(3.19)
$$P_k = \prod_{j \leqslant k} a_j \geqslant \prod_{j \leqslant k} b_j > (\tfrac{3}{2})^k k!,$$

valid for $k \geqslant 63$.

To obtain an upper bound for P_k we start with the divisibility relation

(3.20)
$$P_k = a_1 a_2 \ldots a_k | (k-1)! \prod_{p < k} p,$$

which we shall now prove.

Since all a_i's are square-free, the maximal exponent with which a prime $p < k$ can divide P_k equals the number of those integers among $n+1, \ldots, n+k$ which are divisible by p. If p does not divide k, then this exponent is at most equal to $1 + [k/p] = 1 + [(k-1)/p]$, and if p divides k then it equals $[k/p] = 1 + [(k-1)/p]$. Taking into account that $p^{[(k-1)/p]} | (k-1)!$, we get (3.20).

To fit our purpose (3.20) must be slightly improved. To do this we show that if 2^{c_2} is the highest power of 2 dividing P_k then

(3.21)
$$c_2 \leqslant \frac{k}{3} + \frac{2\log k}{\log 2} + 5,$$

and if 3^{c_3} is the highest power of 3 dividing P_k then

(3.22)
$$c_3 \leqslant \frac{k}{4} + \frac{2\log k}{\log 3} + 8.$$

This results from the following lemma:

LEMMA 3.8. *If p is a prime, then the number T_p of integers among $n+1$, $n+2, \ldots, n+k$, exactly divisible by an odd power of p does not exceed*

$$k/(1+p) + 2\log k/\log p + 3p - 1.$$

Proof. Let $p^M \| n+m$ and let M be maximal. Observe that, if we now replace each number $n+m+j$ for $j = 0, 1, \ldots, k-m$ by its smallest non-negative residue $r_j \pmod{p^M}$ and for $j = -1, -2, \ldots, 1-m$ by $-r_j$, then the divisibility by powers $p^r (r < M)$ will remain unaffected, and since at most $p-1$ integers in the interval $[n+1, n+k]$ can be divisible by p^M it follows that

(3.23)
$$T_p \leqslant p - 1 + A(k-m+1) + A(m-1),$$

where $A(x)$ denotes the number of positive integers $n \leqslant x$ for which $p^r \| n$ with an odd r.

Now

$$A(x) = \sum_{N \leqslant \frac{\log x}{2\log p}} \left(\sum_{\substack{m \leqslant x \\ p^{2N+1}|m}} 1 - \sum_{\substack{m \leqslant x \\ p^{2N+2}|m}} 1 \right) = \sum_{N \leqslant \frac{\log x}{2\log p}} (x/p^{2N+1} - x/p^{2N+2} + 2\theta)$$

$$= x/(1+p) + \theta(\log x/\log p + p) \leqslant x/(1+p) + \log x/\log p + p,$$

where θ has its absolute value bounded by 1, and so (3.23) gives

$$T_p \leqslant k/(p-1) + (2\log k)/\log p + 3p - 1$$

as asserted. □

If d_p is defined by $p^{d_p} \| (k-1)!$, then (3.20) may be put in the refined form

$$P_k | (k-1)!/(2^{d_2 - c_2} 3^{d_3 - c_3}) \prod_{5 \leqslant p < k} p,$$

and because of

$$d_p = \sum_{1 \leqslant j \leqslant \log k/\log p} [(k-1)/p^j] \geqslant (k-1)/(p-1) - \log k/\log p - p$$

we obtain with the aid of (3.21) and (3.22) the inequality

$$P_k \leqslant \tfrac{1}{6}(k-1)! \left(\prod_{p \leqslant k} p \right) 2^{-2k/3} \cdot 3^{-k/2} k^6 \cdot 2^8 \cdot 3^{23/2}.$$

By Proposition 3.2 and (3.19) we see that this implies

$$((2^{2/3} \cdot 3^{1/2})/2)^k < 2^7 \cdot 3^{19/2} k^5,$$

which is contradictory for $k \geqslant 128$.

The theorem is thus proved for all $k \geqslant 128$, and now we have to take care of the remaining k's. The cases $k = 2, 3$ were already treated at the beginning of this chapter. The case $k = 4$ is settled by the observation that $P_{n,4} = (n^2 + 5n + 5)^2 - 1$, which is never a square. For $k = 5$ note that the integers $a_1, \ldots, a_5$ must be distinct, square-free and have to be composed of primes 2, 3 but there are only four such numbers, viz. 1, 2, 3, 6. The same argument is applicable to the remaining values of k. We note that for any given m there can be at most $2^{\pi(m)}$ a_i's composed of primes $\leqslant m$ and take $m = 3$ for $5 \leqslant k \leqslant 20$, $m = 5$ for $20 < k \leqslant 56$ and $m = 7$ for $56 < k \leqslant 127$. A direct although tedious check leads to a contradiction in all these cases except where $k = 6$, $5|a_1$ or $k = 8$, $7|a_1$ and $5|a_2$. In the first of these cases a_1 and a_6 are the only a_i's divisible by a prime exceeding 3 and so $\{a_2, \ldots, a_5\} = \{1, 2, 3, 6\}$, and in the second case we get similarly $\{a_3, \ldots, a_6\} = \{1, 2, 3, 6\}$. Because of $1 \cdot 2 \cdot 3 \cdot 6 = 6^2$ we thus obtain in both cases four consecutive integers whose product equals a square, but we already know that this is impossible. This proves the theorem. □

4. The old conjecture was finally proved by P. Erdös and J. L. Selfridge [75] and we shall now present their proof. The main idea is the same as in the proof of Theorem 3.7, at least for large k, but the details are necessarily more complex and the final stage necessitates some numerical computations.

THEOREM 3.8. *The product of $k \geqslant 2$ consecutive positive integers cannot be a m-th power of an integer for $m \geqslant 2$.*

Proof. Let $P_{n,k} = (n+1) \ldots (n+k)$ be a mth power of an integer with $k \geqslant 2$, $m \geqslant 2$. Since the case $m = 2$ was settled in Theorem 3.7 and the cases $k = 2, 3$ at the beginning of this chapter, we may assume that $k \geqslant 4$, $m \geqslant 3$ and moreover we may suppose that m is a prime, replacing m, if necessary, by any of its prime divisors.

For $i = 1, 2, \ldots, k$ write

$$n+i = a_i x_i^m$$

with m-free integers $a_1, a_2, \ldots, a_k$. Observe first that the product $a_1 a_2 \ldots a_k$ cannot have a prime factor exceeding k and moreover we must have

(3.24) $$n > k^m.$$

Indeed, if $n \leqslant k$ then by Bertrand's postulate there exists a prime p satisfying

$$n < (n+k)/2 < p \leqslant n+k$$

and obviously it must divide $P_{n,k}$ in the first power. But if $n > k$, then by Theorem 3.5 there is a prime $p > k$ dividing $P_{n,k}$. Since only one of the numbers $n+i$ ($1 \leqslant i \leqslant k$) can be a multiple of p, it must be divisible by p^m; hence $(1+k)^m \leqslant p^m < n+k$ and (3.24) follows.

LEMMA 3.9. *All products $a_{i_1} a_{i_2} \ldots a_{i_{m-1}}$ are distinct modulo m-th powers, i.e., the equality*

(3.25) $$a_{i_1} \ldots a_{i_{m-1}} X^m = a_{j_1} \ldots a_{j_{m-1}} Y^m$$

$$(1 \leqslant i_1 \leqslant i_2 \leqslant \ldots \leqslant i_{m-1}, 1 \leqslant j_1 \leqslant j_2 \leqslant \ldots \leqslant j_{m-1})$$

with integral X, Y can hold only if $i_k = j_k$ for $k = 1, 2, \ldots, m-1$.

Proof. Observe first that for $i \neq j$ we have

$$(n+i, n+j) | i-j| < k,$$

and so if $n+i$ divided $P_{n,k}/(n+i)$ then we would have $k^m < n < n+i < k^{m-1} < k^m$, a contradiction. It follows that the products $(n+i_1) \ldots (n+i_{m-1})$ are all different. If now an equality of the form (3.25) holds, then in view of the last observation we may assume that $A_1 = (n+i_1) \ldots (n+i_{m-1}) > (n+j_1) \ldots (n+j_{m-1}) = A_2$. We shall now evaluate the difference $A_1 - A_2$ from above and from below, and this will lead to a contradiction.

Writing

$$\xi = \prod_{k=1}^{m-1} x_{i_k}, \quad \eta = \prod_{k=1}^{m-1} x_{j_k} \quad \text{and} \quad A = A_1/(\xi Y)^m = A_2/(\eta X)^m,$$

we get $A_1 - A_2 = A((\xi Y)^m - (\eta X)^m)$ and thus $\xi Y \geqslant 1 + \eta X$, leading to

(3.26) $$A_1 - A_2 \geqslant A((1 + \eta X)^m - (\eta X)^m) \geqslant Am(\eta X)^{m-1}.$$

To obtain an upper bound for $A_1 - A_2$ we start with

$$A_1 - A_2 < (n+k)^{m-1} - n^{m-1} = (m-1)kn^{m-2} + \sum_{j=2}^{m-1} \binom{m-1}{j} k^j n^{m-1-j}$$

and observe that since $k^m < n$ and $k, m \geqslant 3$ we have $n > km^2$, which in view

of $\binom{m-1}{j} < 2(m/2)^j$ implies

$$k^{-1} n^{2-m} \sum_{j=2}^{m-1} \binom{m-1}{j} k^j n^{m-1-j} \leqslant m \sum_{j=2}^{m-1} (mk/2n)^{j-1}$$

$$\leqslant m \sum_{j=2}^{\infty} (mk/2n)^{j-1} < m^2 k/n < 1;$$

thus $A_1 - A_2 \leqslant mkn^{m-2}$. By comparing this inequality with (3.26) we obtain $mkn^{m-2} \geqslant Am(\eta X)^{m-1}$.

Since $(\eta X)^m = A_2/A > n^{m-1}/A$, we get

$$kn^{m-2} > A^{1/n} n^{(m-1)^2/m} \geqslant n^{m-2+m-1},$$

a clear contradiction. $\square$

COROLLARY. *If for a certain $1 \leqslant j \leqslant m-1$ and $i_1 \leqslant i_2 \leqslant \ldots \leqslant i_j$, $k_1 \leqslant k_2 \leqslant \ldots \leqslant k_j$ we have*

$$a_{i_1} a_{i_2} \ldots a_{i_j} = a_{k_1} a_{k_2} \ldots a_{k_j},$$

then $i_s = k_s$ for $s = 1, 2, \ldots, j$.

Proof. The assumed equality implies

$$a_1^{m-1} a_{i_1} \ldots a_{i_j} = a_1^{m-1} a_{k_1} \ldots a_{k_j},$$

and we may apply the lemma. $\square$

To prove the theorem for all sufficiently large values of k we shall now obtain an upper bound for the product of a suitable subsequence of the a_i's and then we shall derive a contradicting lower bound. For small k we shall use the last lemma to get the required conclusion.

LEMMA 3.10. *There exists a set $A \subset \{1, 2, \ldots, k\}$ containing at most $\pi(k-1)$ elements such that the product $\prod_{i \notin A} a_i$ divides $(k-1)!$.*

Proof. For each prime $p < k$ let a_m $(m = m(p))$ be divisible by the highest power of p, say p^{α_p}, and let A be the set of all numbers $m(p)$ obtained in this way. Since for every j we have $n+m+j \equiv j \pmod{p^{\alpha_p}}$, for $i \notin A$ the condition $p^A |a_i| n+1$ implies $p^A | i-m$; hence the maximal power of p dividing $\prod_{i \notin A} a_i$ does not exceed the maximal power of p which divides $(m-1)! \, (k-m)! | (k-1)!$, and this establishes the lemma. □

To obtain a lower bound for the product occurring in the last lemma we need a bound for the number of a_i's less than a given number, and to do this we shall first prove an auxiliary result from the graph theory:

LEMMA 3.11. *Let G be a bipartite graph with s white and t black vertices. If G does not contain a rectangle (i.e., a pair of white vertices A, B and a pair of black vertices C, D such that G contains the edges AC, AD, BC and BD), then G has at most $t + \binom{s}{2}$ edges.*

Proof. Let N be the number of edges of G and for every i let t_i be the number of black edges of valency i. Then evidently $t = \sum_i t_i$ and $N \leqslant \sum_i i t_i$. As the number of pairs of edges having a common black endpoint equals $\sum_{i \geqslant 2} t_i \binom{i}{2}$, the nonexistence of a rectangle implies

$$\sum_{i \geqslant 2} t_i \binom{i}{2} \leqslant s(s-1)/2$$

and so we obtain

$$N \leqslant \sum_i i t_i = t_1 + 2t_2 + \sum_{i \geqslant 3} i t_i \leqslant t_1 + t_2 + \sum_{i \geqslant 2} \binom{i}{2} t_i \leqslant t + \binom{s}{2}. \quad \square$$

COROLLARY. *Let $1 \leqslant u_1 < \ldots < u_s \leqslant x$, $1 \leqslant v_1 < \ldots < v_t \leqslant x$ be integers such that every integer not exceeding x is of the form $u_i v_j$ for suitable i, j. If now $1 \leqslant A_1 < A_2 < \ldots < A_n \leqslant x$ are integers with the property that all products $A_i A_j$ are distinct, then $N \leqslant t + \binom{s}{2}$.*

Proof. Consider the bipartite graph G defined as follows: the black vertices are $v_1, \ldots, v_t$, the white vertices are $u_1, \ldots, u_s$, and u_i, v_j are joined by an edge if and only if the product $u_i v_j$ is equal to one of the A_k's. Since all products $A_i A_j$ are distinct, G does not contain a rectangle and we may apply the lemma. □

Before we construct suitable sets $\{u_i\}$ and $\{v_j\}$ having the property stated in this corollary, we need a numerical result concerning the number of integers prime to $D \in \{2, 6, 30, 210, 2310\}$ and lying in an interval:

LEMMA 3.12. *If we denote by* $f_D(x)$ *the difference*

$$\sum_{\substack{n \leqslant x \\ (n,D)=1}} 1 - \frac{\varphi(D)}{D} x$$

and $f(D) = \max_x f_D(x)$, *then*

$$f(D) = \begin{cases} 1/2 & \text{if} \quad D = 2, \\ 2/3 & \text{if} \quad D = 6, \\ 14/15 & \text{if} \quad D = 30, \\ 53/35 & \text{if} \quad D = 210, \\ 194/77 & \text{if} \quad D = 2310. \end{cases}$$

Proof. Direct checking. □

(It should be noted that an elementary argument leads to the bound $f(D) \leqslant 2^{\omega(D)-1}$; however this would be insufficient for our purpose.)

In the next lemma we construct two pairs of sets satisfying the assumptions of the corollary to Lemma 3.11.

LEMMA 3.13. *For every* $x \geqslant 36$ *one can find a set* $U_1 = \{u_i\}$ *of 25 integers* $\leqslant x$ *and a set* $V_1 = \{v_j\}$ *of at most* $0.28016x + 4$ *integers not exceeding* x *such that every integer* $\leqslant x$ *is of the form* $u_i v_j$.

Likewise for every $x \geqslant 100$ *there is a set* $U_2 = \{u_i\}$ *of 55 integers* $\leqslant x$ *and a set* $V_2 = \{v_j\}$ *of at most* $0.2297x + 7$ *integers* $\leqslant x$ *with the same property.*

Proof. Let U_1 be the set of all positive integers not exceeding 36 without a prime divisor $\geqslant 11$. One immediately sees that U_1 contains 25 integers. The set V_1 will consist of all multiples of 7 not exceeding $x/6$ and prime to $2 \cdot 3 \cdot 5$, all multiples of 5 not exceeding $x/8$ and prime to $2 \cdot 3$, all odd multiples of 3 up to $x/14$, all even integers up to $x/20$ and finally all integers $\leqslant x$ prime to $2 \cdot 3 \cdot 5 \cdot 7$.

If $m \leqslant x$ is given, then denote by n the maximal divisor of m contained in U_1. If m/n has no prime factor $\leqslant 7$ the proof is complete as in that case $m/n \in V_1$. Otherwise let p be the minimal prime factor of m/n. If we now put

$$c_p = \begin{cases} 6, & p = 7, \\ 8, & p = 5, \\ 14, & p = 3, \\ 20, & p = 2, \end{cases}$$

then from the construction of the set V_1 it follows that if $m/n \leqslant x/c_p$ then $m/n \in V_1$ and so $m \in U_1 V_1$. However, if $m/n > x/c_p$ then $n < c_p m/x \leqslant c_p$ and we obtain

$$pn < \begin{cases} 42, & p = 7, \\ 40, & p = 5, \\ 42, & p = 3, \\ 40, & p = 2; \end{cases}$$

but pn has all its prime factors $\leqslant 7$, and thus in all cases we must have $pn \leqslant 36$, which contradicts the choice of n.

To evaluate the number of elements of V_1 we use Lemma 3.12, which gives

$$|V_1| = \sum_{\substack{n \leqslant x \\ (n, 210) = 1}} 1 + \sum_{\substack{n \leqslant x/6 \\ 7|n \\ (n, 30) = 1}} 1 + \sum_{\substack{n \leqslant x/8 \\ 5|n \\ (n, 6) = 1}} 1 + \sum_{\substack{n \leqslant x/14 \\ 3|n \\ (n, 2) = 1}} 1 + \sum_{\substack{n \leqslant x/20 \\ 2|n}} 1$$

$$\leqslant \frac{\varphi(210)}{210} x + \frac{53}{35} + \frac{\varphi(30)}{30} \cdot \frac{x}{42} + \frac{14}{15} + \frac{\varphi(6)}{6} \cdot \frac{x}{40} + \frac{2}{3} + \frac{\varphi(2)}{2} \cdot \frac{x}{42} + \frac{1}{2} + \frac{x}{40}$$

$$= \frac{353}{1260} x + 3.6143 < 0.28016 x + 4.$$

In the second case we proceed similarly. Here U_2 is the set of all positive integers not exceeding 100 and without a prime divisor $\geqslant 13$, and thus $|U_2| = 55$. The set V_2 consists of all integers not exceeding x prime to $2 \cdot 3 \cdot 5 \cdot 7 \cdot 11$ and, for $p = 2, 3, 5, 7, 11$, of all integers not exceeding x/d_p with the least prime divisor equal to p, where

$$d_p = \begin{cases} 10 & \text{for} \quad p = 11, \\ 15 & \text{for} \quad p = 7, \\ 21 & \text{for} \quad p = 5, \\ 35 & \text{for} \quad p = 3, \\ 54 & \text{for} \quad p = 2. \end{cases}$$

The same argument as in the first case shows that all integers $\leqslant x$ can be written in the form $u_i v_j$ and by Lemma 3.12 we get the bound

$$|V_2| \leqslant \frac{\varphi(2310)}{2310} x + \frac{194}{77} + \frac{\varphi(210)}{210} \cdot \frac{x}{110} + \frac{53}{35} + \frac{\varphi(30)}{30} \cdot \frac{x}{7 \cdot 15} + \frac{14}{15} +$$

$$+ \frac{\varphi(6)}{6} \cdot \frac{x}{5 \cdot 21} + \frac{2}{3} + \frac{\varphi(2)}{2} \cdot \frac{x}{3 \cdot 35} + \frac{1}{2} + \frac{x}{2 \cdot 54}$$

$$\leqslant 0.2297 x + 7.$$

COROLLARY. *If $A_1 < A_2 < \ldots < A_k$ are the a_i's arranged according to their magnitude, then $A_m \geqslant m$, $A_m \geqslant 3.5694 (m - 304)$ and $A_m \geqslant 4.3535 (m - 1492)$.*

Proof. The first inequality is evident and the rest follows from the corollary to Lemma 3.11 with the use of sets constructed in the last lemma, since the corollary to Lemma 3.9 shows that all products $a_i a_j$ are distinct. □

Now we can conclude the proof of the theorem for sufficiently large k in the following way: by Lemma 3.9 there is a set B of at most $\pi(k-1)$

elements such that

$$\prod_{i \in B} A_i \leqslant (k-1)!,$$

but clearly

$$\prod_{i \in B} A_i \geqslant \prod_{i=1}^{k-\pi(k-1)} A_i,$$

and by using the last corollary we obtain, with $a = 3.5694$ and $b = 4.3535$,

$$(k-1)! \geqslant \prod_{i=1}^{k-\pi(k-1)} A_i \geqslant \prod_{i=1}^{422} i \prod_{i=423}^{6900} a(i-304) \prod_{i=6901}^{k-\pi(k-1)} b(i-1492)$$

$$= (k-\pi(k-1)-1492)! \, a^{6478} \, b^{-6900} \, b^{k-\pi(k-1)} \frac{422!}{118!} \cdot \frac{6596!}{5408!}$$

$$\geqslant e^{10110} (k-\pi(k-1)-1492)! \, b^{k-\pi(k-1)}.$$

Using the bound for $\pi(x)$ given by Proposition A.3 (b) and the inequalities

$$N \log N - N + 1 \leqslant \log N! \leqslant N \log N - N + 1 + \log N,$$

we get for $k \geqslant 30000$

$$k \log k - k + 1 \geqslant \log k! - \log k = \log(k-1)!$$

$$\geqslant 10110 + \log\big((k-\pi(k-1)-1492)!\big) + (k-\pi(k-1))\log b$$

$$\geqslant k \log k - 0.9802 k + 1.48 \frac{k}{\log k} - 1492 \log k + 11885,$$

i.e.,

$$0.0198 k + 1.48 \frac{k}{\log k} + 11884 \leqslant 1492 \log k,$$

but for $k \geqslant 30000$ this is false.

It remains to prove the theorem in the range $4 \leqslant k \leqslant 30000$. We shall do this by separating the cases $m = 3$ and $m > 3$. In the case $m = 3$ denote by F_t the number of a_i's without a prime factor larger than the tth consecutive prime number p_t. It is easy to produce a lower bound for F_t which does not depend on n but only on t and k since F_t is at least equal to the number of those integers $n+1, \ldots, n+k$ which do not have a prime divisor in the interval $[1 + p_t, k)$; thus

(3.27) $$F_t = \max_{0 \leqslant j < D} |\{m \leqslant k : m \equiv j \,(\mathrm{mod}\, D)\}|,$$

D being the product of all primes from the interval (p_t, k). Choosing t according to k in the following way:

(3.28)
$$t = \begin{cases} 2 & (4 \leqslant k < 10), \\ 3 & (10 \leqslant k < 28), \\ 4 & (28 \leqslant k < 77), \\ 5 & (77 \leqslant k < 143), \\ 6 & (143 \leqslant k < 340), \\ 7 & (340 \leqslant k < 646), \\ 8 & (646 \leqslant k < 1000) \end{cases}$$

and performing the necessary computations in each case we get

$$F_t(F_t - 1) > 3^t.$$

Now observe that there are 3^t rational numbers built of primes not exceeding p_t which do not differ pairwise by a factor which is a cube of a rational number, and moreover we have $F_t(F_t - 1)$ pairs $[a_i, a_j]$ such that a_i, a_j are divisible by primes $\leqslant p_t$. Since by Lemma 3.8 all ratios a_i/a_j are distinct modulo the cubes, we get a contradiction, and so the case $m = 3$, $4 \leqslant k < 1000$ is settled.

In the case $m > 3$, $4 \leqslant k \leqslant 1000$, we proceed similarly. First observe that the number of possible products $a_{i_1} \ldots a_{i_{m-1}}$ built of those a_i's whose prime factors are all $\leqslant p_t$ equals

$$\binom{F_t + m - 2}{m - 1},$$

since the number of all non-decreasing sequences of r terms taken from a set of N real numbers equals

$$\binom{N + r - 1}{r}.$$

But in view of Lemma 3.8 we can have at most m^t such products, and again a tedious computation shows that, if t is chosen for $k \in [4, 1000]$ according to (3.28) and we use the bound for F_t resulting from this choice, then in our range we have the inequality

$$\binom{F_t + m - 2}{m - 1} > m^t,$$

irrespectible of the value of m. This proves the theorem for $k < 1000$. In the remaining case $(1000 \leqslant k \leqslant 30000)$ we must slightly modify the argument and start again with the case $m = 3$. For each value of k select a number $t = t(k)$ and let $q_1, q_2, \ldots, q_t$ be the t largest primes less than $k^{1/2}$. Denote by

A_t, the set of those a_i's, which have their prime factors bounded by $k^{1/2}$ and which are divisible neither by a square of a q_i nor by a product $q_i q_j$. Let f_t be the cardinality of A_t. Here again we need a lower bound for f_t which is independent of n, and such a bound is provided by

$$f_t \geqslant k - \sum_{k^{1/2} < p < k} ([k/p] + 1) - \sum_{1 \leqslant i < j < r} ([k/q_i q_j] + 1) = \bar{f}_t.$$

Lemma 3.8 implies that there are at most $3^{\pi(q_1) - 1}(t^2 + t + 1)$ ratios a_i/a_j with $a_i, a_j \in A_t$, but obviously at least $\bar{f}_t(\bar{f}_t - 1)$ such ratios are available and it suffices to check that for every $k \in [1000, 30000]$ one can find a suitable t to obtain the inequality

(3.29) $$\bar{f}_t(\bar{f}_t - 1) > 3^{\pi(q_i) - 1}(t^2 + t + 1),$$

which leads to a contradiction.

If $m > 3$ then instead of counting ratios we count the products $a_{i_1} \ldots a_{i_{m-1}}$ with $a_{i_j} \in A_t$ to find that there are

$$\binom{f_t + m - 2}{m - 1}$$

of them and that the upper bound for them implied by Lemma 3.8 equals

$$m^{\pi(q_1) - 1} \binom{m + t - 1}{m - 1}.$$

However, choosing t in the same way as for $m = 3$ one can check that in our range (3.29) implies

$$\binom{f_t + m - 2}{m - 1} > m^{\pi(q_i) - 1} \binom{m + t - 1}{m - 1},$$

and so we get a contradiction. This proves the last remaining case of our assertion. □

Notes and comments

1. The paper of J. J. Sylvester [92], which contains the first proof of the Sylvester–Schur theorem, gives also its generalization to arithmetical progressions: if $k \geqslant n$ and $(n, d) = 1$, then the product $(n+d)(n+2d) \ldots (n+kd)$ is divisible by a prime p exceeding k (cf. also M. Langevin [76b]). The question whether one can restrict p to a particular residue class (mod d) has apparently not been pursued. L. Moser conjectured that this holds for $n \equiv 1 \pmod 4$, $d = 4$ and $p \equiv 1 \pmod 4$.

Other proofs of Theorem 3.5 were given by I. Schur [29a] (cf. also [29b]), P. Erdös [34] and E. F. Ecklund Jr. and R. B. Eggleton [72]. Erdös's proof was based on the estimate $B(n) < 4^n$, but by using better estimates one can obtain sharpened forms of Theorem 3.5. The best possible sharpening was announced by L. Moser [63], who asserted that under the assumptions of Theorem 3.5 there exists a prime $p > 7k/5$ dividing $n(n+1) \ldots (n+k-1)$. With the use of bounds for $B(n)$ proved by J. B. Rosser, L. Schoenfeld [62] this was proved by M. Faulkner [66], and an elementary proof based on Proposition 3.2 (proved earlier in Hanson [72]) was found by D. Hanson [73], who showed also that one can replace the constant 7/5 by 3/2 except in the cases $3 \cdot 4$, $8 \cdot 9$ and $6 \cdot 7 \cdot 8 \cdot 9 \cdot 10$.

The proof of Theorem 3.6 given in the main text is that of D. Hanson [73] with obvious simplifications resulting from the fact that our assertion is weaker.

A complementary result to Theorem 3.6 was obtained by E. F. Ecklund, Jr. [67], who showed that if $n \geqslant 2k$ then there is a prime $p \leqslant \max(n/k, n/2)$ dividing $\binom{n}{k}$ except for $\binom{7}{3} = 5 \cdot 7$.

2. For sufficiently large n the assertion of Theorem 3.5 can be considerably strenghtened. In fact, as early as in 1897 C. Størmer [97] proved the existence of a constant M_k with the property that for n exceeding M_k the product $n(n+1)$ has a prime divisor exceeding k. An analogous result holds also for $n(n+2)$ and n^2+1. (C. Størmer [98].) An explicit bound for M_k was given by D. H. Lehmer [64]. His result implies $\log M_k \leqslant k^2 e^{k/2}$, and thus the maximal prime factor of $n(n+1)$ exceeds $(2+o(1))\log\log n$.

Størmer's results were later extended to other polynomials. Denote by $P(n)$ the maximal prime divisor of the integer n. A. Thue [08] used his theorem on diophantine approximations to deduce

$$\lim_{n \to \infty} P(f(n)) = \infty$$

for the polynomials $f(x) = (ax+b)(cx+d)$ which are non-squares and G. Pólya [18b], using the same method, did this for irreducible quadratic $f(x)$. C. L. Siegel [21] proved that the same assertion holds for all polynomials f which have at least three distinct roots, and this, jointly with the results of Thue and Pólya, shows that the maximal prime divisor of a polynomial tends to infinity for all polynomials which are not powers of a linear polynomial.

The first quantitative result on this topic is due to S. Chowla [35g], who proved

$$P(n^2+1) \gg \log\log n.$$

K. Mahler [35a], [35b] and T. Nagell [37], [55] proved the same evaluation for certain other special quadratic and cubic polynomials, and the results of A. Schinzel [67] and M. Keates [68] give $P(f(n)) \gg \log\log n$ for quadratic and cubic polynomials with distinct roots. Using Baker's method, J. Coates [70a] proved for irreducible polynomials of degree $\geqslant 3$ the evaluation

$$P\big(f(n)\big) \gg (\log\log n)^{1/4}$$

and V. G. Sprindzhuk [71] obtained the bound

$$P\big(f(n)\big) \gg \log\log n/\log\log\log n$$

for irreducible polynomials of degree $\geqslant 5$. Owing to the work of S. V. Kotov [73] it is now known that for all irreducible non-linear polynomials $f(x)$ the following evaluation holds:

$$P\big(f(n)\big) \gg \log\log n.$$

(See T. N. Shorey, R. Tijdeman [76] for a simpler proof.)

3. P. Erdős [55b] denoted by $f(k)$ the least integer with the property that for all $n > k$ at least one of the integers $n+1$, $n+2$, ..., $n+f(k)$ has a prime divisor exceeding k. Theorem 3.1 is equivalent to the inequality $f(k) \leqslant k$, but better bounds are known. In the quoted paper Erdős proved that $f(k) \leqslant (3+\varepsilon)k/\log k$ holds for every $\varepsilon > 0$ and sufficiently large k. This bound was improved by K. Ramachandra [70], whose paper contains a result implying that the coefficient $3+\varepsilon$ in that estimate may be replaced by $1+\varepsilon$, and R. Tijdeman [72] halved this coefficient. Later K. Ramachandra, T. N. Shorey [73] proved $f(k) = o(k/\log k)$, and the best known evaluation of $f(k)$ was given by T. N. Shorey [73], who proved

$$f(k) \ll k\log\log\log k \log^{-1} k \log\log^{-1} k.$$

(Cf. also K. Ramachandra [71] and T. N. Shorey [72].) W. R. Utz [61] and D. H. Lehmer [65] (see also F. Ecklund, Jr., R. B. Eggleton, J. L. Selfridge [74]) computed several values of $f(k)$.

The conjecture $f(k) \ll \log^c k$ for a certain c proposed by P. Erdős [76b] seems to be hopeless at the moment.

If $p(n, k)$ denotes the maximal prime factor of $P_{n,k}$, then for $n \geqslant k^{3/2}$ one has $p(n, k) \gg k\log\log n$ (P. Erdős, T. N. Shorey [76]). Earlier results were obtained by K. Mahler [35b], who had the lower bound $c(k)\log\log n$, and by M. Langevin [75a], [75b]. The latter author showed (Langevin [76b]) that for large n the largest prime factor of $(n+a)(n+2a) \ldots (n+ka)$ (where $(a, n) = 1$) exceeds $(k/8 - \varepsilon)\log\log n$. K. Ramachandra [69] showed that $p(n, [n^{1/2}]) \gg n^{1/2 + 1/13}$ and in Ramachandra [70] improved this bound, obtaining $\gg n^{1/2 + 1/8}$. He showed also (K. Ramachandra [71]) that $p(n, k) \gg k\log k$ with the exception of a range of n depending on k. This restriction was later removed by R. Tijdeman [72]. In the case where the ratio $\log n/\log k$ is not too large M. Jutila [73] improved this bound by showing that if $k^{3/2} \leqslant n \leqslant \exp(c \log^{3/2} k \log\log^{-1} k)$ then

$$p(n, k) \gg \exp\big((1 + c' \log^2 k \log^{-1} n) \log k\big).$$

See also K. Ramachandra [73b]. A survey of problems concerning prime factors of $P_{n,k}$ was given by M. Jutila [75].

4. Proposition 3.2 is a variant of Chebyshev-type evaluations for the product of all primes up to x or for the product of all prime powers up to x or finally for $B(n)$, which can also be written as $\exp(\sum_{n \leqslant x} \Lambda(n))$, $\Lambda(n)$ being v. Mangoldt's function defined as $\log p$ if n is a power of a prime p and 0 in all other cases. The Prime Number Theorem immediately implies $B(n) = \exp(n + o(n))$ and the various bounds for the remainder in the Prime Number Theorem imply bounds for the error term; however, in many applications more explicit evaluations are needed.

The best result is due to J. B. Rosser and L. Schoenfeld [62], who obtained $B(x) < \exp(1.03883\,x) < (2.82591)^x$, the maximal value of $\log B(x)/x$ being attained at $x = 113$. For the function $\theta(x) = \sum_{p \leqslant x} \log p$ the best known bound, namely $\theta(x) < 1.001093\,x$ was provided by L. Schoenfeld [76], who also announced the evaluation $\theta(x) > 1.000081\,x$ for all positive x. (Cf. W. E. L. Grimson, D. Hanson [78] for a weaker but elementary evaluation.) The previous best bound was found by J. B. Rosser and L. Schoenfeld [75].

Bertrand's postulate (Corollary to Theorem 3.5) was first proved by P. Chebyshev [50] and has been sharpened several times. J. Nagura [52] proved that for $n \geqslant 25$ there is always a prime in $[n, 6n/5]$, and H. Rohrbach and J. Weis [64] showed the existence of a prime in $[n, 1.073\,n]$ for $n \geqslant 119$. A simple proof of the existence of a prime in $[3n, 4n]$ for all $n \geqslant 1$ can be found in Hanson [73].

By analytical means one can prove much stronger results. It is known that for sufficiently large n the interval $[n, n+n^c]$ contains a prime for a certain $c < 1$. The first result of this type, namely $c = 32999/33000$, was obtained by G. Hoheisel [30], and this was improved by H. Heilbronn [33] ($c = 249/250$), N. Chudakov [36], ($c = 3/4 + \varepsilon$), A. E. Ingham [37] ($c = 48/77 + \varepsilon$), E. C. Titchmarsh [42] ($c = 192/308 + \varepsilon$), S. H. Min [49] ($c = 38/61 + \varepsilon$), W. Haneke [63] ($c = 61/98 + \varepsilon$), H. L. Montgomery [69], [71] ($c = 3/5 + \varepsilon$), M. N. Huxley [72] ($c = 7/12 + \varepsilon$), H. Iwaniec, M. Jutila [79] ($c = 13/23 < 0.56522$), and D. R. Heath-Brown and H. Iwaniec [79] ($c = 1/2 + 1/20 + \varepsilon$). H. Iwaniec and J. Pintz got recently $c = 1/2 + 1/21 + \varepsilon$. The old conjecture that there is always a prime between two consecutive squares, which would be implied, at least for sufficiently large squares, by $c = 1/2$, is still unproved. J. J. Chen [75] obtained an approximation to it, proving that for large x there is always an integer in $[x, x + x^{1/2}]$ having at most two prime factors. This improves the previous work of V. Brun [20], W. Mientka [61] and S. Uchiyama [63], who had 11, 9, and 4, respectively, in place of 2. Later Chen [79a] proved the existence of such an integer in the smaller interval $[x, x + x^{0.477}]$ and H. Iwaniec, M. Laborde [81] replaced the exponent by 0.45. This result can be improved for almost all x. In fact, Y. Motohashi [79] showed that for almost all integers x there is a product of two primes in the interval $[x, x + x^{\varepsilon}]$ where ε is an arbitrary positive number.

The Riemann Conjecture implies that if $F(x)$ tends to infinity, then for sufficiently large x there are primes in the interval $[x, x + x^{1/2} F(x) \log x]$. This follows from the results of H. Cramér [21]. A. Selberg [43] proved that for almost all x one can replace here $x^{1/2}$ by $\log x$.

The first occurrences of gaps of a given length between consecutive primes were tabulated by L. J. Lander and T. R. Parkin [67], and by R. P. Brent [73], [80].

5. According to L. E. Dickson [HTN] (vol. II, p. 679), the first result concerning the conjecture that the product $P_{n,k} = (n+1) \dots (n+k)$ is never a mth power for $m \geqslant 2$ was published in 1724 by C. Goldbach, who noted that a product of three such integers cannot be a square. Various special cases of Theorems 3.7 and 3.8 were established long ago and up to 1914 the following cases had been settled: $k = 3$, $m \geqslant 2$ (Mlle Adolphine D. [57]), $k = 4$, $m = 2$ (which was one of the examination questions at the École Navale, cf. Nouv. Annales de Mathématique, 16, 1857, pp. 393-394), $k = 4$, $m = 3$ (L. Aubry [13]), $k = 5$, $m = 2, 3$ (V. A. Lebesgue [60a], [60b]), $5 \leqslant k \leqslant 7$, $m = 2$ (G. C. Gerono [60]), $8 \leqslant k \leqslant 11$, $m = 2$ (M. D. A. Guibert [60], [62], who stated also that the same holds for $12 \leqslant k \leqslant 17$), $k = m$ (D. André [71]; this paper contains a small error, pointed out and corrected by R. Obláth [33]). One should also mention a paper by J. Liouville [57], who noted that if one of the factors of $P_{n,k}$ is prime then $P_{n,k}$ cannot be a power.

These results were obtained by a quite straightforward but tedious elementary procedures. In the same style the range $k \leqslant 203$, $m = 2$ was covered by S. Narumi [17] and R. Obláth [33] settled the cases $k = 5, 6, 7$, $m = 3, 5$.

6. Theorem 3.7 was proved independently by P. Erdös [39a] and O. Rigge [39], with similar proofs. The proof of P. Erdös works for $k \geqslant 100$ (but in fact his inequality (7) leads to a contradiction already for $k \geqslant 80$) and for $k \leqslant 99$ Erdös had to quote Narumi's result. The proof presented here avoids this, using a simplification taken from P. Erdös and J. L. Selfridge [75].

The first general result towards Theorem 3.8 was obtained by P. Erdös [39b], who showed that for $m \geqslant 3$ and $k \geqslant k_0(m)$ the product $P_{n,k}$ cannot be a mth power. (Siegel's Theorem 3.3 implies this for m and k fixed and n sufficiently large.) The same result was also obtained by S. S. Pillai [40b] and O. Rigge [40]. Next P. Erdös and C. L. Siegel deduced from Theorem 3.3 that $k_0(m)$ can be replaced here by an absolute constant, but this result remained unpublished. More than ten years later P. Erdös [55a] succeeded in finding an elementary proof, and finally in P. Erdös and J. L. Selfridge [75] the idea of that paper was extended so as to yield a complete proof of the old conjecture. In fact, they prove a stronger result, showing that if $n+k \geqslant p'$, p' being the least prime exceeding k, then there is a prime $p > k$ which divides $P_{n,k}$ with an exponent not divisible by m. It is noted in this paper that the same method can be used to show that no product of consecutive odd integers is a power.

(Added in proof: R. Marszałek (Monatsh. f. Math., in print) showed that if $k \geqslant k_0(d)$ and $(d, n) = 1$ then the product $\prod\limits_{j=1}^{k} (n+jd)$ cannot be a proper power.)

For earlier partial results on Theorem 3.7 see L. L. Johnson [40], R. Obláth [51] and S. S. Pillai [40b].

7. The analogous equation $\binom{n}{k} = y^m$ was treated in P. Erdös [39b], who showed its insolvability in the case $n \geqslant 2k \geqslant 2^{1+m}$. Erdös conjectured that in the case $n \geqslant 2k \geqslant 4$ it has solutions only if $k = m = 2$, in which case there are infinitely many solutions obtained by solving $n^2 - 2y^2 = -1$. He was able to prove this in the case $m = 3$ and in Erdös [51] the truth of the conjecture was established for $k \geqslant 4$. See Stolt [57] for a generalization. In the case $k = 2$, $m \geqslant 3$, E. Z. Chein [79b] announced that m must be a prime satisfying $31 < m < 7.877 \cdot 10^8$.

G. F. Hering [68] and W. Stahl [69] proved that $\binom{n}{k}$ cannot be a prime power for $k \neq 1$, $n-1$. This was improved by H. Scheid [69], who showed that for those k there are at least $k \log 2/\log 2k$ prime divisors of $\binom{n}{k}$, and by P. Erdös [73], who demonstrated the existence of at least k such factors provided n is sufficiently large, say $n \geqslant n(k)$. M. Mignotte [73] and E. S. Selmer [76] studied the function $n(k)$ and obtained the bounds

$$n(k) \leqslant k! + k - 1 \qquad \text{resp.} \qquad n(k) \leqslant B(k),$$

where $B(k)$ is, as in the main text, the least common multiple of positive integers not greater than k. P. Erdös, H. Gupta and S. P. Khare [76] established the lower bound $n(k) \gg k^2 \log k$ and in Erdös and Sarközy [79] this was improved to

$$n(k) \gg k^2 \log^{4/3} k \, (\log\log k)^{-4/3} (\log\log\log k)^{-1/3}.$$

In Erdös, Gupta and Khare [76] it is also shown that for $k \geqslant 4939$ one has the explicit bound $n(k) > k^2$ and the computations of E. S. Selmer [76] verified this also in the range $37 \leqslant k \leqslant 200$.

8. D. J. Newman asked whether for every pair of positive integers k, N one can find a one-to-one map f from the interval $[1, N]$ onto $[k+1, k+N]$ with the property that for $j = 1, 2, ..., N$ one has $(j, f(j)) = 1$. In the case $k = N$ this was confirmed by D. E. Daykin and M. J. Baines [63] and V. Chvátal [71] showed it for all $N \leqslant 1002$. The last step was made by C. Pomerance and J. L. Selfridge [80], who proved the conjecture.

Exercises

1 (J. J. Sylvester [92]). Prove that if $k \geqslant n$ and $(n, d) = 1$ then the product $(n+d) \times (n+2d) ... (n+kd)$ is divisible by a prime greater than k.

2 (D. Hanson [73]). Prove that if $n \geqslant k$ then there is a prime p exceeding $3k/2$ which divides the product $(n+1) ... (n+k)$ except if this product equals $3 \cdot 4$, $8 \cdot 9$ or $6 \cdot 7 \cdot 8 \cdot 9 \cdot 10$.

3. Prove that a product of k consecutive odd integers is never a power if k is sufficiently large.

4 (P. Erdös [39b]). Prove that, for $k \geqslant 2^m$ and $2k < n$, $\binom{n}{k}$ is never a full power.

5 (Ibidem). Show that for $2 \leqslant k \leqslant n-1$ $\binom{n}{k}$ cannot be a cube.

6 (C. L. Siegel [21]). Prove that if $f(x) \in Z[x]$ is not a power of a linear polynomial then the largest prime factor of $f(n)$ tends to infinity with n.

(Hint: For irreducible f of degree $\geqslant 3$ observe that otherwise there would exist a fixed integer A such that the equation $f(x) = Ay^3$ would have infinitely many integral solutions x, y, and then use Theorem 3.3).

7 (P. Erdös [55b]). Using Ingham's bound $O(p_n^{5/8})$ for the difference $p_{n+1} - p_n$ of consecutive primes, prove the existence of a constant C with the property that if $n > k$ and $m > Ck/\log k$ then in the interval $[n+1, n+m]$ there is an integer having a prime divisor larger than k.

(Hint: Use Ingham's result for the case $n \leqslant k^{3/2}$ and in the remaining case consider $\binom{n+t}{t}$ where $t = [ck/\log k]$ with a large c).

§ 3. GRIMM'S CONJECTURE

1. Let $n+1, n+2, ..., n+k$ be k consecutive integers. C. A. Grimm [69] considered the following possible property of this sequence:

(G) *There exist k distinct primes $p_1, ..., p_k$ such that for $j = 1, 2, ..., k$ the number $n+j$ is divisible by p_j.*

It is clear that if k is large enough then this property fails. Indeed, it suffices to take $k = 2n$ since then the interval $[n+1, n+k]$ will contain two powers of 2. If we thus denote by $g(n)$ the largest integer k such that for the sequence $n+1, n+2, ..., n+k$ the above property holds, then $g(n) < 2n$.

Grimm conjectured that property (G) holds in each case where the interval $[n+1, n+k]$ does not contain a prime number. Obviously this conjecture implies the following statement, which we shall call the *weak Grimm's conjecture*:

If there is no prime in the interval $[n+1, n+k]$, then the product $P_{n,k} = \prod_{j=1}^{k} (n+j)$ has at least k distinct prime divisors.

None of these assertions has been proved so far, and certainly they are rather deep in view of the following observation made by P. Erdös and J. L. Selfridge [71]:

PROPOSITION 3.3. *There is a positive constant C such that if $k \geqslant Cn^{1/2} \log^{-1/2} n$, then $\omega(P_{n,k}) < k$.*

Proof. We follow J. W. M. Turk [79]. Let m be the number of distinct prime factors of $P_{n,k}$ and let p_m be the mth prime number. Then

$$(n+k)^k \geqslant P_{n,k} \geqslant k! \prod_{\substack{p > k \\ p \mid P_{n,k}}} p \geqslant k! \prod_{k < p \leqslant p_m} p$$

$$= k! \exp\left\{ \sum_{k < p \leqslant p_m} \log p \right\} = k! \exp\left\{ (p_m - k) + O(p_m/\log^2 p_m) \right\}$$

by the Prime Number Theorem. If we now assume that $m \geqslant k$, and use again the Prime Number Theorem, as well as the inequality $k! > (k/e)^k$, then we arrive at

$$(n+k)^k \geqslant (k/e)^k \exp\left\{ k \log\left((1+o(1)) k \log k \right) + O(k) \right\},$$

which gives

$$n+k \geqslant (k/e) \exp\left(\log k + \log\log k + O(1) \right) \gg k^2 \log k.$$

This shows that if for a sufficiently large constant C, we have $k > Cn^{1/2} \log^{-1/2} n$ then $\omega(P_{n,k}) < k$, as asserted. □

COROLLARY 1. *The weak Grimm conjecture implies that between any two sufficiently large squares lies a prime number.*

Proof. It is enough to observe that for sufficiently large $n = x^2$ we have $(x+1)^2 - x^2 > 2n^{1/2} > Cn^{1/2} \log^{-1/2} n$. □

COROLLARY 2. *We have $g(n) = O(n^{1/2} \log^{-1/2} n)$.*

Proof. The corollary follows immediately from the definition of $g(n)$ and the proposition. □

2. Grimm himself was able to prove the conjecture in the case where $k \leqslant c \log n / \log\log n$ with a certain positive constant c.

We now prove a better result, due to P. Erdös and J. L. Selfridge [71]:

THEOREM 3.9. *We have $g(n) \geqslant \frac{1}{2} \log n$ and also $g(n) \geqslant (1+o(1)) \log n$.*

Proof. We shall use a classical combinatorial result of Ph. Hall [35] concerning a complete system of distinct representatives:

PROPOSITION 3.4. *Let $T_1, \ldots, T_m$ be non-empty sets. A complete system of distinct representatives of those sets, i.e., a sequence $a_1, \ldots, a_m$ of distinct elements with $a_i \in T_i$ $(i = 1, 2, \ldots, m)$ exists if and only if for every non-empty subset A of $\{1, 2, \ldots, m\}$ one has*

$$\left| \bigcup_{i \in A} T_i \right| \geq |A|.$$

Proof. The necessity of the condition is obvious, and so we concentrate on the proof of its sufficiency, proceeding by recurrence in m. The case $m = 1$ being trivial, assume that the assertion is true for all sequences of at most $m-1$ sets and consider any sequence $T_1, \ldots, T_m$ of non-empty sets satisfying the condition of the proposition. We distinguish between two cases. The first case occurs if for $k = 1, 2, \ldots, m-1$ and all choices of distinct indices $i_1, \ldots, i_k$ we have

$$|S_{i_1} \cup \ldots \cup S_{i_k}| \geq k+1.$$

In this case choose an arbitrary element $a_1 \in S_1$ and delete it from the sets $S_2, \ldots, S_{m-1}$, thus giving rise to a new sequence, $S'_2, \ldots, S'_m$, which satisfies the condition of the proposition; thus it is possible to find a complete system of distinct representatives for the new sequence. By joining a to this system we arrive at our assertion.

In the second case we have to assume that there is an integer $k \leq m-1$ and also distinct indices $i_1, \ldots, i_k$ such that

$$|S_{i_1} \cup \ldots \cup S_{i_k}| = k.$$

Clearly we may assume that $i_j = j$ for $j = 1, 2, \ldots, k$. In this case the set $D = S_1 \cup \ldots \cup S_k$ is a complete system of distinct representatives for $S_1, \ldots, S_k$. Now delete from the sets $S_{k+1}, \ldots, S_m$ all elements of D, obtaining thus a new sequence $S^*_{1+k}, \ldots, S^*_m$, and consider a set $j_1, \ldots, j_r$ of indices lying between $k+1$ and m. Since the set

$$S_1 \cup \ldots \cup S_k \cup S^*_{j_1} \cup \ldots \cup S^*_{j_r}$$

has at least $k+r$ elements, D has k elements and the sets D and $S^*_{j_1} \cup \ldots \cup S^*_{j_r}$ are disjoint, it follows that the sequence

$$S^*_{k+1} \cup \ldots \cup S^*_m$$

satisfies the condition of the proposition; hence we may find for this sequence a complete system of distinct representatives, which jointly with D produces such a system for $S_1, \ldots, S_m$. □

The main step in the proof is embodied in the following lemma.

LEMMA 3.14. *For every $n \geq 1$ one can find an integer $t \geq 1$ and $t+1$*

*distinct integers $a_0, a_1, ..., a_t$ lying in the interval $I_n = [n+1,\ n+1+g(n)]$
such that their product P has t distinct prime divisors and moreover the
maximal prime dividing P does not exceed $g(n)$.*

Proof. Denote by T_i the set of all prime divisors of the number $n+i$ for
$i = 1, 2, ..., g(n)+1$. From the definition of $g(n)$ we infer that there cannot
exist a complete system of distinct representatives for the family $\{T_i\}$, and so
Proposition 3.4 shows that there must exist an integer $t \geq 1$ and $t+1$ distinct
integers $a_0, a_1, ..., a_t$ in I_n whose product has at most t distinct prime
divisors. Assume that t is chosen to be minimal with respect to this property.
This implies that the product $a_0 a_1 ... a_{t-1}$ has at least t prime divisors,
showing that $P = a_0 a_1 ... a_t$ also has t prime divisors. To prove that all
prime divisors of P are $\leq g(n)$ assume the contrary and denote by p a prime
divisor of P which is bigger than $g(n)$. Then p divides some a_j, and since
obviously no other integer in I_n can be divisible by p the product P/a_j of
$t-1$ integers a_i would have at most $t-1$ prime divisors. The minimality of t
implies now $t = 1$, but then $P = a_0 a_1$ has p as its only prime divisor and,
since $a_0, a_1 \neq 1$, we obtain

$$g(n) < p \,|a_1 - a_0|\, g(n),$$

a contradiction. □

To prove the theorem choose $t \geq 1$ and the integers $a_0, a_1, ..., a_t$
according to the last lemma. Let $P = a_0 a_1 ... a_t$ and, for every prime $p|P$, let
p^{a_p} be the maximal power of that prime which can divide an integer from I_p.
Choose an integer n_p in I_n such that $p^{a_p} \| n_p$. Since P has t prime divisors,
there must remain at least one integer a_i, say a_N, which differs from all
integers n_p (for $p|P$). If we write $a_N = \prod_{p|P} p^{b_p}$, then obviously $b_p \leq a_p$, and so
p^{b_p} divides both a_N and n_p. Hence p^{b_p} divides the non-zero difference $a_N - n_p$,
and we obtain $p^{b_p} \leq g(n)$, which implies $n \leq a_N \leq g(n)^t$, and

(3.30) $t \geq \log n / \log g(n).$

Since all prime divisors of P are $\leq g(n)$, we get $t = \omega(P) \leq \pi(g(n))$. By the
Prime Number Theorem $t \leq (1+o(1))g(n)/\log g(n)$, and this together with
(3.30) leads to $g(n) \geq (1+o(1))\log n$, as asserted.

By the Brun–Titchmarsh theorem (see Theorem A.2) we get
$t \leq \pi(g(n)) \leq 2g(n)/\log g(n)$ for $n \geq 2$, and this implies $g(n) \geq \frac{1}{2}\log n$
for $n \geq 2$. □

3. We shall now improve upon the last theorem, using Baker's method to
prove the following result:

THEOREM 3.10. *With a suitable positive constant C one has*

$$g(n) \geq C \log^2 n / \log\log^5 n \, \log\log\log^2 n.$$

Proof. (We follow the argument applied by K. Ramachandra, T. N. Shorey and R. Tijdeman [75], who pushed the analysis further along the same lines and obtained a stronger result.)

Obviously we may assume that $g(n) \leqslant \log^3 n$. Choose t and a set $\mathscr{A} = \{a_0, a_1, \ldots, a_t\}$ of $t+1$ integers contained in the interval $I_n = [n+1, n+ +g(n)+1]$ according to Lemma 3.14. Thus the product $P = a_0 a_1 \ldots a_t$ has no prime divisors exceeding $g(n)$ and $\omega(P) \leqslant t$. For every prime $p|P$ choose an integer $f(p) \in \mathscr{A}$ divisible by the maximal power of p and split $\mathscr{A}$ into three subsets: $\mathscr{A} = A_0 \cup A_1 \cup A_2$.

A_0 consists of those elements in $\mathscr{A}$ which are not of the form $f(p)$,

A_1 is the set of all those elements of $\mathscr{A}$ which are of the form $f(p)$ for a unique prime $p|P$ and

A_2 is the set of the remaining elements of $\mathscr{A}$.

Let N_i $(i = 0, 1, 2)$ be the cardinality of A_i.

Our argument will use the following simple lemma:

LEMMA 3.15. *If $a_1, \ldots, a_m$ are integers, all at least equal to a positive integer A and such that for $i \neq j$ one has $(a_i, a_j) \leqslant B$, where B is a given integer, then for the least common multiple $[a_1, \ldots, a_m]$ the following inequality holds:*

$$[a_1, \ldots, a_m] \geqslant \max_{1 \leqslant i \leqslant m} A^i/B^{i(i-1)/2}.$$

Proof. Since for $r = 1, 2, \ldots, m$ we have the inequality

$$[a_1, a_2, \ldots, a_m] \geqslant [a_1, \ldots, a_r],$$

it suffices to show that

$$[a_1, \ldots, a_r] \geqslant A^r/B^{r(r-1)/2}$$

for $r = 1, 2, \ldots, m$. We shall establish this by induction. The case $r = 1$ being trivial, assume that the above inequality holds for a certain $r \geqslant 1$. Then

$$[a_1, \ldots, a_{r+1}] = [[a_1, \ldots, a_r], a_{r+1}]$$
$$= \frac{[a_1, \ldots, a_r] a_{r+1}}{([a_1, \ldots, a_r], a_{r+1})} \geqslant \frac{A^r}{B^{r(r-1)/2}} \frac{a_{r+1}}{([a_1, \ldots, a_r], a_{r+1})}$$

by the inductive assumption and, since

$$([a_1, \ldots, a_r], a_{r+1}) \leqslant \prod_{j=1}^{r} (a_j, a_{r+1}) \leqslant B^r \quad \text{and} \quad a_{r+1} \geqslant A,$$

the asserted inequality follows. $\square$

Using this lemma, we can now improve the bound for t given in (3.30) in the case where N_0 is not very small. We prove

LEMMA 3.16. *If $N_0 > t^{1/2}$ and $g(n) \leqslant \log^3 n$, then*

$$t \geqslant \log^2 n/36 (\log\log n)^2 \quad \text{and} \quad g(n) \gg \log^2 n/\log\log n.$$

Proof. We apply the previous lemma to the set A_0, all elements of which are $\geqslant n$. Since they all lie in an interval of length $g(n)$, the greatest common divisor of any two of them cannot exceed $g(n)$. This gives for their least common multiple M the lower bound

$$M \geqslant \max_{1 \leqslant i \leqslant m} n^i/g(n)^{i(i-1)/2} \geqslant n^T/g(n)^{T(T-1)/2} \geqslant n^{t^{1/2}}/g(n)^t,$$

where $T = 1 + [t^{1/2}] \leqslant N_0$. On the other hand, M cannot exceed $g(n)^t$ because if $p^{\alpha_p} \| f(p)$ then $(M, p^{\alpha_p}) \leqslant g(n)$ and obviously

$$M \leqslant \prod_{p|P} (M, p^{\alpha_p}) \leqslant g(n)^t.$$

Comparing the resulting bounds, we obtain $n^{t^{1/2}} \leqslant g(n)^{2t}$, which leads to $t \geqslant \frac{1}{4}\log^2 n/\log^2 g(n)$, but in our case $\log g(n) < 3\log\log n$, and so the assertion of the lemma follows. $\square$

Now we prove the theorem. We may assume that

$$t \leqslant c(\log n)^2/(\log\log^3 n\log\log\log n)^2$$

holds for a certain constant c, which may be taken arbitrarily small and, since (3.30) implies under our assumptions that $t \geqslant \log n/3\log\log n$, we may assume that t is sufficiently large to meet all our further needs.

Note first that one clearly has $N_2 \leqslant (t+1)/2$, and since in view of Lemma 3.16 we may assume that $N_0 \leqslant t^{1/2} \leqslant t/4$ (for large n) we obtain

$$N_1 \geqslant (t+1) - N_0 - N_1 > t/4.$$

Every element m of A_1 has a unique representation in the form $m = f(p)$ (with $p|P$), and so we may write

(3.31) $m = b_m p_m^{\beta_m}$

with $f(p_m) = m$, $p_m \nmid b_m$ and $p_{m_1} \neq p_{m_2}$ for $m_1 \neq m_2$.

Let M_1 be the least common multiple of the numbers b_m $(m \in A_1)$, let p be a prime dividing M_1 and define a by $p^a \| M_1$. Then with a suitable $m \in A_1$ we have $p^a | b_m | m$ and thus $f(p) \neq m$. Let p^b be the maximal power of p dividing an integer from I_n. Then clearly $a \leqslant b$ and $N = f(p) \neq r$; thus $p^a \| N - r| \neq 0$ and we obtain the inequality $p^a \leqslant g(n)$, leading to $M_1 \leqslant g(n)^t$.

Now we apply Lemma 3.15 to the sequence $c_1 \geqslant c_2 \geqslant \ldots \geqslant c_s = A$ $(s = [t/8])$ of s largest numbers b_m $(m \in A_1)$ with $B = g(n)$. This gives

$$M_1 \geqslant [c_1, \ldots, c_s] \geqslant \max_{1 \leqslant i \leqslant s} A^i g(n)^{-i(i-1)/2} \geqslant A^{t^{1/2}/2} g(n)^{-t/2}$$

(by taking $i = 1 + [t^{1/2}/2]$) and the resulting upper bound for M_1 implies

$$A \leqslant g(n)^{3t^{1/2}}.$$

This shows that we have at our disposal at least $t/4 - [t/8] \geqslant t/8$ numbers b_m

$(m \in A_1)$ with $b_m \leqslant A \leqslant g(n)^{3t^{1/2}} \leqslant \exp(9t^{1/2} \log\log n)$. Let A_3 be the set of those $m \in A_1$ for which b_m has this property. If for all pairs of distinct numbers of A_3 the corresponding exponents β_m (as given by (3.31)) differ by at least $t^{1/2}$, then the largest exponent would be at least equal to $\frac{1}{8} t^{3/2}$ but on the other hand it cannot be larger than $\log(n+g(n)+1)/\log 2$, which is $\ll \log n$, and so t would have to be $\ll \log^{2/3} n$, which fails in our case. Thus we may select a pair $m_1 \neq m_2$ in A_3 for which $|\beta_{m_1} - \beta_{m_2}| < t^{1/2}$, and of course $b_{m_i} \leqslant \exp(9t^{1/2} \log\log n)$ for $i = 1, 2$.

Now we are ready to find a linear form in logarithms to which Baker's method can be applied.

Write, for short, $b_{m_i} = B_i$, $p_{m_i} = q_i$ $(i = 1, 2)$, $\beta_{m_1} = \lambda$, $\beta_{m_2} = \mu$ and $a = \mu - \lambda$. Clearly

(3.32) $|a| < t^{1/2}$

and, in view of

$$m_1 - m_2 = B_1 q_1^\lambda - B_2 q_2^\mu = m_2 (B_1 B_2^{-1} q_2^{-a} (q_1/q_2)^\lambda - 1),$$

we obtain

$$0 < |B_1 B_2^{-1} q_2^{-a} (q_1/q_2)^\lambda - 1| \leqslant g(n)/n.$$

Putting now $q_1/q_2 = \alpha_1$, $B_1/B_2 q_2^a = \alpha_2$ we immediately get for large n the inequality

(3.33) $0 < |\lambda \log\alpha_1 - \log\alpha_2| \leqslant 2g(n)/n \leqslant 2(\log^3 n/n).$

To minorate this linear form we apply Baker's theorem (Theorem A.8); in order to use it we have first to bound the heights of α_1, α_2 and the absolute value of λ. Since the primes q_1, q_2 do not exceed $g(n) < \log^3 n$, the height of α_1 is at most $\log^3 n$. Moreover, B_1, $B_2 \leqslant \exp(9t^{1/2} \log\log n)$, and in view of (3.32) we get $q_2^a \leqslant \exp\{3t^{1/2} \log\log n\}$, which implies that the height of α_2 equals at most $\exp(9t^{1/2} \log\log n)$. Finally $2^\lambda \leqslant n+g(n)+1$ implies

$$\lambda = O(\log n).$$

Having done all this, we apply Theorem A.8 to get

$$|\lambda \log\alpha_1 - \log\alpha_2| > \exp\{-Ct^{1/2}(\log\log n)^3 \log\log\log n\}$$

with a certain effective constant C, which together with (3.33) gives

$$\log n \ll t^{1/2}(\log\log n)^3 \log\log\log n,$$

and so

$$t \gg \log^2 n(\log\log n)^{-6}(\log\log\log n)^{-2}.$$

But $t \leqslant \pi(g(n)) \ll g(n)\log^{-1} g(n)$, and we arrive at

$$g(n) \gg t\log g(n) \gg t\log t \gg \log^2 n(\log\log n)^{-5}(\log\log\log n)^{-2}$$

as asserted. □

Notes and comments

1. Grimm's conjecture was stated in Grimm [69], where also the bound $g(n) \geq [\log n/2 \log \log n]$ for large n was obtained. This was consecutively improved, becoming

$$g(n) \geq (1 + o(1)) \log n$$

(P. Erdös and J. L. Selfridge [71]),

$$g(n) \gg \log n (\log \log n)^{1/2} (\log \log \log n)^{-1/2}$$

(K. Ramachandra [73a], who used Baker's method),

$$g(n) \gg \log^2 n (\log \log n)^{-6}$$

(P. L. Cijsouw and R. Tijdeman [72]) and finally

$$g(n) \gg \log^3 n (\log \log n)^{-3}$$

(K. Ramachandra, T. N. Shorey and R. Tijdeman [75]), who hold the record so far.

The last result implies that for sufficiently large n Grimm's conjecture follows from the conjecture of H. Cramér [37] which states that the difference $p_{n+1} - p_n$ between consecutive prime numbers is $O(\log^2 p_n)$.

The result of Erdös and Selfridge was presented in Theorem 3.9 and Theorem 3.10 uses the method of Ramachandra, Shorey and Tijdeman to get a weaker result.

The weak form of Grimm's conjecture was established by K. Ramachandra, T. N. Shorey and R. Tijdeman [76] for $k \leq \exp(c \log^{1/2} n)$ with a certain positive c. As shown by J. Turk [80], the same assertion holds if one replaces the sequence $n+1, \ldots, n+k$ by $F(n+1), \ldots, F(n+k)$, where $F(x)$ is a non-constant polynomial over Z.

A generalization of Grimm's problem to algebraic number fields was considered by N. S. Sukthankar [73].

Grimm's conjecture was extended by M. Langevin [76b] to the case of consecutive integers in progressions as follows: if $n+d, n+2d, \ldots, n+kd$ are all composite, then there exist distinct primes $p_1, \ldots, p_k$ with $p_j | n+jd$ ($j = 1, 2, \ldots, k$). Langevin established the truth of this in the case where none of the integers in question divides the least common multiple of $1, 2, \ldots, k$.

2. It is stated in Ramachandra, Shorey and Tijdeman [75] that P. Erdös proved the upper bound $g(n) = O(n^c)$ with a constant $c < 1/2$, but the proof of this assertion seems to have never been published. J. W. Turk [79] showed in his Ph.D. thesis that for infinitely many integers n we have

$$g(n) \leq \exp(c \log^{1/2} n (\log \log n)^{1/2})$$

with a certain constant c. The same thesis contains also many other results concerning consecutive integers. In particular, the problem of finding the longest interval $[n, n+k_n]$ not containing a set of multiplicatively dependent integers was considered there and the bounds

$$\log n \log\log n (\log\log\log n)^{-1} \ll k_n \ll n^{1/2} \log^{-1/2} n$$

were proved. Moreover, for infinitely many integers n,

$$k_n \ll \exp\left(c (\log n \log\log n)^{1/2}\right)$$

with a suitable c, and similarly, for infinitely many n's we have the bound

$$k_n \gg \exp\left(c_1 (\log n \log\log n)^{1/2}\right)$$

with a positive c_1. Similar questions were considered by E. M. Nikishin [79], who proved a Baker's type result for linear combinations of the logarithms of consecutive integers.

3. Another question concerning consecutive integers was raised by E. Jacobsthal [60], who in a series of five papers studied the function $\hat{g}(n)$, (it is usually denoted by g) defined as the greatest integer L such that there is a sequence of L consecutive integers none of which is prime to n. Denoting by k the number of distinct prime factors of n, he showed $\hat{g}(n) \leqslant (k+1)(2^k - 1)$ and in a letter to Erdös asked whether the bound $\hat{g}(n) = O(k^2)$ is true. The answer to this question is still unknown but some progress has been made. P. Erdös [62] showed that, for almost all n, $\hat{g}(n)$ is asymptotically equal to $n \log\log n \, \varphi^{-1}(n)$ and observed that a bound of the form $\hat{g}(n) = O(k^C)$ with a certain C follows from the sieve of Brun. On the other hand, a lower bound of the order $k \log^2 k \log\log\log k (\log\log k)^{-2}$ follows from a result of R. A. Rankin [38] on prime differences (Rankin [62]). H. J. Kanold [65] noted that the bound $\hat{g}(N_k) \leqslant (k \log k)^{2-\delta}$ for certain positive δ, where N_k is the product of the first k primes, would imply Linnik's theorem about the least prime in a progression, and in [67] he was able to confirm Jacobsthal's conjecture in certain cases, e.g., for $k \leqslant 12$ and in the case where the least prime dividing n exceeds $k^{0.6}$. He proved also $\hat{g}(n) \leqslant 2^k$ and even $\hat{g}(n) \leqslant 2^{\sqrt{k}}$ provided $k \geqslant \exp 50$.

H. Iwaniec [71] proved that $\hat{g}(N_k) \ll k^2 \log^2 k$ and noted that the Jurkat–Richert sieve (W. B. Jurkat, H. J. Richert [65]) is also applicable and leads to

$$\hat{g}(N_k) \ll k^2 \exp(\log^{13/14} k).$$

R. C. Vaughan [76] used Rosser's sieve in the form given by H. Iwaniec [71] to obtain $\hat{g}(n) \ll k^2 \log^4 k$, and the best result is due to H. Iwaniec [78], who showed $\hat{g}(n) \ll k^2 \log^2 k$. (Cf. also H. Harborth [65], H. J. Kanold [64], [75], [77a], [77b], [77c] and H. Stevens [77].)

For other questions concerning products of consecutive integers see

P. Erdős and E. G. Straus [77], P. Erdős and J. L. Selfridge [67] and E. F. Ecklund, Jr., and R. B. Eggleton [75].

S. S. Pillai [40a] observed that in every set of $k \leqslant 16$ consecutive integers there is one prime to all the others, showed that this fails for $17 \leqslant k \leqslant 430$ and conjectured that it fails also for all larger integers k. Later he (S. S. Pillai [41]) and A. Brauer [41] proved this conjecture. In fact, for $k \geqslant 17$ there are infinitely many sets of k consecutive integers which do not have this property. Other proofs were given later by S. S. Pillai [44a] and R. J. Evans [69].

For $d \geqslant 2$ define $G(d)$ as the minimal integer, if there exists one, with the property that for $m \geqslant G(d)$ there exist infinitely many blocks B of m consecutive integers such that for any x in B one can find $y \neq x$ in B with $(x, y) \geqslant d$. The Brauer–Pillai theorem can be stated as $G(2) = 17$, and Y. Caro [79] proved the existence of $G(d)$ for all $d \geqslant 2$.

An analogue of the Brauer–Pillai theorem for consecutive integers from an arithmetic progression was proved by R. Evans [72].

Exercises

1 (C. A. Grimm [69]). Prove directly, without using Theorem 3.9, that Grimm's conjecture holds for the sequence $n!+2, \ n!+3, \ \ldots, \ n!+n$.

2 (J. W. M. Turk [79]). A set of integers is said to be multiplicatively dependent if the set of the logarithms of those integers is linearly dependent over the rationals. Prove that if $n_1 > 1$ and $n_1 < n_2 < \ldots < n_t$ are multiplicatively dependent then $n_t > n_1 + \frac{1}{4} \log n_1$.

3 (Ibidem). Prove that if the integers $n_1 < n_2 < n_3 \ (n_1 > 1)$ are multiplicatively dependent then $n_3 \geqslant n_1 + 2n_1^{1/2}$ with finitely many exceptions and find all the exceptional cases.

4 (R. Tijdeman [73]). Let $n_1 < n_2 \ (n_1 \geqslant 4)$ be integers composed of the same primes $p_1, \ldots, p_m$. Prove that

$$n_2 - n_1 > n_1 \log^{-C} n_1$$

where $C = C(p_1, \ldots, p_t)$.

5. Prove the Brauer–Pillai theorem: if $k \geqslant 17$ then there is a set of k consecutive integers none of which is prime to the others, and if $k \leqslant 16$ then this cannot happen.

OPEN PROBLEMS

1 (E. Catalan). Prove that 2^3 and 3^2 are the only consecutive powers.

2 (S. S. Pillai [45]). Prove that for a given m the equation $a^x - b^y = m$ has only finitely many integral solutions $a, \ b \geqslant 2, \ x, \ y \geqslant 2$.

3 (M. Hall, Jr.). Prove that the inequality $0 < |x^3 - y^2| < x^{1/2}$ has only a finite number of integral solutions $x, \ y$.

4 (F. Beukers [79]). Let A be positive and let $p \neq 2$ be a prime not dividing A. Prove that if the equation $x^2 + A = p^n$ has more than one solution then for a certain integer m and $\varepsilon = \pm 1$ we have $p = 4m^2 + \varepsilon$ and $A = 3m^2 + \varepsilon$.

5 (F. Beukers [81b]). Is it possible to find a negative integer A and an odd prime p not dividing A such that the equation $x^2 + A = p^n$ has exactly four integral solutions x, n?

6 (A. Schinzel, R. Tijdeman [76]). Let f be a polynomial over Z with at least three simple roots. Prove that f can represent only finitely many square-full numbers, i.e., that the equation $f(x) = y^2 z^3$ has only finitely many integral solutions x, y, z.

7 (L. Moser). Prove that if $k \geqslant n$ and $n \equiv 1 \pmod 4$ then there is a prime $k < p \equiv 1 \pmod 4$ which divides the product $(n+4)(n+8) \ldots (n+4k)$.

8 (P. Erdős [76b]). Let $f(k)$ be defined as the least integer with the property that for all $n > k$ the product $\prod_{j=1}^{k} (n+j)$ is divisible by a prime exceeding k. Prove that $f(k) \ll \log^c k$ with a certain constant c, or perhaps at least $f(k) \ll k^t$ with $t < 1$.

9 (C. A. Grimm [69]). Prove that if p is a prime, and p' is the smallest prime bigger than p, then $g(p) \geqslant p' - p$, where $g(n)$ is defined in § 3.

10 (Weak Grimm conjecture). Prove that if there is no prime in the interval $\lfloor n+1, n+k \rfloor$ then the product $(n+1)(n+2) \ldots (n+k)$ has at least k distinct prime divisors.

11. Improve the lower and upper bounds for $g(n)$.

12 (E. Jacobsthal [60]). Prove the existence of a constant B with the property that every sequence of at least $B\omega^2(n)$ consecutive integers contains at least one coprime with n.

IV

Waring's
theorem

---

§ 1. HILBERT'S PROOF

1. Although the problem of representing positive integers as sums of squares was considered already by Diophantes and Fermat, the general question of representing positive integers as sums of nth powers was first stated in 1770 by Edward Waring, who on pp. 204–205 of his *Meditationes Algebraicae* (E. Waring [70]) stated that all integers are sums of four squares, nine cubes, nineteen biquadrates and so forth. He did not give any substantiation for this assertion.

It is customary to denote by $g(k)$ the smallest number of non-negative integral kth powers sufficient to represent every positive integer. Thus Waring's conjecture can be interpreted as the statement that $g(k)$ is finite. Similarly by $G(k)$ one denotes the minimal number of such powers sufficient to represent all sufficiently large integers. Of course to prove Waring's conjecture it is enough to show that for all k the number $G(k)$ exists.

The first result in this direction was obtained by J. L. Lagrange [70], who proved the four squares theorem, confirming thus an old conjecture going back to C. G. Bachet and P. Fermat:

THEOREM 4.1. *Every positive integer is a sum of at most four squares of integers.*

(There are many proofs of this result; we shall give a simple one, found by A. Brauer and T. L. Reynolds [51] and based on Minkowski's convex body theorem.)

Proof. We start with two easy lemmas.

LEMMA 4.1. *If $m_1, \ldots, m_k$ are positive integers and $n > k$, then for any system $L_1(X_1, \ldots, X_n), \ldots, L_k(X_1, \ldots, X_n)$ of linear forms with integral coefficients the system of congruences*

(4.1) $$L_j(X_1, \ldots, X_n) \equiv 0 \pmod{m_j} \quad (j = 1, 2, \ldots, k)$$

has a solution in which not all X_i's vanish and which satisfies

(4.2) $|X_i| \leqslant (m_1 \dots m_k)^{1/n}$ $(i = 1, \dots, n)$.

Proof. Let Λ be the set of all those points $\langle X_1, \dots, X_n \rangle$ with integral coordinates which satisfy (4.1). One immediately sees that Λ is a lattice and its determinant does not exceed $m_1 \dots m_k$. Since the set of all points $(X_1, \dots, X_n)$ with real coordinates which satisfy (4.2) is compact, convex, and symmetrical about the origin, and its volume equals $2^n m_1 \dots m_k$, the application of Minkowski's theorem (Theorem A.5) gives the required assertion. □

LEMMA 4.2. *If p is a given odd prime, then one can find a multiple pm of it which can be written in the form*

$$pm = 1 + x^2 + y^2$$

with certain integers x, y and satisfies $0 < pm < p^2$.

Proof. The numbers $0^2, 1^2, \dots, ((p-1)/2)^2$ are pairwise incongruent $(\operatorname{mod} p)$ and the same applies to the numbers

$$-1, \; -1-1^2, \; -1-2^2, \dots, \; -1-((p-1)/2)^2.$$

As we have together more than p integers, at least two of them must be congruent $(\operatorname{mod} p)$; thus we can find x, y not exceeding $(p-1)/2$ and such that

$$x^2 \equiv -1 - y^2 \, (\operatorname{mod} p);$$

since $1 + x^2 + y^2$ is positive and does not exceed p^2 our assertion follows. □

Now we can deduce from these lemmas that every prime p is a sum of at most four squares. For $p = 2$ this is trivial, and so we may assume that p is an odd prime. By Lemma 4.2 one can find integers x, y such that the equality

$$pm = 1 + x^2 + y^2$$

holds for a certain positive m not exceeding $p-1$.

The system

$$X_1 \equiv xX_2 + yX_3 \, (\operatorname{mod} p),$$

$$X_4 \equiv yX_2 - xX_3 \, (\operatorname{mod} p)$$

has by Lemma 4.1 a solution with $|X_i| \leqslant p^{1/2}$ $(i = 1, 2, 3, 4)$ with not all X_i's being zero. This implies that $X_1^2 + \dots + X_4^2$ is divisible by p, positive and bounded by $3p$, thus $X_1^2 + \dots + X_4^2 = Ap$ where $A = 1, 2,$ or 3. In the case $A = 1$ we are ready. If $A = 2$ then, after renumbering the X_i's if necessary, we may assume that $X_1 - X_2$ and $X_3 - X_4$ are both even, and this leads to

$$p = \left(\frac{X_1+X_2}{2}\right)^2 + \left(\frac{X_1-X_2}{2}\right)^2 + \left(\frac{X_3+X_4}{2}\right)^2 + \left(\frac{X_3-X_4}{2}\right)^2.$$

Finally, if $C = 3$, then we may assume that X_1 is divisible by 3 (if none of the X_i's is divisible by 3, then $0 \equiv X_1^2 + \ldots + X_4^2 \equiv 1 \pmod{3}$) and moreover, changing if necessary the signs of X_2, X_3, X_4, that these numbers are congruent (mod 3). This leads to

$$p = \left(\frac{X_2+X_3+X_4}{3}\right)^2 + \left(\frac{X_1+X_3-X_4}{3}\right)^2 +$$
$$+ \left(\frac{X_1-X_2+X_4}{3}\right)^2 + \left(\frac{X_1+X_2-X_3}{3}\right)^2.$$

We have thus obtained the representability of every prime as a sum of four squares of integers. However, the representability of any positive integer in this form now follows from Euler's identity

$$(x_1^2 + \ldots + x_4^2)(y_1^2 + \ldots + y_4^2)$$
$$= (x_1 y_1 + x_2 y_2 + x_3 y_3 + x_4 y_4)^2 + (x_1 y_2 - x_2 y_1 + x_3 y_4 - x_4 y_3)^2 +$$
$$+ (x_1 y_3 - x_3 y_1 + x_4 y_2 - x_2 y_4)^2 + (x_1 y_4 - x_4 y_1 + x_2 y_3 - x_3 y_2)^2. \quad \square$$

One cannot replace in this theorem four summands by three since no number congruent to $7 \pmod 8$ can be equal to a sum of three integral squares, thus $g(2) = 4$.

The three squares theorem of A. M. Legendre [98], which we shall now prove, gives a necessary and sufficient condition for a positive integer to be a sum of three squares.

PROPOSITION 4.1. *A positive integer N can be written as a sum of three integral squares if and only if N does not have the form $4^a M$ with $M \equiv 7 \pmod 8$.*

Proof. The necessity of this condition for odd N is proved immediately by reducing (mod 8) the equality $N = x^2 + y^2 + z^2$, and if $N = 4^a M$ with $a > 0$ and $M \equiv 7 \pmod 8$ is a sum of three squares then they must all be even, and so $N/4$ is again of this form. In this way we arrive at a representation of M as a sum of three squares, which, as we have seen, is impossible.

The proof of the sufficiency will be based on the fact that every positive definite ternary quadratic form $f = \sum a_{ij} x_i x_j$ $(a_{ij} = a_{ji} \in Z)$ of discriminant $\det(a_{ij}) = 1$ is equivalent (over the rational integers) to the form $x^2 + y^2 + z^2$. (See Proposition A.5.) In view of this one has only to show that any number N not of the form $4^a M$ with $M \equiv 7 \pmod 8$ is represented by such a form. We need a simple fact which further reduces our problem:

If N is a positive integer and there exists a positive number D such that
$-D$ *is a quadratic residue* $(\mathrm{mod}\,(DN-1))$, *then N is a sum of three integral squares.*

Let u, z be integers satisfying

$$-D = u^2 - z(DN - 1),$$

which exist by our assumptions. Note that z must be positive, and consider the form

$$zx_1^2 + 2ux_1 x_2 + (DN - 1)x_2^2 + 2x_1 x_3 + Nx_3^2.$$

It clearly has a unit discriminant, represents N, and looking at the principal minors we find that it is positive definite.

The remainder is easy. If $N \equiv 2 \,(\mathrm{mod}\,4)$ and p is any prime congruent to $N - 1 \,(\mathrm{mod}\,4N)$, then $D = (p + 1)/N$ satisfies the assumptions stated above. Similarly, for $N \equiv 1 \,(\mathrm{mod}\,4)$ choose a prime $p \equiv (3N - 1)/2 \,(\mathrm{mod}\,4N)$ and for $N \equiv 3 \,(\mathrm{mod}\,8)$ choose $p \equiv (N - 1)/2 \,(\mathrm{mod}\,4N)$, in both cases putting $D = (1 + 2p)/N$. A simple calculation of the relevant quadratic residue symbols shows that the assumptions of the lemma are satisfied. This proves that every number not divisible by 4 and incongruent to $7 \,(\mathrm{mod}\,8)$ is a sum of three integral squares. To conclude the proof observe that every number divisible by 4 and not of the form $4^a(8k + 7)$ can be written in the form $4^a M$ where M is not divisible by 4 and incongruent to $7 \,(\mathrm{mod}\,8)$; thus, by the previous argument, M is a sum of three squares and the same follows for $4^a M$.

2. The proof of Theorem 4.1 was based on Euler's identity, which expresses the fact that the quaternion norm is multiplicative. Using suitable identities, one can show that for certain integers k every positive integer is a sum of a bounded number of kth powers. We shall illustrate this by the following result, proved by J. Liouville (see V. A. Lebesgue [59]).

PROPOSITION 4.2. *Every positive integer is a sum of at most 53 biquadrates, i.e.,* $g(4) \leqslant 53$.

Proof. We start with an identity which may be checked without difficulty, provided one has enough patience:

$$6(x_1^2 + x_2^2 + x_3^2 + x_4^2)^2 = \sum_{1 \leqslant i < j \leqslant 4} (x_i + x_j)^4 + \sum_{1 \leqslant i < j \leqslant 4} (x_i - x_j)^4.$$

This identity in conjunction with Theorem 4.1 implies that every integer of the form $6n^2$ is a sum of at most 12 biquadrates, and so, using that theorem again, we obtain for every integer N the representation of $6N$ as a sum of 48 biquadrates. Finally, if N is any given positive integer, we may write $N = 6q + r$ with $r \in 0, 1, 2, 3, 4, 5$ and positive integral q, and since every integer in $[0, 5]$ is a sum of at most 5 fourth powers we conclude that N is a sum of at most 53 such powers. $\square$

An analogous result for cubes is more difficult, but the result obtained has the remarkable property that it cannot be improved.

THEOREM 4.2 (A. Wieferich [09a]). *Every positive integer is a sum of at most nine cubes of positive integers and there are integers which are not sums of at most eight such cubes. In other words* $g(3) = 9$.

Proof. The second part is very easy. In fact, the numbers 23 and 239 cannot be represented as sums of less than 9 cubes of positive integers.

The proof of the first part, however, is more complicated and will be based on Proposition 4.1 and the identity

$$(4.3) \qquad \sum_{i=1}^{3} \left((y+x_i)^3 + (y-x_i)^3\right) = y\left(6y^2 + 6(x_1^2 + x_2^2 + x_3^2)\right)$$

which is easily checked; in view of Proposition 4.1 it immediately implies that every integer N which can be written in the form

$$(4.4) \qquad N = a^3 + b^3 + c^3 + y(6y^2 + 6m)$$

where a, b, c, y are non-negative integers and m is a positive integer not of the form $4^a(8b+7)$, is a sum of at most nine positive integral cubes.

Now we show that this indeed happens for every integer $N \geqslant 8^{10} = 1\,073\,741\,824$. Let N be such an integer and let

$$8^{3k+1} < N \leqslant 8^{3(k+1)+1}$$

(thus $k \geqslant 3$). Define n by

$$N - (n+1)^3 < 8^{3k+1} \leqslant N - n^3$$

and observe that

$$8 \cdot 8^{3k} \leqslant N - n^3 < N - (n-1)^3 < 11 \cdot 8^{3k}.$$

One of the numbers $N - n^3$, $N - (n-1)^3$ is odd; let us call it X and let $a^3 = N - X$. If $0 < b < 8^k$ is a solution of $b^3 \equiv X \pmod{8^k}$ then we may write $X - b^3 = q \cdot 8^k$. It follows that

$$N = a^3 + b^3 + q \cdot 8^k$$

and in view of $7 \cdot 8^{3k} < X - b^3 < 11 \cdot 8^{3k}$ we obtain

$$7 \cdot 8^{2k} < q < 11 \cdot 8^{2k};$$

thus finally $q = 6 \cdot 8^{2k} + r$ with an integer r satisfying $8^{2k} < r < 5 \cdot 8^{2k}$. This leads to

$$N = a^3 + b^3 + 8^k(6 \cdot 8^{2k} + r),$$

and it suffices to show that we can write

$$r = c^3 + 6m$$

where c is a non-negative integer and m is a sum of three integral squares. For this purpose note that, if m is not a sum of three integral squares, then from Proposition 4.1 if follows that $6m$ must be congruent to 0, 42, 72 or 90 (mod 96). Now it is a straightforward numerical check that for any r one can find a cube c^3 with $r - c^3 \equiv 0 \pmod 6$ and $r - c^3 \not\equiv 0, 42, 72, 90 \pmod{96}$. In fact it suffices to make the following choice: for $r \equiv 42, 72, 90 \pmod{96}$ take $c = 6$, for $r \equiv 43, 73, 91 \pmod{96}$ take $c = 7$, for $r \equiv 2, 50, 80 \pmod{96}$ take $c = 8$, for $r \equiv 21, 27, 69 \pmod{96}$ take $c = 9$, for $r \equiv 10, 58, 64 \pmod{96}$ take $c = 10$, for $r \equiv 5, 23, 71 \pmod{96}$ take $c = 11$, for $r \equiv 1 \pmod{96}$ take $c = 13$, for $r \equiv 8 \pmod{96}$ take $c = 14$, for $r \equiv 3 \pmod{96}$ take $c = 15$, for $r \equiv 29 \pmod{96}$ take $c = 17$, for $r \equiv 40 \pmod{96}$ take $c = 22$, for $r \equiv 0 \pmod{96}$ take $c = 18$ and for the remaining residues $r \pmod{96}$ take c equal to the smallest non-negative residue of $r \pmod 6$.

This choice shows that we can even assert $0 \leqslant c^3 \leqslant 22^3 = 10\,648$, and so $6m = r - c^3$ will be positive provided $8^{2k} - 22^3$ is positive, and this is indeed true for $k \geqslant 3$. Thus every number $N \geqslant 8^{10}$ is a sum of at most nine positive integral cubes.

To deal with the numbers $N \leqslant 8^{10}$ we shall make use of the fact that all integers in the range $[1, 4 \cdot 10^4]$ are sums of at most nine cubes and the integers in the interval $[10^4, 2 \cdot 10^4]$ need only six cubes. This can be checked in the tables prepared by R. D. v. Sterneck [03]. Believing that this is in fact true, we proceed in the following way: if $4 \cdot 10^4 \leqslant N \leqslant 8^{10}$ then choose n_1 so that

$$N - (n_1 + 1)^3 < 10^4 < N - n_1^3$$

and observe that in view of $n_1 \leqslant N^{1/3}$ we obtain

$$N - (n_1 - 1)^3 - (N - n_1^3) = 3n_1^2 - 3n_1 + 1 < 3N^{2/3};$$

thus

$$10^4 < N - n_1^3 < 10^4 + 3N^{2/3}.$$

Apply the same procedure with $N - n_1^3$ in place of N to obtain an integer n_2 and then do this again with $N - n_1^3 - n_2^3$ in place of N to obtain an integer n_3. If now $M = N - n_1^3 - n_2^3 - n_3^3$, then it follows that

$$10^4 < M < 10^4 + 3(10^4 + 3(10^4 + 3 \cdot 8^{20/3})^{2/3})^{2/3},$$

and this is less than $2 \cdot 10^4$; hence M is a sum of at most six cubes and so N must be a sum of at most nine cubes. $\square$

3. We have already seen that no integer congruent to $7 \pmod 8$ can be a

sum of three squares of integers, and hence Theorem 4.1 cannot be improved even for large integers. The situation in the case of cubes is quite different. E. Landau [09] was the first to show that for large integers eight cubes suffice and later Yu. V. Linnik [43a] was able to reduce this bound to seven. We now give the proof of the seven cube theorem, following G. L. Watson [51], who found a remarkably simple way to deal with the problem.

THEOREM 4.3. *Every sufficiently large integer is a sum of at most seven cubes of positive integers.*

Proof. We first give a rather complicated sufficient condition for the representability of an integer as a sum of six positive integral cubes. It is based on a suitable identity.

LEMMA 4.3. *Let p_1, p_2, p_3 be distinct primes, congruent to $5 \pmod 6$ and such that $p_2 < p_3 < 1.01\, p_2$. If N is an integer satisfying*

$$N \equiv 3p_1 \pmod{6p_1},$$

$$4N \equiv p_2^{18}\, p_1^3 \pmod{p_3^6},$$

$$2N \equiv p_3^{18}\, p_1^3 \pmod{p_2^6}$$

and lying in the interval $(3p_3^{18}\, p_1^3/4,\ p_3^{18}\, p_1^3)$, then N is a sum of six positive integral cubes.

Proof. Denote the number $(4p_3^{18} + 2p_2^{18})\, p_1^3 + 18p_3^6\, p_2^6\, p_1$ by M and note that our assumptions imply that $8N \equiv M \pmod{p_1\, p_2^6\, p_3^6}$ and

$$(4.5) \qquad (4p_3^{18} + 2p_2^{18})\, p_1^3 < 8N < (4p_3^{18} + 8p_2^{18})\, p_1^3.$$

Moreover, one sees without difficulty that $M \equiv 24 \pmod{48}$ and, since we have also $8N \equiv 24 \pmod{48}$ and none of the primes p_1, p_2, p_3 divides 48, the congruence $8N \equiv M \pmod{48\, p_1\, p_2^6\, p_3^6}$ follows. Denoting by u the integer $(8N - M)/48\, p_1\, p_2^6\, p_3^6$, we obtain in view of (4.5)

$$0 < 8u + 3 < p_1^2\, p_2^{12}/p_3^6.$$

By Proposition 4.1 we may write $8u + 3 = x^2 + y^2 + z^2$, where x, y, z are odd and positive integers none of which exceeds $p_1\, p_2^6/p_3^3$; finally note that

$$8N = (2p_2^{18} + 4p_3^{18})\, p_1^3 + 6p_3^6\, p_2^6\, p_1\, (x^2 + y^2 + z^2)$$

$$= (p_1\, p_3^6 + p_2^3\, x)^3 + (p_1\, p_3^6 - p_2^3\, x)^3 + (p_1\, p_3^6 + p_2^3\, y)^3 +$$

$$+ (p_1\, p_3^6 - p_2^3\, y)^3 + (p_1\, p_2^6 + p_3^3\, z)^3 + (p_1\, p_2^6 - p_3^3\, z)^3$$

is, as every polynomial identity, trivially true. As the bases of the cubes appearing here are even and positive, we obtain our assertion. □

Our second lemma is a direct consequence of the Siegel–Walfisz theorem on primes in progressions:

LEMMA 4.4. *If x is a sufficiently large number and $k < \log^{100} x$, then for every l prime to k there is a prime $p \equiv l \pmod k$ in the interval $[x, 1.01x]$.*

Proof. Indeed, the Siegel–Walfisz theorem (see Theorem A.3) shows that under our assumptions we have

$$\pi(x, k, l) = \frac{1}{\varphi(k)} \operatorname{li} x + O\left(x \exp(-C \log^{1/2} x)\right)$$

and hence

$$\pi(1.01x, k, l) - \pi(x, k, l) = \frac{1}{\varphi(k)} \left(\operatorname{li}(1.01x) - \operatorname{li} x\right) + O\left(x \exp\{-C \log^{1/2} x\}\right).$$

But

$$\operatorname{li}(1.01x) - \operatorname{li} x = \int\limits_x^{1.01x} \frac{dt}{\log t} > \frac{0.01x}{\log(1.01x)} \gg \frac{x}{\log x},$$

and so, using $\varphi(k) < k < \log^{100} x$, we obtain

$$x \exp\{-C \log^{1/2} x\} = o(x \log^{-300} x) = o\left(x \varphi^{-1}(k) \log^{-1} x\right),$$

which shows that the difference $\pi(1.01x, k, l) - \pi(x, k, l)$ is positive for sufficiently large x. □

Now let n be a large positive integer. We can find two primes p_2, p_3, both congruent to $5 \pmod 6$, which satisfy $p_2 < p_3 < 1.01p_2$ and neither of which divides n. We may even find such primes in the interval $[2, \log^2 n]$ because there are at most $O(\log n)$ distinct prime factors of n and the interval $[c \log^2 n, \log^2 n]$ contains at least $B(c) \log^2 n / \log \log n$ primes congruent to $5 \pmod 6$ for any positive $c < 1$ with a suitable positive $B(c)$.

Moreover, let m be a solution of the system

$$4n \equiv p_2^{18} m^3 \pmod{p_3^6},$$

$$2n \equiv p_3^{18} m^3 \pmod{p_2^6},$$

which is solvable since in view of $p_2 \equiv p_3 \equiv 5 \pmod 6$ every integer prime to p_2 and p_3 is a cubic residue $\pmod{p_2}$ and $\pmod{p_3}$. Lemma 4.4 (applied with $k = 6p_2^6 p_3^6$) now implies the existence of a prime p_1 satisfying

$$n^{1/3} p_3^{-6} < p_1 < 1.01 n^{1/3} p_3^{-6},$$

$$p_1 \equiv 5 \pmod 6 \quad \text{and} \quad p_1 \equiv m \pmod{p_2^6 p_3^6}$$

at least for sufficiently large n.

Having done all this, we may now conclude the proof of the theorem. Let t be a positive integer, not exceeding $6p_1 p_2^2 p_3^2$, which satisfies the congruences

$$t^3 \equiv n - 3p_1 \pmod{6p_1},$$

$$t \equiv 0 \pmod{p_2^2 p_3^2}.$$

(The first of these congruences is solvable since 2, 3 and p_1 are not congruent to unity (mod 3).)

A straightforward check reveals that the number $N = n - t^3$ satisfies the assumptions of Lemma 4.3, and so it is a sum of six positive integral cubes, and the representability of $n = N + t^3$ as a sum of at most seven positive integral cubes follows. □

4. Now we turn to the general case and present a proof of the Waring conjecture given by D. Hilbert [09a], [09b], in which we include later simplifications due to F. Hausdorff [09], E. Stridsberg [12], E. Schmidt [13] and W. J. Ellison [71].

THEOREM 4.4. *To every integer* $k \geqslant 1$ *there corresponds an integer* $C = C(k)$ *such that every positive integer can be written as a sum of at most* C *positive integral k-th powers.*

Proof. We shall actually prove an assertion which seems weaker than our theorem; however, the two are easily shown to be equivalent:

THEOREM 4.5. *To every integer* $k \geqslant 1$ *there correspond a positive integer* $M = M(k)$ *and positive rational numbers* $c_1, \ldots, c_M$ *such that every sufficiently large integer* n *can be written in the form*

$$n = \sum_{j=1}^{M} c_j n_j^k$$

with suitable non-negative integers $n_1, \ldots, n_M$.

Clearly Theorem 4.5 follows from Theorem 4.4 and we shall now prove the converse implication:

LEMMA 4.5 (A. Hurwitz [08]). *If Theorem 4.5 is true for an integer* k, *then Theorem 4.4 is also true for the same* k.

Proof. If m is the least common denominator of the numbers $c_1, c_2, \ldots, c_M$, then Theorem 4.5 implies that every sufficiently large multiple of m is a sum of at most $\sum_{j=1}^{M} mc_j$ kth powers. Now, if $B = B(k)$ denotes the minimal number of kth powers needed to represent all numbers of the interval $[1, m-1]$, then every sufficiently large integer will be the sum of at most $B + \sum_{j=1}^{M} mc_j$ kth powers; this finishes the proof since those integers which are not covered by the above argument form a finite set and we can represent them as sums of a bounded number of positive kth powers. □

The next lemma was stated in the special case $x_5 = 0$ by A. Hurwitz [08], who recognized its importance for the problem of Waring but could not find a proof of it except for $k = 4$. (In the case $k = 2$ Hurwitz's identity appears in the proof of Proposition 4.2, and for $k = 3$ it was proved by A. Fleck [06].)

In the general case it was proved in a rather complicated way by D. Hilbert [09a], [09b]. Our proof is based on Schmidt [13].

LEMMA 4.6. *For every positive integer k one can find a positive integer N, positive rational numbers $b_0, b_1, \ldots, b_N$ and integers a_{ij} $(i = 1, 2, \ldots, N; j = 1, 2, \ldots, 5)$ such that the following identity holds:*

$$(x_1^2 + \ldots + x_5^2)^k = \sum_{i=0}^{N} b_i \left(\sum_{j=1}^{5} a_{ij} x_j \right)^{2k}.$$

Proof. Consider the linear space over the reals whose elements are homogeneous forms of degree $2k$ in five variables and real coefficients. Its dimension N equals the number of representations of the number $2k$ as a sum of at most five positive integers.

Denote by A the subset of this space consisting of all forms $\left(\sum_{i=1}^{5} \alpha_i x_i \right)^{2k}$ with rational $\alpha_1, \ldots, \alpha_5$ and let $\mathrm{Conv}(A)$ be its convex hull. Observe that it suffices to show that for a certain positive rational number r

(4.6) $r(x_1^2 + \ldots + x_5^2)^k \in \mathrm{Conv}(A).$

Indeed, if this is true, then using Carathéodory's theorem (Theorem A.6') we may write

$$r(x_1^2 + \ldots + x_5^2)^k = \sum_{i=0}^{N} \beta_i \left(\sum_{j=1}^{5} \gamma_{ij} x_j \right)^{2k}$$

with suitable non-negative reals β_i and rational γ_{ij}. If P is the least common denominator of the numbers γ_{ij}, then $\delta_{ij} = P\gamma_{ij}$ are integral and we get

$$(x_1^2 + \ldots + x_5^2)^k = \sum_{i=0}^{N} \beta_i / rP^2 \left(\sum_{j=1}^{5} \delta_{ij} x_j \right)^{2k}.$$

To prove (4.6) denote, for given $x_1, \ldots, x_5$, by $g(x_1, \ldots, x_5)$ the gravity centre of the set

$$\{(\lambda_1 x_1 + \ldots + \lambda_5 x_5)^{2k} : \langle \lambda_1, \ldots, \lambda_5 \rangle \in S\},$$

where S denotes the unit sphere, i.e.,

$$g(x_1, \ldots, x_5) = \left(\int_S (\lambda_1 x_1 + \ldots + \lambda_5 x_5)^{2k} d\lambda_1 \ldots d\lambda_5 \right) \left(\int_S d\lambda_1 \ldots d\lambda_5 \right)^{-1}.$$

If $[b_{ij}]$ is a five-dimensional orthogonal matrix such that $b_{1j} = x_j(x_1^2 + \ldots + x_5^2)^{-1/2}$ holds for $j = 1, 2, \ldots, 5$, then putting $t_i = \sum_{j=1}^{5} b_{ij} \lambda_j$ we obtain

$$g(x_1, \ldots, x_5) = c(x_1^2 + \ldots + x_5^2)^k$$

with a certain positive c because our transformation preserves the unit sphere. Finally, taking for r a rational number from the interval $(0, c)$, we get

$$r(x_1^2 + \ldots + x_5^2)^k = \frac{r}{c} g(x_1, \ldots, x_5) \in \text{Conv}(A)$$

because $\text{Conv}(A)$ is symmetrical about the origin. This proves (4.6) and the lemma follows. □

COROLLARY 1. *If k and y are given positive integers, then we can find integers $a_0, \ldots, a_N$ (N being as in the lemma), positive rationals $b_0, \ldots, b_N$ which depend only on k, and integers $c_0, \ldots, c_N$ depending on k and y such that for all x we have the identity*

$$(x^2 + y)^k = \sum_{i=0}^{N} b_i (a_i x + c_i)^{2k}.$$

Proof. It suffices to put in the lemma $x_1 = x$ and $x_2^2 + \ldots + x_5^2 = y$, which is possible in view of Theorem 4.1. □

COROLLARY 2. *If Theorem 4.5 is true for a certain integer $k = m$, then it is also true for $k = 2m$.*

Proof. Put in the previous corollary $k = m$ and $x = 0$. □

To formulate the next corollary we need a simplified notation, which was introduced by E. Stridsberg. If m is a given positive integer, then we shall denote by $\Sigma(m)$ every positive integer which can be written in the form $u_1 n_1^m + \ldots + u_M n_M^m$ where M is a positive integer depending only on m and the u_i's are positive rational numbers also depending only on m. Thus Theorem 4.5 asserts that every positive integer is a $\Sigma(m)$. (Formally one should make explicit the dependence of the symbol $\Sigma(m)$ on the choice of M and the u_i's, but this is exactly what we want to avoid.)

Now we formulate the last corollary:

COROLLARY 3. *If $1 \leqslant r < m$ are integers, then one can find integers $B_i^{(r)} \geqslant 2$ such that*

$$B_i^{(r)} x^{2i} (x^2 + y)^{m-i} = \Sigma(m)$$

for all positive integral x and y.

Proof. Put $k = m + r$ in Corollary 1 and differentiate the resulting equality $2r$ times with respect to x. □

To prove the theorem we use induction on k. For $k = 2$ our assertion follows from Theorem 4.1. Assume that the theorem holds for all integers $< m$. By Corollary 2 it holds also for all even integers $< 2m$. Using this, we shall now deduce two auxiliary results to be used in the main part of the proof (see Lemma 4.8 below).

LEMMA 4.7. *Let $1 \leqslant r < m$ be given integers and let $B_i^{(r)}$ be as in Corollary*

3. *If $1 \leqslant n < T$ are given integers, then there exist integers $x_1, \ldots, x_h$ depending on n and an integer $h = h(m)$ such that*

$$hB_0^{(r)} T^m + \sum_{k=1}^{r-1} B_k^{(r)} \Big(\sum_{i=1}^{h} x_i^{2k} \Big) T^{m-k} + B_r^{(r)} n T^{m-r} = \Sigma(m).$$

Proof. By the inductive assumption we may write

$$n = x_1^{2r} + \ldots + x_h^{2r}$$

with a certain $h = h(m)$. Putting $y_i = T - x_i^2$ in Corollary 3 and adding the resulting equalities, we arrive at our assertion.

COROLLARY. *If T is a given sufficiently large positive integer and N_r, for $r = 1, 2, \ldots, m-1$, is an integer from $(0, T)$, then there exist numbers $C_k^{(r)}$ $(r = 1, 2, \ldots, m-1; k = 0, 1, \ldots, r-1)$ such that the inequalities*

$$C_r^{(k)} < T, \qquad C_{r-1}^{(r)} + B_r^{(r)} < T$$

hold and moreover

$$\sum_{k=0}^{r-2} C_k^{(r)} T^{m-k} + (C_{r-1}^{(r)} + B_r^{(r)}) T^{m-r+1} - B_r^{(r)} N_r T^{m-r} = \Sigma(m).$$

Proof. To establish the last assertion put in the lemma $n = T - N_r$ for $r = 1, 2, \ldots, m-1$. This gives the required equality with

$$C_k^{(r)} = B_k^{(r)} (x_{1r}^{2k} + \ldots + x_{hr}^{2k})$$

where $T - N_r = x_{1r}^{2r} + \ldots + x_{hr}^{2r}$. Taking T bigger than

$$\max_{k,r} \{(1+h)((B_k^{(r)})^{2(m-1)})/(B_k^{(r)} - 1)\},$$

we obtain, writing B for $B_k^{(r)}$,

$$C_k^{(r)} < B\Big(1 + \sum_{i=1}^{h} x_{ir}^{2(m-1)}\Big) = B\Big(1 + \sum_{x_{ir} \leqslant B} x_{ir}^{2(m-1)}\Big) + B \sum_{x_{ir} > B} x_{ir}^{2(m-1)}$$

$$\leqslant (1+h) B^{2m-1} + (1/B) \sum_{x_{ir} > B} x_{ir}^{2(m-1)} (B/x_{ir})^2$$

$$\leqslant (1+h) B^{2m-1} + (1/B) \sum_{i=1}^{h} x_{ir}^{2(m-1)}$$

$$< (1+h) B^{2m-1} + T/B \leqslant \frac{B-1}{B} T + T/B = T.$$

This proves the first inequality. To obtain the second write

$$C_{r-1}^{(r)} + B_r^{(r)} = B_{r-1}^{(r)} \sum_{i=1}^{h} x_{ir}^{2(r-1)} + B_r^{(r)} \leqslant \max(B_{r-1}^{(r)}, B_r^{(r)}) \Big(1 + \sum_{i=1}^{h} x_{ir}^{2(m-1)}\Big);$$

replacing in the previous argument $B_k^{(r)}$ by $\max(B_{r-1}^{(r)}, B_r^{(r)})$ we obtain our assertion for sufficiently large T. $\square$

Now we may make the principal step of the proof, stated in the following lemma:

LEMMA 4.8. *If q is a non-negative integer not exceeding m then there exist an integer $T_0 = T_0(m)$ and an integer A_q such that for T exceeding T_0 and arbitrary integers $b_{m-1}, b_{m-2}, \ldots, b_{m-q} \in [-T, T)$ we have*

$$A_q T^m + \sum_{i=m-q}^{m-1} b_i T^i = \Sigma(m).$$

Proof. We proceed by induction on q, the case $q = 0$ being clearly true with $A_0 = 1$. Assume the truth of the lemma for all integers less than q.

Let T be a large integer and R an integer in $[-T, T)$. Lemma 4.7 and its corollary imply that if R is non-zero then one can find integers $a_1, \ldots, a_{q-1}$ satisfying $0 < a_i < T$ for $i = 1, 2, \ldots, q-1$ and also positive integers a_0, b, depending only on q and m and such that

(4.7) $\qquad a_0 T^m + a_1 T^{m-1} + \ldots + a_{q-1} T^{m-q+1} + bR T^{m-q} = \Sigma(m).$

The inductive assumption shows that (4.7) is true also for $R = 0$.

Denote by λ the minimal positive integer satisfying $\lambda b \geqslant A_{q-1} + a_0$. Then $\lambda b - A_{q-1} - a_0$ does not exceed a constant depending only on m, since it is bounded by b. This shows that

$$(\lambda b - A_{q-1} - a_0) T^m = \Sigma(m).$$

The inductive assumption gives

$$A_{q-1} T^m - \sum_{i=0}^{q-1} a_i T^{m-i} = \Sigma(m),$$

and thus

$$\lambda b T^m - \sum_{i=0}^{q-1} a_i T^{m-i} = (\lambda b - A_{q-1} - a_0) T^m + A_{q-1} T^m - \sum_{i=1}^{q-1} a_i T^{m-i} = \Sigma(m),$$

which together with (4.7) leads to $b(\lambda T^m + RT^{m-q}) = \Sigma(m)$ and finally to

(4.8) $\qquad\qquad\qquad\qquad \lambda T^m + RT^{m-q} = \Sigma(m).$

If $b_{m-q}, b_{m-q+1}, \ldots, b_{m-1}$ are given integers in $[-T, T)$, then by the inductive assumption we get

$$A_{q-1} T^m + b_{m-q+1} T^{m-q+1} + \ldots + b_{m-1} T^{m-1} = \Sigma(m)$$

and if we add to it the expression in (4.8) with $R = b_{m-q}$ we arrive at our assertion with $A_q = A_{q-1}$.

COROLLARY. *There exist positive integers A and T_0 which depend only on m*

and are such that if $T \geqslant T_0$ and n is an integer lying-in $(-T^{m-1}, T^{m-1})$ then $AT^m + nT = \Sigma(m)$. $\square$

Now we can complete the proof of the theorem. Let A and T_0 be the positive integers whose existence is asserted in the last corollary and let N be a sufficiently large integer. Moreover, let T be the largest integer satisfying $N \geqslant A((T+1)^m + T^m)$.

If N was taken sufficiently large, T exceeds T_0 and
$$0 \leqslant r = N - A((T+1)^m + T^m) \leqslant T^m.$$

Let x, y be solutions of $r = x(1+T) - yT$, about which we may assume that $0 \leqslant x \leqslant T-1$ and $|y| < T^{m-1}$. In view of the equality
$$N = A(T+1)^m + x(1+T) + AT^m - yT$$

it is sufficient to show that the numbers $A(T+1)^m + x(1+T)$ and $AT^m - yT$ are both of the form $\Sigma(m)$; indeed this is guaranteed by the corollary to the previous lemma. $\square$

Notes and comments

1. It seems that the four squares theorem (our Theorem 4.1) was first conjectured by C. G. Bachet in 1621 in his comments in an edition of Diophantes. (Although it is rather difficult to find this book, its essential points can be found in an edition of Fermat's works (P. Fermat [70]).) Bachet notes in it that Diophantes apparently assumed the truth of this theorem and stated that he himself had verified it for all integers up to 325. Fermat claimed to have found a proof of it; however, no indication of that proof appears in his works. The first proof was given by J. L. Lagrange [70]. He made use of some ideas from an earlier paper of L. Euler [54], in particular of his identity, which is used also in the proof presented in this book.

C. F. Gauss [01] (art. 293) deduced Theorem 4.1 from the three squares theorem. Of the many other proofs let us quote only a few classical ones: L. Euler [73] (note that earlier Euler [54] showed that every positive integer is a sum of four squares of rational numbers), C. G. J. Jacobi [28], [29], [34] (who also proved that the number of representations of $n = 2^a b$ with b odd as a sum of four squares equals $8\sigma(n)$ if $a = 0$ and $24\sigma(b)$ otherwise), C. Hermite [53] (whose proof used Dirichlet's prime number theorem and the theory of the minima of quadratic forms), P. G. Dirichlet [56] (who modified Jacobi's approach) and J. J. Sylvester [80b] (who based his proof on Lemma 4.2). More recently two geometrical proofs of Theorem 4.1 were given by J. H. Grace [27] and J. D. Dixon [64], L. E. Dickson [24a] availed himself of the theory of quaternions and D. Barbilian [46] deduced the four squares theorem from Wedderburn's theorem concerning the commutativity of finite division rings. The proof presented in this book is that of A. Brauer, T. L. Reynolds [51].

2. Proposition 4.1 was first proved by A. M. Legendre [98] and other proofs of it were supplied by C. F. Gauss [01] (art. 291) (a variant of Gauss's proof is given in J. W. S. Cassels [78]) and P. G. Dirichlet [50]. The proof given in this book is that of Dirichlet.

In J. V. Uspensky, M. A. Heaslett [39] we find an elementary proof based on algebraic identities. N. C. Ankeny [57], L. J. Mordell [58] and J. Wójcik [71] also proved the three squares theorem. L. J. Risman [74] noted that it is equivalent to the theorem proved by B. Fein, B. Gordon, J. H. Smith [71] about the representation of -1 as a sum of two squares in a quadratic number field. For an elementary proof see A. R. Rajwade [76].

C. F. Gauss [01] (art. 291, 292) expressed the number of representations of a given integer as a sum of three squares in terms of class numbers of quadratic forms. (Cf. also L. Kronecker [60], [83] and A. Weil [74] for a fresh exposition.) H. Maass [38], P. T. Bateman [51] and T. Estermann [59] used analytical methods to find this number.

Proposition 4.1 immediately implies that if $F(x)$ denotes the number of positive integers not exceeding x which are sums of at most three integral squares then $F(x) = (5/6 + o(1))x$. The error term $R(x) = F(x) - (5/6)x$ is $O(\log x)$ and this cannot be improved. In fact, M. C. Chakrabarti [40] and H. Gupta [41] proved that

$$\limsup R(x)/\log x = 1/8 \quad \text{and} \quad \liminf R(x)/\log x = 0.$$

There are only finitely many positive integers not divisible by 4 which are sums of three non-negative integral squares, but not sums of three positive integral squares. This was shown by E. Grosswald, A. Calloway, J. Calloway [59] and A. Schinzel [59] (cf. also L. J. Mordell [60b], H. P. Baltes, P. K. J. Draxl, E. R. Hilf [74]). It is conjectured that these integers are 1, 2, 5, 10, 13, 25, 37, 58, 85 and 130 and it is known that there can be at most one more and none below $5 \cdot 10^{10}$ (P. J. Weinberger [73], cf. A. Schinzel [59]). There is a close connection between these numbers and *idoneal numbers* studied in 1778 by L. Euler [95] (see J. Steinig [66] for a historical account) which are now usually defined as those positive integers N for which in every genus of positive definite binary quadratic forms of discriminant $-4N$ there is a single class (cf. Chapter V). In fact the set of those numbers coincides with the set of idoneal numbers which do not have a prime factor congruent to $3 \pmod 4$.

3. Proposition 4.2, which gives a bound for $g(4)$, was improved several times. S. Réalis [78] got $g(4) \leqslant 47$, É. Lucas [78a] reduced this bound to 45 and then (É. Lucas [78b]) observed that the use of Proposition 4.1 in Liouville's argument leads to $g(4) \leqslant 41$. The next steps were made by A. Fleck [06], who obtained 39, E. Landau [07] with 38 and A. Wieferich [09b], who arrived at 37, improving upon Landau's proof. W. S. Baer [13a] showed that for $n \equiv 1 \pmod{48}$ and $n \equiv 33 \pmod{48}$ as few as 34 biquadrates suffice, and then L. E. Dickson [33] obtained $g(4) \leqslant 35$, using the tables of decomposition into biquadrates prepared by C. A. Bretschneider [53] and extended by E. Chandler [33] (they covered the range $1 \leqslant n \leqslant 28\,561$) and his asymptotic results (see § 3). The next step was only made almost forty years later, when F. Dress [71a] reduced the bound first to 34 and then (F. Dress [73]) to 30. This was superseded by J. J. Chen [74] with 27 and later by H. E. Thomas [74], who did a great deal of computing to prove $g(4) \leqslant 22$. (In his Ph.D. thesis he had $g(4) \leqslant 23$.) The best known result is due to R. Balasubramanian [79], who holds the record with 21.

On the other hand, it is known that the number 79 needs nineteen biquadrates and that for $n \geqslant 10^{1409}$ nineteen such powers suffice. (H. E. Thomas [74]. The previous bound was due to F. C. Auluck [40], viz. $n \geqslant 10^{10^{88 \cdot 39}}$.) This makes the conjecture $g(4) = 19$ highly plausible.

For sufficiently large integers the situation looks better, since the value $G(4)$ is known. After previous bounds obtained by G. H. Hardy, J. E. Littlewood [21] ($G(4) \leqslant 21$) and H. Davenport, H. Heilbronn [36], T. Estermann [36] (who independently proved $G(4) \leqslant 17$), H. Davenport [39c] got $G(4) \leqslant 16$, and since A. Kempner [12] (by noting that the numbers $16^m \cdot 31$ ($m = 1, 2, \ldots$) need at least 16 biquadrates) had already established $G(4) \geqslant 16$ the equality $G(4) = 16$ resulted.

G. H. Hardy, J. E. Littlewood [25] showed that almost all integers are sums of at most 15 biquadrates and H. Davenport [39c] proved the existence of a set of positive density for which as few as 14 biquadrates suffice. This set consists of all sufficiently large integers not congruent to 0 or 15 (mod 16) and so its density equals 7/8.

R. D. James [38] showed that all positive rationals can be written as sums of at most 16 biquadrates of rational numbers.

4. Theorem 4.2 was proved by A. Wieferich [09a], whose proof unfortunately omitted certain cases. The omissions were noticed by P. Bachmann [10] (p. 344), and A. Kempner [12] supplied the missing argument. The proof given in the main text is a modification of Wieferich's argument due to B. Scholz [55]. As pointed out by E. Herzog [38], the last step of the proof can be replaced by a less numerical argument; however, this would not shorten it.

Previously E. Maillet [95] proved $g(3) \leqslant 17$ and A. Fleck [06] reduced this bound to 13.

Tables giving decompositions into cubes were provided by E. Waring [70] for integers $n \leqslant 3000$, C. G. J. Jacobi [51] for $n \leqslant 12000$ and R. D. v. Sterneck [03] for $n \leqslant 40000$. They imply that for $240 \leqslant n \leqslant 454$ eight, for $n \in [455, 8042]$ seven and for $n \in [8043, 40000]$ six cubes are sufficient. Jacobi conjectured that for sufficiently large n five cubes will be sufficient, i.e., $G(3) \leqslant 5$, but this is still unproved. (A numerical investigation of this question was made by A. E. Western [26].) E. Landau [09] proved $G(3) \leqslant 8$

and for other proofs of this see L. K. Hua [35e] and G. L. Watson [53].
L. E. Dickson [39] showed that eight cubes suffice for all integers except 23
and 239. An arithmetic progression of positive integers for which seven cubes
are sufficient was produced by W. S. Baer [13b], and Yu. V. Linnik [43a]
proved the celebrated seven cubes theorem (Theorem 4.2). His proof was
fairly complicated, and later G. L. Watson [51] found a much simpler
approach which we presented above.

(Added in proof: R. J. Cook (Bull. Austral. Math. Soc. 30 (1984), 381–385)
and K. S. McCurley (J. Number Theory 19 (1984), 176–183) effectivized the
proof of Theorem 4.2. McCurley showed that all integers exceeding $e^{e^{14}}$ are
sums of seven cubes.)

H. Davenport [39b] proved that almost all integers are sums of four
cubes (the number of exceptions less than x being $O(x^{29/30+\varepsilon})$ for every
$\varepsilon > 0$). Cf. also G. Szekeres [78]. Previously G. H. Hardy, J. E. Littlewood
[25] had obtained this result for sums of five cubes. Davenport's theorem is
the best possible, since although the precise order of the number $N_3(x)$ of
integers $\leqslant x$ which are sums of three cubes is unknown the numbers $9k \pm 4$
are not such sums. The best lower bound for $N_3(x)$ was given by
H. Davenport [50], who proved $N_3(x) \gg x^{47/54-\varepsilon}$ (for every positive ε),
improving upon previous results of G. H. Hardy and J. E. Littlewood [25]
and his own (H. Davenport [38]), where the exponents were equal to 7/9 and
$13/15 - \varepsilon$ respectively.

(Added in proof: R. C. Vaughan (Bull. London Math. Soc. 17 (1985),
17–20) got $N_3(x) \gg x^{8/9-\varepsilon}$.)

The precise order of magnitude for the number $N_2(x)$ of integers $\leqslant x$
which are sums of two positive cubes was found by C. Hooley [80], who
showed that $N_2(x) = cx^{2/3} + O(x^{5/9+\varepsilon})$ with $c = \Gamma^2(1/3)/12\Gamma(2/3)$. Previously
(C. Hooley [63]) the error term here had been shown to be
$O(x^{2/3} \log\log x (\log x)^{-1/2})$. On the other hand, this error term is $\gg x^{1/3} \log x$
(C. Hooley [80]). The first result in this direction goes back to G. H. Hardy
and J. E. Littlewood [25], who proved $N_2(x) \gg x^{2/3-\varepsilon}$ for every positive ε.
The factor $x^{-\varepsilon}$ was replaced by $\log^{-a} x$ for a certain $a \in (0, 1)$ by S. S. Pillai
[28] and removed completely by P. Erdös and K. Mahler [38] (cf. P. Erdös
[39c]).

Denote by $c_4(n)$ the number of representations of an integer n as a sum
of four non-negative cubes. It is conjectured that $c_4(n)$ is close to $n^{1/3}$ and
the best result towards this conjecture is due to C. Hooley [78], who
obtained $c_4(n) \ll n^{11/18+\varepsilon}$ (for every $\varepsilon > 0$). On the other hand, C. Hooley
[77] showed that $c_4(n) \neq o(n^{1/3} (\log\log n)^{-4})$. S. Chowla [30] considered an
analogous problem for eight cubes and proved that for large n the number of
representations is $\gg n^{2/9}$.

H. W. Richmond [22a], [22b] proved that every positive rational number
is a sum of three positive rational cubes and H. Davenport and E. Landau
[69] showed that in the representation $n = x^3 + y^3 + z^3$ one can obtain the

bound $O(n^2)$ for the denominators of x, y and z. A simple proof of the weaker bound $O(n^{8/3})$ was given by L. J. Mordell [71].

R. E. Dressler, T. Parker [74] showed that 12758 is the largest integer which is not a sum of distinct cubes. The fact that for every k there are only finitely many positive integers which are not sums of distinct kth powers was established by R. Sprague [48b], who also showed (R. Sprague [48a]) that the largest integer which is not a sum of distinct squares equals 128. E. Krubeck [53] generalized Sprague's result to arbitrary polynomials and J. L. Brown Jr. [76] made a further generalization.

5. The first proof of Theorem 4.4 which solved Waring's problem was given by D. Hilbert [09a], [09b]. In its first version he used in the proof of Lemma 4.6 integrals in the 25-dimensional real space and in the second version only quintuple integrals. F. Hausdorff [09] reduced the proof of that lemma to the study of binomial coefficients and E. Stridsberg [10], [12], [17], [19] simplified it further. Cf. also G. Frobenius [12a] and R. Remak [12] for further simplifications. In particular, Remak eliminated the integrals completely.

E. Schmidt [13] resorted in the proof of Lemma 4.6 to the theory of convex bodies, and our proof of that lemma uses his approach. Another proof was given by V. Veselý [33a].

Our proof of Theorem 4.4 is essentially due to E. Stridsberg [12] and follows Hilbert's ideas. We incorporated further simplifications due to W. J. Ellison [71] and the clarifications contained in H. Koch, H. Pieper [76].

F. Dress [71b], [72] found another way of deducing Theorem 4.4 from Hilbert's identity. Hilbert's proof can be used to obtain an effective bound for $g(k)$, and this was done by G. J. Rieger [53], who showed that it leads to the exorbitant bound

$$g(k) \leqslant (2k+1)^{260(k+3)^{3k+8}}.$$

Exercises

1 (E. Lucas [78b]). Use Proposition 4.1 to prove the inequality $g(4) \leqslant 41$.

2 (R. Sprague [48a]). Prove that all integers exceeding 128 can be written as sums of distinct squares.

3 (R. Sprague [48b]). Prove that for every $k \geqslant 2$ all sufficiently large integers are sums of distinct positive kth powers.

4 (E. Krubeck [53]). Prove that if $f(x)$ is any real polynomial of positive degree and positive leading coefficient then every positive number can be written in the form

$$r + f(n_1) + \ldots + f(n_s)$$

where $n_1, \ldots, n_s$ are positive integers with $f(n_1), \ldots, f(n_s)$ distinct and r is bounded by a constant depending only on f.

5 (A. Hurwitz [07], O. Fraser, B. Gordon [69]). Prove that the equation $n^2 = x^2 + y^2 + z^2$ is solvable in positive integers x, y, z if and only if $n \neq 2^k$ and $n \neq 5 \cdot 2^k$, $k = 0, 1, 2, \ldots$

6 (B. Fein, B. Gordon, J. H. Smith [71], L. J. Risman [74], A. R. Rajwade [76]). Prove that

an integer N is a sum of three integral squares if and only if -1 is a sum of two squares in the field $Q(\sqrt{-N})$.

7 (H. W. Richmond [22a], [22b]). Show that every positive rational number can be written as a sum of at most three cubes of positive rationals.

8 (A. Hurwitz [07]). Prove that the integers which are sums of at most three non-negative cubes form a set of density less than 7/9.

9 (A. Kempner [12]). Prove that there are infinitely many positive integers congruent to unity (mod 9) which are not sums of at most three positive cubes.

10 (Ibidem). Prove that if k is a power of two then there are infinitely many positive integers which are not sums of at most $4k-1$ positive kth powers.

§2. BOUNDS FOR $G(k)$

1. Hilbert's proof of the Waring conjecture presented in the foregoing section does not immediately give any explicit bound for $g(k)$ or $G(k)$, although such a bound can be derived from it, as shown by G. J. Rieger [53]. Unfortunately this bound is very large and roughly equivalent to $\log \log g(k) \leqslant (3+\varepsilon) k \log k$ for arbitrary positive ε and sufficiently large k.

An analytic approach based on the circle method of G. H. Hardy and J. E. Littlewood, developed later by I. M. Vinogradov, leads to much stronger estimates. In this section we shall prove $G(k) \ll k \log k$, which was first obtained by I. M. Vinogradov in 1934. We present a proof due to H. Heilbronn [36], which seems to be the simplest available proof of this bound. However, we shall complicate it by making explicit all the constants occurring in it, so as to pave the way for the proof of the formula for $g(k)$, to which the next section will be devoted. Thus we shall attempt to prove:

THEOREM 4.6. *If $k \geqslant 9$ is an integer then every sufficiently large integer N can be written as a sum of at most*

$$g = 6k \log k + 4k + 3 \left(\log (3 + 2/k)\right) k + 4 \leqslant 6k \log k + 8k + 4$$

k-th powers of positive integers. It suffices here to take $N \geqslant \exp(18k^6)$.

Proof. Let N be a large integer about which we assume $N \geqslant 2^k$. To show that it can be represented as a sum of g kth powers it suffices to prove that the integral

$$(4.9) \qquad J(N) = \int_0^1 T^{4k}(x) R^2(x) S(x) \exp(-2\pi i N x)\, dx$$

is non-zero, where

$$(4.10) \qquad T(x) = \sum_{m^k \leqslant N} \exp(2\pi i m^k x)$$

and $R(x)$, $S(x)$ are defined as follows: denote by U the set of all positive integers which are sums of at most $t = [k \log(3k^2 + 2k)] + 2$ kth powers of positive integers and put

(4.11)
$$R(x) = \sum_{\substack{m \leqslant N/4 \\ m \in U}} \exp(2\pi imx),$$

and finally

(4.12)
$$S(x) = \sum_{\substack{m \leqslant N^{1/k(k+1)}}} \sum_{\substack{n \leqslant \frac{1}{4} N^{1-(1/(k+1))} \\ n \in U}} \exp\{2\pi im^k nx\}.$$

Indeed, the integral $J(N)$ counts the number of solutions of the diophantine equation

$$N = x_1^k + \ldots + x_{4k}^k + u_1 + u_2 + z^k u_3$$

with $0 \leqslant x_i \leqslant N^{1/k}$, $u_i \in U$, $0 \leqslant u_1$, $u_2 \leqslant N/4$, $0 \leqslant u_3 \leqslant \frac{1}{4} N^{1-(1/(k+1))}$, $0 \leqslant z \leqslant N^{1/k(k+1)}$; thus $J(N) \neq 0$ implies that N is a sum of $4k + 3t \leqslant g$ non-negative kth powers.

To investigate the integral $J(N)$ we shall divide the range of integration into the so-called *major* and *minor arcs*. It will turn out later that the contribution of the major arcs is closely connected with a series built from trigonometrical sums involving kth powers; the *singular series*. That is why we shall start with the investigation of this series. This will form the arithmetical part of the proof. By using it we shall be able to obtain a decent lower bound for the real part of the contribution of the major arcs to $J(N)$ and afterwards we shall use a lemma of Vinogradov to get a proper upper bound for the contribution of minor arcs, which will fortunately be of a lower order of magnitude.

We start with the definition of the singular series. Let q be a positive integer and let $(a, q) = 1$. Define

(4.13)
$$S_{a,q} = \sum_{m=1}^{q} \exp(2\pi im^k a/q),$$

for any given integers n and s put

(4.14)
$$A_q = A_q(n, s) = \sum_{\substack{1 \leqslant a \leqslant q \\ (a,q) = 1}} (S_{a,q} q^{-1})^s \exp(-2\pi ina/q),$$

and finally define

(4.15)
$$S = S(s, n, k) = \sum_{q=1}^{\infty} A_q.$$

The series S is called the *singular series for the problem of representing n as a sum of s k-th powers* and it is closely connected with the congruences

(4.16)
$$X_1^k + \ldots + X_s^k \equiv n \pmod{p^l}$$

(for prime p and $t \geqslant 1$) and thus with the analogue of Waring's problem in p-adic fields (see Lemma 4.9).

To study the convergence of the singular series we have to obtain first an upper bound for the sums $S_{a,q}$. This bound is the subject of the next proposition.

PROPOSITION 4.3. *If* $k \geqslant 3$ *and* $(a, q) = 1$ *then*

$$(4.17) \qquad |S_{a,q}| \leqslant Cq^{1-1/k}$$

where

$$C = C(k) = \exp\left(\pi \left(k^{2k/(k-2)} \log k\right)\right) \leqslant \begin{cases} \exp\{81k^2\} & (k \geqslant 3), \\ \exp\{3.6k^2\} & (k \geqslant 9). \end{cases}$$

Moreover, if p *is a prime and* $t \geqslant 1$ *then we have*

$$(4.18) \qquad |S_{a,p^t}| \leqslant \begin{cases} kp^{1/2} & if \quad t = 1, \\ p^{t(1-1/k)} & if \quad p \geqslant k^{2k/(k-2)}, \\ kp^{t(1-1/k)} & if \quad p < k^{2k/(k-2)}. \end{cases}$$

Proof. We shall first prove (4.18) for primes and then for all prime powers, and finally we shall deduce (4.17). Although the case of primes is covered by Theorem A.9, we give an independent proof, which is quite simple. Let p be a prime. Since our assertion in the case $p = 2$ is evident, the sum $S_{1,2}$ being zero, we may assume that p is odd. Put $d = (p-1, k)$ and let $\tau_a(\chi)$ be the Gaussian sum associated with a character $\chi \pmod p$. Since

$$\sum_{\substack{\chi \\ \chi^k = 1}} \chi(m) = \begin{cases} d & \text{if } m \text{ is a } k\text{th power residue mod } p, \\ 0 & \text{otherwise} \end{cases}$$

and

$$S_{a,p} - 1 = \frac{1}{d} \sum_r \exp(2\pi i r a / p)$$

where the last sum is taken over all kth power residues $\pmod p$, we obtain

$$(4.19) \qquad S_{a,p} = 1 + \sum_{\substack{\chi \\ \chi^k = 1}} \tau_a(\chi),$$

and by Proposition 2.1 (i), (iii), (iv) we get

$$(4.20) \qquad |S_{a,p}| \leqslant \sum_{\substack{\chi \neq \chi_0 \\ \chi^k = 1}} |\tau_a(\chi)| = (d-1)p^{1/2} \leqslant (k-1)p^{1/2}.$$

This implies the first and the third inequality in (4.18). However, if $p \geqslant k^{2k/(k-2)}$ then (4.20) gives

$$|S_{a,p}| < kp^{1/2} \leqslant p^{(k-2)/2k + 1/2} = p^{1-1/k},$$

and thus the second inequality in (4.18) also holds.

Now let $q = p^t$ be a prime power with $t \geq 2$. We shall distinguish two cases:

(a) $p \nmid k$

and

(b) $p \mid k$.

In the first case observe that every integer m from the interval $[1, p^t]$ can be uniquely written in the form

(4.21) $$m = y + p^{t-1} x$$

with $0 \leq x < p$, $0 \leq y < p^{t-1}$. Since $m^k \equiv y^k + k y^{k-1} p^{t-1} x \pmod{p^t}$ we get

$$S_{a,p^t} = \sum_{y \pmod{p^{t-1}}} \exp\left\{\frac{2\pi i a}{p^t} y^k\right\} \sum_{x \pmod p} \exp\left\{\frac{2\pi i a k x}{p} y^{k-1}\right\}$$

$$= p \sum_{\substack{y(\mod p^{t-1}) \\ p \mid y}} \exp\left\{\frac{2\pi i a}{p^t} y^k\right\} = p \sum_{u \pmod{p^{t-2}}} \exp\left\{\frac{2\pi i a u}{p^t} p^k\right\},$$

and so in case (a) we obtain the formula

(4.22) $$S_{a,p^t} = \begin{cases} p^{t-1} & \text{if} \quad t = 2, 3, \ldots, k, \\ p^{k-1} S_{a,p^{t-k}} & \text{if} \quad t > k. \end{cases}$$

This already implies (4.18) in the case (a). Indeed, if $2 \leq t \leq k$ then (4.22) shows that

$$|S_{a,p^t}| \, p^{-t(1-1/k)} = p^{-1+t/k} \leq 1,$$

the case $t = 1$ was settled earlier, and if $t > k$ then by recurrence we infer from (4.22) that

$$|S_{a,p^t}| \, p^{-t(1-1/k)} = p^{k-1-t+t/k} |S_{a,p^{t-k}}| \leq 1$$

as asserted.

In case (b) define α by $p^\alpha \| k$ and proceed along the same lines as in the previous case but write instead of (4.21)

$$m = y + p^{t-\alpha-1} x$$

with $0 \leq x < p^{1+\alpha}$, $0 \leq y < p^{t-\alpha-1}$. This permits us to write

$$S_{a,p^t} = \sum_{y \pmod{p^{t-\alpha-1}}} \sum_{x \pmod{p^{1+\alpha}}} \exp\left\{\frac{2\pi i a}{p^t}(y + p^{t-\alpha-1} x)^k\right\}$$

$$= \sum_{y \pmod{p^{t-\alpha-1}}} \exp\left\{\frac{2\pi i a}{p^t} y^k\right\} \times$$

$$\times \sum_{x \pmod{p^{1+\alpha}}} \exp\left\{\frac{2\pi i a}{p^{1+\alpha}}\left(k y^{k-1} x + \sum_{r=2}^{k} \binom{k}{r} y^{k-r} p^{(r-1)(t-\alpha-1)} x^r\right)\right\}.$$

If t exceeds k, then for $r = 2, 3, \ldots, k$ we have

(4.23)
$$p^{1+\alpha} \left| \binom{k}{r} p^{(r-1)(t-\alpha-1)}. \right.$$

In fact, if we assume the contrary, then since $\binom{k}{r}$ is for $r = 2, 3, \ldots, k-1$ divisible by at least the $(\alpha - r)$th power of p we get

$$1 + \alpha > \alpha - r + (r-1)(t-\alpha-1)$$

and so

$$2 \leqslant r < 1 + 2/(t-\alpha-2)$$

which in view of $t > k \geqslant p^\alpha \geqslant 2^\alpha$, $\alpha < \log t/\log 2$, leads for $t \geqslant 7$ to $r < 2$, a contradiction. A similar computation in the case $r = k$ leads to a contradiction for $t \geqslant 10$. As $t > k \geqslant p^\alpha$, in the remaining cases we have only finitely many possibilities to check, and a tedious verification leads to (4.23) in all cases. Thus for $t > k$ we obtain

$$S_{a,p^t} = \sum_{y \,(\mathrm{mod}\, p^{t-\alpha-1})} \exp\left\{ \frac{2\pi i a}{p^t} y^k \right\} \sum_{x \,(\mathrm{mod}\, p^{1+\alpha})} \exp\left\{ \frac{2\pi i a}{p^{1+\alpha}} k y^{k-1} x \right\}.$$

As the inner sum vanishes for $p \nmid y$ and equals $p^{1+\alpha}$ otherwise, this leads to

(4.24)
$$S_{a,p^t} = p^{k-1} S_{a,p^{t-k}}.$$

Finally for $t \leqslant k$, we have

$$|S_{a,p^t}| \, p^{-t(1-1/k)} \leqslant p^{t/k} \leqslant p \leqslant k;$$

and thus

(4.25)
$$|S_{a,p^t}| \leqslant k p^{t(1-1/k)}.$$

Since (4.18) holds for primes and from $p \mid k$ we get $p \leqslant k < k^{2k/(k-2)}$, inequalities (4.24) and (4.25) imply (4.18) in our case.

To prove (4.17) it suffices now to observe that if $(q_1, q_2) = 1$ and $(a, q_1 q_2) = 1$ then with suitable a_1, a_2 satisfying $(a_i, q_i) = 1$ for $i = 1, 2$ we have

$$S_{a,q_1 q_2} = S_{a_1,q_1} S_{a_2,q_2}.$$

This, however, is easy because

$$(x_1 q_2 + x_2 q_1)^k \equiv x_1^k q_2^k + x_2^k q_1^k \;(\mathrm{mod}\, q_1 q_2)$$

implies that

$$S_{a,q} = \sum_{x_1 \,(\mathrm{mod}\, q_1)} \sum_{x_2 \,(\mathrm{mod}\, q_2)} \exp\left\{ \frac{2\pi i}{q_1 q_2} a(x_1 q_2 + x_2 q_1)^k \right\}$$

$$= \sum_{x_1 \,(\mathrm{mod}\, q_1)} \exp\left\{ \frac{2\pi i}{q_1} a q_2^{k-1} x_1^k \right\} \sum_{x_2 \,(\mathrm{mod}\, q_2)} \exp\left\{ \frac{2\pi i}{q_2} a q_1^{k-1} x_2^k \right\} = S_{a_1,q_1} \cdot S_{a_2,q_2}$$

with $a_1 = a q_2^{k-1}$ and $a_2 = a q_1^{k-1}$.

The bounds for $C(k)$ immediately follow from $\pi(x) \leqslant 2x/\log x$ and the fact that $k^{2k/(k-2)} = f(k)k^2$, where $f(k) = k^{4/(k-2)}$ decreases for $k \geqslant 3$, $f(3) = 81$ and $f(9) < 3.6$. $\Box$

2. Using the previous proposition we shall now show that for sufficiently large s the singular series converges to a positive sum.

PROPOSITION 4.4. *For $s > 2k$ the singular series converges absolutely and, if $s \geqslant 4k$ and $k \geqslant 9$, then its sum $S(n, k)$ satisfies*

$$S(n, k) \geqslant \lambda_k = \exp(-7.1\, k^3).$$

Proof. For $s > 2k$ Proposition 4.3 implies

$$|A_q| \leqslant C^s q^{1-s/k} \leqslant C^s q^{-3},$$

which shows that the singular series converges absolutely. For any prime p put

$$T(p) = 1 + \sum_{j=1}^{\infty} A_{p^j}$$

and denote by $B_s(n, p^t)$ the number of solutions of the congruence (4.16). The next lemma gives an interpretation of $T(p)$ in terms of $B_s(n, p^t)$.

LEMMA 4.9. (i) A_q *is a multiplicative function of q.*
(ii) *For $s \geqslant 4k$ we have $S(n, k) = \prod_p T(p)$.*

(iii) *For any $t \geqslant 1$ and any prime p we have*

$$1 + \sum_{j=1}^{t} A_{p^j} = B_s(n, p^t)\, p^{-t(s-1)}.$$

(iv) *For any prime p we have*

$$T(p) = \lim_{t \to \infty} B_s(n, p^t)\, p^{-t(s-1)}.$$

Proof. (i) If $(q_1, q_2) = 1$ then

$$A_{q_1} A_{q_2} = \sum_{\substack{1 \leqslant a_1 \leqslant q_1 \\ (a_1, q_1) = 1}} \sum_{\substack{1 \leqslant a_2 \leqslant q_2 \\ (a_2, q_2) = 1}} (S_{a_1, q_1} S_{a_2, q_2}\, q_1^{-1} q_2^{-1})^s \exp\left\{ -2\pi i n \left(\frac{a_1}{q_1} + \frac{a_2}{q_2} \right) \right\}$$

but a direct computation shows

$$S_{a_1, q_2} \cdot S_{a_2, q_2} = S_{a_1 q_2 + a_2 q_1, q_1 q_2}$$

and so it is sufficient to observe that if for $i = 1, 2$ a_i runs over all restricted residue classes $(\mathrm{mod}\, q_1)$ and $(\mathrm{mod}\, q_2)$ respectively, then $a_1 q_2 + a_2 q_1$ runs over all such classes $(\mathrm{mod}\, q_1 q_2)$.

Part (ii) follows directly from (i), and since (iv) is a consequence of (iii) it remains to establish (iii). To do this write

$$A_{p^j} = p^{-js} \sum_{\substack{1 \leqslant a \leqslant p^j \\ p \nmid a}} S^s_{a,p^j} \exp\left\{-\frac{2\pi i a n}{p^j}\right\}$$

$$= p^{-js} \sum_{a=1}^{p^j} S^s_{a,p^j} \exp\left\{-\frac{2\pi i a n}{p^j}\right\} - p^{-js} \sum_{\substack{1 \leqslant a \leqslant p^j \\ p \mid a}} S^s_{a,p^j} \exp\left\{-\frac{2\pi i a n}{p^j}\right\}.$$

The second summand (by putting $a = pb$) equals

$$p^{-js+s} \sum_{b=1}^{p^{j-1}} S^s_{b,p^{j-1}} \exp\left\{-\frac{2\pi i b n}{p^{j-1}}\right\},$$

and in view of

$$p^t B_s(n, p^t) = \sum_{x=1}^{p^t} S^s_{x,p^t} \exp\left\{-\frac{2\pi i x n}{p^t}\right\}$$

we get

$$A_{p^j} = p^{-j(s-1)} B_s(n, p^j) - p^{-(j-1)(s-1)} B_s(n, p^{j-1}),$$

which, through summing over $j = 0, 1, \ldots, t$, gives equality (iii). $\square$

Lemma 4.9 indicates that in order to obtain a lower bound for the sum of the singular series we have to bound $T(p)$ away from zero, which amounts to obtaining good lower evaluations for $B_s(n, p^t)$. This we shall do now. Since a direct treatment of $B_s(n, p^t)$ presents certain technical difficulties, we define $B^*_s(n, p^t)$ as the number of solutions of congruence (4.16) in which not all X_i's are divisible by p, study this function in the next lemma, and finally use the obvious inequality $B_s(n, p^t) \geqslant B^*_s(n, p^t)$ to obtain the required bounds.

We need another piece of notation. For any prime p define a_p as the maximal power of p which divides k and put

$$\Omega_p = \begin{cases} a_p + 1 & \text{if} \quad p \text{ is odd,} \\ a_p + 2 & \text{if} \quad p = 2. \end{cases}$$

LEMMA 4.10. (i) *If* $p \nmid m$ *and the congruence* $X^k \equiv m \pmod{p^{\Omega_p}}$ *is solvable, then so is the congruence* $X^k \equiv m \pmod{p^t}$ *for all* $t \geqslant 1$.

(ii) *For* $t \geqslant \Omega_p$ *we have*

$$B^*_s(n, p^{t+1}) \geqslant p^{s-1} B^*_s(n, p^t).$$

(iii) *If* p *is odd and* $s \geqslant 2k$, *or* $p = 2$ *and* $s \geqslant 4k$ *then for all* n *and* $t \geqslant 1$ *one has*

$$B^*_s(n, p^t) \geqslant 1.$$

Proof. The proof of (i) is based on the following simple fact from group theory:

If C_d denotes the cyclic group of d elements and $A = \prod_{j=1}^{r} C_{n_j}$, $B = \prod_{j=1}^{r} C_{m_j}$ are two finite abelian groups written multiplicatively such that $m_j | n_j$ for $j = 1, 2, \ldots, r$ and $f: A \to B$ is a homomorphism mapping each C_{n_j} onto C_{m_j}, then the following two properties are equivalent:

(a) For $x \in A$, $f(x)$ is a kth power in B if and only if x itself is a kth power,

(b) For $j = 1, 2, \ldots, r$ one has $(k, n_j) | m_j$.

Indeed, if g_j is a generator of C_{n_j} $(j = 1, 2, \ldots, r)$, then

(a) $\Leftrightarrow \operatorname{Ker} f \subset A^k \Leftrightarrow g_1^{m_1} \ldots g_r^{m_r} \in A^k \Leftrightarrow$ the congruence $m_j = kx_j \pmod{n_j}$ is solvable for $j = 1, \ldots, r \Leftrightarrow$ (b).

Taking $A = (Z/p^t Z)^*$, $B = (Z/p^u Z)^*$ with $t > u$, we infer that the solvability of $X^k \equiv m \pmod{p^u}$ implies that of $X^k \equiv m \pmod{p^t}$ if and only if $(k, p^{t-1}(p-1)) | p^{u-1}(p-1)$ if p is odd, resp. $(k, 2) | 2$ and $(k, 2^{t-2}) | 2^{u-2}$ if $p = 2$, which in both cases is equivalent to $u \geqslant \Omega_p$.

Assertion (ii) is an easy consequence of (i). Let $x_1, \ldots, x_s$ be a solution of congruence (4.16) for a certain $t \geqslant \Omega_p$ and assume that not all x_i's are divisible by p. Say, $p \nmid x_1$. Then the congruence

$$X^k \equiv n - \sum_{j=2}^{s} (x_j + p^t y_j)^k \pmod{p^t}$$

is solvable for any choice of $0 \leqslant y_2, \ldots, y_s < p$ and the right-hand side is prime to p. By (i) the analogous congruence $\pmod{p^{t+1}}$ is solvable, and so every solution of (4.16) counted in $B_s^*(n, p^t)$ leads to at least p^{s-1} solutions counted by $B_s^*(n, p^{t+1})$ and (ii) follows by recurrence.

We now prove (iii). First let $p \nmid n$ and denote by $g(n, p^t)$ the smallest positive integer s for which (4.16) has a solution. (As $p \nmid n$, every such solution will be counted by $B_s^*(n, p^t)$.) Observe that if n_1 and n_2 lie in the same coset of $G = (Z/p^t Z)^*$ with respect to the subgroup G^k of kth powers then $g(n_1, p^t) = g(n_2, p^t)$. Thus the sets $A_c = \{n: p \nmid n, g(n, p^t) = c\}$ consist of full cosets of $G \pmod{G^k}$. Let r denote the cardinality of G/G^k and observe that by considering the structure of G one gets

$$(4.26) \qquad\qquad r \leqslant \begin{cases} k & \text{if} \quad p \text{ is odd,} \\ 2k & \text{if} \quad p = 2. \end{cases}$$

From every set A_c choose the smallest positive integer and arrange the numbers obtained in an increasing sequence: $1 = M_1 < M_2 < \ldots < M_r$.

We prove the inequality $g(M_j, p^t) \leqslant 2j - 1$. Since it is obvious for $j = 1$, we assume that it holds for $j = 1, 2, \ldots, i < r$. At least one of the integers $M_{i+1} - 1$, $M_{i+1} - 2$, say M', is not divisible by p and, as it is smaller than

M_{i+1}, we get $g(M', p^t) \leqslant 2i-1$; hence

$$g(M_{i+1}, p^t) \leqslant 2+g(M', p^t) \leqslant 2(i+1)-1,$$

as asserted. Applying the resulting bound in the case of $j = r$ we see that if $p \nmid n$ then $g(n, p^t) \leqslant 2r-1$, and if $p \mid n$ then it suffices to note that $p \nmid n-1$; hence

$$g(n, p^t) \leqslant 1+g(n-1, p^t) \leqslant 2r.$$

Thus (iii) follows from (4.26). $\square$

COROLLARY. *If* $s \geqslant 4k$ *then for odd* p *one has*

$$B_s^*(n, p^t) \geqslant p^{(s-1)t-(2k-1)\Omega_p}$$

whereas for $p = 2$ *one has*

$$B_s^*(n, 2^t) \geqslant 2^{(s-1)t-(4k-1)\Omega_2}.$$

Proof. If p is odd, then by (iii) the congruence

$$X_1^k + \ldots + X_{2k}^k \equiv n - x_{2k+1}^k - \ldots - x_s^k \pmod{p^{\Omega_p}}$$

has a solution with not all X_i's divisible by p for any choice of $x_{2k+1}, \ldots, x_s \in [0, p^{\Omega_p})$. This shows that

$$B_s^*(n, p^{\Omega_p}) \geqslant p^{\Omega_p(s-2k)}$$

and since (ii) implies

$$B_s^*(n, p^t) \geqslant B_s^*(n, p^{\Omega_p}) p^{(s-1)(t-\Omega_p)}$$

we get our assertion. In the case of $p = 2$ the same argument applies, provided $2k$ is replaced by $4k$. $\square$

The resulting bounds for $B_s^*(n, p^t)$ enable us now to evaluate $T(p)$, which leads to the lower bound for the singular series stated in the theorem.

LEMMA 4.11. (i) *If* $p \nmid 2kn$, *then* $T(p) = 1 + A_p$.

(ii) *If* $p \nmid 2kn$, *then*

$$|T(p)-1| < k^s p^{1-s/2}$$

and if $s \geqslant 4k$ *we have for any* p

$$|T(p)-1| < \tfrac{4}{3}\varepsilon(p) p^{1-s/k},$$

where

$$\varepsilon(p) = \begin{cases} k^s & \text{if } p \leqslant k^{2k/(k-2)}, \\ 1 & \text{otherwise}. \end{cases}$$

Proof. (i) In this case $B_s(n, p^t) = B_s^*(n, p^t)$ and $\Omega_p = 1$. In view of Lemma 4.9 (iii) and Lemma 4.10 (ii) it suffices thus to show that

$$B_s^*(n, p^t) \leqslant p^{s-1} B_s^*(n, p^{t-1})$$

holds for $t \geqslant 2$. Let $x_1^k + \ldots + x_s^k \equiv n \pmod{p^{t-1}}$ and assume that there are more than p^{s-1} solutions of

$$y_1^k + \ldots + y_s^k \equiv n \pmod{p^t}$$

satisfying $y_i \equiv x_i \pmod{p^{t-1}}$ for $i = 1, 2, \ldots, s$. Permuting, if necessary, the x_i's we may assume that $p \nmid x_s$. Our assumption implies that we can find two sets of solutions of the last congruence, say $Y_1, \ldots, Y_s$ and $Y_1', \ldots, Y_s'$, such that for $i = 1, 2, \ldots, s-1$ we have $Y_i \equiv Y_i' \pmod{p^t}$. Since we can write $Y_s = x_s + up^{t-1}$, $Y_s' = x_s + vp^{t-1}$ with $0 \leqslant u$, $v < p$, it follows that

$$(x_s + up^{t-1})^k \equiv (x_s + vp^{t-1})^k \pmod{p^t};$$

hence

$$kx_s^{k-1} up^{t-1} \equiv kx_s^{k-1} vp^{t-1} \pmod{p^t}$$

and finally $u = v$ and $Y_s \equiv Y_s' \pmod{p^t}$, a contradiction.

(ii) If $p \nmid 2kn$ then we may apply (i) to get

$$|T(p) - 1| = |A_p| \leqslant \sum_{1 \leqslant a \leqslant p-1} |S_{a,p} p^{-1}|^s \leqslant k^s p^{1-s/2}$$

by Proposition 4.3, and if $p \mid 2kn$ then the same proposition implies

$$|T(p) - 1| \leqslant \sum_{t=1}^{\infty} |A_{p^t}| \leqslant \varepsilon(p) p^{1-s/k} (1 - p^{1-s/k})^{-1} \leqslant \tfrac{4}{3} \varepsilon(p) p^{1-s/k}. \quad \square$$

COROLLARY. *If $s \geqslant 4k$, then for $p \geqslant k^{2+4/(k-2)}$ one has*

$$T(p) \geqslant 1 - p^{-3/2}.$$

If $p \nmid 2kn$ then the same inequality already holds for $p > k^{2s/(s-5)}$. In all the remaining cases

$$T(p) \geqslant \begin{cases} 2^{-(4k-1)\Omega_2} & \text{if} \quad p = 2, \\ p^{-(2k-1)\Omega_p} & \text{if} \quad p \neq 2. \end{cases}$$

In particular, $T(p)$ is positive for all primes p.

Proof. If $T(p) \leqslant 1 - p^{-3/2}$ then in view of (ii) we get

$$\tfrac{4}{3}\varepsilon(p) p^{1-s/k} \geqslant |T(p) - 1| \geqslant p^{-3/2};$$

thus

$$\tfrac{4}{3}\varepsilon(p) \geqslant p^{s/k - 5/2} = p^{(2s-5k)/2k}.$$

If $p \geqslant k^{2+4/(k-2)}$ then $\varepsilon(p) = 1$, and since $s \geqslant 4k$ we obtain $4/3 > p^{3/2} \geqslant 2^{3/2} > 2$, a contradiction. If $p \nmid 2kn$ then $T(p) < 1 - p^{-3/2}$ implies

$$k^s p^{1-s/2} \geqslant |T(p) - 1| \geqslant p^{-3/2},$$

which easily gives $p \leqslant k^{2s/(s-5)}$.

The remaining assertions follow immediately from the corollary to Lemma 4.10 and Lemma 4.9 (iv). □

To complete the proof of the proposition let us write, using the last corollary,

$$S(s, n, k) = \prod_p T(p) \geqslant 2^{-(4k-1)\Omega_2} \prod_{p \in A} p^{-(2k-1)\Omega_p} \prod_{\substack{p \notin A \\ p \neq 2}} (1 - p^{-3/2})$$

where A denotes the set of all odd primes not exceeding $k^{2+4/(k-2)}$. This implies

$$S(s, n, k) \geqslant \zeta^{-1}(3/2) \exp(-C_1)$$

where

$$C_1 = (4k-1)\Omega_2 \log 2 + \sum_{p \in A} \Omega_p(2k-1) \log p$$

$$\leqslant (2k-1) \log k + 2k\Omega_2 \log 2 + (2k-1) \sum_{p \in A} \log p.$$

Using Proposition A.3 (a) and noting that $\Omega_2 \leqslant \log k / \log 2$, we arrive at

$$C_1 \leqslant (4k-1) \log k + 1.01(2k-1)k^{2+4/(k-2)}$$

$$\leqslant 4k \log k + 1.01(2k-1)3.51 k^2 < 7.1 k^3 + 4k \log k - 3.55 k^2;$$

thus

(4.27) $$C_1 < 7.1 k^3.$$

Since $\zeta^{-1}(3/2) > 1/3$, this implies our assertion. □

3. Now we turn to the integral $J(N)$, defined by (4.9). In order to evaluate it we shall now divide the range of integration into a finite collection of intervals. To define them put $P = N^{1/k}$, $d = k/(k+1)$ and consider for any $q \in [1, P^d]$ and $a = 1, 2, \ldots, q-1$ coprime with q the interval $I(a, q)$ of length P^{d-k}/q centred at a/q. Every such interval will be called a *major arc*. We denote by $\mathscr{M}$ the family of all major arcs. Clearly the major arcs do not intersect, and since their union does not cover the full unit interval, its complement consists of a finite set of intervals, which we shall call the *minor arcs*.

Observe that if x belongs to a minor arc, then it lies in an interval of length P^{d-k}/q centred at a rational number a/q with $P^d < q \leqslant 2P^{k-d}$. Indeed, by Proposition A.6 we can find integers $p \geqslant 1$ and $1 \leqslant q \leqslant 2P^{k-d}$ such that

$$|x - p/q| < P^{d-k}/2q,$$

and if we had $q \leqslant P^d$ then x would lie in a major arc, contrary to our assumption.

That part of $J(N)$ which stems from the major arcs will give the dominant term, whereas the contribution of the minor arcs will go into the error term. The terminology traditionally used here is misleading, since the major arcs are not really large, their union having measure less than P^{2d-k} and thus tending to zero for $P \to \infty$, but their influence on $J(N)$ is greater than that of the minor arcs.

We shall first obtain a good approximation for $T(x)$ on a major arc.

LEMMA 4.12. *If $I(a, q)$ is a major arc, then for $x \in I(a, q)$ we have*

$$\Delta(x) = \left| T(x) - S(a, q) q^{-1} \int_0^P \exp\{2\pi i \beta u^k\}\, du \right| \leqslant 15 k P^d,$$

where $\beta = x - a/q$.

Proof. We write

$$T(x) = \sum_{j=1}^{q} \sum_{\substack{m \leqslant P \\ m \equiv j \,(\mathrm{mod}\, q)}} \exp\{2\pi i m^k x\}$$

$$= \sum_{j=1}^{q} \exp\{2\pi i j^k a/q\} \sum_{(1-j)/q \leqslant n \leqslant (P-j)/q} \exp\{2\pi i (Aq+j)^k \beta\}.$$

Applying to the inner sum Proposition A.0 with $f(x) = (xq+j)^k \beta$, $B_0 = P^k |\beta| \leqslant P^d/2q$, $B_1 = kqP^{k-1} |\beta| \leqslant k P^{d-1}/2$, we get

$$T(x) = \sum_{j=1}^{q} \exp\{2\pi i j^k a/q\} \left(\int_{(1-j)/q}^{(P-j)/q} \exp\{2\pi i (yq+j)^k \beta\}\, dy + R \right)$$

$$= S_{a,q}/q \int_1^P \exp\{2\pi i t^k \beta\}\, dt + R \cdot S_{a,q},$$

where $|R| \leqslant 2 + 4k P^{d-1} + 10k P^{2d-1}/q$.

Because of

$$\left| \int_0^1 \exp\{2\pi i t^k \beta\}\, dt \right| \leqslant 1$$

we obtain, estimating $|S_{a,q}|$ trivially,

$$\Delta(x) \leqslant \frac{2|S_{a,q}|}{q} + (1 + 4k P^{d-1} + 10k P^{2d-1} q^{-1}) |S_{a,q}|$$

$$\leqslant 2 + (1 + 4k P^{d-1} + 10k P^{2d-1} q^{-1}) q \leqslant 2 + (1 + 4k P^{d-1}) P^d + 10k P^{2d-1}$$

$$\leqslant 2 + (1 + 14k) P^d < 15k P^d$$

since $2d - 1 < d$ and $q \leqslant P^d$. □

COROLLARY. *For $s \geqslant 4k$ and $k \geqslant 9$ one has*

$$\sum_{I(a,q) \in \mathscr{H}} \int_{I(a,q)} \left| T^s(x) - \left(\frac{S_{a,q}}{q} I(\beta) \right)^s \right| dx \leqslant 75 skC_0^s P^{s+d-k-1}$$

where

$$I(\beta) = \int_0^P \exp\{2\pi i\beta u^k\}\, du, \qquad \beta = x - a/q,$$

$$C_0 = C_0(k) = 2C(k) + 15k \leqslant \exp(3.7k^2).$$

Proof. Observe first that both integrals

$$\int_0^\infty \exp(\pm 2\pi i t^k)\, dt$$

converge and for every positive T we have

$$\left| \int_0^T \exp(\pm 2\pi i t^k)\, dt \right| < 2.$$

Indeed, the first assertion results from

$$\left| \int_{N_1}^{N_2} \exp(\pm 2\pi i t^k)\, dt \right| \leqslant \sum_{j=N_1}^{N_2+1} \left| \int_j^{j+1} \frac{d(\exp\{\pm 2\pi i t^k\})}{2\pi i k t^{k-1}} \right|$$

$$\leqslant (\pi k)^{-1} \sum_{j=N_1}^\infty j^{1-k} \ll N_1^{2-k} \qquad \text{(for } 1 < N_1 < N_2\text{)},$$

and to prove the second observe that the same argument leads to

$$\left| \int_0^T \exp\{\pm 2\pi i t^k\}\, dt \right| \leqslant 1 + \left| \int_1^T \exp\{\pm 2\pi i t^k\}\, dt \right| \leqslant 1 + (\pi k)^{-1} \zeta(k-1)$$

$$\leqslant 1 + (\pi k)^{-1} \zeta(2) < 2.$$

Hence

(4.28) $$|I(\beta)| = |\beta|^{-1/k} \left| \int_0^{|\beta|^{1/k}P} \exp\{2\pi i t^k\, dt\} \right| < 2|\beta|^{-1/k}.$$

If $|\beta|$ is small, this bound is of little use, and in those cases we shall apply the trivial bound $|I(\beta)| \leqslant P$. Taking into account the resulting evaluations and using Proposition 4.3, we obtain

$$|I(\beta) S_{a,q} q^{-1}| \leqslant \begin{cases} 2C(k) q^{-1/k} P & \text{if} \quad |\beta| \leqslant P^{-k}, \\ 2C(k) q^{-1/k} |\beta|^{-1/k} & \text{if} \quad |\beta| > P^{-k}. \end{cases}$$

The obvious inequality

$$|z_1^s - z_2^s| \leqslant s|z_1 - z_2| Z^{s-1}$$

(where $Z = \max(|z_1|, |z_2|)$) implies the evaluation

$$\Delta_s(x) = \left| T^s(x) - \left(\frac{S_{a,q}}{q} I(\beta) \right)^s \right| \leqslant s \cdot \Delta(x) \left(\left| \frac{S_{a,q}}{q} I(\beta) \right| + \Delta(x) \right)^{s-1}.$$

We now consider separately the cases $|\beta| \leqslant P^{-k}$ and $p^{d-k}/2q \geqslant |\beta| > P^{-k}$. In the first case we have

$$|S_{a,q} I(\beta) q^{-1}| \leqslant 2CPq^{-1/k}$$

and $\varDelta(x) \leqslant 15kP^d \leqslant 15kPq^{-1/k}$, which leads to

$$(4.29) \qquad \varDelta_s(x) \leqslant 15ksP^d (C_0 Pq^{-1/k})^{s-1} = 15ksC_0^s q^{-(s-1)/k} P^{s+d-1}.$$

Similarly, in the second case

$$P^{-k} < |\beta| \leqslant P^{d-k}/2q,$$

and so

$$P^{k-d} \leqslant 1/2q |\beta|^{-1}, \qquad P^d \leqslant (2q)^{-1/k} |\beta|^{-1/k} < q^{-1/k} |\beta|^{-1/k};$$

thus

$$\varDelta(x) \leqslant 15kP^d \leqslant 15kq^{-1/k} |\beta|^{-1/k}.$$

Because of $|S_{a,q} I(\beta) q^{-1}| \leqslant 2C(k) q^{-1/k} |\beta|^{-1/k}$ we obtain

$$(4.30) \qquad \varDelta_s(x) \leqslant 15skP^d C_0^{s-1} q^{-(s-1)/k} |\beta|^{-(s-1)/k}.$$

Inequalities (4.29) and (4.30) give

$$\int\limits_{I(a,q)} \varDelta_s(x)\,dx = \int\limits_{|\beta| \leqslant P^{-k}} \varDelta_s(x)\,dx + \int\limits_{|\beta| > P^{-k}} \varDelta_s(x)\,dx$$

$$\leqslant 30ksC_0^s q^{-(s-1)/k} P^{s+d-k-1} + 30skP^d C_0^s q^{-(s-1)/k} \int\limits_{P^{-k}}^{\infty} \beta^{-(s-1)/k}\,d\beta,$$

and since the integral here does not exceed $P^{s-k-1}/2$ we finally get

$$\int\limits_{I(a,q)} \varDelta_s(x)\,dx \leqslant 45skC_0^s q^{-(s-1)/k} P^{s+d-k-1} \sum\limits_{I(a,q) \in \mathscr{M}} \int\limits_{I(a,q)} \varDelta_s(x)\,dx$$

$$\leqslant 45skC_0^s P^{s+d-k-1} \sum\limits_{q \leqslant P^d} \sum\limits_{\substack{1 \leqslant a \leqslant q \\ (a,q)=1}} q^{-(s-1)/k}$$

$$\leqslant 45skC_0^s P^{s+d-k-1} \sum\limits_{q=1}^{\infty} q^{1-(s-1)/k} \leqslant \frac{45\pi^2}{6} skC_0^s P^{s+d-k-1},$$

which implies our assertion.

Before completing the evaluation of the contribution of major arcs to $J(N)$ we need another auxiliary result, concerning an integral connected with $I(\beta)$.

LEMMA 4.13. (i) *If* $0 < n \leqslant P^k$, $s \geqslant 4k$ *and* $q \leqslant P^d$, *then*

$$\int\limits_{|\beta| \leqslant P^{d-k}/2q} I^s(\beta) \exp\{-2\pi in\beta\}\,d\beta = \int\limits_{-\infty}^{\infty} I^s(\beta) \exp\{-2\pi in\beta\}\,d\beta + E,$$

where

$$|E| \leqslant \tfrac{1}{3} 2^{s(1+1/k)} (P^{d-k} q^{-1})^{1-s/k}.$$

(ii) *If* $0 < n \leqslant P^k$, *then*

$$\mathscr{I}(n) = \int_{-\infty}^{\infty} I^s(\beta) \exp\{-2\pi in\beta\} \, d\beta = \frac{\Gamma^s(1+1/k)}{\Gamma(s/k)} n^{s/k-1}.$$

Proof. (i) Using (4.28), we find that the integral is bounded by

$$2 \int_{P^{d-k}/2q}^{\infty} |I(\beta)|^s \, d\beta \leqslant 2^{1+s} \int_{P^{d-k}/2q}^{\infty} \beta^{-s/k} \, d\beta$$

$$= 2^{1+s} \frac{k}{s-k} P^{(d-k)(1-s/k)} (2q)^{s/k-1}$$

$$\leqslant \tfrac{1}{3} 2^{s(1+1/k)} (P^{d-k} q^{-1})^{(1-s/k)}. \quad \sqcap$$

(ii) We follow E. Landau [30b]. Changing the variables $u = Pv$, $\beta P^k = t$, we obtain for $c = nP^{-k} < 1$

$$\mathscr{I}(n) = \lim_{T \to \infty} P^{s-k} \int_{-T}^{T} \exp(-2\pi ict) \left(\int_0^1 \exp(2\pi itv^k) \, dv \right)^s dt$$

$$= \lim_{T \to \infty} P^{s-k} \int_0^1 \cdots \int_0^1 dv_1 \ldots dv_s \int_{-T}^{T} \exp\left(2\pi it(v_1^k + \ldots + v_s^k - c)\right) dt$$

$$= \lim_{T \to \infty} P^{s-k} \pi^{-1} \int_0^1 \cdot \int_0^1 \frac{\sin\left(2\pi T(v_1^k + \ldots + v_s^k - c)\right)}{v_1^k + \ldots + v_s^k - c} \, dv_1 \ldots dv_s$$

$$= \lim_{T \to \infty} P^{s-k} (k\pi)^{-1} \int_{-c}^{s-c} \frac{\sin(2\pi Tx)}{x} \int \cdots \int_{V(x)} \frac{dv_1 \ldots dv_{s-1}}{(c+x-v_1^k - \ldots - v_{s-1}^k)^{1-1/k}}$$

where

$$V(x) = \{\langle v_1, \ldots, v_{s-1} \rangle : 0 \leqslant v_i \leqslant 1 \ (i = 1, \ldots, s-1),$$

$$c - 1 + x \leqslant v_1^k + \ldots + v_{s-1}^k \leqslant c + x\};$$

hence

$$\mathscr{I}(n) = \lim_{T \to \infty} P^{s-k} (k\pi)^{-1} \int_{-c}^{s-c} \frac{\sin(2\pi Tx)}{x} (c+x)^{s/k-1} \times$$

$$\times \int_{W(x)} \frac{dy_1 \ldots dy_{s-1}}{(1 - y_1^k - \ldots - y_{s-1}^k)^{1-1/k}},$$

where

(4.31) $W(x) = \{\langle y_1, \ldots, y_{s-1}\rangle:$

$0 \leqslant y_i \leqslant (c+x)^{-1/k} (i = 1, \ldots, s-1), 1 - 1/(c+x) \leqslant y_1^k + \ldots + y_{s-1}^k \leqslant 1\}.$

If $-c \leqslant x \leqslant 1-c$ then $1/(c+x) \geqslant 1$; hence the inner integral equals

$$\int \cdots \int_{\substack{0 \leqslant y_i \leqslant 1 \\ y_1^k + \ldots + y_s^k \leqslant 1}} (1 - y_1^k - \ldots - y_{s-1}^k)^{1/k-1} \, dy_1 \ldots dy_{s-1} = \frac{k\Gamma^s(1+1/k)}{\Gamma(s/k)},$$

as computed already by P. G. Dirichlet [39a].

It follows that

$$\mathscr{I}(n) = \lim_{T \to \infty} P^{s-k} \pi^{-1} \frac{\Gamma^s(1+1/k)}{\Gamma(s/k)} \int_{-c}^{1-c} \frac{\sin(2\pi Tx)}{x} (c+x)^{s/k-1} \, dx +$$

$$+ \lim_{T \to \infty} \frac{P^{s-k}}{k} \int_{1-c}^{s-c} \frac{\sin(2\pi Tx)}{x} \Phi(x) \, dx$$

where

$$\Phi(x) = (c+x)^{s/k-1} \int \cdots \int_{W(x)} \frac{dy_1 \ldots dy_{s-1}}{(1 - y_1^k - \ldots - y_{s-1}^k)^{1-1/k}},$$

the set $W(x)$ being defined by (4.31).

The function $\Phi(x)(c+x)^{1-s/k}$ is decreasing, and thus $\Phi(x)$ is of bounded variation in the interval $[1-c, s-c]$, which implies that the second summand tends to zero as T goes to infinity.

Finally, for $\alpha = s/k - 1$, we have

$$\int_{-c}^{1-c} \frac{\sin(2\pi Tx)}{x} (c+x)^\alpha \, dx - \int_{-c}^{1-c} \frac{\sin(2\pi Tx)}{x} c^\alpha \, dx$$

$$= \int_{-2\pi Tc}^{2\pi T(1-c)} \frac{\sin u}{u} \left\{ \left(c + \frac{u}{2\pi T}\right)^\alpha - c^\alpha \right\} du$$

$$= \int_{-2\pi Tc}^{-2\pi T(1-c)} \frac{\sin u}{u} \left(\frac{\alpha u}{2\pi T} c^{\alpha-1} + O(uT^{-2}) \right) du$$

$$= \frac{\alpha c^{\alpha-1}}{2\pi T} \int_{-2\pi Tc}^{2\pi T(1-c)} \sin u \, du + O(T^{-1}) \ll T^{-1};$$

thus

$$\lim_{T \to \infty} \int_{-c}^{1-c} \frac{\sin(2\pi Tx)}{x} (c+x)^\alpha \, dx = \lim_{T \to \infty} \int_{-c}^{1-c} \frac{\sin(2\pi Tx)}{x} c^\alpha \, dx = \pi c^\alpha$$

and

$$\mathscr{I}(n) = P^{s-k} c^\alpha \Gamma^s(1+1/k) \Gamma^{-1}(s/k) = n^\alpha \Gamma^s(1+1/k) \Gamma^{-1}(s/k)$$

as asserted. □

COROLLARY 1. *If* $s \geqslant 4k$ *and* $0 < n \leqslant P^k$, *then*

$$\int_{I(a,q) \in \mathscr{M}} \int_{I(a,q)} T^s(x) \exp\{-2\pi inx\} \, dx = S(s, n, k) \frac{\Gamma^s(1+1/k)}{\Gamma(s/k)} n^{s/k-1} + R,$$

where

$$|R| \leqslant P^{s-k} \left\{ 75skC_0^s P^{d-1} + \tfrac{1}{3} C^s 2^{s+s/k} P^{d(2-s/k)} + \frac{2^{1/2} C^s}{\Gamma(s/k)} P^{-2d} \right\}.$$

P r o o f. The corollary to Lemma 4.12 implies that

$$\left| \sum_{I(a,q) \in \mathscr{M}} \int_{I(a,q)} T^s(x) \exp\{-2\pi inx\} \, dx - \right.$$

$$\left. - \sum_{q \leqslant P^d} \sum_{\substack{1 \leqslant a \leqslant q \\ (a,q)=1}} (S_{a,q} \cdot q^{-1})^s \int_{I(a,q)} I^s(x-a/q) \exp\{-2\pi inx\} \, dx \right|$$

$$\leqslant 75skC_0^s P^{s+d-k-1}.$$

But Lemma 4.13 shows that

$$\int_{I(a,q)} I^s(x-a/q) \exp\{-2\pi inx\} \, dx = \exp\left\{-2\pi in\frac{a}{q}\right\} \frac{\Gamma^s(1+1/k)}{\Gamma(s/k)} n^{s/k-1} + R_1$$

where

$$|R_1| \leqslant \tfrac{1}{3} 2^{s(1+1/k)} (P^{d-k} q^{-1})^{1-s/k},$$

and since Proposition 4.3 implies

$$\left| \sum_{q \leqslant P^d} A_q - S(s, n, k) \right| \leqslant \sum_{q > P^d} |A_q| \leqslant C^s \sum_{q > P^d} q^{-3} \leqslant 2C^s (P^d-1)^{-2}$$

we obtain

$$|R| \leqslant 75skC_0^s P^{s+d-k-1} + \sum_{q \leqslant P^d} \sum_{\substack{1 \leqslant a \leqslant q \\ (a,q)=1}} \left| \frac{S_{a,q}}{q} \right|^s |R_1| +$$

$$+ 2 \frac{\Gamma^s(1+1/k)}{\Gamma(s/k)} n^{s/k-1} C^s (P^d-1)^{-2}.$$

The second summand is equal to

$$\tfrac{1}{3} 2^{s(1+1/k)} P^{(d-k)(1-s/k)} \sum_{\substack{q \leqslant P^d}} \sum_{\substack{1 \leqslant a \leqslant q \\ (a,q)=1}} \left|\frac{S_{a,q}}{q}\right|^s q^{s/k-1}$$

$$\leqslant \tfrac{1}{3} 2^{s(1+1/k)} C^s P^{(d-k)(1-s/k)} \sum_{q \leqslant P^d} 1$$

$$\leqslant \tfrac{1}{3} C^s 2^{s(1+1/k)} P^{(s/k-1)(k-d)+d} = \tfrac{1}{3} C^s 2^{s(1+1/k)} P^{s-k+d(2-s/k)},$$

and the third is bounded by

$$\frac{2^{3/2} C^s P^{s-k-2d}}{\Gamma(s/k)}$$

because for $P \geqslant 2$ we have $(P^d-1)^2 > 2^{-1/2} P^{2d}$, $0 < \Gamma(1+1/k) < 1$ and $n \leqslant P^k$. $\square$

If we now specialize s, putting $s = 4k$, we obtain the following result, which will be crucial in the final step of our proof of Theorem 4.6.

COROLLARY 2. *If* $k \geqslant 9$ *and* $P^k/4 \leqslant n \leqslant P^k$, *then for*

(4.32) $$P \geqslant P_0 = \exp 15k^4$$

the real part of the sum

$$\sum_{I(a,q) \in \mathcal{M}} \int_{I(a,q)} T^{4k}(x) \exp\{-2\pi i n x\}\, dx$$

is at least equal to $\alpha_k P^{3k}$ *where*

$$\alpha_k = \lambda_k (4/5)^{4k} \cdot 3^{-1} \cdot 2^{-8} \quad and \quad \lambda_k = \exp(-7.1k^3).$$

Proof. By Corollary 1 and Proposition 4.4 the real part of the above sum is at least equal to

$$\tfrac{1}{6} \lambda_k \Gamma^{4k}(1+1/k)(P^k/4)^3 - |R| \geqslant \lambda_k(4/5)^{4k} 3^{-1} 2^{-7} P^{3k} - |R| = 2\alpha_k P^{3k} - |R|$$

because the minimal value of $\Gamma(1+x)$ for positive x exceeds 0.885.

Consequently it suffices to prove that $|R| P^{-3k}$ is for $P \geqslant P_0$ smaller than α_k. Now in our case the bound for $|R|$ given in Corollary 1 takes the form

$$|R| \leqslant P^{3k}\left\{300k^2 C_0^{4k} P^{d-1} + \left(\tfrac{1}{3} C^{4k} 2^{4k+4} + \frac{2^{3/2}}{6} C^{4k}\right) P^{-2d}\right\};$$

thus, making use of the equalities $1-d = 1/(k+1)$ and $2d = 2k/(k+1)$, as well as $P_0 \geqslant \exp k^4$, we arrive at

$$|R| P^{-3k} \leqslant P^{-1/(k+1)} \exp(14.82\,k^3).$$

It follows that the ratio $|R| P^{-3k}$ will be smaller than α_k provided P exceeds

$$\exp\left(14.82 k^3 (k+1) - \log \alpha_k\right)$$
$$= \exp\left(14.82 (k^4 + k^3) - \log \lambda_k - 4k \log (4/5) + \log 3 + 8 \log 2\right),$$

which will certainly be satisfied if $P \geqslant \exp(15 k^4) = P_0$. $\square$

4. Now we turn to the study of minor arcs and start with a lemma of I. M. Vinogradov:

LEMMA 4.14. *Let I, J be two intervals of lengths X and Y respectively and let A, B be certain sets of integers satisfying $A \subset I$, $B \subset J$. If x is a real number and the rational number p/q $((p, q) = 1)$ satisfies*

$$|x - p/q| \leqslant q^{-2},$$

then

$$\left| \sum_{\substack{a \in A \\ b \in B}} \exp\{2\pi i a b x\} \right|^2 \leqslant 6 |A|\, |B| (1 + Y/q)(X + q \log q).$$

Proof. Without restricting generality we may assume that $0 < x < 1$ (the case $x = 0$ or 1 being trivial). Denoting by $\|t\|$ the distance of a real number t from the nearest integer, we get by Cauchy's inequality

$$\left| \sum_{\substack{a \in A \\ b \in B}} \exp\{2\pi i a b x\} \right|^2 \leqslant \sum_{a \in A} 1 \sum_{m \in I} \left| \sum_{b \in B} \exp\{2\pi i m b x\} \right|^2$$

$$= |A| \sum_{b_1, b_2 \in B} \sum_{m \in I} \exp\{2\pi i m (b_1 - b_2) x\}$$

$$\leqslant |A| \sum_{b_1, b_2 \in B} \min\left(X, \frac{1}{\|(b_1 - b_2) x\|}\right)$$

$$\leqslant |A| \cdot |B| \sum_{|y| \leqslant Y - 1} \min(X, \|xy\|^{-1}).$$

If now $mq \leqslant Y < (m+1)q$, then

$$\sum_{|y| \leqslant Y - 1} \min(X, \|xy\|^{-1}) \leqslant \sum_{r = -1 - m}^{m+1} \sum_{y = 1 + qr}^{rq + q} \min(X, \|xy\|^{-1});$$

writing

$$x = p/q + \varepsilon/q^2$$

with $(p, q) = 1$, $|\varepsilon| \leqslant 1$, and putting $z = y - rq$ and $\xi_r = \varepsilon r/q$, we obtain

$$\sum_{y = 1 + qr}^{rq + q} \min(X, \|xy\|^{-1}) = \sum_{z = 1}^{q} \min(X, \|xz + \xi\|^{-1}).$$

This shows that it suffices to prove for all ξ the inequality

$$S(\xi) = \sum_{z=1}^{q} \min(X, \|xz+\xi\|^{-1}) \leqslant 6(X+q \log q).$$

If $q \leqslant 2$ then $S(\xi) \leqslant 2X$, and so we may assume $q \geqslant 3$ and $|\xi| \leqslant 1$. Write

$$xz+\xi = pz/q+\varepsilon z/q^2+\xi = (pz+[\xi q])/q+\eta/q^2$$

where $\eta = \varepsilon z + q(\xi q - [\xi q])$ satisfies

$$|\eta| < 2q.$$

Observe now that if z ranges over the interval $[1, q]$ then, in view of $(p, q) = 1$, $y = pz+[\xi q]$ ranges over a complete system of residues $(\bmod\, q)$, and since the function $\|u\|$ is of period 1 we get

$$S(\xi) = \sum_{|y| \leqslant q/2} \min(X, \|yq^{-1}+\eta q^{-2}\|^{-1}).$$

For $3 \leqslant |y| \leqslant q/2$ we have

$$\|yq^{-1}+\eta q^{-2}\| \geqslant (|y|-2)q^{-1};$$

thus, finally,

$$S(\xi) \leqslant 5X + \sum_{3 \leqslant |y| \leqslant q/2} q(|y|-2)^{-1}$$

$$= 5X+2q \sum_{y=3}^{q/2} (y-2)^{-1} = 5X+2q \sum_{n=1}^{q/2-2} 1/n \leqslant 5X+2q(1+\log(q/2-1)),$$

but $2(1+\log(q/2-1)) < 2\log(2e/q) < 4+2\log q < 6\log q$ (in view of $q \geqslant 3$) and thus

$$S(\xi) \leqslant 6(X+q\log q). \qquad \square$$

COROLLARY 1. *Under the assumptions of the lemma, if moreover* $2 \leqslant Y \leqslant q \leqslant X$, *then*

$$\left| \sum_{\substack{a\in A \\ b\in B}} \exp\{2\pi iabx\}\right|^2 \leqslant 24|A|\,|B|\,X\log X.$$

Proof. In this case $Y/q \leqslant 1$ and $X+q\log q \leqslant 2X\log X$. $\square$

COROLLARY 2. *If* $x\in(0, 1)$ *and lies in a minor arc, $S(x)$ is defined by* (4.12) *and finally U is the set of all positive integers which are sums of at most* $t = 1+[k\log(3k^2+2k)]$ *k-th powers of positive integers, then*

$$|S(x)|^2 \leqslant 24P^{k-d+d/k}\log P \cdot U(P^{k-d}/4)$$

where $U(X)$ denotes the counting function of the set U.

Proof. We apply the preceding corollary with A being the set of all kth powers not exceeding P^d and B being the set of all elements of U lying in

$[1, P^{k-d}/4]$. If x lies in a minor arc, then by Proposition A.6 we can find a rational number p/q such that

$$|x - p/q| \leqslant P^{d-k}/2q \leqslant q^{-2}$$

and $P^d < q \leqslant 2P^{k-d}$. The previous corollary implies now the required evaluation. □

COROLLARY 3. *If* $\mathfrak{M} = \{\mathfrak{m}\}$ *denotes the collection of all minor arcs, then for* $T(x)$, $R(x)$ *and* $S(x)$ *defined by* (4.10)–(4.12) *we have*

$$\sum_{\mathfrak{m} \in \mathfrak{M}} \int_{\mathfrak{m}} |T^s(x) R^2(x) S(x)| \, dx \leqslant 5P^{s+d/2k+(k-d)/2} \log^{1/2} P \cdot U^{1/2}(P^{k-d}/4) U(P^k/4).$$

Proof. Since the minor arcs are disjoint, the previous corollary implies that the sum in question does not exceed

$$\max_{0 \leqslant x \leqslant 1} |T(x)|^s \max_{\substack{x \in \bigcup \mathfrak{m} \\ \mathfrak{m} \in \mathfrak{M}}} |S(x)| \int_0^1 |R(x)|^2 \, dx$$

$$\leqslant P^s \cdot 5P^{k/2-d/2+d/2k} \log^{1/2} P \cdot U^{1/2}(P^{(k-d)/4}) \cdot U(P^k/4). \quad \square$$

Before making the final step we need an evaluation of $U(X)$ from below. This is given by the next lemma, which goes back to G. H. Hardy and J. E. Littlewood [25], where it was proved in a slightly sharper form.

LEMMA 4.15. *If* $k \geqslant 4$, $t \geqslant 1$ *and* $A_t(x)$ *denotes the number of positive integers* $\leqslant x$ *which are sums of at most* t k-*th powers of positive integers, then for* $x \geqslant 3^k$ *we have*

$$A_t(x) \geqslant C(k, t) x^{a_t}$$

where $a_t = 1 - (1 - 1/k)^t$ *and* $C(k, t) = d_k^{t-1} k^{-1} 2^{1-k}$ *with* $d_k = (2/3)^k k^{-1+1/k}$.

Proof. In the case $t = 1$ we have $a_1 = 1/k$ and $C(k, 1) = (k2^{k-1})^{-1} < 1/2$ and thus for $x \geqslant 2^k$

$$A_1(x) = [x^{1/k}] \geqslant x^{1/k}/2 \geqslant C(k, 1) x^{a_1}.$$

Assume now that our assertion is valid for a certain $t \geqslant 1$. Since between two consecutive kth powers u^k and $(u+1)^k$ we can insert at least

$$A_t((u+1)^k - u^k) \geqslant A_t(ku^{k-1})$$

integers which are sums of t kth powers, we get for $x \geqslant 3^k$ the inequality

$$A_{t+1}(x) \geqslant A_t(k) + A_t(k2^{k-1}) + \sum_{3 \leqslant n \leqslant x^{1/k} - 1} A_t(kn^{k-1})$$

$$\geqslant A_t(k) + A_t(k2^{k-1}) + \sum_{3 \leqslant n \leqslant x^{1/k} - 1} C(t) k^{a_t} n^{(k-1)a_t}$$

$$\geqslant C(t) k^{a_t} + C(t)(k2^{k-1})^{a_t} + C(t) k^{a_t} \sum_{3 \leqslant n \leqslant x^{1/k} - 1} n^{(k-1)a_t}$$

$$= C(t) k^{a_t} \int_0^{x^{1/k} - 1} y^{(k-1)a_t} \, dy = \frac{C(t) k^{a_t}}{a_t(k-1) + 1} (x^{1/k} - 1)^{a_t(k-1)+1}$$

due   to $A_t(k) \geqslant 1 = k/k \geqslant C(t)k^{a_t}$ and $A_t(k2^{k-1}) \geqslant 1 = k2^{k-1}/k2^{k-1}$
$\geqslant C(t)(k2^{k-1})^{a_t}$.

Since
$$\frac{(x^{1/k}-1)^{a_t(k-1)+1}}{x^{a_t+1}} = (1-x^{-1/k})^{a_t(k-1)+1} \geqslant (2/3)^{a_t(k-1)+1} \geqslant (2/3)^k,$$

we finally get
$$A_{t+1}(x) \geqslant \frac{C(t)k^{a_t}}{a_t(k-1)+1}\left(\frac{2}{3}\right)^k x^{a_t+1} \geqslant \left(\frac{2}{3}\right)^k \frac{C(t)k^{1/k}}{k} x^{a_t+1} = C(t+1)x^{a_t+1}. \quad \square$$

Now we can made the final step and show that the integral $J(N)$ given
by (4.9) is positive for large N. Corollary 3 to Lemma 4.14 implies that

$$\text{Re } J(N) = \sum_{I(a,q)\in \mathcal{M}} \text{Re} \int_{I(a,q)} T^{4k}(x)R^2(x)S(x)\exp\{-2\pi i Nx\}\,dx +$$

$$+ \sum_{\mathfrak{m}\in\mathfrak{M}} \text{Re} \int_{\mathfrak{m}} T^{4k}(x)R^2(x)S(x)\exp\{-2\pi i Nx\}\,dx$$

$$\geqslant \sum_{\substack{u_1,u_2\in U \\ u_1,u_2 \leqslant P^k/4}} \sum_{y\leqslant P^{d/k}} \sum_{\substack{u_3\in U \\ u_3 \leqslant P^{k-d}/4}} \sum_{I(a,q)\in\mathcal{M}} \text{Re} \int_{I(a,q)} T^s(x) \times$$

$$\times \exp\{-2\pi i(N-u_1-u_2-y^k)x\}\,dx -$$

$$- 5P^{4k+d/2k+(k-d)/2}\log^{1/2}P\cdot U^{1/2}(\tfrac{1}{4}P^{k-d})U(\tfrac{1}{4}P^k)$$

$$= \mathcal{A} - \mathcal{B}.$$

Since
$$\tfrac{1}{4}P^k \leqslant P^k/2 - P^d \leqslant N - P^k/2 - P^d \leqslant N - u_1 - u_2 - y^k \leqslant N = P^k,$$

we may apply to the first summand Corollary 2 to Lemma 4.13, and so it
follows that for $P \geqslant P_0 = \exp(15k^4)$ we have

$$\mathcal{A} \geqslant \alpha_k P^{3k+d/k}U(\tfrac{1}{4}P^{k-d})U^2(\tfrac{1}{4}P^k)$$

where
$$\alpha_k = (4/5)^{4k}3^{-1}\cdot 2^{-8}\exp\{-7.1k^3\} \geqslant \exp\{-7.13k^3\}.$$

We infer, using Lemma 4.15, that for $P \geqslant 5$ (so that $\tfrac{1}{4}P^{k-d} \geqslant 3^k$)

$$\mathcal{A}/\mathcal{B} \geqslant \frac{\alpha_k}{5}P^{-k+d/k-d/2k+(d-k)/2}\log^{-1/2}P\cdot U^{1/2}(\tfrac{1}{4}P^{k-d})U(\tfrac{1}{4}P^k)$$

$$\geqslant \frac{\alpha_k}{5}P^{-3k/2+d/2+d/2k}\log^{-1/2}P\cdot C(k,t)^{3/2}(\tfrac{1}{4}P^{k-d})^{a_t/2}(\tfrac{1}{4}P^k)^{a_t}$$

$$= \frac{\alpha_k\cdot C(k,t)^{3/2}}{5\cdot 8^{a_t}}P^{-3k/2+d/2+d/2k+a_t(3k/2-d/2)}\log^{-1/2}P$$

$$= \frac{\alpha_k\cdot C(k,t)^{3/2}}{5\cdot 8^{a_t}}P^{(a_t-1)((3k-d)/2)+d/2k}\log^{-1/2}P.$$

Observe now that our choice of t $(= 2 + [k \log (3k^2 + 2k)])$ implies that the exponent of P in the last expression is positive. In fact, with this choice of t we have the inequalities

$$1 - a_t = (1 - 1/k)^t < (1 - 1/k)^{1 + k \log (3k^2 + 2k)}$$

$$< (1 - 1/k) \exp \{ - \log (3k^2 + 2k) \} = \frac{k-1}{k} \cdot \frac{1}{3k^2 + 2k},$$

$$(a_t - 1) \left(\frac{3k - d}{2} \right) + \frac{d}{2k} > -\frac{k-1}{k} \cdot \frac{3k^2 - 2k}{2(3k^2 + 2k)(k+1)} + \frac{1}{2(k+1)}$$

$$= \frac{1}{2(k+1)} - \frac{k-1}{2k(k+1)} = \frac{1}{2k(k+1)},$$

$$\frac{\mathscr{A}}{\mathscr{B}} \geqslant \frac{\alpha_k \cdot C(k, t)^{3/2}}{5 \cdot 8^{a_t}} P^{k(k+1)/2} \log^{-1/2} P.$$

The inequalities

$$C(k, t) \geqslant \exp(-k(t-1) \log (3/2) - t \log k - k \log 2) \quad \text{and} \quad t \leqslant 2.84 k \log k$$

imply

$$C(k, t) \geqslant \exp(-1.9 k^2 \log k),$$

which leads to

$$\mathscr{A} \mathscr{B}^{-1} \geqslant \tfrac{1}{40} \exp(-7.13k^3 - 2.85k^2 \log k) P^{k(k+1)/2} \log^{-1/2} P$$

$$\geqslant \exp(-7.84k^3) P^{k(k+1)/2} \log^{-1/2} P.$$

Since $P^{k(k+1)/2} \log^{-1/2} P$ increases for $P \geqslant \exp(k^2 + k)$, we obtain for $P \geqslant P_1 = \exp(18k^5)$ the evaluation

$$\mathscr{A} \mathscr{B}^{-1} \geqslant \exp(-7.84k^3 + 9k^4/(k+1)) 18^{-1/2} k^{-5/2} \geqslant \exp(0.16k^3) \geqslant 1.$$

Since P_1 satisfies (4.32), we get for $N \geqslant P_1^k = \exp \{18k^6\}$ the inequality $J(N) \geqslant \mathscr{A} - \mathscr{B} > 0$, which completes the proof of the theorem. $\square$

Notes and comments

1. The circle method, which is essential in all analytical proofs of Waring's conjecture appeared for the first time in G. H. Hardy and S. Ramanujan [18], who applied it to the study of the partition function $p(n)$. Their results had been announced two years earlier at the Stockholm Congress of Scandinavian mathematicians (G. H. Hardy [16]). This application is much simpler than that to Waring's or Goldbach's problems since neither the distinction between major and minor arcs nor the study of the singular series is needed. The generating function $1 + \sum_{n=1}^{\infty} p(n) X^n$ is divided by $2\pi i X^{n+1}$ and integrated along a suitable circle $|z| = r < 1$ to get $p(n)$ and this task is beautifully executed in the paper in question. This first approach to the problem led only to an asymptotic formula for $p(n)$; however, H. Rademacher [37] showed later that an elaboration of the method leads to an explicit formula presenting $p(n)$ as a sum of a convergent series. (See R. Ayoub [63], § 3.)

The *singular series* appears for the first time in G. H. Hardy's study ([20]) of $r_s(n)$, the number of representations of a positive integer n as a sum of $3 \leqslant s \leqslant 8$ squares. Hardy gave there a uniform proof of the classical formulas for $r_s(n)$ due to C. G. J. Jacobi [29] (§ 40–42, $s = 4, 6, 8$), G. Eisenstein [47], H. J. S. Smith [87] and H. Minkowski [87], who dealt with $s = 5$. (In this case Eisenstein stated the formula and Smith and Minkowski gave independent proofs of it, which brought them the Grand Prix of the Paris Academy.) In Hardy's paper the singular series appeared in a shape which formally differs from (4.15) since the factor $\pi^{s/2} n^{s/2-1} \Gamma^{-1}(s/2)$ was incorporated in it. No error terms appeared in the final formulas and the reason for their absence was explained by C. L. Siegel [35], who extended Hardy's results to arbitrary positive definite quadratic forms over Z. It follows from his results that the error term in the formula for $r_s(n)$ disappears if and only if there is a single class in the genus of $X_1^s + \ldots + X_s^s$ and this happens only for $s \leqslant 8$. Hardy did not use complex integration and his methods are taken from the theory of modular forms. Cf. also T. Estermann [37a], [59].

Note that the formulas for $r_s(n)$ (including the classical result for $s = 2$ and the trivial one for $s = 1$) imply that the function $r_s(n)/2s$ is multiplicative for $s = 1, 2, 4$ and 8. P. T. Bateman [69] proved that this happens only in these cases. (Cf. J. Lagrange [72], where it was shown that the function $r_s(n^2)/2s$ is multiplicative if and only if $s \leqslant 8$.) Note that formulas for $r_s(n^2)$ in cases $s = 3, 5$ were obtained by A. Hurwitz [07], [84]. A uniform proof, covering also the case $s = 7$, was given by G. Pall [30]. Cf. also H. F. Sandham [53].

All features of the circle method including the singular series and the distinction between major and minor arcs appear in the first part of the celebrated series *Some problems of 'Partitio Numerorum'*. (G. H. Hardy, J. E. Littlewood [20], [21], [22], [25], [28]. In the sequel we shall denote papers from that series by PN I, PN II etc.) Their paper [20] brings the first analytical proof of Waring's theorem (Theorem 4.4) as well as an asymptotic expression valid for sufficiently large s for $r_{k,s}(n)$, defined as a sum with weights taken over all representations of n as a sum of s kth powers of non-negative integers. The important point is that $r_{k,s}(n)$ is positive if and only if n is a sum of s kth powers, and so to prove Theorem 4.4 it suffices to establish $r_{k,s}(n) > 0$. The proof, however, does not give any explicit bound for the minimal values of s for which the assertions are valid. To evaluate the terms of the singular series the authors use the results of H. Weyl [16], which lead to a worse bound than (4.17), namely

$$|S_{a,q}| = O(q^{1-a})$$

with $a = 1/2^{k-1}$. The same type of argument is also used to bound the integrand on minor arcs.

The first explicit bound for $G(k)$ appears in PN IV (Hardy, Littlewood [22]), where a detailed study of the singular series is made. In particular, we find there a proof of Lemma 4.9, parts of which appeared in PN II (Hardy, Littlewood [21]), where the case $k = 4$ was treated in detail and the bound $G(4) \leqslant 21$ was obtained. In Hardy, Littlewood [22] we find also the bound $|S_{a,p}| \leqslant (k-1) p^{1/2}$ for prime p. These improvements lead to the first bound for $G(k)$, namely $G(k) \leqslant (k-2) 2^{k-1} + 5$ and to an asymptotic formula for $r_{k,s}(n)$ valid for $s \geqslant (k-2) 2^{k-1} + 5$. Unfortunately one of the lemmas in this paper had an incorrect proof, which was later rectified in PN VI (Hardy, Littlewood [25]).

The main result of PN VI is the improved bound for $G(k)$, namely

$$G(k) \leqslant (k-2) 2^{k-2} + k + 5 + [\zeta_k] \qquad (k \geqslant 4)$$

where

$$\zeta_k = \frac{(k-2)\log 2 + \log(1 - 2/k)}{\log(1 + 1/(k-1))},$$

which gives $G(4) \leqslant 19$, $G(5) \leqslant 41$, ... It is also shown in PN VI that almost all numbers require at most $(k-2) 2^{k-2} + 3$ kth powers, and so, in particular, almost all integers are sums of 5 cubes.

A major part of PN VI is devoted to the study of the consequences of *hypothesis K*, stating that the number of representations $R_k(n)$ of an integer n as a sum of k kth powers is $O(n^\varepsilon)$ for every positive ε. This hypothesis was then known to be true for $k = 2$ (E. Landau [12]). Its consequences are fairly strong, e.g., it implies, as shown in PN VI, that for $k \neq 2^m$ ($m = 1, 2, \ldots$) one has $G(k) \leqslant 1 + 2k$ and $G(2^m) \leqslant 4 \cdot 2^m$. Unfortunately hypothesis K was disproved for $k = 3$ by K. Mahler [36], who produced the identity

$$(9x^4)^3 + (3xy^3 - 9x^4)^3 + (y^4 - 9x^3 y)^3 = y^{12},$$

implying that infinitely often we have

$$R_3(N) > cN^{1/12} \qquad \text{with } c = 9^{-1/3}.$$

Whether this hypothesis is true for $k \geqslant 4$ is still an open question. In any case $R_k(N)$ is unbounded, which was proved by S. Chowla [35e], [35f] and P. Erdös [36b]. In fact Erdös showed that for infinitely many N one has $R_k(N) > \exp(c \log N (\log \log N)^{-1})$ with a positive constant $c = c(k)$.

S. Chowla [36b] showed that many consequences of "hypothesis K" can already be deduced from certain assertions about the mean value of $R_k(N)$; however, these assertions have never been proved.

For biquadrates K. Mahler [34a] showed that already the number of representations of an integer N as a sum of three biquadrates is unbounded and S. Chowla [33] proved that this number is infinitely often larger than $c \log N (\log \log N)^{-1}$ with a positive c. Later M. Parthasarathy [53] replaced this bound by

$$\exp(c \log N (\log \log N)^{-1}) \quad \text{with } c > 0.$$

2. Certain simplifications in the Hardy–Littlewood proof of the Waring theorem were introduced by E. Landau [21], [22], [26a], [30a], A. Ostrowski [21] and H. Weyl [21], [22]. In particular, Weyl in his second paper showed that if one is satisfied with a proof of the existence of $g(k)$ then the study of the major arcs can be replaced by a more elementary argument, and Ostrowski proved that if for a certain value of s the singular series exceeds a positive constant c then the same holds also for all larger values of s. E. Landau showed in [22] that the argument can be slightly modified to yield an asymptotic formula for the number of representations of a given large integer as a sum of $s \geqslant (k-2) 2^{k-1} + 5$ kth powers. All subsequent authors dealt directly with this number rather than with the slightly artificial function $r_{k,s}(N)$ used by Hardy and Littlewood. Landau's book (E. Landau [27a]) gives the Hardy–Littlewoods proof with all details and his paper [30c] introduces further simplifications in the study of the singular series. A study of the major arcs is contained in Bessel-Hagen [29].

In 1924 I. M. Vinogradov [24] published the first of his proofs of Waring's theorem. A version of it was presented by E. Landau [26b] and included also in Landau [27a]. Vinogradov's novelty lies in very clever estimations of trigonometrical sums. He does not have to use either the singular series or complex integration (because he noticed the simple fact overlooked by previous writers that the number of representations of an integer n as a sum of s kth powers does not depend on the terms of degree $\geqslant n+1$ of the generating series). Vinogradov's approach gives the finiteness of $g(k)$ but does not lead to any bound for $g(k)$ or $G(k)$.

Four years later I. M. Vinogradov [28a] returned to this subject and succeeded in simplifying and amending the original Hardy–Littlewood approach to obtain the first really simple proof of Waring's theorem, which implied the bound $G(k) \leqslant (k-2) 2^{k-1} + 5$.

Certain technical improvements in this proof were introduced in Landau [30b] and Gelbcke [31].

In Vinogradov [34a] a new approach was devised, this time avoiding the use of Weyl's sums and leading to $G(k) \leqslant 32\,k^2 \log^2 k$, a very substantial improvement over previous bounds. This was later improved by the same author (Vinogradov [34b], [34c], [35a], [35d]) to

$$G(k) \leqslant 6\,k \log k + (\log 216 + 4)\,k.$$

Paper [35b] of I. M. Vinogradov gives the weaker bound

$$G(k) \leqslant (\log 4)\,k^2 + (2 - \log 16)\,k$$

by a method using Weyl's sums. The next improvement appeared in Vinogradov [38], where $G(k) \leqslant 4k \log k + O(k \log \log k)$ was proved, and in Vinogradov [47], where one finds $G(k) \leqslant 3k \log k + 11$.

For sufficiently large k one can do better, and in fact in Vinogradov [59] the evaluation $G(k) \leqslant k(2\log k + 4\log\log k + 2\log\log\log k + 13)$ was obtained for $k > 170000$. This is the best known bound valid for large k. Weaker bounds, which, however, are valid for all $k \geqslant 15$ were obtained by K. C. Tong [57]: $G(k) \leqslant 3\log k + 9k$, J. J. Chen [58], [67]: $G(k) \leqslant 3k \log k + 5.2k$ and K. Thanigasalam [80b]: $G(k) \leqslant 3k \log k + 4.7k$.

B. M. Bredikhin and T. I. Grishina [78] obtained in an elementary way a proof of $G(k) \ll k \log k$, using Linnik's dispersion method.

The proof of Theorem 4.6 presented here is that of H. Heilbronn [36], in which all constants are explicitly evaluated.

3. The exact value of $G(k)$ is known only in two cases: $G(2) = 4$ and $G(4) = 16$, quoted already in § 1. For certain small values of k upper bounds are known which are better than those resulting from general theorems. We now quote the consecutive improvements of those bounds for $k \leqslant 10$:

$G(5) \leqslant 35$ (R. D. James [34b]), $\leqslant 29$ (T. Estermann [37b]), $\leqslant 28$ (L. K. Hua [37b]), $\leqslant 24$ (K. Sambasiva Rao [41], $\leqslant 23$ (H. Davenport [42b]).

$G(6) \leqslant 42$ (T. Estermann [37b]), $\leqslant 36$ (K. Sambasiva Rao [41], H. Davenport [42b]).

$G(7) \leqslant 64$ (R. D. James [34b]), $\leqslant 59$ (T. Estermann [37b]), $\leqslant 52$ (K. Sambasiva Rao [41]).

$G(8) \leqslant 78$ (T. Estermann [37b]), $\leqslant 73$ (V. Narasimhamurti [41]).

$G(9) \leqslant 824$ (R. D. James [34b]), $\leqslant 101$ (T. Estermann [37b]), $\leqslant 99$ (V. Naramsimhamurti [41]), $\leqslant 96$ (R. J. Cook [73]), $\leqslant 91$ (R. C. Vaughan [77]), $\leqslant 90$ (K. Thanigasalam [80b]), $\leqslant 88$ (K. Thanigasalam [82]).

$G(10) \leqslant 125$ (T. Estermann [37b]), $\leqslant 122$ (V. Narasimhamurti [41]), $\leqslant 121$ (J. J. Chen [58], R. J. Cook [73]), $\leqslant 107$ (R. C. Vaughan [77]), $\leqslant 106$ (K. Thanigasalam [80b]), $\leqslant 104$ (K. Thanigasalam [82]).

(Added in proof. A. Schinzel informed me that R. C. Vaughan got for $k = 5, 6, \ldots, 10$ the bounds 21, 31, 45, 62, 82 and 102 respectively.)

For $11 \leqslant k \leqslant 20$ the best evaluations of $G(k)$ are due to K. Thanigasalam

[82], who obtained 119, 134, 150, 165, 181, 197, 213, 229, 245 and 262 respectively.

4. In PNIV the asymptotic formula for $r_{k,s}(N)$ was obtained for $s \geqslant (k-2) 2^{k-1} + 5$ and E. Landau [22] showed that it holds also for the number of representation of N as a sum of s non-negative kth powers in the same range of s. I. M. Vinogradov, in a series of papers ([35c], [36a], [36b], [36c]), obtained drastic improvements of this bound, starting with $s \geqslant 91k^8 (1 + \log k)^2$ (for $k \geqslant 20$) in [35e]. Later I. M. Vinogradov [47] reduced the bound further to $s \geqslant 10k^2 \log k$ and L. K. Hua [47], [49] showed that $s \geqslant k^2 (4 \log k + 2 \log^{1/2} k + \log \log k + 1)$ already suffices.

In Vinogradov [71] the asymptotical formula is proved for $k \geqslant 12$ and $s \geqslant k^2 (4 \log k + 2 \log \log k + 6)$, which is slightly better.

Proofs that $s \geqslant 2^k + 1$ is sufficient for the asymptotical formula were given by L. K. Hua [38a] and T. Estermann [48a]. L. K. Hua [57] showed also that the asymptotics for the contribution of the major arcs can already be obtained for $s \geqslant 1 + k$ but the minor arcs still present serious difficulties.

Detailed expositions of the analytical method of dealing with Waring's problem can be found in Landau [27a], Davenport [62], and R. C. Vaughan [81].

5. The method of L. Schnirelman [33] was successfully applied to the proof of Waring's theorem by Yu. V. Linnik [43b], who produced a completely elementary proof. Later G. J. Rieger [54] effectivized his arguments and so obtained the rather huge bound

$$g(k) \leqslant \exp(2 \cdot 16^k (k+1)! \log 2).$$

Combining the analytical method with Schnirelman's approach one gets perhaps the simplest proof of Waring's theorem, as demonstrated by D. J. Newman [60]. Cf. also K. Thanigasalam [74].

6. Proposition 4.3 in the case of prime q appears for the first time in PNIV as Lemma 13, although the case $q = 2$ goes back to C. F. Gauss [01], art. 356. It seems that it was first stated in full generality by E. Landau [27a].

Later the bounds for $S_{a,q}$ were carried over to more general situations. Let f be a polynomial of degree k over Z, let q be a given integer, and assume that the greatest common divisor of the coefficients of f is prime to q. Put

$$S_q(f) = \sum_{x=0}^{q-1} \exp(2\pi i f(x) q^{-1}).$$

The first non-trivial bound for this sum in the general case was obtained by E. Kamke [24], who proved

$$|S_q(f)| \ll q^{1 - 2^{1-k} + \varepsilon} \qquad \text{for every positive } \varepsilon.$$

Later L. J. Mordell [32] considered the case of prime q and showed that if q does not divide the leading coefficient of f then

$$|S_q(f)| \ll q^{1-1/k}.$$

This was improved by H. Davenport [33], who replaced the exponent by $1 - 1/r$ where r is the largest integer of the form 2^m or $3 \cdot 2^m$ not exceeding k.

In the case of composite q L. K. Hua [38b], [40a], [40b] obtained for every positive ε the bound

$$|S_q(f)| \ll q^{1-1/k+\varepsilon}$$

provided the greatest common divisor of the coefficients of f is prime to q. In Hua [51] this was generalized to polynomials with integral algebraic coefficients, and the proof turned out to be simpler than that in Hua [40b]. V. I. Nechaev [53] removed the ε from the exponent and at the same time effectivized the bound by proving

$$|S_q(f)| \leqslant \exp(2^{1+k}) q^{1-1/k} \quad \text{for} \quad k \geqslant 12.$$

Denote by $B(k)$ the maximal value of $|S_q(f) q^{1/k-1}|$ taken over all pairs f, q of polynomials over Z of degree k and positive integers q for which the previous condition concerning the coefficients of f is satisfied. Nechaev's bound $B(k) \leqslant \exp(2^{1+k})$ was improved by J. J. Chen [59b] to $B(k) \leqslant \exp(Ck^2)$ with a fixed C, and V. I. Nechaev [75] proved that, for $k \geqslant 3$, $B(k) \leqslant \exp(5k^2 \log^{-1} k)$. For large k S. B. Stechkin [77] obtained $B(k) \leqslant \exp(k + O(k/\log k))$ and the best bound valid for all $k \geqslant 3$ was given by J. J. Chen [77], who showed that $B(k) \leqslant \exp(c_k k)$ with $c_3 = 6.1$, $c_4 = 5.5$, $c_5 = 5$, $c_6 = 4.7$, $c_7 = 4.4$, $c_8 = 4.2$, $c_9 = 4.05$ and $c_k = 4k$ for $k \geqslant 10$. O. Körner and H. Stähle [79] obtained a result of similar nature, proving

$$|S_q(f)| \leqslant (k^2 - k)^{v(q,k)} q^{1-1/k}$$

where $v(q, k)$ is the number of prime divisors of q which do not exceed either 2^k or $(k-1)^{2k(k-2)}$. This result is stronger than Chen's in cases where q does not have many small prime divisors. They also showed that if $q = p^m$ is a prime power with $m \geqslant 2$ then

$$|S_q(f)| \leqslant (k^2 - k) q^{1-1/t},$$

where $t = \min(k, m)$. In certain cases this can be further improved. Cf. also L. K. Hua [57].

Note that for the polynomials of the form $f(x) = ax^k$ S. B. Stechkin [75] proved

$$|S_q(f)| \leqslant \exp(Ck^2 \varphi^{-2}(k)) q^{1-1/k}$$

with an absolute constant C (cf. also D. A. Mit'kin [75]). For certain values of k and prime p the sum $G_k(p) = S_p(x^k)$ can be evaluated explicitly. For $k = 2$ such an evaluation follows easily from Theorem 2.1. Formulas for G_3 and G_4 can be found in Hasse [50], but with a sign ambiguity. Other known cases include $k = 5$ (E. Lehmer [51]), $k = 6, 8, 12, 24$ (B. C. Berndt, R. Evans [79]) and $k = 16$ (Evans [80]).

The proof of the Riemann hypothesis for zeta-functions of curves obtained by A. Weil [48] gave the possibility of obtaining very accurate bounds in the case of prime q. This was shown by L. Carlitz and S. Uchiyama [57], who deduced in this case the evaluation

$$|S_q(f)| \leqslant (k-1) q^{1/2}.$$

This bound seems to be very close to the best possible, since L. A. Knizhnerman and V. Z. Sokolinskij [79] stated that with positive probability $|S_q(f)|$ exceeds, for prime q, $(1.38\,k^{1/2} - \varepsilon) q^{1/2}$, which means that the number of polynomials of degree k which are pairwise incongruent (mod q), vanish at 0 and satisfy

$$|S_q(f)| \geqslant (1.38 k^{1/2} - \varepsilon) q^{1/2} \quad \text{with a fixed } \varepsilon > 0$$

is at least equal to $(C(\varepsilon) + o(1)) q^k$ with a positive $C(\varepsilon)$ for q tending to infinity through all primes.

7. Proposition 4.4 was first proved in PN I; however, no effective bound for the sum of the singular series was obtained. It was only shown that for sufficiently large s this sum exceeds $1/2$. The first effective bound appears to be due to R. D. James [34a], who evaluated all constants appearing in Gelbcke's proof (M. Gelbcke [31]), which led him to the first explicit upper bound for $g(k)$. Later R. D. James [35] improved his evaluations for odd $k \geqslant 7$ and L. E. Dickson [36b] evaluated the constants occurring in the proof of I. M. Vinogradov [35d]. In fact, he did this not only for the Waring problem but also for the Waring–Kamke problem with polynomial summands.

Lemma 4.9 (i), (ii) appears in PN II in the case of sufficiently large s and the connection of the singular series with congruences (Lemma 4.9 (iii), (iv)) appears as Lemma 2 in PN IV. Theorem 2 of that paper gives an explicit formula for $T(p)$ (for a simple proof cf. H. D. Kloosterman [39]), and it is also shown there that A_{p^r} vanishes for sufficiently large r; hence the limit in Lemma 4.9 (iv) is attained already at a finite stage.

The study of the singular series $S(n)$ leads immediately to the consideration of the analogue of Waring's problem in GF (p) and in the ring Z_p of p-adic integers. Denote by $\Gamma(k, p)$ the *Waring constant for the field* GF (p), i.e., the minimal integer s such that every element of that field is a sum of at most s kth powers, and let $\Gamma_p(k)$ be the corresponding constant for

Z_p. Following Hardy and Littlewood we put

$$\Gamma(k) = \max_p \Gamma_p(k) \geqslant \max_p \Gamma(k, p).$$

Lemma 4.10 (iii), which goes back to PN IV, shows that $\Gamma(k) \leqslant 4k$, and in PN VIII one finds the bound $\Gamma(k, p) \leqslant k$. M. M. Dodson [71] showed that for sufficiently large k one has $\Gamma(k, p) < k^{7/8}$ and this was improved by A. Tietäväinen [73] to $\Gamma(k, p) \ll k^{3/5 + \varepsilon}$ (for all $\varepsilon > 0$) and M. M. Dodson and A. Tietäväinen [76] to

$$\Gamma(k, p) < 68k^{1/2} \log^2 k.$$

The last result is not far from being the best possible since in the same paper the authors show that if $p = 3k + 1$ is a prime then

$$\Gamma(k, p) > 3^{1/2} k^{1/2}/2 - \tfrac{1}{2}.$$

If d is a divisor of $p - 1$ and $p - 1 = td$, then a conjecture of H. Heilbronn [64] states that for $t > t_0(\varepsilon)$ one has

$$\Gamma(d, p) < d^\varepsilon \quad \text{(for every positive } \varepsilon\text{)}.$$

H. Heilbronn himself showed that

$$\Gamma(d, p) \leqslant C(t) p^{1/\varphi(t)}$$

and J. D. Bovey [77] proved

$$\Gamma(d, p) \ll \varphi(t) d^\varepsilon$$

for all positive ε.

It was noted already in PN IV that if k is not divisible by $(p-1)/2$ then $\Gamma_p(k) \leqslant k$. I. Chowla [43] improved this to $\Gamma_p(k) \leqslant k^c$ with any c exceeding $1 - 0.122936$, and later M. Dodson [71] showed that in this case the bound $\Gamma_p(k) \leqslant k^{7/8}$ holds for large k. Finally J. D. Bovey [76] obtained the evaluation $\Gamma_p(k) \ll k^{1/2 + \varepsilon}$ for every $\varepsilon > 0$.

The corresponding problem for the ring of integers in a finite extension of a p-adic field was also considered, and it was shown that in this case the Waring constant can be bounded by a function depending only on k but not on the ring in question. This was proved independently by B. J. Birch [64], who got the bound k^{16k^2} and C. P. Ramanujam [63], whose bound was $8k^5$. It should be pointed out that Birch's proof is much simpler and shorter.

The study of the function $\Gamma(k)$ was initiated in PN VIII. We find there, among other things, a list of all cases in which $\Gamma(k)$ exceeds k, as well as a nice characterization of this number for $k \neq 4$, stating that $\Gamma(k)$ equals the smallest integer s such that every arithmetical progression contains infinitely many sums of at most s kth powers.

Later I. Chowla [37b] showed that for infinitely many primes p we have

$\Gamma(p) < 2p/3$ (cf. also I. Chowla [37a] for a study of an analogous function) and more recently M. Dodson [73] obtained the bound $\Gamma(k) < k^{7/8}$ for an infinite sequence of k's which includes infinitely many primes as well as infinitely many even numbers.

The mean value of $\Gamma(k)$ was found by M. M. Dodson [69], who proved that

$$\sum_{k \leqslant x} \Gamma(k) = (c + o(1)) x^2 / \log x \quad \text{with} \quad c = 5\pi^2/24.$$

8. There are many possibilities of defining the Farey dissection of the integration interval in the proof of Waring's theorem. In PN I Farey fractions of order $N^{1-1/k}$ were used. H. Weyl [21] and E. Landau [22] used them up to the order N^{1-a} with $a = k^{-1} 2^{k-1}/(1+2^{k-1})$ and in PN VI two other choices were made. In Vinogradov's proofs various types of dissection were used; sometimes he considered not only major and minor arcs but up to four types of arcs.

Lemma 4.13 (ii) is due to E. Landau [30a]. Cf. H. Kestelman [37] for an evaluation of a more general integral. Lemma 4.14 is due to I. M. Vinogradov and the proof given is that of H. Heilbronn [36].

The lower bounds for $A_t(x)$ given in Lemma 4.15 are weaker than those proved in PN VI, where the case $t = 2$ was treated separately and the inductive argument started with that case.

E. Landau [26c] showed that $A_2(x) \gg x^{2/k} \log^{-1} x$ and this was slightly improved by S. S. Pillai [28]. From a general result of P. Erdös and K. Mahler [38] it follows that in Landau's result the logarithm may be removed. For odd k an elementary proof of that was given by P. Erdös [39c]. (See also Davenport, Erdös [39] and Davenport [42a].) In the case of odd k the asymptotical behaviour of $A_2(x)$ was determined by C. Hooley [81], who proved

$$A_2(x) = C(k) x^{2/k} + O(x^{5/3k+\varepsilon})$$

(for all $\varepsilon > 0$) with a positive constant $C(k)$. Previously Hooley [64] dealt with the case of prime $k \geqslant 5$ and in [63] with $k = 3$.

9. The methods used in various proofs of Theorem 4.6 can also be successfully applied to the study of representations of integers as sums of the values of a given polynomial. For certain special polynomials this question was already considered by P. Fermat [70] (art. 305), who asserted that every positive integer is a sum of at most n polygonal numbers of order n, defined as integers of the form $x + (n-2)(x^2-x)/2$. Note that for $n = 4$ this is equivalent to Theorem 4.1. In the case $n = 3$ Fermat's assertion was confirmed by C. F. Gauss [01] (art. 293) and the general case was settled by A. Cauchy [13]. Other proofs were given by T. Pepin [92] and by L. E. Dickson [27b]. (Cf. also L. E. Dickson [34e].)

A more general approach was initiated by E. Kamke [21], who proved that if f is a non-constant polynomial with integral coefficients which assumes non-negative values at positive arguments, then there exists a constant $C(f)$ such that every positive integer can be written in the form

$$f(x_1) + \ldots + f(x_n) + m$$

where $x_1, \ldots, x_n$ are positive integers, $m \geqslant 0$ and $m + n \leqslant C$.

This result holds also if one assumes that f is integer-valued and for certain polynomials f one can eliminate the summand m in the above expression.

For polynomials of degrees not exceeding 5 Kamke's theorem is essentially equivalent to an older result of E. Maillet [96]. If the polynomial f is without a constant term and has no fixed prime divisor, then the constant $C(f)$ can be made dependent only on the degree of f (E. Kamke [22]). Earlier E. Landau [22] proved Kamke's theorem with $C(f)$ depending only on the degree and the leading coefficient of f. Obviously one cannot have this for all polynomials, as the example of $f(x) = Nx^2$ shows.

The earliest proofs of Kamke's theorem (E. Kamke [21], [22]) were elementary, but it is also possible to prove it by using analytical means (E. Landau [22], [26b], E. Kamke [24], I. M. Vinogradov [28b]). Note that most of the papers of I. M. Vinogradov concerning the original Waring problem which we quoted earlier cover also Kamke's theorem. A. V. Kuzel' [56] gave a proof based on Schnirelman's method.

Asymptotics for the number of representations was obtained by L. K. Hua [36b], who using Gelbcke's approach to the Waring problem (M. Gelbcke [31]) showed that for polynomials f without a fixed divisor of degree $k \geqslant 3$ at most $2^{k-1}(k-2) + 5$ summands are needed to represent large numbers as sums of values of f. Later (Hua [37a]) he applied the method of H. Heilbronn [36] and obtained a weaker result. S. S. Pillai [37b] sharpened this bound to $O(k^3 \log k)$. In Hua [38a] the asymptotical formula is proved for $s \geqslant 1 + 2^k$.

The problem of obtaining bounds for $C(f)$ for various particular polynomials f and classes of polynomials has been intensively studied. Quadratic polynomials were considered by L. E. Dickson [27b], [28a], [28b], [28c], [37] and G. Pall [31], [32a], [32b].

It is easy to establish that every cubic integral-valued polynomial has the form

$$f(x) = a(x^3 - x)/6 + b(x^2 - x)/2 + cx + d.$$

Denote by $g(a, b, c, d)$ the minimal number of summands $f(x_j)$ needed to represent every positive integer, and similarly let $G(a, b, c, d)$ be the minimal number of such summands which is sufficient for representing all large integers. R. D. James [33] proved that $G(1, 0, 0, 0) \leqslant 8$ and $g(1, 0, 0, 0) \leqslant 9$

and later (R. D. James [34c]), using the method of E. Landau [30b], got $G(a, b, c, d) \leqslant 9$ in the case $(a, b, c) = 1$, $a > 0$ and $a \not\equiv 4c \,(\mathrm{mod}\, 8)$. The last restriction turned out to be irrelevant (R. D. James [37]). In Dickson [34a], certain particular cases of this result were obtained. After studying several particular cases (Hua [35a], [35b], [35d]) L. K. Hua [40c], [40d] proved under the same assumptions the bound $G(a, b, c, d) \leqslant 8$.

About the value of $g(a, b, c, d)$ not much is known. G. C. Webber [34] proved $g(6, 6, 1, 0) = 15$, L. E. Dickson [34f] showed that for $m = 1, 2, \ldots, 6$ and for no other value of m one has $g(m, 0, 1, 0) \leqslant 9$ and later (L. E. Dickson [36d]) listed 116 cubic polynomials such that every integer is a sum of at most nine of its values. Rather huge bounds for $g(a, b, c, d)$ in certain particular cases were obtained by A. Sugar [36], [37], and G. L. Watson [52] showed that $g(1, 0, 1, 0) \leqslant 8$ and $g(1, 0, 0, 0) \leqslant 8$.

Corresponding results for certain particular polynomials of higher degrees can be found in Dickson [34f].

V. I. Nechaev [51], [53] considered the polynomial

$$P_k(x) = x(x+1)\ldots(x+k-1)/k!$$

and showed that every large integer is a sum of at most $6k \log k + 4k \log \log k$ of its values for $k \geqslant 12$. This number was reduced by J. J. Chen [59b] to $5k \log k + 60$.

10. E. M. Wright [33a] considered decomposition of an integer into sums of s squares which are approximately proportional to a given sequence of s integers, and proved that if $s \geqslant 5$ and $a_1, \ldots, a_s$ are positive numbers adding up to unity then every integer N can be written in the form

$$N = x_1^2 + \ldots + x_s^2,$$

so that the following additional condition holds:

$$|x_i^2 - a_i N| \ll N^{1-c}$$

where $c = c(s)$ is an explicit positive constant. Under certain conditions the same can be asserted in the case $s = 4$ (E. M. Wright [36]). F. C. Auluck and S. Chowla [37] showed that $c(4)$ can be taken to be $1/4$ and E. M. Wright [37a] proved that it cannot be made larger. (Cf. also E. M. Wright [37b].)

For cubes a similar result was proved by S. Chowla [35d] and N. Chudakov [36].

An analogous result holds also for higher powers, provided

$$s \geqslant (k-2)2^{k-1} + 5$$

(E. M. Wright [33b], [34a]). M. Laborde [76] proved that for $s \geqslant g(k)$ one can solve

$$N = x_1^k + \ldots + x_s^k \quad \text{with} \quad |x_i^k - a_i N| < \varepsilon N$$

for any $\varepsilon > 0$ and $a_i \geqslant 0$ with $a_1 + \ldots + a_s = 1$.

11. Denote by $v(k)$ the least number s such that every integer N can be written in the form

$$N = \varepsilon_1 x_1^k + \ldots + \varepsilon_s x_s^k \quad \text{with} \quad \varepsilon_i = \pm 1.$$

Clearly $v(k) \leqslant g(k)$, and so Theorem 4.4 implies that $v(k)$ is well-defined and finite for all values of k. The first to consider the problem of determining $v(k)$, called now the *"easier"* Waring problem, was V. Veselý [33b], who gave a simple direct proof of the finiteness of $v(k)$. The only previous result in this respect seems to be that of G. Otramare [94], viz. $v(3) \leqslant 5$. (Cf. H. W. Richmond [22c].)

The first upper bound for $v(k)$ was given by E. M. Wright [34b], who proved

$$v(k) \leqslant 2^{k-1} + \Delta(k, k!)$$

where $\Delta(k, m)$ denotes the *Waring constant for the ring of residue classes* (mod m). Since from the results of Hardy and Littlewood [28] it follows that $\Delta(k, k!) \leqslant 4k$, we obtain the inequality $v(k) \leqslant 2^{k-1} + 4k$. The true order of magnitude of $v(k)$ is not known and neither are the values of $v(k)$ except $k = 2$, in which case one easily gets $v(2) = 3$. For large k E. M. Wright [34b] established

$$v(k) \ll \exp(0.267 k),$$

and so, as expected, $v(k)$ turned to be of a much lower order than $g(k)$, which is, as we shall see in the next section, asymptotical to $2^k = \exp(0.693\ldots k)$.

The number $v(k)$ can be very small. S. Chowla [35b] proved that we infinitely often get $v(k) < Bk^2$ with a certain constant B, and in [35c] he made this result more precise by proving $v(k) \leqslant k^2 + 7k - 2$ for infinitely many values of k.

We have already noted the bound $v(3) \leqslant 5$. It is an open problem whether $v(3) = 4$. Chao Ko [36] checked that all positive integers $N \leqslant 100$ can be represented by at most four cubes and this was extended to $N \leqslant 1000$ by V. A. Demyanenko [66]. L. J. Mordell [36] showed that if $N \not\equiv \pm 4 \pmod 9$ and $N \not\equiv \pm 2 \pmod{18}$ then four cubes suffice. The last two exceptions were eliminated by V. A. Demyanenko [66] (for certain N see A. Schinzel, W. Sierpiński [58a]), who showed also that if $N \not\equiv \pm 4 \pmod 9$ then there are infinitely many representations. However, the case $N \equiv \pm 4 \pmod 9$ is still open, although H. Davenport and H. Heilbronn [37a] proved that four cubes are sufficient for almost all integers.

The first bound for biquadrates, $v(4) \leqslant 12$ was given by E. M. Wright [34b]. Later H. Davenport [41] and W. Hunter [41] improved this, giving $v(4) \leqslant 11$ and $v(4) \leqslant 10$ respectively and Hunter noted also that $v(4) \geqslant 9$.

Evaluations of $v(k)$ for $5 \leqslant k \leqslant 20$ can be found in Wright [34b], Chowla

[35a], Fuchs, Wright [39] and Rai [50] and, in the range $21 \leqslant k \leqslant 30$, in Banerjee [42]. An analogous problem for polynomials (the *"easier" Waring–Kamke problem*) was treated by L. K. Hua [35f], [36a], who showed that if $P(x)$ is an integer-valued polynomial of degree $k \geqslant 1$ then every integer N can be written in the form

$$N = \sum_{j=1}^{s} \pm P(x_j) + C$$

with integers $x_1, \ldots, x_s$, C and $s + |C| \leqslant 2^k - 2 + (a_{k-1}, a_{k-2})$ where the numbers a_{k-1}, a_{k-2} are obtained from the canonical representation

$$P(x) = \sum_{j=0}^{k} a_j \binom{x}{j}.$$

The particular polynomials $f_N(x) = x + N(x^3 - x)/6$ were earlier treated by L. K. Hua [35c], who showed that every integer is a sum of seven values of $\pm f_N$ at integral arguments x.

12. The problem of representing positive integers as sums of powers with not necessarily the same exponent has been considered by several authors. The first result of this type seems to be due to G. K. Stanley [31], who showed that every sufficiently large integer can be written as a sum of two squares and four cubes, and proved that the same holds for sums of one square and six cubes. Later H. Davenport and H. Heilbronn [37a] showed that almost all integers are sums of two cubes and a square and in [37b] they obtained the same result for two squares and a kth power, with an arbitrary odd k. K. F. Roth [49] showed that almost all integers are of the form $x^2 + y^3 + z^4$ and in [51] he considered the question of the smallest possible k that can be chosen to ensure that every sufficiently large integer could be written in the form $x_1^2 + x_2^3 + \ldots + x_k^{k+1}$. He showed that $k = 50$ is enough and this was later consecutively reduced to $k = 35$ (K. Thanigasalam [68]), $k = 30$ (R. C. Vaughan [70b]), $k = 26$ (R. C. Vaughan [71]), $k = 22$ (K. Thanigasalam [80a]) and $k = 20$ (K. Thanigasalam, to appear), which is the best result to date. T. Kløve [72] checked that, for integers up to $250\,000$, $k = 6$ is enough and conjectured that for sufficiently large integers $k = 4$ works; however there is no hope of proving this conjecture in the near future.

Denote by $g_2(k)$ the minimal integer s such that every positive integer can be written as a sum of at most s powers with exponents $\geqslant k$. The question of determining $g_2(k)$ was first considered by M. Haberzetle [39], who proved that under certain assumptions on k one has

$$g_2(k) = 2^k + [\log q / \log 2] - 1,$$

where $q = [3^k / 2^k]$. This equality was later shown to hold for all $k \geqslant 32$ by S. S. Pillai [40d].

A related result was announced by G. A. Freiman [49]: if $2 \leqslant n_1 \leqslant n_2 \leqslant \dots$ is a given sequence of integers then for every n_j one can find an integer $r = r(n_j)$ with the property that all sufficiently large integers can be written in the form $x_1^{n_j} + \dots + x_r^{n_j + r - 1}$ if and only if the series $\sum\limits_{j=1}^{\infty} n_j^{-1}$ diverges. This assertion was proved by E. J. Scourfield [60].

There are many results showing that all large integers are sums of a certain number of various powers. The interested reader should consult W. J. Leveque [74], vol. 4.

Exercises

1. Obtain lower bounds for the sum of the singular series in the cases $4 \leqslant k \leqslant 8$.

2 (L. J. Mordell [32]). Let f be a polynomial of degree $k \geqslant 1$ such that $f(0) = 0$ and let p be a prime not dividing the leading coefficient of f. Put

$$S_p(f) = \sum_{x=0}^{p-1} \exp\{2\pi i f(x) p^{-1}\}.$$

(a) For $1 \leqslant a \leqslant p-1$, $0 \leqslant b \leqslant p-1$ let $f_{a,b}(x) = f(ax+b) - f(b)$. Prove that

$$|S_p(f)|^{2k} = \frac{1}{p(p-1)} \sum_{a=1}^{p-1} \sum_{b=0}^{p} |S_p(f_{a,b})|^{2k},$$

and for every polynomial g over $GF(p)$ there are at most k^2 polynomials $f_{a,b}$ whose reduction (mod p) equals g.

(b) Interpret the sum

$$\sum_{g(0)=0} |S_p(g)|^{2k},$$

where g runs over all polynomials of degree k over $GF(p)$, as the number of solutions of a certain system of congruences.

(c) Deduce from (a) and (b) the bound

$$|S_p(f)| \leqslant kp^{1 - 1/k}.$$

3. Prove that the number $r_{2,k}(n)$ of representations of an integer n as a sum of two kth powers is $\ll n^\varepsilon$ for every $\varepsilon > 0$.

4. Prove that $\sum\limits_{n \leqslant x} r_{2,k}(n) = (C_k + o(1)) x^{2/k}$.

5. Using Exercises 3 and 4, improve Lemma 4.15 to obtain

$$A_t(x) \gg x^{b_t - \varepsilon} \quad \text{(for every positive } \varepsilon)$$

with $b_t = 1 - (1 - 2/k)(1 - 1/k)^{t-2}$.

6. Obtain a closed expression for the value of $T(p)$ defined before Lemma 4.9.

7. Prove that $v(2) = 3$ and $v(3) \leqslant 5$, where $v(k)$ denotes the smallest integer s such that every integer is a sum of at most s integers of the form $\pm x^k$.

8 (T. H. Jackson, F. Rehman [74], J. D. Bovey [77]). Prove that, if A is a subset of Z/mZ

such that every element of Z/mZ is a difference of two elements of A, then every element of Z/mZ can be written as a sum of at most $1+[\log m/\log 2]$ elements of A.

9 (J. D. Bovey [77]). Let p be a prime and k a divisor of $p-1$, and denote by $t(k, p)$ the minimal integer s with the property that every element of $GF(p)$ is a sum of at most s elements of the form $\pm x^k$. Prove that

$$\Gamma(k, p) \ll (\log k)\, t(k, p).$$

§3. THE VALUE OF $g(k)$

1. In this section we shall prove a formula for $g(k)$ (for all k's except finitely many), which was proved by L. E. Dickson in the thirties. We start with a lower bound for $g(k)$, which according to L. E. Dickson [HTN] is due to J. A. Euler. Write

(4.33) $3^k = 2^k q + r \qquad (0 < r < 2^k).$

PROPOSITION 4.5. *For all $k \geqslant 2$ one has*

$$g(k) \geqslant 2^k + q - 2.$$

Proof. Consider the number $N = 2^k q - 1 < 3^k$. The shortest representation of N as a sum of kth powers is

$$N = (q-1)\, 2^k + (N - (q-1)\, 2^k)\, 1^k,$$

and so N requires at least $q - 1 + N - (q-1)\, 2^k = 2^k + q - 2$ kth powers. $\square$

The number $I(k) = 2^k + q - 2$ is called the *ideal Waring constant for the exponent k*. It was conjectured by C. A. Bretschneider [53] that for all $k \geqslant 2$ we have the equality $g(k) = I(k)$, and it is known that this is indeed true for $2 \leqslant k \leqslant 200\,000$, with a possible exception of $k = 4$, as well as for all sufficiently large k. This last result will be the subject of our Theorem 4.7.

In the next lemma we collect certain elementary facts about the integer r appearing in (4.33) in order to refer to them later.

LEMMA 4.16. *For $k \geqslant 5$ we have $r \geqslant 5$, $2 \nmid r$, $r \neq 2^k - 1$ and $r \neq 2^k - q - 1$.*

Proof. Clearly r must be an odd number. If $r = 1$ or $r = 2^k - 1$ then $3^k \equiv \pm 1 \pmod{2^k}$ and thus $3^{2k} \equiv 1 \pmod{2^k}$ and 3 has the order $2^{k-2} \pmod{2^k}$; it follows that $2^{k-2} \mid 2k$, which is impossible for $k \geqslant 5$. If $r = 3$ then $3^{k-1} \equiv 1 \pmod{2^k}$, and the same argument gives $k \leqslant 5$, and if finally $r = 2^k - q - 1$ then $3^k = (2^k - 1)(q + 1)$. Hence for a certain $a < k$ we have $2^k - 1 = 3^a$; thus $3^{2a} \equiv 1 \pmod{2^k}$ and again $2^{k-2} \mid 2a < 2k$, leading to $k \leqslant 5$. It remains to observe that all assertions hold also for $k = 5$. $\square$

The main result of this section is the following theorem:

THEOREM 4.7 (L. E. Dickson [36e]). *Let $k \geqslant 9$ and let $A = [(4/3)^k]$. If $r \leqslant 2^k - q - 3$ then we have the equality $g(k) = I(k)$, and if $r \geqslant 2^k - q + 2$*

then

(4.34) $$g(k) = \begin{cases} I(k)+A & \text{if} \quad qA+q+A = 2^k, \\ I(k)+A-1 & \text{otherwise}. \end{cases}$$

In particular, we have $g(k) = I(k)$ *for* $9 \leqslant k \leqslant 33$.

This theorem leaves out the case $2^k - q - 2 \leqslant r \leqslant 2^k - q + 1$. It was shown by L. E. Dickson [36e] that for r exceeding $2^k - q - 1$ the alternative (4.34) holds, and later I. Niven [44] showed that $r = 2^k - q - 2$ implies $g(k) = I(k)$. We do not give the proofs of these results, which are based on the same idea as the proof of Theorem 4.7 but involve additional technical details. We shall see later (Theorem 4.8) that these cases can occur only for finitely many numbers k, and one conjectures that in fact they never occur. The same conjecture applies to those cases in Theorem 4.7 which lead to (4.34).

2. We begin the proof with the description of Dickson's ascent argument, which will lead us quickly to the equality $g(k) = I(k)$ for $9 \leqslant k \leqslant 33$ (corollary to Lemma 4.20).

Theorem 4.6 shows that for $k \geqslant 9$ and $N \geqslant N_0(k) = \exp(18k^6)$ the integer N is a sum of less than $I(k)$ kth powers. Hence we have to study numbers from the interval $J_0 = [1, N_0(k)]$. For an interval J denote by $g_k(J)$ the minimal number of kth powers needed to represent every number from J. We now have to obtain bounds for $g_k(J_0)$ sharp enough to imply our assertion. This will be established by the *method of ascent*, introduced by L. E. Dickson [27a]. This method is based on the following easy observation:

LEMMA 4.17. *If* m, n *are positive integers and* $n \geqslant m+1$ *then there exists a positive integer* x *such that* $n-x^k$ *lies in the interval* $[m, m+kn^{1-1/k}]$.

Proof. Put $y = (n-m)^{1/k} \geqslant 1$ and let $x = [y]$. Then $0 \leqslant n-x^k-m = y^k - x^k \leqslant y^k - (y-1)^k \leqslant ky^{k-1} \leqslant kn^{1-1/k}$. □

COROLLARY (Dickson's ascent lemma). *Let* $m < M$ *be integers chosen so that under the notation* $v = (1-m/M)k^{-1}$ *one has* $v^k M > 1$.

If $g_k([m, M]) \leqslant g$ *and we define for* $t = 1, 2, \ldots$

(4.35) $$M_t = M_t(m, M) = \exp\big((k/(k-1))^t \log(Mv^k) - \log(v^k)\big)$$

then $g_k([m, M_t]) \leqslant g+t$.

Proof. First let $t = 1$. In this case $M_1 = (Mv)^{k/(k-1)}$ and if $M \leqslant n \leqslant M_1$ then by the lemma we can find a positive integer x such that

$$m \leqslant n-x^k \leqslant m+kn^{1-1/k} \leqslant m+kM_1^{1-1/k}$$
$$= m+kvM^{1-1/k} = m+(1-m/M)M^{1-1/k} \leqslant M;$$

hence n requires at most $1+g$ kth powers.

The corollary follows by recurrence. □

The ascent described in the above corollary is applicable only to relatively large values of M. To start the ascent at a level that is not too high we need a lemma which gives another type of ascent.

LEMMA 4.18. *If* $m \geqslant 0$ *and* $g_k([m, m+2^k]) \leqslant g$ *then*

$$g_k([m, m+(k+1)^k]) \leqslant g+s(k)$$

where

(4.36)
$$s(k) = \sum_{j=2}^{k} [(1+1/j)^k].$$

Proof. For $t = 2, 3, \ldots, k+1$ denote by I_t the interval $[m, m+t^k]$. We prove by recurrence the inequality

$$g_k(I_t) \leqslant g + \sum_{j=2}^{t-1} [(1+1/j)^k].$$

For $t = 2$ the inequality holds by assumption; so let us assume that it is true for a certain $t < k$. If $n \in I_{t+1} \setminus I_t$, i.e.,

$$m+t^k < n \leqslant m+(t+1)^k,$$

then we may choose an integer u in such a way that $m < n-ut^k < m+t^k$, and so n will need at most $u+g+\sum_{j=2}^{t-2} [(1+1/j)^k]$ kth powers. But $u < (1+1/j)^t$ and our assertion follows. □

COROLLARY 1. *We have*

$$g_k([2^k q, 2^k q+(k+1)^k]) \leqslant \max \{2^k-r, q+r-1\} + s(k).$$

Proof. We want to apply the lemma to $m = 2^k q$, and hence we need a bound for $g_k([2^k q, 2^k(q+1)])$. But clearly

$$g_k([2^k q, 3^k-1]) = g([2^k q, 2^k q+r-1]) = q+r-1,$$

$$g_k([3^k, 2^k(q+1)-1]) = 2^k-r$$

and $2^k(q+1)$ requires $\leqslant q+1 < q+r-1$ kth powers.

Thus

(4.37)
$$g_k([2^k q, 2^k(q+1)]) = \max(2^k-r, q+r-1). \quad □$$

Combining this corollary with Lemma 4.17, we obtain

COROLLARY 2. *If* M_t *is defined by* (4.35) *with* $m = 3^k$ *and* $M = (k+1)^k$, *then*

$$g_k(3^k, M_t) \leqslant t+s(k)+\max(2^k-r, q+r-1)$$

where $s(k)$ *is given by* (4.36).

Proof. Note first that $2^k q < 3^k$; hence by Corollary 1 we have

$$g_k\left([3^k, (k+1)^k]\right) \leqslant s(k) + \max(q+r-1, 2^k-r).$$

Now we apply the corollary to Lemma 4.17 with $m = 3^k$, $M = (k+1)^k$. In this case $v > (1 - 3/(k+1)^k)k^{-1}$ and, since for $k \geqslant 9$

$$(3/(k+1))^k < c/(k+1)$$

where $c = 2 \cdot 10^{-4}$, we obtain $v^k M \geqslant (1+(1-c)/k)^k > 1$; so the assumptions of the corollary are satisfied and our assertion follows. □

By choosing t sufficiently large so that (with the choice of m and M made in the last corollary)

(4.38) $$M_t \geqslant \exp(18k^6),$$

and using Theorem 4.6, we shall obtain an upper bound for $g(k)$, provided we first dispose of the numbers not exceeding 3^k. This is done in the next lemma:

LEMMA 4.19. *Every integer* $\leqslant 3^k$ *is a sum of at most* $I(k)$ *k-th powers.*

Proof. If $n \leqslant 2^k q - 1$ then $n = 2^k x + y$ with $0 \leqslant x \leqslant q-1$ and $0 \leqslant y \leqslant 2^k - 1$, so n requires at most $x + y \leqslant I(k)$ kth powers. If $2^k q \leqslant n \leqslant 3^k$, we invoke Corollary 1 to Lemma 4.18. □

Now we want to establish for which integers t inequality (4.38) is satisfied; we shall do this in the next lemma.

LEMMA 4.20. *If* $k \geqslant 9$, $1 \leqslant m \leqslant 4^k$ *and* $M \geqslant (k+1)^k$, *then for* $t \geqslant 6k \log k + 3k$ *inequality* (4.38) *holds.*

Proof. Since

$$v \geqslant \left(1 - (4/(k+1))^k\right)k^{-1},$$

the inequality

$$\log M_t(m, M) \geqslant k(1 + 1/(k-1))^t \log\left((1 + 1/k)\left(1 - (4/(k+1))^k\right)\right)$$

holds for $t \geqslant 1$. Observe that for $k \geqslant 9$ we have

$$(1 + 1/k)\left(1 - (4/(k+1))^k\right) = 1 + 1/k - (4/(k+1))^2(1 + 1/k)(4/(k+1))^{k-2}$$
$$\geqslant 1 + 1/k - 16/9k \cdot 10/9 \cdot (2/5)^7 \geqslant 1 + 0.996/k,$$

and since $\log(1+t) \geqslant t - t^2/2$ holds for $|t| < 1$ we obtain

$$\log M_t(m, M) \geqslant (1 + 1/(k-1))^t k \log(1 + 0.966/k)$$
$$\geqslant (1 + 1/(k-1))^t (0.966 - 0.966^2/18) \geqslant 0.91(1 + 1/(k-1))^t.$$

This shows that if t exceeds

$$\log(19.781 \, k^6)/\log(1 + 1/(k-1))$$

then inequality (4.38) will be satisfied. Since the function $t \log(1 + 1/(t-1))$ decreases to 1 as t tends to infinity, we have

$$\log(1 + 1/(k-1)) \geqslant 1/k;$$

thus $\log(19.781\,k^6)/\log(1 + 1/(k-1)) \leqslant 6k \log k + 3k$ and our assertion follows. $\square$

COROLLARY. *For* $9 \leqslant k \leqslant 33$ *one has* $g(k) = I(k)$.

Proof. Applying Corollary 2 to Lemma 4.18 with $t = [6k \log k + 3k] + 1$, we infer that all integers between 3^k and $(k+1)^k$ are sums of at most

$$a(k) = s(k) + 1 + [6k \log k + 3k] + \max(2^k - r, q + r - 1)$$

kth powers. An easy check on a pocket programmable calculator convinces us that in the range $9 \leqslant k \leqslant 33$ we have the inequality $a(k) \leqslant I(k)$. By Lemma 4.19 all integers up to 3^k require at most $I(k)$ kth powers and the last lemma shows that we may use Theorem 4.6 to infer that $g(k)$ does not exceed $\max(I(k), 6k \log k + 8k + 4)$. Since for $10 \leqslant k \leqslant 33$ we have $6k \log k + 8k + 4 \leqslant 961$ and $I(k) \geqslant 2^k + (3/2)^k - 3 \geqslant 2^{10} = 1024$, we obtain in this range $g(k) = I(k)$ and finally for $k = 9$ we have $I(9) = 548$ but $6 \cdot 9 \cdot \log 9 + 8 \cdot 9 + 4 < 195$. $\square$

3. To deal with $k \geqslant 34$ we need a good bound for $s(k)$, which will be provided by the next lemma.

LEMMA 4.21. *If* $k \geqslant 34$ *then*

$$s(k) \leqslant q + s - t - 97$$

where $t = 6k \log k + 3k$ *and* $s = [(4/3)^k] + 2[(5/4)^k]$.

Proof. Write the assertion is the slightly stronger form

$$t + \sum_{j=5}^{k} [(1 + 1/j)^k] \leqslant (5/4)^k - 98.$$

Since the left-hand side of this inequality does not exceed

$$t + \sum_{j=5}^{34} [(1 + 1/j)^k] + (k - 34)(36/35)^k,$$

it suffices to show that for $k \geqslant 34$

$$F(k) = (4/5)^k(t + 98) + (4/5)^k \sum_{j=5}^{34} [(1 + 1/j)^k] + (k - 34)(144/175)^k < 1.$$

The functions $k(4/5)^k$, $k \log k(4/5)^k$ and $[(1 + 1/j)^k](4/5)^k$ decrease for $k \geqslant 9$ and the function $(k - 34)(144/175)^k$ decreases for $k \geqslant 40$; hence it is enough to prove that $F(k) < 1$ for $k = 34, 35, \ldots, 40$. Now for $k \geqslant 34$ we have $(4/5)^k(t + 98) < 0.467$, and since $\sum_{j=5}^{34} [(1 + 1/j)^{34}] = 1022$ we obtain

$F(34) < 0.985$. Since for $k \geqslant 34$ we have $(144/175)^k < 0.0014$, for $34 \leqslant k \leqslant 40$ we get the bound

$$(k-34)(144/175)^k < 6 \cdot 0.0014 < 0.008;$$

thus finally $F(k) < 0.993 < 1$ for $k = 34, \ldots, 40$. $\square$

COROLLARY. *If $k \geqslant 34$ and for a certain integer $m \leqslant 4^k$ one has $g_k([m, m+2^k]) \leqslant g$, then every integer $\geqslant m$ is a sum of at most $g+q+s-95$ k-th powers.*

Proof. Lemma 4.18 shows that

$$g_k\big([m, m+(k+1)^k]\big) \leqslant g+s(k) \leqslant g+q+s-\hat{t}-97$$

where $\hat{t} = 6k \log k + 3.04 k$. Applying the corollary to Lemma 4.17 with $M = m+(k+1)^k$ and $t = [\hat{t}]+1$, we get

$$g_k([m, M_t]) \leqslant g+q+s+t-\hat{t}-96 \leqslant g+q+s-95.$$

By Lemma 4.20 we have $M_t \geqslant \exp(18k^6)$; hence Theorem 4.6 gives

$$g_k([m, \infty]) \leqslant \max(6k \log k + 8k + 4, \, g+q+s-95),$$

and since for $k \geqslant 15$ we have

$$6k \log k + 8k + 4 \leqslant q < q+s-95,$$

our assertion follows. $\square$

It proves be necessary to split the proof of the theorem into several cases, according to the mutual behaviour of q, r and s. We shall consider the following possibilities, always assuming $k \geqslant 34$:

(A) $s \leqslant r \leqslant 2^k - q - s$,
(B) $r \leqslant s$,
(C) $2^k - q - s \leqslant r \leqslant 2^k - q - 5$,
(D) $2^k - q - 4 \leqslant r \leqslant 2^k - q - 3$ and
(E) $2^k - q + 2 \leqslant r$.

(As already said, the case $2^k - q + 1 \geqslant r \geqslant 2^k - q - 2$ is left out.)

Our starting point will be the following inequality, which is a direct consequence of the corollary to Lemma 4.21 and equality (4.37):

$$g_k([2^k, \infty]) \leqslant q+s+\max(2^k-r, \, q+r-1)-95;$$

this equality jointly with Lemma 4.19 implies

(4.39) $g(k) \leqslant \max\big(I(k), \, q+s+\max(2^k-r, \, q+r-1)-95\big).$

The easiest case is (A). Indeed, if in this case $2^k - r \geqslant q+r-1$ then (4.39) gives

$$g(k) \leqslant \max\big(I(k), \, q+s+2^k-r-95\big) = I(k),$$

and if $2^k - r < q + r - 1$ then we get

$$g(k) \leqslant \max\left(I(k),\, 2q + s + r - 96\right) = I(k).$$

The same approach works in case (B) provided $2^k - r \leqslant q + r - 1$. Indeed, (4.39) then implies

$$g(k) \leqslant \max\left(I(k),\, 2q + s + r - 96\right),$$

and if we had $2q + s + r - 96 > I(k) = 2^k + q - 2$, then $2^k + 94 < q + 2s$, but this is impossible in our range of k.

Assume thus that $r \leqslant s$ and $2^k > q + 2r - 1$. Here we shall again use the corollary to Lemma 4.21; however, we have to start our ascent with a different interval. Put

$$u = 1 + [s/4]$$

and consider the interval $I = [2^k qu,\, 2^k qu + 2^k]$. We shall prove the inequality

(4.40) $$g_k(I) \leqslant 2^k - s - 1,$$

which will lead (in view of the corollary to Lemma 4.21) to the bound

$$g_k([2^k qu,\, \infty]) \leqslant 2^k + q - 95 \leqslant I(k),$$

and it will only remain to show that the numbers from the interval $[3^k,\, 2^k qu - 1]$ are sums of at most $I(k)$ kth powers.

If $n \in I$ then we may write $n = 2^k qu + x$ with $x \leqslant 2^k$. In the case $x \leqslant ru - 1$ such an integer requires at most $qu + x \leqslant (q + r)u - 1$ kth powers, and if $2^k - s \leqslant (q + r)u - 1 \leqslant (q + s)(1 + s/4) - 1$ then

$$4 \cdot 2^k \leqslant (q + s)(1 + s/4) + s$$

$$< \left\{ \left(\frac{3}{2}\right)^k + \left(\frac{4}{3}\right)^k + 2\left(\frac{5}{4}\right)^k \right\} \left\{ \frac{1}{2}\left(\frac{4}{3}\right)^k + \left(\frac{5}{4}\right)^k \right\} + \left(\frac{4}{3}\right)^k + 2\left(\frac{5}{4}\right)^k$$

$$\leqslant \frac{3}{2}\left\{ \left(\frac{3}{2}\right)^k + 3\left(\frac{4}{3}\right)^k \right\} \left\{ \left(\frac{4}{3}\right)^k + 3\left(\frac{4}{3}\right)^k \right\}$$

$$= \frac{3}{2} \cdot 2^k + \frac{9}{2}\left(\frac{16}{9}\right)^k + 3\left(\frac{4}{3}\right)^k \leqslant \frac{3}{2} \cdot 2^k + \frac{15}{2}\left(\frac{16}{9}\right)^k;$$

thus

$$\frac{5}{2} \cdot 2^k \leqslant \frac{15}{2}\left(\frac{16}{9}\right)^k,$$

and so

$$54 < \left(\frac{18}{16}\right)^{34} \leqslant \left(\frac{18}{16}\right)^k < 3,$$

a contradiction.

Thus

$$g_k([2^k qu,\ 2^k qu + ru - 1]) \leqslant 2^k - s - 1.$$

If $ru - 1 \geqslant 2^k$ then (4.40) is proved. However, if the converse inequality holds, then we have to consider integers $n = 2^k qu + x \in I$ with $ur \leqslant x < 2^k$ (because $n = 2^k qu + 2^k$ requires at most $qu + 1 \leqslant 2^k - s - 1$ kth powers). We can write $n = 2^k qu + ur + y = 3^k u + y$ with $0 \leqslant y \leqslant 2^k - ur - 1$, thus n needs at most $u + y \leqslant u + 2^k - ur - 1$ kth powers and if $u + 2^k - ur - 1 \geqslant 2^k - s$ then $s/4 \leqslant u \leqslant (s-1)/(r-1)$; hence $r < 5$, which is ruled out by Lemma 4.16. Thus (4.40) follows.

To complete the consideration of case (B) it suffices now to establish the inequality

(4.41) $$g_k([3^k + 1,\ 3^k u]) \leqslant I(k)$$

because $2^k qu \leqslant 3^k u$.

Write $n = 3^k a + 2^k b + c$ where $0 \leqslant a \leqslant u - 1$, $0 \leqslant b \leqslant q$, $0 \leqslant c \leqslant 2^k - 1$, and observe that if $b \leqslant q - u$ then n requires at most $a + b + c \leqslant (u-1) + (q-u) + (2^k - 1) = I(k)$ kth powers. Assuming $b \geqslant q - u + 1$, write $b = q - u + j$ with $1 \leqslant j \leqslant u$. Then $a + b + c = q + c + j - 1$, and so in the case $c \leqslant 2^k - 1 - j$ again $I(k)$ kth powers suffice. Thus let $c \geqslant 2^k - j$. Choosing $m \geqslant 1$ so that $mr \geqslant 2^k - c > (m-1)r$, we can write

$$n = 3^k a + 2^k (q - u + j) + c = 3^k (a - m) + 2^k qm + mr + 2^k (q - u + j) + c,$$

and so n requires at most $\alpha = a - m + qm + q - u + j + 1 + mr + c - 2^k$ kth powers. We shall now show that this number is much less than $I(k)$. Indeed, it does not exceed $q(m+1) - m + j + 1 + r \leqslant q(m+1) - m + u + 1 + r \leqslant q(m+1) - m + u + 1 + s$ and in view of

$$5(m-1) \leqslant r(m-1) < 2^k - c \leqslant u \leqslant 1 + s/4$$

we get $m \leqslant 6/5 + s/20$; thus α is at most equal to $(11/5 + s/20) q + 2 + 5s/4$. But for $k \geqslant 34$ we have $s/2^k < 10^{-4}$, $q/2^k < 10^{-4}$ and $sq/2^k < 2$; thus

$$\alpha \leqslant 2^k \left\{ \frac{11}{5} \cdot 10^{-4} + 0.1 + \frac{5}{4} \cdot 10^{-4} \right\} + 2 < 0.11 \cdot 2^k + 2 < I(k).$$

This settles case (B).

In case (C) we have $2^k - q - s < r \leqslant 2^k - q - 5$, and we may also assume that $r > s$. If $2^k - r \geqslant q + r - 1$ then (4.39) implies $g(k) \leqslant I(k)$; hence we may further assume that $2^k - r < q + r - 1$. As in the previous case, put $u = 1 + [s/4]$, write $D = uq + u - 1$ and consider the interval

$$I = [2^k D,\ 2^k D + 2^k].$$

If $n \in I$, $n = 2^k D + x < 3^k u$, then n requires at most

$$D + x \leqslant D + 3^k u - 2^k D - 1 = 2^k - u(2^k - r - q - 1) - 2$$

kth powers. If this number exceeded $2^k - s - 1$, then

(4.42) $\qquad s \geqslant u(2^k - r - q - 1) + 2 \geqslant 4u + 2 > s,$

a contradiction.

The remaining integers in I can be written in the form

$$n = 3^k u + y \quad (0 \leqslant y \leqslant 2^k(D+1) - 3^k u),$$

and they require at most $u + y \leqslant 2^k(D+1) - (3^k - 1)u$ kth powers. If this number were $\geqslant 2^k - s$, we would have

$$u(2^k - r + 1) + s \geqslant 2^k$$

and hence

$$\frac{u(q+s+1)+s}{2^k} \geqslant 1;$$

however, this inequality fails in our range of k. The corollary to Lemma 4.21 implies now $g_k([2^k D, \infty]) \leqslant I(k)$ and to conclude case (C) we have to look at the integers from the interval

$$J = [3^k, 2^k D] \subset [3^k, 3^k u].$$

Let $n = a3^k + b2^k + c$ ($1 \leqslant a \leqslant u - 1$, $0 \leqslant b \leqslant q$, $0 \leqslant c \leqslant 2^k - 1$ in the case $b \leqslant q - 1$ and $0 \leqslant c \leqslant r - 1$ in the case $b = q$) be such an integer. Clearly n requires at most $a + b + c$ kth powers, and hence if c does not exceed $2^k - u - 1$ then $I(k)$ kth powers are sufficient. We may thus assume that $c \geqslant 2^k - u$. We write

$$n = (b + aq)2^k + c + ar = (b + aq + a)2^r + (c + ar - 2^k a)$$

and note that $c + ar - 2^k a \geqslant 0$. Indeed, $2^k - r = q + y$ with a certain positive $y \leqslant s$; thus $c + ar - 2^k a \geqslant 2^k - u - a(q+y)$, and as

$$u + a(q+y) \leqslant u(1+q+s) \leqslant (1+(3/4)(4/3)^k)\ (1+(3/2)^k + 3(4/3)^k) < 2^k$$

for $k \geqslant 34$ the positiveness of $c + ar - 2^k a$ results. It follows that n can be written as a sum of at most $b + aq + a + c + ar - 2^k a$ kth powers and this number equals

$$b + a(1-y) + c \leqslant \begin{cases} q + r - 1 < I(k) & \text{if} \quad b = q, \\ q - 1 + 2^k - 1 = I(k) & \text{if} \quad b \leqslant q - 1. \end{cases}$$

This settles case (C).

In case (D) the same argument applies as in the foregoing case, except that we put

$$u = \begin{cases} 1+[s/3] & \text{if} \quad r = 2^k-q-4, \\ 1+[s/2] & \text{if} \quad r = 2^k-q-3. \end{cases}$$

In fact, such a choice requires only a slight change in (4.42), in place of which we get

$$s \geqslant u(2^k-r-q-1)+2 = \begin{cases} 3u+2 > s & \text{if} \quad r = 2^k-q-4, \\ 2u+2 > s & \text{if} \quad r = 2^k-q-3. \end{cases}$$

We now turn to our last case, namely (E), in which $r \geqslant 2^k-q+2$. Here we are forced to start our ascent with a larger number, close to 4^k. Write

$$4^k = A3^k + B2^k + C$$

with $A = [(4/3)^k]$, $0 \leqslant B \leqslant q$ and $0 \leqslant C \leqslant 3^k - 2^k B$, $C \leqslant 2^k - 1$. The exact values of B and C are easy to determine. Indeed, in view of $4^k = A(2^k q + r) + B2^k + C$ we get $A + C \equiv 0 \pmod{2^k}$ and so $C - A(2^k - r) \equiv 0 \pmod{2^k}$. But $0 < A(2^k - r) \leqslant Aq < 2^k$ and so we have the equality $C = A(2^k - r)$. This leads immediately to $B = 2^k - Aq - A$.

We shall consider the interval $I = [3^k A + 2^k B, 3^k A + 2^k B + 2^k]$. Write $n = 4^k + x \in I$. If x does not exceed $2^k - A(2^k - r) - 1 = 3^k A + 2^k B + 2^k - 1$ then n requires at most $2^k - A(2^k - r)$ kth powers. However, if $n \in I$ is larger, then we can write $n = 3^k A + 2^k B + y$ with $y \leqslant 4^k - 3^k A - 2^k B$, and so n requires at most $A + B + 4^k - 3^k A - 2^k B = 2^k - A(q + r - 2^k) - 1$ kth powers, which shows that

$$g_k(I) \leqslant \max(2^k - A(2^k - r), \, 2^k - A(q + r - 2^k) - 1).$$

The corollary to Lemma 4.21 implies now that all numbers larger than $3^k A + 2^k B$, and in particular all numbers $\geqslant 4^k$, require at most

$$q + s - 95 + \max(2^k - A(2^k - r), \, 2^k - A(q + r - 2^k) - 1)$$

kth powers. If this number exceeds $I(k)$ then either

(a) $s > A(2^k - r) + 93$ or
(b) $s > A(q + r - 2^k) + 98$.

In case (i) note that by Lemma 4.16 we have $r \neq 2^k - 1$, hence $2^k - r \geqslant 2$ and so $A + 2(5/4)^k > s > 2A + 93$, which for $k \geqslant 34$ is not possible. In case (ii) we use $r \geqslant 2^k - q + 2$ to obtain $s > 2A + 98$, which again is not possible for $k \geqslant 34$.

Thus

(4.43) $$g_k(4^k, \infty) \leqslant I(k).$$

Now we have to deal with integers from $[3^k, 4^k]$. Write such an integer n in the form $n = a3^k + b2^k + c$ $(0 \leqslant b2^k + c \leqslant 3^k, 0 \leqslant c \leqslant 2^k)$. Then $a \leqslant A$,

$b \leqslant q$ and $c \leqslant 2^k - 1$. If $b = q$ then clearly $c \leqslant r - 1$, hence $a + b + c \leqslant A + q + r - 1 \leqslant A + q + 2^k - 4 = I(k) + A - 2$. If $a = A$, then $b \leqslant B = 2^k - Aq - A \leqslant q$ and if, moreover, $b = B$ then $c \leqslant C = A(2^k - r)$; thus in this case $a + b + c \leqslant 2^k - A(q + r - 2^k) < I(k)$. However, if $a = A$ but $b \leqslant B - 1$, then $a + b + c \leqslant A + B - 1 + 2^k - 1 = I(k) + A$. Finally, if $a \leqslant A - 1$ and $b \leqslant q - 1$, then $a + b + c \leqslant A + q - 2 + 2^k - 1 = I(k) + A - 1$. This shows that

(4.44)
$$g_k([3^k, 4^k]) \leqslant I(k) + A.$$

The argument above shows also that the only integer which may possibly require $I(k) + A$ kth power is

$$n = A3^k + (q - 1)2^k + 2^k - 1,$$

which can happen only if $B = q$, i.e.,

(4.45)
$$2^k - Aq - A = q.$$

If this equality holds then our n really requires $I(k) + A$ kth powers, because by writing

$$n = (A - j)3^k + (q - 1 + jq)2^k + 2^k + jr - 1$$
$$= (A - j)3^k + (q - jq - 1 + v)2^k + 2^k + jr - 1 - v2^k$$

with $0 \leqslant j \leqslant A$ and $v = v(j) = [(2^k + jr - 1)/2^k]$ we get a decomposition of n into kth powers using

$$A - j + q + jq - 1 + v + 2^k + jr - 1 - v2^k$$

summands; this number is equal to at least

$$A + j(q + r - 1) + q - 2 + 2^k + (1 - 2^k)(jr - 1)2^{-k} \geqslant A + I(k),$$

but it is the only way of reducing the number of kth powers involved.

This proves the theorem in case (E), provided (4.45) holds. Assuming that (4.45) fails observe that our argument shows that the only integers which may require $I(k) - 1 + A$ kth powers are

$$n = 3^k A + (q - 2)2^k + 2^k - 1 \quad \text{(if } B = q - 1),$$
$$n = 3^k A + (q - 1)2^k + 2^k - 2 \quad \text{(if } B = q)$$

and

$$n = 3^k(A - 1) + (q - 1)2^k + 2^k - 1 \quad \text{(in the remaining subcases of (E))}.$$

It is now easy to check that these numbers ideed require $I(k) + A - 1$ kth powers and this completes the proof of the theorem. $\square$

4. We conclude with the determination of the value of $g(k)$ for all sufficiently large integers k. Unfortunately the proof will be ineffective, being based on the Roth–Ridout theorem; hence it will not be possible to check numerically the remaining finite number of values of k.

THEOREM 4.8 (K. Mahler [57]). *For sufficiently large k one has* $g(k) = I(k)$.

Proof. In view of the preceding theorem it suffices to show that the inequality $r > 2^k - q - 3$ can hold only for finitely many integers k. Assuming that this inequality holds, we obtain

$$2^k > r > 2^k - q - 3;$$

thus

$$|r - 2^k| < q + 3 < 2(3/2)^k,$$

and we shall show that this is contradictory for sufficiently large k. Let $m = 2^k(q+1)$, $n = 3^k$ and apply the Roth–Ridout theorem (see Theorem A.7) with $A_1 = \{2\}$, $A_2 = \{3\}$, $\alpha = 1 - (\log 2)/(\log 3)$, $\beta = 0$, $\gamma = \alpha + 1/(20 \log 3)$ and $C = 2$. In our case $n_1 = 1$, $m_1 = q + 1 < 2(3/2)^k$; since $m^\alpha \geqslant 3^{k\alpha} = (3/2)^k$ $\geqslant m_1/2$ the assumptions of that theorem are satisfied, and thus we obtain

$$|1 - 2^k(q+1)3^{-k}| > M \cdot 3^{-\gamma k},$$

i.e.,

$$|3^k - 2^k q - 2^k| > M \cdot 3^{(1-\gamma)k},$$
$$2(3/2)^k > |r - 2^k| > M \cdot 3^{(1-\gamma)k}.$$

Thus finally $(2/3^\gamma)^k < 2/M$, which in view of $3^\gamma = 3\exp(1/20)/2 < 2$ gives a contradiction for all large values of k. □

Notes and comments

1. The method of ascent, on which the proof of Theorem 4.7 is based, originated in Dickson [27a], where Lemma 4.16 may be found. Its corollary appears in Dickson [33] and Lemma 4.17 in Dickson [36c]. An application of this method to obtain bounds for $g(k)$ in special cases was made by L. E. Dickson [31], [33], [34b], [34c], [34d], R. D. James [34a], A. Sugar [35].

The first asymptotic result for $g(k)$ was obtained by E. Landau [26b], who proved

$$\limsup_{k \to \infty} g(k)/k2^k \leqslant 1/2.$$

This bound was later halved by M. Gelbcke [33] and R. D. James [34a].

The first determination of the exact value of $g(k)$ after the classical cases $k = 2, 3$ was made by H. S. Zuckerman [36], who proved the equality

$g(k) = I(k)$ for $15 \leqslant k \leqslant 20$, and L. E. Dickson [36a], who proved this for $k = 12$. In the same year Dickson [36b] first proved this equality for $11 \leqslant k \leqslant 15$ and $k = 17$ and later (Dickson [36c]) for $7 \leqslant k \leqslant 180$. Shortly afterwards he was able (Dickson [36e]) to determine the value of $g(k)$ for all integers $k \geqslant 7$ except in the case $r = 2^k - q - 2$, which was left out completely, and $r = 2^k - q$, where only the final result was indicated. Part of Dickson's result is proved in our Theorem 4.7. Later, in the case $r = 2^k - q - 2$, I. Niven [44] showed that $g(k) = I(k)$, and the case $r = 2^k - q$ was successfully treated by R. Rubugunday [42], who showed that it never occurs. S. S. Pillai [36a], [36b], [36d], [36e] also proved that part of Theorem 4.7 in which $r \leqslant 2^k - q - 3$ is assumed and obtained the equality $g(k) = I(k)$ for $7 \leqslant k \leqslant 100$. By using this S. Chowla [36a] proved that $g(k) = I(k)$ holds infinitely often (cf. also S. Chowla [39]). A simple proof of Chowla's result was given by E. Trost [58].

The result of Dickson ([36e]) implies that the ideal Waring theorem, namely $g(k) = I(k)$, holds for all k in the interval [7, 400]. This interval was later extended by R. M. Stemmler [64] to [7, 200 000]. Cf. Ehlich [65], who considered the interval [7, 50 000].

2. Theorem 4.8 was proved by K. Mahler [57]. It is non-effective, and this deficiency could be removed if we had a proof of the inequality

$$\|(3/2)^k\| \geqslant 2(3/4)^k$$

(where $\|x\|$ denotes the distance from x to the nearest integer) for $k \geqslant k_0$, with an effective k_0. The best known result of this type is due to F. Beukers [81a], who showed that for $k \geqslant 5000$ one has

$$\|(3/2)^k\| \geqslant (0.37)^k.$$

(Cf. A. Baker, J. Coates [75].)

3. The first bound for $g(5)$ is due to E. Maillet [96], who proved that it does not exceed 192. L. E. Dickson [31] reduced this number to 54 and later J. J. Chen [59a] first obtained $g(5) \leqslant 40$ and then showed (Chen [64]) that $g(5) = I(5) = 37$.

The consecutive bounds obtained for $g(6)$ were as follows: A. Fleck [07] got $g(6) \leqslant 2451$, W. S. Baer [13a] and L. E. Dickson [27a] had $g(6) \leqslant 478$, later L. E. Dickson [36f] showed $g(6) \leqslant 110$ and the last two steps were made by S. S. Pillai [37a], [40c], who in the first paper reduced the bound to 104 and in the second settled the problem, showing that $g(6) = I(6) = 73$.

Thus in principle all values of $g(k)$ are known except $g(4)$.

4. Questions analogous to the Waring problem can be stated in a more general setting. Let R be a commutative ring with a unit element and let $k \geqslant 2$ be given. Then one can pose the following two problems:

(a) Determine the set R_k of all those elements of R which can be written as sums of kth powers of elements of R, and

(b) Evaluate the *Waring constant* $g(R, k)$ *of the ring* R, defined as the smallest integer s with the property that every element of R_k can be written as a sum of at most s kth powers of elements of R.

These problems may be modified, e.g. by the requirement that the summands are to lie in a prescribed subset of R. This is usually done in the study of the Waring problem in rings of algebraic integers, where one mostly considers totally positive kth powers. This applies in particular to the usual Waring problem, in which we restrict the summands to non-negative ones.

Many general results concerning this form of the Waring problem in arbitrary rings are contained in J. R. Joly [70]. One of the questions posed there was answered by T. Chinburg [79], who showed that if p is a prime which cannot be written in the form

$$p = (p_1^{bc} - 1)/(p_1^c - 1)$$

with $b \geqslant 2$, $c \geqslant 1$ and a prime p_1 then every element of R can be written in the form

$$\pm x_1^p \pm \ldots \pm x_s^p$$

with $x_i \in R$ and s bounded by a constant depending only on p, and not on R. This constant is asymptotically equal to $3p^2 \cdot \log p$.

Waring's problem in the rings of polynomials over a finite field was studied by R. E. A. C. Paley [33], M. Car [71], W. A. Webb [72], [73] and R. M. Kubota [74]. (Cf. also L. Verner [79] for the case of squares.) Car and Kubota obtained evaluations for the Waring constant in the case where the exponent does not exceed the characteristic of the field. They both use an adaptation of the circle method.

The Waring constant in finite fields was considered by S. Schwarz [48], who proved that if q is a power of the prime p and $d = (q - 1, k) \leqslant p - 1$, then the Waring constant for the field $GF(q)$ does not exceed d. C. Small [77a], [77b], [78] considered the Waring problem for the ring of residue classes (mod N). Recursion formulas for the number of representation of such a residue class as a sum of s kth powers were given by R. Hull [32].

There is a huge literature connected with Hilbert's 17-th problem, concerning representations of rational functions as sums of squares, and with the generalization of Waring's problem to algebraic number fields, but we shall not tackle this question. A good survey of topics related to Waring's problem has been written by W. J. Ellison [71].

Exercises

1 (C. Small [77a]). Prove that every element of Z/mZ is a sum of at most four cubes.

2 (T. Nagell [54]). Show that if p is a prime $\neq 7$ then every element of Z/pZ is a sum of at most two cubes.

3 (O. H. Keller [64]). Let $N \geqslant 2$ and assume $(m, N) = 1$. If N is divisible by 4, assume further that $m \equiv 1 \pmod 4$. Find the number of representations of m as a sum of two squares in Z/NZ.

4 (C. Small [77c]). Prove that if p is a prime exceeding k^4 then every element of Z/pZ is a sum of at most two kth powers.

OPEN PROBLEMS

1. Prove that the largest positive integer not divisible by 4 which is a sum of three non-negative integral squares but is not a sum of three positive integral squares equals 130.

2 (C. G. J. Jacobi). Prove that $G(3) \leqslant 5$.

3. Prove that $g(4) = 19$.

4. Obtain the asymptotics for the number of integers $\leqslant x$ which are sums of three cubes.

5. Prove that the number of representations of an integer n as a sum of four non-negative cubes is $\ll n^{1/3 + \varepsilon}$ for every positive ε.

6. Prove that $G(k) \ll k$.

7 ("Hypothesis K"). Prove that for $k \geqslant 4$ the number $R_k(n)$ of representations of an integer n as a sum of k kth powers is $\ll n^\varepsilon$ for every positive ε.

8. Determine the smallest integer $s = s(k)$ such that the number of representations of integers as sums of s kth powers is unbounded.

9. Determine the value of $G(k)$ for $k \geqslant 5$.

10. Determine the smallest value of s such that the asymptotic formula for the number of representations of an integer as a sum of s kth powers holds.

11. Determine the exact value for the Waring's constant in finite fields.

12. Do the same for the rings of p-adic integers.

13. Determine the Waring–Kamke constant for cubic polynomials.

14. Find the values of $v(k)$ (the "easy" Waring constant) for $k \geqslant 3$. In particular prove or disprove the equality $v(3) = 4$.

15 (T. Kløve [72]). Prove that every sufficiently large integer can be written in the form $x_1^2 + x_2^3 + x_3^4 + x_4^5$.

16. Prove that for all $k \geqslant 2$ one has $g(k) = I(k)$.

V

Binary
quadratic
forms

---

§ 1. THE CLASS NUMBER

1. In this chapter we shall consider the problem of determination of all negative discriminants of binary quadratic forms with class number one or, which means the same, of all imaginary quadratic fields with only one class of ideals. The interest in this problem is due mostly to the fact that these fields are the only quadratic imaginary fields whose ring of integers is a unique factorization domain.

This problem goes back to C. F. Gauss [01], who in Chapter V studied extensively *binary quadratic forms*

$$(5.1) \qquad\qquad f(x, y) = ax^2 + 2bxy + cy^2$$

(with integral a, b, c) and their equivalence classes under the action of the unimodular group $\mathrm{SL}(2, Z)$ defined by

$$(\mathfrak{A}f)(x, y) = f(Ax + By, Cx + Dy)$$

for

$$\mathfrak{A} = \begin{bmatrix} A & B \\ C & D \end{bmatrix} \in \mathrm{SL}(2, Z).$$

Since all forms in the same equivalence class have the same *determinant* $D(f)$, defined by $D(f) = b^2 - ac$, and (as we shall see later) there are only finitely many equivalence classes of forms with a given determinant, one can consider the *class number* $H(d)$, which Gauss defined as the number of equivalence classes of forms (5.1) which satisfy $(a, 2b, c) = 1$, (Gauss called them *properly primitive*, reserving the name "primitive" for forms satisfying

$(a, b, c) = 1$), have determinant D and, in the case of negative D, are positive definite. In art. 303 and 304 of Gauss [01] he listed small negative determinants d for which $H(d)$ is small and put forward the conjecture that there are only finitely many determinants with a given class number, i.e., that $H(d)$ tends to infinity when $-d$ tends to infinity.

Nowadays more general quadratic forms are usually considered, without restriction on the middle coefficient, following in this respect the classical work of J. L. Lagrange [73] and L. Kronecker [85]. One writes

(5.2) $$f(x, y) = ax^2 + bxy + cy^2$$

(with a, b, $c \in Z$), calling such form *primitive* provided $(a, b, c) = 1$ and defining its *discriminant* by $d(f) = b^2 - 4ac$. It is immediately seen that for a Gaussian form (5.1) we have $d(f) = 4D(f)$ and that all forms (5.2) with a discriminant divisible by 4 are Gaussian.

The equivalence classes of forms (5.1) are defined in the same way as before, and so we arrive at the number $h(d)$ of equivalence classes of primitive forms (5.2) with a given discriminant d, (restricting our attention in the case $d < 0$ to positive definite forms). From previous remarks it is clear that $H(d) = h(4d)$, and so Gauss's conjecture can be written as $\lim\limits_{d \to -\infty} h(4d)$ $= \infty$.

It should be pointed out that, contrary to the common belief, Gauss nowhere conjectured that his list of determinants $D < 0$ for which $H(D) = 1$ is complete; neither did he conjecture anything about the number $h(d)$, with which he was never concerned. However, as noted by D. Shanks [69], the assertion that Gauss's list of negative determinants D with $H(D) = 1$ or 3 is complete is equivalent to the statement that $h(d) = 1$ holds for negative d if and only if $-d$ is one of the numbers 3, 4, 7, 8, 11, 19, 43, 67, 163, which is often quoted as Gauss's conjecture.

2. First we shall show that the number of equivalence classes of primitive quadratic forms with a given discriminant is finite. We shall obtain this as a corollary to the *reduction process* described in the following proposition:

PROPOSITION 5.1. (i) *Every primitive positively definite quadratic form is equivalent to a form* $g(x, y) = ax^2 + bxy + cy^2$ *which satisfies*

(5.3.i) $$|b| \leqslant a \leqslant c.$$

(ii) *Every primitive indefinite quadratic form* f *with a non-square discriminant is equivalent to a form* $g(x, y) = ax^2 + bxy + cy^2$ *which satisfies*

(5.3.ii) $$|b| \leqslant |a|, \qquad |b| \leqslant |c|.$$

(iii) *Every primitive indefinite quadratic form* f *with a square discriminant* $d = D^2 \neq 0$ *is equivalent to a form* $g(x, y) = ax^2 + Dxy$ *where* $0 \leqslant a \leqslant D - 1$.

Proof. (i) Let $a = f(x_1, y_1)$ be the minimal positive value attained by f at points with integer coordinates, and let $c = f(x_2, y_2)$ be the minimal value attained by f at points (x, y) with $x, y \in Z$ and

$$\det \begin{bmatrix} x_1 & x \\ y_1 & y \end{bmatrix} = 1.$$

On solving the equation

$$\begin{bmatrix} A & B \\ C & D \end{bmatrix} \begin{bmatrix} x_1 & x_2 \\ y_1 & y_2 \end{bmatrix} = \begin{bmatrix} 1 & 0 \\ 0 & 1 \end{bmatrix}$$

for A, B, C, D we get, with a certain integral b and $\mathfrak{A} = \begin{bmatrix} A & B \\ C & D \end{bmatrix}$,

$$\mathfrak{A}^{-1} f = ax^2 + bxy + cy^2 = g(x, y),$$

because $f(x_1, y_1) = g(1, 0) = a$ and $f(x_2, y_2) = g(0, 1) = c$.

By construction we have $a \leqslant c$ and in view of

$$\det \begin{bmatrix} x_1 & x_2 \pm x_1 \\ y_1 & y_2 \pm y_1 \end{bmatrix} = 1$$

we get $g(\mp 1, 1) = f(\pm x_1 + x_2, \pm y_1 + y_2) \geqslant c$, which implies $a \mp b + c \geqslant c$; thus $|b| \leqslant a$, as asserted. $\square$

(ii) In this case it suffices to show that if a form $ax^2 + bxy + cy^2$ with a positive and non-square discriminant does not satisfy (5.3.ii), then it is equivalent to a form with the absolute value of the middle coefficient strictly less than $|b|$. Our assumptions imply that neither a nor c vanishes; hence if $|b| > |a|$ then we can select an integer t satisfying the inequality $|2at + b| \leqslant |a| < |b|$, and thus for

$$\mathfrak{A} = \begin{bmatrix} 1 & t \\ 0 & 1 \end{bmatrix}$$

the form $\mathfrak{A} f$ has its middle coefficient equal to $2at + b$, of absolute value smaller than $|b|$. In the case $|b| > |c|$ the same argument applies to

$$\mathfrak{A} = \begin{bmatrix} 1 & 0 \\ t & 1 \end{bmatrix}.$$

(iii) Let $f(x, y) = Ax^2 + Bxy + Cy^2$. If $AC \neq 0$ then $(D - B)/2A = -2C/(D + B) = \beta/\delta$ with coprime integers β, δ. If we now solve the equation $\alpha\delta - \beta\gamma = 1$ for $\alpha, \gamma \in Z$ and define

$$\mathfrak{A} = \begin{bmatrix} \alpha & \beta \\ \gamma & \delta \end{bmatrix},$$

then the form $\mathfrak{A} f$ will be equal to $A_1 x^2 + Dxy$ with a certain integer A_1.

Applying to this form the matrix $\begin{bmatrix} 1 & 0 \\ k & 1 \end{bmatrix}$ with a suitable k, we obtain the form $A_2 x^2 + Dxy$ where A_2 is an arbitrary integer congruent to $A_1 \pmod D$. In particular, we can choose k in such a way that $0 \leqslant A_2 < D$.

If $C = 0$, then $f(x, y) = Ax^2 \pm Dxy$, and it suffices to observe that the form $Ax^2 - Dxy$ is equivalent to $A_1 x^2 + Dxy$ with a certain A_1 since writing $a/D = \delta/\beta$ with $(\delta, \beta) = 1$, and solving $\alpha\delta - \beta\gamma = 1$ we are led to the matrix $\begin{bmatrix} \alpha & \beta \\ \gamma & \delta \end{bmatrix}$, which satisfies our needs. Since the last step of the previous case is applicable, our proof is complete.

Finally the case $A = 0$ readily reduces to the previous one via the matrix $\begin{bmatrix} 0 & -1 \\ 1 & 0 \end{bmatrix}$. □

Every primitive, positive definite form satisfying (5.3.i), every indefinite form with a non-square discriminant satisfying (5.3.ii) and every form $ax^2 + Dxy$ with $0 \leqslant a \leqslant D - 1$ will be called a *reduced form*.

COROLLARY 1. *The numbers $h(d)$ and $H(d)$ are finite for all non-zero d and in fact*

$$h(d) \leqslant 2|d|/3 \quad \text{for } d \text{ negative},$$

$$h(d) \leqslant (2/5 + o(1))d \quad \text{for } d \text{ positive and non-square},$$

and finally for $d = D^2 \neq 0$

$$h(d) = D.$$

Proof. In view of $H(d) = h(4d)$ it suffices to consider only the class number $h(d)$. If d is negative, then the number of triplets $\langle a, b, c \rangle$ satisfying (5.3.i) and $b^2 - 4ac = d$ is finite since

$$3a^2 \leqslant 4ac - a^2 \leqslant 4ac - b^2 = |d|;$$

thus $|b| \leqslant a \leqslant |d|^{1/2}/3^{1/2}$ and there is only one possibility for c. Counting all possible triplets, we find that there are at most $2|d|/3$ of them.

If d is positive and non-square and the triplet $\langle a, b, c \rangle$ satisfies (5.3.ii), then clearly ac must be negative; thus

$$5b^2 \leqslant b^2 + 4|ac| = d,$$

and we get $|b| \leqslant (d/5)^{1/2}$. Since ac is a divisor of $(b^2 - d)/4$, it follows that

$$h(d) \leqslant 2 \sum_{|b| \leqslant (d/5)^{1/2}} \sum_{\substack{a|(d-b^2)/4 \\ a \geqslant 1}} 1 \leqslant 4 \sum_{0 \leqslant b \leqslant (d/5)^{1/2}} \sum_{a|(d-b^2)/4} 1$$

$$\leqslant 4 \sum_{d/5 \leqslant a \leqslant d/4} \sum_{\substack{1 \leqslant b \leqslant (d/5)^{1/2} \\ b^2 \equiv d \pmod a}} 1 \leqslant 4 \sum_{d/5 \leqslant a \leqslant d/4} 2(a^{-1}(d/5)^{1/2} + 1)$$

$$\leqslant \tfrac{2}{5}d + (8/\sqrt{5})d^{1/2} \sum_{a \leqslant d} 1/a \leqslant (2/5 + o(1))d.$$

To obtain the last assertion it suffices to check that the two forms $f = ax^2 + Dxy$ and $g = Ax^2 + Dxy$ with $0 \leqslant a < A \leqslant D - 1$ are not equivalent. Assuming that for a matrix

$$\mathfrak{A} = \begin{bmatrix} \alpha & \beta \\ \gamma & \delta \end{bmatrix}$$

of determinant 1 we have $g = \mathfrak{A}f$ and, comparing the coefficients in the resulting equality, we immediately obtain

$$\beta(a\beta + D\delta) = 0,$$

$$2a\alpha\beta + D(\alpha\delta + \beta\gamma) = D;$$

thus

$$-D\beta = 2\alpha\beta(a\beta + D\delta) = 2a\alpha\beta^2 - D\beta(\alpha\delta + \beta\gamma)$$

$$= \alpha\beta\delta D - \beta^2\gamma D = \beta D(\alpha\delta - \beta\gamma) = \beta D,$$

which implies $\beta = 0$. Hence $\alpha\delta = 1$, i.e., $\alpha = \delta = \pm 1$; however, this is incompatible with the equality

$$a\alpha^2 + D\alpha\gamma = A,$$

obtained by comparing the coefficients of x^2 in g and f. Indeed, from this inequality and the equality $\alpha^2 = 1$ we get $a \equiv A \pmod{D}$, which contradicts our assumptions. $\square$

COROLLARY 2. If $f = ax^2 + bxy + cy^2$ is a positive definite primitive reduced form, then $a = f(1, 0)$ is the smallest positive value attained by f at points with integral coordinates, $c = f(0, 1)$ is the smallest value attained by f at points with integral coordinates (x, y) with $y \neq 0$ and finally $a - |b| + c$ is the smallest value attained by f at points with integral coordinates, both non-zero. (The last value is attained at $(-1, 1)$ if b is non-negative and at $(1, 1)$ otherwise.)

Proof. Since f is reduced, we have

$$f(1, 0) = a \leqslant f(0, 1) = c \leqslant a - |b| + c = \begin{cases} f(1, 1) & \text{if} \quad b = 0, \\ f(-\text{sgn } b, 1) & \text{if} \quad b \neq 0, \end{cases}$$

and so it suffices to show that if $xy \neq 0$ then $f(x, y) \geqslant a - |b| + c$. If $|x| \geqslant |y|$ then

$$f(x, y) = |x| \left(a|x| + b\frac{x}{|x|}y \right) + cy^2$$

$$\geqslant |x|(a|x| - |by|) + cy^2 \geqslant |x|^2(a - |b|) + cy^2 \geqslant a - |b| + c,$$

and if $|x| \leqslant |y|$ then interchanging in the above argument x with y and a with c we arrive at the same inequality. $\square$

COROLLARY 3. If $f(x, y)$ is a reduced Gaussian form of determinant $D < 0$ equivalent to $x^2 - Dy^2$, then $f(x, y) = x^2 - Dy^2$.

Proof. Since $f(x, y)$ and $x^2 - Dy^2$ represent the same integers, Corollary 2 shows that $f(x, y) = x^2 + 2bxy + cy^2$ and, since f is reduced, this implies $b = 0$, i.e., $f(x, y) = x^2 + cy^2$; comparing the determinants we get $c = -D$. $\square$

Even with these elementary tools we can now determine all negative determinants D with class number one:

THEOREM 5.1 (E. Landau [02]). *If D is negative, then $H(D) = 1$ if and only if $D \in \{-1, -2, -3, -4, -7\}$.*

Proof. The "if" part is very easy. Indeed, if $f(x, y) = ax^2 + 2bxy + cy^2$ is a reduced, properly primitive Gaussian form of determinant $0 > D \geqslant -7$, then because of $|2b| \leqslant a \leqslant c$ we get $b^2 \leqslant ac/4$, and so

$$ac = b^2 - D \leqslant ac/4 - D \leqslant ac/4 + 7,$$

which implies $ac \leqslant 9$. If $b \neq 0$ then $c \geqslant a \geqslant 2$ and we get for the pair $[a, c]$ the following possibilities: $[2, 2]$, $[2, 3]$, $[2, 4]$ and $[3, 3]$, whereas $b = \pm 1$. The pairs $[2, 2]$ and $[2, 4]$ correspond to forms which are not properly primitive, and the pair $[3, 3]$ leads to a form of determinant -8, and so we are left with the forms $2x^2 \pm 2xy + 3y^2$ of determinant -5. However, if $b = 0$, then we have first of all the forms $x^2 - Dy^2$ of determinant D, and if $a \neq 1$ then in view of $D = ac$ we get for $[a, c]$ the possibilities $[2, 2]$ and $[2, 3]$. The first gives rise to a form of determinant -6. We thus see that if $0 > D \geqslant -7$ then there are two such forms, and this establishes the "if" part of the theorem.

Now assume that $D < 0$ and $H(D) = 1$. Corollary 3 to Proposition 5.1 shows that there exists only one reduced properly primitive form of determinant D; hence in order to eliminate a particular value of D it suffices to produce such a form distinct from $x^2 - Dy^2$.

Putting $|D| = D_0$, observe that D_0 must be equal either to unity or to a prime power. Indeed, otherwise we could factorize D_0 in two relatively prime factors $\neq 1$, say $D_0 = ac$, $1 < a < c$, $(a, c) = 1$, and in this case the form $ax^2 + cy^2$ would be reduced and distinct from $x^2 - Dy^2$.

The case $D_0 = 1$ leading to $D = -1$, we may write $D_0 = p^m$ with a certain prime p and $m \geqslant 1$. If $p = 2$ and $m \geqslant 4$, then the form $4x^2 + 4xy + (2^{m-2} + 1)y^2$ satisfies our needs. In the case $m = 3$ we consider the form $3x^2 + 2xy + 3y^2$ and in the cases $m = 1, 2$ we arrive at $D = -2, -4$, which are on our list.

Now let p be odd. If the even number $D_0 + 1$ is not a power of 2 then we can write $D_0 + 1 = ac$ with $2 \leqslant a < c$ and $(2, a, c) = 1$, and so the form $ax^2 + 2xy + cy^2$ serves our purpose. Thus $D_0 = p^m = 2^k - 1$ with a certain $k \geqslant 1$. In the cases $k = 1, 2, 3$ we get $D = -1, -3, -7$, which are on our list; for $k = 4$ we have $D_0 = 15$, which is not a prime power; for $k = 5$ we consider the form $5x^2 + 4xy + 7y^2$; finally, if $k \geqslant 6$, then we take the form $8x^2 + 6xy + (2^{k-3} + 1)y^2$. $\square$

3. To avoid certain technical complications which are inessential for our purpose we shall henceforth restrict our attention to those discriminants of quadratic forms which are at the same time discriminants of quadratic number fields. Such discriminants are called *fundamental* and are defined as integers which either are square-free and congruent to unity (mod 4) or are of the form $4m$, where m is square-free and congruent to 2 or to 3 (mod 4). It is an easy exercise to show that d is a fundamental discriminant if and only if it is the discriminant of the field $Q(d^{1/2})$.

We shall now establish an intimate connection between equivalence classes of primitive positive definite binary quadratic forms of a given fundamental discriminant d and the ideal classes in the ring Z_K of all integers in the field $K = Q(d^{1/2})$. A similar connection can be established also for a non-fundamental discriminant, but in this case the ring Z_K must be replaced by its suitable subring (see e.g. B. W. Jones [49]), and an analogous result holds for positive discriminants, although in this case parts (iii) and (iv) of Proposition 5.2 below must be modified. (Cf. E. Hecke [23], Theorem 154, W. Narkiewicz [74], Theorem 8.3, Z. I. Borevich, I. R. Shafarevich [72], Ch. II, §7, Theorem 5.)

Let d be a negative fundamental discriminant, K the field generated by $d^{1/2}$ (which we assume to lie in the upper half-plane) and Z_K the ring of integers of K. By $N(a)$ and $N(I)$ we shall denote the norms of elements of K and of ideals of Z_K respectively.

Consider the set S of all pairs $\alpha = [a_1, a_2]$ of elements of Z_K such that $Za_1 \oplus Za_2 = I_\alpha$ is an ideal in Z_K ordered in such a way that the number $a_1 \bar{a}_2 - \bar{a}_1 a_2$ lies in the upper half-plane, the bars denoting complex conjugation.

With every such pair α we associate the quadratic form

$$f_\alpha(x, y) = N(a_1 x + a_2 y)/N(I_\alpha),$$

the variables being restricted to Z.

PROPOSITION 5.2. (i) *For every α in S the form $f_\alpha(x, y)$ is a primitive positive definite quadratic form over Z of discriminant d.*

(ii) *If $\alpha = [a_1, a_2]$, $\beta = [b_1, b_2]$ are in S and determine equivalent ideals, then the corresponding forms f_α and f_β are equivalent and conversely.*

(iii) *The correspondence*

$$f_\alpha \to \text{class of } I_\alpha$$

induces a one-to-one mapping between the set of all classes of primitive positive definite binary quadratic forms of discriminant d and the group of ideal classes $H(K)$ of the field K.

(iv) *If $\alpha \in S$ and $X \in H(K)$ is the ideal class containing I_α then the set of values attained by f coincides with the set of norms of ideals from the class*

X^{-1}, *and the number of ideals in* X^{-1} *having norm m is equal to*

$$\varepsilon^{-1}(d) \sum_{\substack{x,y \\ f_\alpha(x,y)=m}} 1$$

where

(5.4)
$$\varepsilon(d) = \begin{cases} 6 & if \quad d = -3, \\ 4 & if \quad d = -4, \\ 2 & otherwise. \end{cases}$$

Proof. (i) Obviously

$$f_\alpha(x, y) = \frac{N(a_1)x^2 + (a_1\bar{a}_2 + \bar{a}_1 a_2)xy + N(a_2)y^2}{N(I)}$$

is a binary quadratic form, and if we write $a_i = x_i + y_i d^{1/2}$ with rational x_i, y_i ($i = 1, 2$) then

$$a_1\bar{a}_2 + \bar{a}_1 a_2 = 2(x_1 x_2 - y_1 y_2 d),$$

and

$$N(a_i) = x_i^2 - dy_i^2,$$

which implies $d(f_\alpha) = d$. Since for every integral x, y the number $a_1 x + a_2 y$ lies in I_α, our form attains integral values for integral arguments; hence its coefficients $f(1, 0)$, $f(0, 1)$ and $f(1, 1) - f(1, 0) - f(0, 1)$ are integers and in view of $N(a_1) > 0$ we find that f is positive definite. The fact that d is a fundamental discriminant implies that f is primitive, because if a prime p divided all its coefficients then the form $f_\alpha(x, y)/p$ would have integral coefficients and discriminant d/p^2, which could happen only if $p = 2$; thus $d/4$ would be a discriminant of a quadratic form, thus congruent to 0 or 1 (mod 4), which contradicts the definition of the fundamental discriminant.

(ii) Observe first that if $\alpha = [a_1, a_2]$ and $\beta = [b_1, b_2]$ determine the same ideal I then f_α and f_β are equivalent. Indeed, there is a matrix $\mathfrak{A} \in GL_2(Z)$ such that

$$\mathfrak{A} \begin{bmatrix} a_1 \\ a_2 \end{bmatrix} = \begin{bmatrix} b_1 \\ b_2 \end{bmatrix},$$

and our convention about the ordering of our pairs implies that $\mathfrak{A} \in SL_2(Z)$. Since

$$f_\beta(x, y) = f_\alpha\left(\mathfrak{A}^T \begin{bmatrix} x \\ y \end{bmatrix}\right) = \mathfrak{A}^T f_\alpha$$

(where $\mathfrak{A}^T$ denotes the transposed matrix), we see that f_α and f_β are equivalent. The first part of our assertion follows now from the observation that the quadratic forms corresponding to the pairs $[a_1, a_2]$ and $[ca_1, ca_2]$, where c is any non-zero element of Z_K, coincide; hence if $\alpha = [a_1, a_2]$, $\beta = [b_1, b_2]$ determine equivalent ideals, say $c_1 I_\alpha = c_2 I_\beta$ ($c_1, c_2 \in Z_K$, and non-zero), then $\alpha' = [c_1 a_1, c_1 a_2]$ and $\beta' = [c_2 b_1, c_2 b_2]$ determine the same ideals and we have

$$f_\alpha = f_{\alpha'}, \quad f_\beta = f_{\beta'},$$

and f_α, f_β are equivalent.

Conversely, if f_α, f_β are equivalent, then we have

$$f_\beta(x, y) = f_\alpha(A_{11} x + A_{12} y, A_{21} x + A_{22} y)$$

with a certain matrix $(A_{ij}) \in SL_2(Z)$. Using the definition of f_β, we now find that the solutions of $f_\beta(1, Y) = 0$ are equal on the one hand to $-b_1/b_2$ and $-\bar{b}_1/\bar{b}_2$ and on the other hand to

$$-\frac{a_1 A_{11} + a_2 A_{21}}{a_1 A_{12} + a_2 A_{22}} \quad \text{and} \quad -\frac{\bar{a}_1 A_{11} + \bar{a}_2 A_{21}}{\bar{a}_1 A_{12} + \bar{a}_2 A_{22}}.$$

If we had

$$\frac{\bar{b}_1}{\bar{b}_2} = \frac{a_1 A_{11} + a_2 A_{21}}{a_1 A_{12} + a_2 A_{22}} = \frac{A_{11}(a_1/a_2) + A_{21}}{A_{12}(a_1/a_2) + A_{22}},$$

then $\bar{b}_1/\bar{b}_2$ would lie in the upper complex half-plane, contrary to our ordering of b_1, b_2. This shows that we must have

$$\frac{b_1}{b_2} = \frac{a_1 A_{11} + a_2 A_{21}}{a_1 A_{12} + a_2 A_{22}},$$

and so, with a suitable non-zero $t \in K$,

$$b_1 = t(a_1 A_{11} + a_2 A_{21}), \quad b_2 = t(a_1 A_{12} + a_2 A_{22}).$$

Writing $t = U/V$ with $U, V \in Z_K$ and observing that $c_1 = a_1 A_{11} + a_2 A_{21}$ and $c_2 = a_1 A_{12} + a_2 A_{22}$ form a Z-basis of I_α, we get $Ub_i = Vc_i$ ($i = 1, 2$), which implies that the ideals I_α and I_β are equivalent.

(iii) To prove this assertion it suffices to show that every primitive and positive definite quadratic form f of discriminant d equals f_α with a suitable choice of $\alpha = [a_1, a_2]$. Write $f(x, y) = Ax^2 + Bxy + Cy^2$ and put

$$a_1 = \begin{cases} B + d^{1/2} & \text{if} \quad C > 0, \\ B - d^{1/2} & \text{if} \quad C < 0 \end{cases}$$

and $a_2 = 2C$. An easy check shows that this is a good choice.

(iv) If $\alpha = [a_1, a_2]$ and $I = I_\alpha$ then every element ξ of I can be uniquely written in the form $\xi = xa_1 + ya_2$ with integral x, y. With every such element we can associate a unique ideal $J_\xi \in X^{-1}$ defined by $J_\xi = I(\xi)/I$ where $I(\xi)$ denotes the principal ideal generated by ξ. Conversely, if $J \in X^{-1}$ is given, then the ideal IJ is principal, and taking for ξ any of its generators we get $J = J_\xi$. This shows that there is a one-to-one correspondence between ideals $J \in X^{-1}$ and classes of associated elements in I, and it remains to observe that if $\xi = xa_1 + ya_2$, then $f_\alpha(x, y) = N(\xi)/N(I) = N(I(\xi)I^{-1})$ $= N(J_\xi)$ and that every class of associated elements in Z_K is of cardinality $\varepsilon(d)$. $\square$

COROLLARY. *If $K = Q(d^{1/2})$ and d is a fundamental discriminant, then $h(d) = h(K)$.* $\square$

4. We now give the classical definition of the *genera of quadratic forms*. We follow C. F. Gauss [01] (art. 231) adapting his approach to cover the more general forms (5.2) but restrict ourselves to the case of fundamental negative discriminants.

Thus, let d be a negative fundamental discriminant. With every prime p dividing d we shall associate a real character χ_p. For p odd put $\chi_p(m) = \left(\dfrac{m}{p}\right)$, and if $p = 2$ then $\chi_2(m)$ is defined as follows: if $d/4$ is odd then $\chi_2(m)$ is the only real primitive character (mod 4), and if $d/4$ is even then $\chi_2(m)$ is one of the primitive real characters (mod 8), namely

$$\chi_2 = \begin{cases} \varphi_8 & \text{if} \quad d/4 \equiv 2 \pmod 8, \\ \psi_8 & \text{if} \quad d/4 \equiv 6 \pmod 8, \end{cases}$$

where φ_8 and ψ_8 are distinguished by putting $\operatorname{Ker} \varphi_8 = \{-1, 1\}$, $\operatorname{Ker} \psi_8 = \{1, 3\}$.

Now, for $m \in Z$, $(m, d) = 1$, define

$$X(m) = [\chi_p(m)]_{p|d} \in \{-1, 1\}^{\omega(d)}.$$

The definition of the genera depends on the following result:

PROPOSITION 5.3. *If $f(x, y) = ax^2 + bxy + cy^2$ is a primitive form of discriminant d, then for all integers m represented by f which are coprime with d the value $X(m)$ depends only on f but not on m.*

Proof. Let m, n be two integers represented by f and coprime with d, say $m = f(x, y)$ and $n = f(u, v)$. Then

(5.5) $mn = \left(axu + \tfrac{1}{2}b(xu + yv) + cyx\right)^2 - \tfrac{1}{4}d(xu - yv)^2$;

thus $4mn$ can be written in the form $A^2 - dB^2$ with integral A, B and we get $mn \equiv A^2 \pmod d$. This implies that if p is an odd prime divisor of d then $\chi_p(m) = \chi_p(n)$.

If d is even then it must be divisible by 4 and b must be even.

If $d/4 \equiv 3 \pmod 4$ then by (5.5) mn is congruent to a sum of two squares (mod 4), which is possible only if $mn \equiv 1 \pmod 4$; thus $\chi_4(m) = \chi_4(n)$. If $d/4 \equiv 2 \pmod 8$ then by (5.5) we can write $mn \equiv C^2 - 2D^2 \pmod 8$. Here C must be odd; hence $C^2 \equiv 1 \pmod 8$, and since $2D^2 \equiv 0, 2 \pmod 8$ we see that $mn \equiv 1, -1 \pmod 8$; thus $\varphi_8(m) = \varphi_8(n)$. The same argument applies also to the case $d/4 \equiv 6 \pmod 8$ and leads to $\psi_8(m) = \psi_8(n)$ in that case. □

Proposition 5.3 allows us to define for every primitive form f the sequence $X(f) = \langle \chi_p(f) \rangle_{p|d}$ by putting $\chi_p(f) = \chi_p(m)$ for $p|d$, m being any number coprime with d and represented by f.

To show the correctness of this definition we must show that any primitive form represents at least one integer coprime with its discriminant, but this can be seen in the following way:

If p is a prime dividing $d(f)$, then at least one of the numbers $a = f(1, 0)$, $c = f(0, 1)$ is not divisible by p, since otherwise p would divide b, contradicting the primitiveness of f. Now, for every such prime p, define

$$x_p = \begin{cases} 1, & p \nmid a, \\ 0, & p | a \end{cases} \quad \text{and} \quad y_p = \begin{cases} 0, & p \nmid a, \\ 1, & p | a \end{cases}$$

and let x, y be a solution of the system of congruences

$$x \equiv x_p \pmod p,$$

$$y \equiv y_p \pmod p.$$

Then $m = f(x, y)$ cannot be divisible by any prime divisor of $d(f)$; thus $(m, d(f)) = 1$.

We shall say that two forms f, g of the same discriminant d belong to the same genus if and only if the equality $X(f) = X(g)$ holds. (In modern terminology this is equivalent to the following: two primitive binary forms of the same discriminant belong to the same genus if and only if they are equivalent in R and in Z_p, the ring of p-adic integers for all p.) From this definition it is clear that equivalent forms belong to the same genus.

The main result of Gauss's theory of genera is the following theorem, which we find (for Gaussian forms) in art. 287 of his *Disquisitiones Arithmeticae* (C. F. Gauss [01]):

THEOREM 5.2. *If $d = -D$ is a negative fundamental discriminant, then there are $2^{\omega(D)-1}$ different genera of positive definite primitive forms of discriminant d.*

Proof. We shall first show that there are at most $2^{\omega(D)-1}$ genera. Let m be an integer satisfying $(m, 2d) = 1$ and assume that $m = f(x_0, y_0)$ where f is a form of discriminant d and $(x_0, y_0) = 1$. (Such a representation of m by the form f is called *proper*.) Extending the point $\langle x_0, y_0 \rangle$ to a basis of Z^2 and writing f in this basis, we find that f is equivalent to $mx^2 + Bxy + Cy^2$ with suitable integers B, C. Since $B^2 - 4Cm = d$, we obtain $\left(\dfrac{d}{m}\right) = 1$. Write

$d = -2^a D Q^2$ with $a = 0$ or 1, D odd and square-free, $Q = 1$ or 2. Using the quadratic reciprocity law, we now obtain

$$(5.6) \quad 1 = \left(\frac{d}{m}\right) = \left(\frac{-1}{m}\right)\left(\frac{2}{m}\right)^a\left(\frac{D}{m}\right) = \chi_4(m)\,\varphi_8^a(m)\prod_{p|D}\chi_p(m)\cdot(-1)^{(m-1)(D-1)/4}.$$

Now, if d is odd, then $a = 0$ and $D = -d \equiv 3\,(\mathrm{mod}\,4)$; thus the last equality gives

$$1 = \chi_4(m)\prod_{p|D}\chi_p(m)\,\chi_4(m) = \prod_{p|D}\chi_p(m) = \prod_{p|d}\chi_p(m),$$

and we see that $X(f)$ can attain at most $2^{\omega(D)-1}$ values.

If d is even, then $4|d$ and we must consider three cases, according to the residue of $d/4\,(\mathrm{mod}\,8)$. Clearly the cases $d/4 \equiv 0\,(\mathrm{mod}\,8)$ and $d/4 \equiv 4\,(\mathrm{mod}\,8)$ are excluded since d is fundamental.

If $d/4$ is odd, then $a = 0$ and $D \equiv 1\,(\mathrm{mod}\,4)$; thus (5.6) leads to

$$1 = \chi_4(m)\prod_{p|D}\chi_p(m) = \prod_{p|m}\chi_p(m),$$

and again we have at most $2^{\omega(D)-1}$ possibilities for $X(f)$. If $d/4 \equiv 2\,(\mathrm{mod}\,8)$ then $a = 1$ and $D \equiv 3\,(\mathrm{mod}\,4)$; thus (5.6) gives

$$1 = \chi_4(m)\cdot\varphi_8(m)\prod_{p|D}\chi_p(m)\cdot\chi_4(m) = \varphi_8(m)\prod_{p|D}\chi_p(m) = \prod_{p|d}\chi_p(m),$$

and if $d/4 \equiv 6\,(\mathrm{mod}\,8)$ then $a = 1$, $D \equiv 1\,(\mathrm{mod}\,4)$, and again using (5.6) we get

$$1 = \chi_4(m)\cdot\varphi_8(m)\prod_{p|D}\chi_p(m) = \psi_8(m)\prod_{p|D}\chi_p(m) = \prod_{p|d}\chi_p(m);$$

in both cases we see that there are at most $2^{\omega(D)-1}$ possibilities for the value of $X(f)$.

To prove that there are exactly $2^{\omega(D)-1}$ different genera it suffices to produce for every discriminant d an integer m which is properly represented by a primitive form of that discriminant and which, moreover, satisfies the condition

$$\chi_p(m) = \varepsilon_p$$

for every prime divisor p of d, except for the largest such divisor p_0, with $\varepsilon_p = \pm 1$ arbitrarily chosen.

Observe that if a prime q satisfies $\left(\dfrac{d}{q}\right) = 1$ then by Proposition A.10 it splits in the extension $Q(d^{1/2})/Q$; hence, in view of Proposition 5.2 (iv), it is represented by a form of discriminant d, and of course this representation is a proper one. Because of

$$\left(\frac{d}{m}\right) = \prod_{p|d}\chi_p(m)$$

it suffices thus to find a prime q such that

$$\chi_p(q) = \begin{cases} \varepsilon_p & \text{if} \quad p \neq p_0, \\ \prod_{\substack{p|d \\ p \neq p_0}} \varepsilon_p & \text{if} \quad p = p_0. \end{cases}$$

The condition $\chi_p(m) = \varepsilon$ (with $\varepsilon = 1$ or -1) determines for odd p a set of $(p-1)/2$ non-zero residue classes $(\mathrm{mod}\, p)$ and for $p = 2$ a non-empty set of odd residue classes $(\mathrm{mod}\, 8)$, and thus, by the Chinese remainder theorem, the conditions above are satisfied by all integers lying in a certain non-empty set of residue classes $(\mathrm{mod}\, 8d)$ coprime with $8d$.

Any prime belonging to a residue class from that set will satisfy our demands and Dirichlet's Prime Number Theorem guarantees the existence of such primes. □

5. The first important result concerning class numbers after Gauss's Theorem 5.2 was obtained by G. Dirichlet [38], who succeeded in obtaining a simple expression for $h(d)$. It turned out later that this formula is only a particular case of a general result valid for the class numbers of all abelian extensions of the rationals, but we shall restrict ourselves to the imaginary quadratic case.

THEOREM 5.3. *If d is a fundamental negative discriminant, $X(n) = X_d(n)$ is the character $\left(\dfrac{d}{n}\right)$ and $L(s, X_d)$ denotes the corresponding L-function, then*

$$(5.7) \qquad h(d) = \varepsilon(d)|d|^{1/2}(2\pi)^{-1} L(1, X_d)$$

and

$$(5.8) \qquad h(d) = \varepsilon(d)(2d)^{-1} \sum_{x=1}^{|d|} \left(\frac{d}{x}\right) x$$

where $\varepsilon(d)$ is given by (5.4).

Proof. We shall first prove (5.7) and then give two different proofs of (5.8). The first of them will be analytical and essentially due to Dirichlet and the second, discovered recently by H. L. S. Orde [78], will be completely elementary. In the first proof we shall freely use fundamental facts from the theory of quadratic fields, which may be found e.g. in E. Hecke [23], H. B. Mann [55] or W. Narkiewicz [74]. An analytical proof which does not use algebraic numbers is contained in Exercises 3–8.

We start with the analytic approach. Denote by $F(m)$ the number of ideals of norm m in the ring of integers of the field $Q(d^{1/2})$ and for any ideal class X denote by $F_X(m)$ the number of those ideals which belong to X. From the theory of quadratic fields we shall here use the following facts:

(a) the function $F(m)$ is multiplicative, and

(b) for a prime power p^m we have

$$F(p^m) = \begin{cases} 0 & \text{if} \quad X(p) = -1 \text{ and } 2 \nmid m, \\ 1 & \text{if} \quad X(p) = -1 \text{ and } 2 \mid m, \\ 1 & \text{if} \quad p \mid d, \\ m+1 & \text{if} \quad X(p) = +1. \end{cases}$$

The proof of (a) is immediate and (b) follows from the law of factorization of rational primes in quadratic fields (Proposition A.10). From (a) and (b) we obtain the equality

(5.9) $$F(m) = \sum_{k \mid m} X(k) = \prod_{p^\alpha \| m} \left(1 + X(p) + \ldots + X(p^\alpha)\right),$$

which, for $x > 1$, leads to

$$\sum_{m=1}^{\infty} \frac{F(m)}{m^x} = \sum_{m=1}^{\infty} \frac{1}{m^x} \cdot \sum_{m=1}^{\infty} \frac{X(n)}{n^x} = \zeta(x) L(x, X),$$

and so

(5.10) $$\lim_{x \to 1} (x-1) \sum_{m=1}^{\infty} \frac{F(m)}{m^x} = L(1, X).$$

Now we evaluate the limit in the last equality in another way. Using Proposition 5.2 (iv), we may write

$$\sum_{m=1}^{\infty} \frac{F(m)}{m^x} = \sum_{i=1}^{h} \sum_{m=1}^{\infty} \frac{F_{X_i}(m)}{m^x} = \frac{1}{\varepsilon(d)} \sum_{i=1}^{h} \sum_{m=1}^{\infty} \frac{A_i(m)}{m^x},$$

where by $A_i(m)$ we denote the number of representations of the integer m by a quadratic form of discriminant d, which corresponds in view of Proposition 5.2 (iii) to an ideal lying in the class X_i, the set $\{X_1, X_2, \ldots, X_h\}$ ($h = h(d)$) being the set of all ideal classes in $Q(d^{1/2})$. If we denote such a form by $f_i(x, y)$ ($i = 1, 2, \ldots, h$), then

$$\sum_{m \leqslant t} A_i(m) = \sum_{\substack{x, y \\ 0 < f_i(x,y) \leqslant t}} 1,$$

which (when t tends to infinity) is asymptotically equal to the area bounded by the ellipse $f_i(x, y) = t$; this equals

$$\left(2\pi |d|^{-1/2} + o(1)\right) t.$$

Abelian summation shows that for $x \to 1$

$$\sum_{m=1}^{\infty} \frac{A_i(m)}{m^x} = \left(1 + o(1)\right) \frac{2\pi x}{|d|^{1/2}} \zeta(x);$$

hence

$$\lim_{x \to 1} (x-1) \sum_{m=1}^{\infty} \frac{F(m)}{m^x} = \frac{2\pi h}{\varepsilon(d)|d|^{1/2}}$$

and by using (5.10) we arrive at (5.7).

The deduction of (5.8) from formula (5.7) will be based on the following lemma, which gives a closed expression for the value of $L(1, \chi)$ for an arbitrary primitive character χ.

LEMMA 5.1. *If χ is a primitive character* (mod m), *then*

$$L(1, \chi) = -\frac{\tau(X)}{|m|} \sum_{j=1}^{m} \bar{\chi}(j) \left\{ \log\left(2 \sin \frac{\pi j}{m} \right) + \pi i \left(\frac{1}{2} - \frac{j}{|m|} \right) \right\}.$$

Proof. For x in $(-1, 1)$ define

$$f(x) = \sum_{n=1}^{\infty} \chi(n) n^{-1} x^n$$

and observe that $\lim_{x \to 1} f(x) = L(1, \chi)$. Now it is easy to see that

$$f(x) = \sum_{r=1}^{m} \chi(r) \sum_{n \equiv r (\mathrm{mod}\, m)} n^{-1} x^n = \sum_{r=1}^{m} \chi(r) \sum_{n=0}^{\infty} (r+nm)^{-1} x^{r+nm},$$

and after computing the derivative of $f(x)$ we obtain

$$f(x) = -\int_0^x \sum_{r=1}^{m} \left(\chi(r) t^{r-1}/(t^m-1) \right) dt = -\int_0^x \sum_{j=0}^{m} \left(a_j/(t-\zeta_m^j) \right) dt$$

(where $\zeta_m = \exp\{2\pi i/m\}$) with certain coefficients $a_0, a_1, \ldots$, which can be explicitly determined in the following way:

Since

$$\sum_{r=1}^{m} \chi(r) t^{r-1} = \sum_{j=0}^{m} a_j \frac{t^m - 1}{t - \zeta_m^j},$$

we get, taking limits on both sides as t tends to ζ_m^j,

$$\sum_{r=1}^{m} \chi(r) \zeta_m^{jr-j} = m a_j \zeta_m^{-j};$$

hence $a_j = m^{-1} \tau_j(X)$. Using Proposition 2.1 (i) and noting that

$$\int_0^1 \frac{dt}{t - \zeta_m^j} = \log\left(2 \sin \frac{\pi j}{m} \right) + \pi i \left(\frac{1}{2} - \frac{j}{m} \right),$$

we arrive at

$$L(1, \chi) = -\tau(X) m^{-1} \sum_{j=1}^{m} \bar{\chi}(j) \left\{ \log\left(2 \sin \frac{\pi j}{m} \right) + \pi i \left(\frac{1}{2} - \frac{j}{m} \right) \right\}. \quad \square$$

COROLLARY. *If d is a fundamental discriminant and $X_d(n) = \left(\dfrac{d}{n}\right)$, then for* $d < 0$ *we have*

$$L(1, X_d) = \frac{\pi}{d|d|^{1/2}} \sum_{j=1}^{|d|} j\left(\frac{d}{j}\right),$$

whereas for $d > 0$

$$L(1, X_d) = -d^{-1/2} \sum_{j=1}^{d} \left(\frac{d}{j}\right) \log\left(\sin\left(\pi j/d\right)\right).$$

Proof. The character X_d is a primitive character $(\bmod |d|)$ in view of Proposition A.8. Since Theorem 2.1 implies that

$$\tau(X_d) = \begin{cases} d^{1/2}, & d > 0, \\ i|d|^{1/2}, & d < 0 \end{cases}$$

and $L(1, X_d)$ is real, the asserted formulas follow by a simple computation. $\square$

Formula (5.8) follows immediately. $\square$

Now we give the elementary proof of (5.8). We assume that $d < -4$ since in the cases $d = -3$ and $d = -4$ one can check equality (5.8) directly. Hence we have to prove that

$$h(d) = d^{-1} \sum_{x=1}^{|d|} \left(\frac{d}{x}\right) x.$$

Let $f_1, \ldots, f_h$ (where $h = h(d)$) be a complete set of representatives of classes of quadratic forms of discriminant d. Clearly the forms $-f_1, \ldots, -f_h$ constitute a similar system for negative definite primitive forms of the same discriminant. Denoting by $A(F, m)$ the number of representations of a given integer m by the form F and using Proposition 5.2 (iv) and formula (5.9), we obtain for

$$s(m) = \sum_{i=1}^{h} \left(A(f_i, m) + A(-f_i, m)\right)$$

the equality

$$s(m) = \begin{cases} 2 \sum_{k \mid |m|} \left(\dfrac{d}{k}\right), & m \neq 0, \\ 2h(d), & m = 0. \end{cases}$$

We now define a function $S(m)$ putting $S(m) = s(m)$ for $m \neq 0$ and

$$S(0) = \frac{2}{d} \sum_{x=1}^{|d|} x\left(\frac{d}{x}\right)$$

and consider for integral $N \geqslant 1$ and $0 < q < 1$ the polynomials

$$a_N(x) = \sum_{|k| \leqslant N} s(k) q^{|k|}, \qquad b_N(x) = \sum_{k \leqslant N} S(k) x^{|k|}.$$

Moreover, for $m = [N/4]$, put

$$A_N(q) = 4 a_m(q^4) - a_N(q) \qquad \text{and} \qquad B_N(q) = 4 b_m(q^4) - b_N(q).$$

Then

$$A_N(q) - B_N(q) = 6 \left(\frac{1}{d} \sum_{x=1}^{d} x \left(\frac{d}{x} \right) - h(d) \right),$$

which is a rational number whose denominator is a divisor of d; hence to establish the theorem it is sufficient to show that for a suitable choice of q and N we have

$$|A_N(q) - B_N(q)| \leqslant 2/d^2.$$

In fact, we shall prove the existence of q and N such that both numbers $|A_N(q)|$ and $|B_N(q)|$ will be less than $1/d^2$. Let us start with $A_N(q)$. We have

$$a_N(q) = \sum_{j=1}^{h} \sum_{m=1}^{N} A(f_j, m) q^m + \sum_{j=1}^{h} \sum_{m=1}^{N} A(-f_j, -m) q^m + 2h$$

$$= 2 \sum_{j=1}^{h} \left(1 + \sum_{m=1}^{N} A(f_j, m) q^m \right) = 2 \sum_{j=1}^{h} \sum_{\substack{x,y \\ f_j(x,y) \leqslant N}} q^{f_j(x,y)};$$

thus

$$A_N(q)/2 = \sum_{j=1}^{h} \left\{ 4 \sum_{\substack{x,y \\ f_j(x,y) \leqslant N/4}} q^{4 f_j(x,y)} - \sum_{\substack{x,y \\ f_j(x,y) \leqslant N}} q^{f_j(x,y)} \right\}.$$

Now note that

$$\sum_{\substack{x,y \\ f_j(x,y) \leqslant N}} (1 + (-1)^x + (-1)^y + (-1)^{x+y}) q^{f_j(x,y)}$$

$$= 4 \sum_{\substack{x,y \text{ even} \\ f_j(x,y) \leqslant N}} q^{f_j(x,y)} = 4 \sum_{\substack{x,y \\ f_j(x,y) \leqslant N/4}} q^{4 f_j(x,y)};$$

thus

(5.11) $$\tfrac{1}{2} A_N(q) = \sum_{j=1}^{h} \sum_{\substack{x,y \\ f_j(x,y) \leqslant N}} ((-1)^x + (-1)^y + (-1)^{x+y}) q^{f_j(x,y)}.$$

To bound $A_N(q)$ we use the following lemma:

LEMMA 5.2. *If r, s are integers, $r \geqslant |s|$, $r \neq 0$, $0 < q < 1$, $N \geqslant 4$ and*

$$S = S(r, s; N, q) = \sum_{\substack{x \\ rx^2 + sx \leqslant N}} (-1)^x q^{rx^2 + sx},$$

we have the bound

$$|S| \leqslant r^2(1 - q) + 2q^{N/4}..$$

Proof. Denote by m the largest positive integer for which $rm^2 + sm \leqslant N$ holds and similarly let $-n$ be the smallest negative integer such that $rn^2 - sn \leqslant N$. Thus

$$S = \sum_{x=n}^{m} (-1)^x q^{rx^2 + sx} = 1 + \sum_{x=1}^{m} (-1)^x q^{rx^2 + sx} + \sum_{x=1}^{n} (-1)^x q^{rx^2 - sx}.$$

First we consider the case $m = n = 0$. Then necessarily $r + s$ and $r - s$ exceed N; thus $r \geqslant N/2$ and obviously $S = 1$. If it were $S = 1 \geqslant r^2(1 - q) + q^N$ then

$$N^2/4 \leqslant r^2 < (1 - q^N)/(1 - q) = 1 + q + \ldots + q^{N-1} < N;$$

thus $N < 4$, contrary to our assumption. Thus in this case $S < r^2(1 - q) + q^N$.

Now assume that at least one of the numbers m, n is non-zero. If $s = 0$ then obviously $m = n$. If s is negative, then either $n = m$ or $n = m - 1$. This is clear if $m = 0$, and if $m > 0$ then for $x = -m - 1$ we get

$$rx^2 + sx = r(m + 1)^2 - s(m + 1) \geqslant r(m + 1)^2 + s(m + 1) > N$$

and for $x = -m + 1$ we get

$$rx^2 + sx = r(m - 1)^2 - s(m - 1) \leqslant rm^2 + sm \leqslant N.$$

A similar argument shows that in the case $s > 0$ one has either $n = m$ or $n = m + 1$. Thus in all cases we have n equal to $m - 1$, m or $m + 1$; hence, putting $T = \max(m, n) > 0$, we may write

$$S = 1 + \sum_{x=1}^{T} (-1)^x (q^{rx^2 + sx} + q^{rx^2 - sx}) + \varepsilon_1 (-1)^{u+1} q^{ru^2 + su} + \varepsilon_2 (-1)^{v+1} q^{rv^2 - sv},$$

where in the case $n = m - 1$ we have $\varepsilon_1 = 0$, $\varepsilon_2 = 1$, $v = m$, in the case $n = m$ we have $\varepsilon_1 = \varepsilon_2 = 0$ and in the case $n = m + 1$ we have $\varepsilon_1 = 1$, $\varepsilon_2 = 0$ and $u = n$. This shows that in all cases

$$S = 1 + \sum_{x=1}^{T} (-1)^x (q^{rx^2 + sx} + q^{rx^2 - sx}) + R$$

where $|R| \leqslant q^N$.

Observe now that

$$\sum_{x=1}^{T} (-1)^{x-1} (q^{rx^2+r} + q^{rx^2-r}) = 1 + (-1)^{T-1} q^{r(T^2+T)};$$

hence the polynomial

$$P_T(x) = \sum_{x=1}^{T} (-1)^{x-1} q^{rx^2-rx} (1-q^{rx-sx})(1-q^{rx+sx})$$

equals $(-1)^{T-1} q^{r(T^2+T)} + S - R$.

If we had $r(T^2+T) \leqslant N/4$ then in view of $r(T+1)^2 + r(T+1) > N$ the inequality

$$N \leqslant N/4 + 2r(T+1)$$

would result, but $r(T+1) \leqslant N/4$ and so finally we would have $N \leqslant 3N/4$, a contradiction. It follows that the difference between S and the polynomial $P_T(q)$ does not exceed $2q^{N/4}$. Now we bound $P_T(q)$ from above, which leads to a bound for S.

We apply to the terms of $P_T(x)$ and $-P_T(x)$ the inequalities

$$tq^t \leqslant (1-q^t)/(1-q) = 1 + q + \ldots + q^{t-1} \leqslant t$$

(for $t = 1, 2, 3, \ldots$), which lead to

$$(r^2-s^2) x^2 (1-q)^2 q^{2rx} \leqslant (1-q^{rx-sx})(1-q^{rx+sx}) \leqslant (r^2-s^2) x^2 (1-q)^2$$

and thus imply

$$P_T(q) \leqslant (r^2-s^2)(1-q)^2 \Big\{ \sum_{\substack{1 \leqslant x \leqslant T \\ x \, \text{odd}}} x^2 q^{rx^2-rx} - \sum_{\substack{1 \leqslant x \leqslant T \\ x \, \text{even}}} x^2 q^{rx^2+rx} \Big\}$$

$$\leqslant r^2(1-q)^2 \Big\{ 1 + \sum_{1 \leqslant k \leqslant [(T-1)/2]} (2k+1)^2 q^{2rk(2k+1)} -$$

$$- \sum_{1 \leqslant k \leqslant [T/2]} 4k^2 q^{2rk(2k+1)} \Big\}$$

$$\leqslant r^2(1-q)^2 \Big\{ 1 + \sum_{1 \leqslant k \leqslant [(T-1)/2]} (4k+1) q^{2rk(2k+1)} \Big\}$$

$$\leqslant r^2(1-q)^2 \Big\{ 1 + \sum_{1 \leqslant k \leqslant [(T-1)/2]} (4k+1) q^{4k^2+2k} \Big\}$$

$$\leqslant r^2(1-q)^2 \Big\{ 1 + \sum_{1 \leqslant k \leqslant [(T-1)/2]} (q^{4k^2-2k} + q^{4k^2-2k+1} + \ldots + q^{4k^2+2k}) \Big\}$$

$$\leqslant r^2(1-q)^2 \sum_{0 \leqslant k \leqslant [(T-1)/2]} q^k < r^2(1-q)$$

because we have

$$4(k-1)^2 + 2(k-1) < 4k^2 - 2k$$

for $k \geqslant 1$.

The same approach gives

$$-P_T(q) < r^2(1-q),$$

and so finally we arrive at $|P_T(q)| < r^2(1-q)$ and

$$|S| < r^2(1-q) + 2q^{N/4}$$

as asserted. □

COROLLARY. *If f is a positive definite quadratic form of discriminant d, $N \geqslant 4$ and*

$$F(q) = \sum_{f(x,y) \leqslant N} ((-1)^x + (-1)^y + (-1)^{x+y}) q^{f(x,y)},$$

then for $0 < q < 1$ we have

$$|F(q)| < 4N^{1/2} \left\{ \frac{|d|}{3}(1-q) + 2q^{N/4} \right\}.$$

Proof. Note first that for equivalent forms the corresponding polynomials coincide. Indeed, it suffices to show that if f_1, f_2 are equivalent forms then the numbers of representations

(5.12) $f_1(x, y) = m,$

(5.13) $f_2(u, v) = m$

with even x, y, u and v coincide; however, this follows from the observation that if $f_2 = \mathfrak{A} f_1$ with a certain matrix $\mathfrak{A}$ in $SL_2(Z)$ then the map $\begin{bmatrix} u \\ v \end{bmatrix} \to \mathfrak{A} \begin{bmatrix} u \\ v \end{bmatrix} = \begin{bmatrix} x \\ y \end{bmatrix}$ gives a one-to-one correspondence between solutions of (5.12) and (5.13) preserving the greatest common divisor.

We may thus assume that the form f is reduced, i.e., $f(x, y) = ax^2 + bxy + cy^2$ with $|b| \leqslant a \leqslant c$. For any y write $by = 2aQ + r$ with $Q = Q(y)$, $r = r(y)$ and $|r| < a$. Then

$$f(x, y) = a(x+Q)^2 + r(x+Q) - aQ^2 - rQ + cy^2;$$

thus, putting $z = x + Q$ and denoting by $S(N)$ the set of those integers y for which there exists an integer x such that $f(x, y) \leqslant N$, we can write, for $\varDelta = \varDelta(y) = cy^2 - aQ^2 - rQ$,

(5.14) $\displaystyle \sum_{f(x,y) \leqslant N} (-1)^x q^{f(x,y)} = \sum_{y \in S(N)} (-1)^Q q^{\varDelta(y)} \sum_{\substack{z \\ az^2 + rz \leqslant N - \varDelta}} (-1)^z q^{az^2 + rz}.$

Now observe that $\varDelta(y)$ is non-negative. Indeed, from

$$|2aQ| = |by - r| \leqslant |b||y| + a \leqslant (1+|y|)a$$

we infer that

$$|Q| \leqslant (1+|y|)/2,$$

and thus if $y \neq 0$ then $|Q| \leqslant |y|$. This settles the case of negative Q since

$$cy^2 - aQ^2 - rQ \geqslant a(y^2 - Q^2 + |Q|) \geqslant 0.$$

If Q is positive, then

$$\Delta \geqslant a(y^2 - Q^2 - Q) \geqslant a(y^2 - (|y|+1)^2/4 - (|y|+1)/2) \geqslant 0$$

for $|y| \geqslant 2$. In the remaining cases, viz. $y = 0, 1$ and -1, we have $Q = 0$ and the assertion becomes evident.

It follows that $|(-1)^Q q^{\Delta(y)}| \leqslant 1$, and hence, using Lemma 5.2, we obtain

$$\left| \sum_{f(x,y) \leqslant N} (-1)^x q^{f(x,y)} \right| \leqslant \sum_{y \in S(N)}' q^{\Delta(y)} \{a^2(1-q) + 2q^{(N-\Delta(y))/4}\}$$

$$= a^2(1-q) \sum_{y \in S(N)} 1 + 2 \sum_{y \in S(N)} q^{N/4 + 3\Delta(y)/4}$$

$$\leqslant (a^2(1-q) + 2q^{N/4}) \sum_{y \in S(N)} 1.$$

Writing $|d| = 4ac - b^2 \geqslant 4ac - a^2 \geqslant 3a^2$, we get $a \leqslant |d|^{1/2}/3^{1/2}$, and to bound the cardinality of $S(N)$ observe that from

$$f(x, y) = a(x + by/2a)^2 + (|d|/4a) y^2 \leqslant N$$

one gets

$$|y| \leqslant 2N^{1/2}(a/|d|)^{1/2} \leqslant 2N^{1/2} \left(\frac{1}{|d|^{1/2} \sqrt{3}} \right)^{1/2} \leqslant \left(\frac{2}{\sqrt{2}} \right)^{1/2} N^{1/2} < \frac{2}{3} N^{1/2}$$

because d is a fundamental discriminant and so $d < -4$ implies the inequality $|d| \leqslant 7$. Thus finally $S(N) \leqslant 4N^{1/2}/3$ and we arrive at

$$(5.15) \qquad \left| \sum_{f(x,y) \leqslant N} (-1)^x q^{f(x,y)} \right| \leqslant \frac{4}{3} N^{1/2} \left\{ \frac{|d|}{3}(1-q) + 2q^{N/4} \right\}.$$

The same bound is true for the sum

$$\sum_{f(x,y) \leqslant N} (-1)^y q^{f(x,y)}$$

since it suffices to apply (5.15) to the reduced form, equivalent to $g(x, y) = f(y, x)$. Finally, to the sum

$$\sum_{f(x,y) \leqslant N} (-1)^{x+y} q^{f(x,y)}$$

we apply the same procedure, arriving immediately at

$$\left| \sum_{f(x,y) \leqslant N} (-1)^{x+y} q^{f(x,y)} \right| = \sum_{y \in S(N)} (-1)^{Q+y} q^{\Delta(y)} \sum_{az^2 + rz \leqslant N - \Delta(y)} (-1)^z q^{az^2 + rz},$$

to which the argument used to evaluate (5.14) applies *verbatim*. The corollary follows immediately. □

Using this corollary, we now obtain from (5.11) the following bound for $A_N(q)$:

$$|A_N(q)| \leqslant 8hN^{1/2}\left(\frac{|d|}{3}(1-q)+2q^{N/4}\right);$$

thus, applying Corollary 1 to Proposition 5.1, we obtain

(5.16) $$|A_N(q)| \leqslant \frac{16}{3}N^{1/2}\left(\frac{|d|}{3}(1-q)+2q^{N/4}\right).$$

Now we turn to the evaluation of $B_N(q)$, which will be based on the following lemma:

LEMMA 5.3. *If* $N \geqslant 1$ *and for* $q \in (0, 1)$

$$T_N(q) = \frac{1}{d}\sum_{1 \leqslant n \leqslant |d|} n\left(\frac{d}{n}\right)+2\sum_{mn \leqslant N}(-1)^m\left(\frac{d}{n}\right)q^{mn}$$

then

$$|T_N(q)| < 13|d|^2\{1-q+Nq^N\}.$$

Proof. Since

$$\sum_{mn \leqslant N}(-1)^m\left(\frac{d}{n}\right)q^{mn} = \sum_{n=1}^{N}\left(\frac{d}{n}\right)\sum_{m=1}^{[N/n]}(-q^n)^m = -\sum_{n=1}^{N}\left(\frac{d}{n}\right)\frac{q^n+(-q^n)^{1+[N/n]}}{1+q^n}$$

and

$$\left|\sum_{n=1}^{N}\left(\frac{d}{n}\right)(-q^n)^{1+[N/n]}(1+q^n)^{-1}\right| \leqslant \sum_{n=1}^{N}\frac{q^{N+n}}{1+q^n} \leqslant Nq^N,$$

we obtain

(5.17) $$\left|T_N(q)-\frac{1}{d}\sum_{n=1}^{|d|}n\left(\frac{d}{n}\right)+\sum_{n=1}^{N}\left(\frac{d}{n}\right)\frac{2q^n}{1+q^n}\right| \leqslant 2Nq^N.$$

Now write

$$A = d^{-1}\sum_{n=1}^{|d|}n\left(\frac{d}{n}\right), \quad a_m = \sum_{k=1}^{m}\left(\frac{d}{k}\right) \quad \text{and} \quad A_n = a_1+a_2+\ldots+a_n.$$

Since $\left(\frac{d}{x}\right)$ is a non-principal character (mod $|d|$), we have $a_m = 0$ for m divisible by d, and thus a_m is periodic with period $|d|$ and satisfies $|a_m| \leqslant |d|$. Moreover, writing $n = q|d|+r$ with $1 \leqslant r < |d|$, we get

$$A_n = \sum_{m=1}^{q|d|}a_m+\sum_{m=1+q|d|}^{q|d|+r}a_m = q\sum_{m=1}^{|d|}a_m+\sum_{m=1}^{r}a_m,$$

and since $n/|d| - 1 \leqslant q \leqslant n/|d|$ we get

$$A_n = \frac{n}{|d|} \sum_{m=1}^{|d|} a_m + \theta \sum_{m=1}^{|d|} a_m + \sum_{m=1}^{r} a_m$$

where $0 \leqslant \theta = \theta(n, d) \leqslant 1$; thus

$$A_n = \frac{n}{|d|} \sum_{m=1}^{d} a_m + R(n, d)$$

where $|R(n, d)| \leqslant 2 \sum_{m=1}^{|d|} |a_m| < 2|d|^2$. But

$$\sum_{m=1}^{|d|} a_m = \sum_{k=1}^{|d|} \left(\frac{d}{k}\right) \sum_{m=k}^{|d|} 1 = \sum_{k=1}^{|d|} (|d| - k + 1)\left(\frac{d}{k}\right) = -\sum_{k=1}^{|d|} k \left(\frac{d}{k}\right) = -dA = |d| A,$$

and so we finally obtain

(5.18) $A_n = nA + R(n, d)$ $(n = 1, 2, \ldots)$.

Writing $x_n = 2q^n/(1 + q^n)$, we get

$$\Delta x_n = x_n - x_{n+1}$$
$$= 2q^n (1 - q)(1 + q^n)^{-1}(1 + q^{n+1})^{-1};$$

hence $0 < \Delta x_n < 2(1 - q)$ and

$$\Delta^2 x_n = \Delta x_n - \Delta x_{n+1}$$
$$= 2(1 - q^2) q^n (1 - q^{n+1})(1 + q^n)^{-1}(1 + q^{n+1})^{-1}(1 + q^{n+2})^{-1} > 0.$$

Now we apply partial summation to get

$$\sum_{n=1}^{N} \left(\frac{d}{n}\right) x_n = \sum_{n=1}^{N-1} \left(\sum_{k=1}^{n} \left(\frac{d}{k}\right)\right) \Delta x_n + x_N \sum_{n=1}^{N} \left(\frac{d}{n}\right) = \sum_{n=1}^{N-1} a_n \Delta x_n + x_n a_n$$

and further

$$\sum_{n=1}^{N} \left(\frac{d}{n}\right) x_n = \sum_{m=1}^{N-2} {}' A_m \Delta^2 x_m + A_{N-1} \Delta x_{N-1} + a_N x_N.$$

Applying (5.18) we obtain

$$A - \sum_{n=1}^{N} \left(\frac{d}{n}\right) x_n$$

$$= A - \sum_{m=1}^{N-2} (mA + R(m, d)) \Delta^2 x_m - \{(N-1)A + R(N-1, d)\} \Delta x_{N-1} - a_N x_N$$

$$= A \{1 - \sum_{m=1}^{N-2} m\Delta^2 x_m - (N-1)\Delta x_{N-1}\} - \sum_{m=1}^{N-2} R(m, d) \Delta^2 x_m -$$

$$- R(N-1, d) \Delta x_{N-1} - a_N x_N.$$

Since

$$\sum_{m=1}^{N-2} m\Delta^2 x_m = x_1 - x_{N-1} - (N-2)\Delta x_{N-1},$$

we finally get

$$A - \sum_{n=1}^{N}\left(\frac{d}{n}\right)x_n = A + A(x_N - x_1) - \sum_{m=1}^{N-2} R(m, d)\Delta^2 x_m - R(N-1, d)\Delta x_N - a_N x_N.$$

Now

$$|A| \leqslant \sum_{n=1}^{|d|} n|d|^{-1} \leqslant |d|, \qquad |a_N x_N| \leqslant 2|d|\,q^N,$$

and since

$$\left|\sum_{m=1}^{N-2} R(m, d)\Delta^2 x_m\right| \leqslant 2|d|^2 \sum_{m=1}^{N-2}\Delta^2 x_m = 2|d|^2(\Delta x_1 - \Delta x_{N-1}) \leqslant 8|d|^2(1-q)$$

and

$$|R(N-1, d)\Delta x_N| \leqslant 4|d|^2(1-q),$$

this leads to

$$|A(1 + x_N - x_1)| \leqslant |d|(1-q)(1-q^N)(1+q)^{-1}(1+q^N)^{-1} \leqslant |d|(1-q)$$

and

$$\left|A - \sum_{n=1}^{N}\left(\frac{d}{n}\right)x_n\right| \leqslant |d|(1-q) + 12d^2(1-q) + 2|d|\,q^N;$$

hence by (5.17)

$$|T_N(q)| \leqslant 13d^2(1-q) + 2(|d| + N)q^N \leqslant 13d^2(1-q+q^N)$$

since $2|d| + N \leqslant 13d^2 N$. $\square$

COROLLARY. *If* $N \geqslant 1$ *and* $q \in (0, 1)$ *then*

$$|B_N(q)| \leqslant 78d^2(1-q) + 52d^2 Nq^{N-2}.$$

Proof. We first prove the equality

(5.19) $$B_N(q) = 4T_{[N/2]}(q^2) + 2T_N(q).$$

Writing $m = [N/4]$ and denoting, as before, the sum $\sum_{n=1}^{|d|} nd^{-1}\left(\frac{d}{n}\right)$ by A, we have

$$B_N(q)/2 = 2b_m(q^4) - b_N(q)/2 = 3A + 8\sum_{4mn \leqslant N}\left(\frac{d}{m}\right)q^{4mn} - 2\sum_{mn \leqslant N}\left(\frac{d}{m}\right)q^{mn},$$

but, on the other hand,

$$2T_{[N/2]}(q^2) + T_N(q) - 3A + 4 \sum_{2mn \leqslant N} (-1)^n \left(\frac{d}{m}\right) q^{2mn} + \sum_{mn \leqslant N} (-1)^n \left(\frac{d}{m}\right) q^{mn};$$

thus the coefficient of q^k in the difference of the two sides of (5.19) equals

$$-2 \sum_{mn=k} \left(\frac{d}{m}\right) - 2 \sum_{mn=k} (-1)^n \left(\frac{d}{m}\right) = 0 \quad \text{if } k \text{ is odd,}$$

$$-2 \sum_{mn=k} \left(\frac{d}{m}\right) - 4 \sum_{2mn=k} (-1)^n \left(\frac{d}{m}\right) - 2 \sum_{mn=k} (-1)^n \left(\frac{d}{m}\right)$$

$$= -4 \sum_{\substack{mn=k \\ 2|n}} \left(\frac{d}{m}\right) + 4 \sum_{2mn=k} \left(\frac{d}{m}\right) = 0 \quad \text{if } 2\|k$$

and

$$8 \sum_{4mn=k} \left(\frac{d}{m}\right) - 2 \sum_{mn=k} \left(\frac{d}{m}\right) - 4 \sum_{2mn=k} (-1)^n \left(\frac{d}{m}\right) = 2 \sum_{mn=k} (-1)^n \left(\frac{d}{m}\right)$$

$$= 8 \sum_{4mn=k} \left(\frac{d}{m}\right) - 4 \sum_{\substack{mn=k \\ 2|n}} \left(\frac{d}{m}\right) - 4 \sum_{2mn=k} (-1)^n \left(\frac{d}{m}\right)$$

$$= 8 \sum_{4mn=k} \left(\frac{d}{m}\right) - 8 \sum_{\substack{mn=k \\ 4|n}} \left(\frac{d}{m}\right) = 0 \quad \text{if } 4|k,$$

and so (5.19) is established.

Applying Lemma 5.3, we get

$$|B_N(q)| \leqslant 52d^2 (1 - q + [N/2] q^{2[N/2]}) + 26d^2 (1 - q + Nq^N)$$
$$\leqslant 78d^2 (1 - q) + 26d^2 (Nq^{N-2} + Nq^N) \leqslant 78d^2 (1 - q) + 52d^2 Nq^{N-2}. \quad \square$$

Now we can complete the proof of the theorem. Using the last corollary and inequality (5.16), we get for $N \geqslant 3$

$$|A_N(q) - B_N(q)| \leqslant |A_N(q)| + |B_N(q)|$$
$$\leqslant 2N^{1/2} |d| (1 - q) + 3N^{1/2} q^{N/4} + 78d^2 (1 - q) + 52d^2 Nq^{N-2}$$
$$\leqslant (1 - q)(78d^2 + 2|d| N^{1/2}) + 55d^2 Nq^{N/4}.$$

Now let a be a large fixed integer, and put $q = 1 - |d|^{-a}$ and $N = [|d|^{4a/3}]$. Then

$$q^{N/4} = \exp(N/4 \cdot \log q) \leqslant \exp(-|d|^{a/3}/4);$$

hence

$$|A_N(q) - B_N(q)| \leqslant |d|^{-a} (78d^2 + 2|d|^{2a/3+1}) + 55|d|^{2+4a/3} \exp\{-\tfrac{1}{4}|d|^{a/3}\},$$

and this is clearly smaller than $2/d^2$ provided a is sufficiently large. $\square$

COROLLARY. *If $d \neq -3, -4$ is a fundamental negative discriminant, then*

$$h(d) \leqslant \frac{1}{\pi} |d|^{1/2} (\log|d| + 2).$$

Proof. This inequality follows from (5.7) and the following simple lemma:

LEMMA 5.4. *If $D > 1$ and χ is any non-principal character* (mod D), *then*

$$|L(1, \chi)| \leqslant 2 + \log D.$$

Proof. For $N > D$ we have

$$\left| \sum_{n=1}^{N} \chi(n) n^{-1} \right| = \left| \sum_{n=1}^{D} \chi(n) n^{-1} + N^{-1} \sum_{n=1+D}^{N} \chi(n) + \sum_{j=1+D}^{N-1} \left(\frac{1}{j} - \frac{1}{j+1} \right) \sum_{n=1+D}^{j} \chi(n) \right|$$

$$\leqslant \sum_{n=1}^{D} n^{-1} + DN^{-1} + \sum_{j=1+D}^{N-1} \left(\frac{1}{j} - \frac{1}{j+1} \right) D$$

$$= \sum_{n=1}^{D} n^{-1} + \frac{D}{D+1} \leqslant \log D + 2. \quad \square$$

Notes and comments

1. The first general study of binary quadratic forms was made by J. L. Lagrange [73], who treated the problem of representing divisors of integers of the form $ax^2 + bxy + cy^2$ by a form of the same discriminant. He used a reduction process which is essentially equivalent to Proposition 5.1 (i), (ii); however, he considered the action of GL(2, Z) rather than that of SL(2, Z).

A more systematic treatment, in which most of the currently used definitions concerning binary forms already appear, is given in the fifth chapter of Gauss [01]. As we have already noted, Gauss restricted himself to the study of forms with an even middle coefficient, i.e., of forms with a discriminant divisible by four; however, most of his results carry over *verbatim* to the general case. Reduced forms are defined by Gauss in the case of a negative determinant in the same way as we do in this book (Proposition 5.1 (i) appears in a slightly stronger form in art. 171) whereas for positive determinants his approach is different: a form $ax^2 + 2bxy + cy^2$ of a positive non-square determinant D he calls reduced if $0 < 2b \leqslant D^{1/2}$ and $D^{1/2} - B \leqslant |A| \leqslant D^{1/2} + B$. In contrast to Lagrange, Gauss considered also forms with square determinants and part (iii) of Proposition 5.1 is due to him (art. 206).

The finiteness of $h(d)$ already follows from the results of Lagrange [73], and this is the way chosen in the present book (Corollary 1 to Proposition 5.1). See L. Kronecker [64] for an analytical proof.

Since for fundamental discriminants the number $h(d)$ is equal to the number of ideal classes of the quadratic field $Q(d^{1/2})$, its finiteness can also be obtained via the theory of algebraic numbers. Two classical proofs of the finiteness of the ideal class group are due to H. Minkowski [91] (who utilized the geometry of numbers) and A. Hurwitz [95] (whose proof is completely elementary and is based on a lemma providing a substitute for the Euclidean algorithm in an arbitrary algebraic number field). The earliest proofs of this result go back to E. E. Kummer [47] (in the case of cyclotomic fields), R. Dedekind [71] and L. Kronecker [82]. More recent proofs can be found in E. Artin, G. Whaples [45], K. Mahler [64] and J. W. S. Cassels, A. Fröhlich [67].

A list of inequivalent forms of discriminant d with $|d| \leqslant 100$ was prepared by A. Cayley [62] and an extension of it up to $|d| \leqslant 200$ was made by A. E. Cooper [25].

2. Theorem 5.1, which solves Gauss's original question about negative determinants with class number one, is due to E. Landau [02]. Another proof of it is contained in Lerch [03] and is based on the formula

$$h(dQ^2) = 2\varepsilon^{-1} Q \prod_{p|Q} (1 - X(p) p^{-1}) h(d),$$

in which $X(n) = \left(\dfrac{d}{n}\right)$, d is a negative fundamental discriminant, Q is an arbitrary integer and $\varepsilon = \varepsilon_d$ is defined by (5.4).

Using the theorem on genera (Theorem 5.2), one easily disposes of all cases except the case where $d \equiv 3 \pmod 4$ is a prime. In that case Lerch had to proceed in the same way as Landau, producing explicitly two non-equivalent forms.

A proof of Theorem 5.1 was also given by D. Shanks [69], who proved moreover that Gauss's lists of negative determinants with h equal to 5, 7 or 11 are complete.

3. Proposition 5.2, due to R. Dedekind [71], gives a one-to-one correspondence between classes of positive definite forms of fundamental discriminant d and ideal classes in the field $Q(d^{1/2})$. An analogous result holds also for positive fundamental discriminants; in this case, however, one has to consider *ideal classes in the narrow sense*, where two ideals I, J are said to lie in the same class if for two totally positive integers a, b we have $aI = bJ$. A number $a \in Q(d^{1/2})$ $(d > 0)$ is called *totally positive*, if a and its conjugate are both positive. This correspondence induces a group structure in the set of classes of forms, because the set of ideal classes has such a structure. In fact, the induced multiplication of form classes was already known to Gauss, who in art. 235 of Gauss [01] introduced it in a rather complicated way and called *class composition*. For a modern exposition of

Gauss's composition theory see G. Pall [73] and for its generalizations to the case where the form coefficients belong to certain integral domain see H. S. Butts, D. Estes [68], B. J. Dulin, H. S. Butts [72], I. Kaplansky [68]. A new approach to this theory, based on a correspondence between the set of all primitive binary quadratic forms of not necessarily the same discriminant and a certain set of modules was given by H. S. Butts and G. Pall [68].

Our proof of Proposition 5.2 follows that of E. Hecke [23]. For other proofs (which sometimes give more general assertions) see B. W. Jones [49], R. König [13].

The corollary to Proposition 5.2 implies in particular that all forms of discriminant d are equivalent if and only if the ring Z_K of integers of the field $K = Q(d^{1/2})$ forms a unique factorization domain. An elementary proof, not using ideals, of the unique factorization in Z_K in the case $h(d) = 1$ was given by L. E. Dickson [24b].

Another condition equivalent to $h(d) = 1$ in the case of $d = 1 - 4p$ with a prime p goes back to G. Frobenius [12b], who observed that the equality $h(1 - 4p) = 1$ holds if and only if the polynomial $X^2 + X + p$ attains prime values for $X = 0, 1, \ldots, p-2$ (such polynomials attracted the attention of L. Euler [72]; however, he did not obtain any conclusive results). The same result was obtained with the use of the theory of algebraic numbers by G. Rabinowitsch [13]. (Cf. H. H. Mitchell [25].) Recently G. Szekeres [74] expressed the number of divisors of $X^2 + X + p$ in the case $h(1 - 4p) = 1$ by the number of solutions of a diophantine equation. An analogue of the Frobenius–Rabinowitsch theorem for the case $h(d) = 2$ was given by M. D. Hendy [74]. See also H. Möller [76b] for a generalization.

4. Theorem 5.2, which gives explicitly the number of genera, is considered the central result of the Gaussian theory of quadratic forms. Our proof uses Dirichlet's prime number theorem but there exist also elementary proofs, starting with Gauss's own (C. F. Gauss [01], art. 263–264, 286–287), which, however, is very complicated and based on the theory of ternary quadratic forms. For other proofs see G. Dirichlet [39b], F. Arndt [59], L. Kronecker [64], D. Hilbert [97], F. Mertens [05] and I. Reiner [45]. Cf. also J. M. Shyr [79], where Theorem 5.2 is obtained as a special case of a much more general result.

If the *principal genus* $G_0(K)$ in the class-group $H(K)$ of an imaginary quadratic field is defined as the subgroup consisting of all squares and different genera are defined as cosets with respect to this subgroup, then the correspondence given in Proposition 5.2 provides also a one-to-one map between genera of forms and genera of ideal classes. Obviously the quotient group $H(K)/G_0(K) = G(K)$ must be a power of C_2 and Theorem 5.2 shows that $G(K) = C_2^{m-1}$ where m is the number of prime divisors of the discriminant of K. However, the last equality can be proved independently of the theory of forms and proofs of this can be found e.g. in E. Hecke [23] (Satz 145) or W. Narkiewicz [74] (Theorem 8.6). A further development of the concept of the genus is to be found in Frei [79].

5. Theorem 5.3 is due to G. Dirichlet [38], [39b]; however, he considered only Gaussian forms. He obtained also an analogous result for positive discriminants. Formula (5.7) holds also for non-fundamental discriminants (see Exercises 3–8). The general case is due to L. Kronecker [85]. A huge literature concerning Dirichlet's formulas (5.7) and (5.8) is quoted in L. E. Dickson [HTN]. We only point to another proof of them, given by L. J. Mordell [18a].

For a long time it was an open problem to find an elementary proof of (5.8). For discriminants not congruent to $1 \pmod 8$ this was achieved by B. A. Venkov [31] and in certain other cases by R. W. Davis [76]. For all negative discriminants the problem was finally settled by H. L. S. Orde [78], and we present his proof in this book along with the classical analytical approach.

Lemma 5.1 appears in Dirichlet's proof of the infinitude of primes in an arithmetical progression (G. Dirichlet [37b]).

6. Owing to Proposition 5.2 a compact expression for the class number of an imaginary quadratic number field follows from formula (5.7). An analogous result holds for the class number of an arbitrary abelian extension of the rationals. For cyclotomic extensions $Q(\exp(2\pi i/p))$ with prime p this was proved by E. E. Kummer [50]. In the general case a formula of this kind was proved by N. G. W. H. Beeger [19], [22b] and M. Gut [29]. It states that if K is an abelian extension of the rationals and m is the smallest integer with the property $K \subset Q(\exp(2\pi i/m))$ (which exists by the Kronecker–Weber theorem, cf. e.g. W. Narkiewicz [74], Theorem 6.5), then $h(K)$, the class group of K, differs from the product

$$\prod_{j=1}^{t} L(1, \chi_j)$$

(where $\chi_1, \ldots, \chi_t$ are certain characters $\pmod m$ canonically determined by m and extended to primitive characters) only by an explicit factor involving the discriminant and regulator of K.

For a thorough study of this formula and its consequences see H. Hasse [52c].

Exercises

1. Prove an analogue of Proposition 5.2 for positive fundamental discriminants.

2. Prove that if f, g are two forms of the same discriminant d and the integers m, n are coprime and representable in the form $m = f(x, y)$, $n = g(u, v)$ with integral x, y, u, v then mn can be represented by a form of discriminant d.

3. Prove that if d is a negative discriminant, $k > 0$ and $(k, d) = 1$ then the congruence

$$X^2 \equiv d \pmod{4k}$$

has

$$w \sum_{m|k} \mu^2(m) \left(\frac{d}{m}\right)$$

solutions where $w = 6$ for $d = -3$, $w = 4$ for $d = -4$ and $w = 2$ in all other cases.

4. Prove that if $f = ax^2 + bxy + cy^2$ then all matrices

$$\mathfrak{A} = \begin{bmatrix} \alpha & \beta \\ \gamma & \delta \end{bmatrix} \quad \text{satisfying} \quad \mathfrak{A}f = f$$

are given by

$$\alpha = (t - bu)/2, \quad \beta = -cu, \quad \gamma = au, \quad \delta = (t + bu)/2$$

where t, u are integers satisfying $t^2 - du^2 = 4$, d being the discriminant of f.

5. Prove that if d is a negative discriminant, $n > 0$ and $(d, n) = 1$ then n has

$$w \sum_{m|n} \left(\frac{d}{m}\right)$$

representations by quadratic forms of discriminant d, where w is defined as in Exercise 3.

6. Let d be a negative discriminant, denote by $A(k)$ the number of representations of an integer k by quadratic forms of discriminant d and put

$$S(n) = \sum_{\substack{1 \le k \le n \\ (k,d) = 1}} A(k).$$

Prove that

$$\lim_{n \to \infty} S(n)/n = w \sum_{p|d} (1 - p^{-1}) L(1, X)$$

where w is as in Exercise 3 and $X = X(n)$ denotes the character $\left(\dfrac{d}{n}\right)$.

7. Prove that if $f(x, y)$ is a form of discriminant $d < 0$, $A_F(k)$ denotes the number of representation of an integer k by F and

$$S_F(n) = \sum_{\substack{1 \le k \le n \\ (k,d) = 1}} A_F(k)$$

then

$$\lim_{n \to \infty} S_F(n)/n = \frac{2\pi}{\sqrt{|d|}} \prod_{p|d} (1 - p^{-1}).$$

8. Prove that for all negative discriminants d we have

$$h(d) = \frac{w \sqrt{|d|}}{2\pi} L(1, X)$$

where X denotes the character $X(n) = \left(\dfrac{n}{d}\right)$ and w is defined in Exercise 3.

9. Let d be a negative fundamental discriminant and Q a positive integer. Prove that

$$h(dQ^2) = \frac{2}{w(d)} Qh(d) \prod_{p|Q}(1 - X(p)p^{-1})$$

where $X(n) = \left(\dfrac{d}{n}\right)$ and w is the same as in Exercise 3.

10 (G. Frobenius [12b], G. Rabinowitsch [13]). Let p be an odd prime. Prove that $h(1-4p) = 1$ holds if and only if the polynomial $X^2 + X + p$ attains for $X = 0, 1, \ldots, p-2$ exclusively prime values.

11. Prove directly, without the use of ideals and ideal classes, that $h(d) = 1$ implies a unique factorization in the ring of integers of $Q(d^{1/2})$.

§ 2. THE CLASS NUMBER PROBLEM

1. The first step towards the proof of Gauss's conjecture that $h(d)$ tends to infinity as $d \to -\infty$ was made by T. H. Gronwall [13] and E. Hecke (see E. Landau [18]). Gronwall's paper contains implicitly the conclusion that if Dirichlet's L-function corresponding to the real primitive character mod d does not vanish in the interval $[1 - a/\log d, 1]$ then we have $h(-d) > c(a)d^{1/2}\log^{-1}d(\log\log d)^{-1/2}$ for a certain positive $c(a)$. Hecke's result, which we shall now prove, gives a better bound for $h(-d)$. Of course both results show that Gauss's conjecture is a consequence of the Extended Riemann Hypothesis.

We now prove Hecke's result, using a simple argument due to J. Pintz [76a]:

THEOREM 5.4. *If $X(n)$ is a real non-principal character* (mod d) *where $d > 200$ and the corresponding L-function $L(s, X)$ has no real zero in the interval $[1-a, 1]$ for a certain a satisfying $0 < a < (10\log d)^{-1}$, then*

$$L(1, X) > 0.11837\, a.$$

(This bound is far from being the best possible. It will be clear from the proof that for large d one can replace it by ca where c is any number larger than $71/150 = 0.4722\ldots$; J. Hoffstein [80] showed that one can have $c = 1.507$.)

Proof. Let P_+, P_-, P_0 be the sets of all those primes p for which the character X attains the values 1, -1 and 0, respectively. If $n = \prod_p p^{a_p}$ is a positive integer, then we write $n = n_+ n_- n_0$ where n_t denotes the maximal divisor of n whose all prime factors lie in the set P_t. If we define $F(n) = \sum_{d|n} X(d)$ then

$$F(n) = \prod_p \left(1 + X(p) + \ldots + X(p)^{a_p}\right) = \prod_{p|N_+}(1 + a_p) \prod_{p|N_-}(1 + (-1)^{a_p})/2,$$

and hence $F(n)$ equals $d(n_+)$ if n_- is a square and vanishes otherwise. This implies that $F(n)$ is non-negative and $F(n^2) \geqslant 1$ holds for all $n \geqslant 1$. Now let a satisfy the assumptions of the theorem. Then for $x \geqslant 49$ we have

$$1.5 \leqslant \sum_{m^2 \leqslant x} m^{-2} \leqslant \sum_{n \leqslant x} F(n)/n \leqslant \sum_{n \leqslant x} F(n)\, n^{a-1} = \sum_{d \leqslant x} X(d)\, d^{a-1} \sum_{m \leqslant x/d} m^{a-1}.$$

We evaluate the inner sum using Lemma A.1, which gives

$$\sum_{m \leqslant x} m^{a-1} = (x^a - 1)/a + c(a) + \theta(a, x)\, x^{a-1}$$

where $0 < c(a) < 1$ and $|\theta(a, x)| \leqslant 1$. It follows that

$$1.5 \leqslant x^a a^{-1} \sum_{d \leqslant x} X(d)\, d^{-1} - (a^{-1} - c(a)) \sum_{d \leqslant x} X(d)\, d^{a-1} + O\left(x^{a-1} \sum_{d \leqslant x} |X(d)|\right),$$

where the constant implied by the O-symbol does not exceed 1. Partial summation gives

$$\left| \sum_{d > x} X(d)\, d^{-1} \right| = \sum_{d > x} \left| \sum_{x < m \leqslant d} X(m) \right| d^{-1}(d+1)^{-1} \leqslant D \sum_{d > x} d^{-1}(d+1)^{-1} \leqslant D/x;$$

thus

$$x^a a^{-1} \sum_{d \leqslant x} X(d)\, d^{-1} = x^a L(1, X)\, a^{-1} + R(x)$$

where $|R(x)| \leqslant Dx^{a-1}/a$, and similarly

$$(1/a - c(a)) \sum_{d \leqslant x} X(d)\, d^{a-1} = (1/a - c(a))\, L(1-a, X) + R_1(x)$$

with $|R_1(x)| \leqslant Dx^{a-1}/a$, which leads in view of $L(1-a, X) \geqslant 0$ to

$$1.5 \leqslant (x^a/a)\, L(1, X) - (1/a - c(a))\, L(1-a, X) + 2Dx^{a-1}/a + x^a$$

$$\leqslant (x^a/a)\, \{a + 2D/x + L(1, X)\};$$

this in turn permits us to bound $L(1, X)$ from below

$$L(1, X) \geqslant 1.5\, ax^{-a} - a - 2D/x.$$

To obtain our assertion we now choose x to be equal to $75D/a$, which leads to

$$L(1, X) \geqslant a(1.5x^{-a} - 1 - 2/75).$$

To bound x^{-a} from below observe first that $0 < a < (1/10) \log 200 < 0.02$ and $D^a < \exp(0.1) \leqslant 1.11$; hence

$$x^a \leqslant 1.11 \cdot 75^{0.02}/\min\{a^a : 0 < a \leqslant 0.02\} = 1.11 \cdot 75^{0.02}/(0.02)^{0.02} < 1.31,$$

and so finally

$$L(1, X) \geqslant 0.11837\, a,$$

as asserted. $\square$

COROLLARY 1. *If X is a real non-principal character (mod D) with D ⩾ 200 and the corresponding L-function does not vanish in the interval* $[1-(B \log D)^{-1}, 1]$ *for a certain B > 10, then*

$$L(1, X) \geqslant (10 \, B \log D)^{-1},$$

and if −D is a fundamental discriminant ≠ −4, −6 then

$$h(-D) \geqslant D^{1/2}/10\pi B \log D.$$

COROLLARY 2. *If X is as in the previous corollary and the corresponding L-function does not vanish in* $(\frac{1}{2}, 1]$, *then*

$$L(1, X) \geqslant (100 \log D)^{-1}. \quad \square$$

COROLLARY 3. *Under the assumption of the Extended Riemann Hypothesis one has for fundamental discriminants d < −200 the inequality*

$$h(d) \geqslant |d|^{1/2}/(100\pi \log |d|),$$

and if h(d) = 1 then |d| ⩽ 29 158 366.

Proof. It suffices to apply the previous corollary and formula (5.7). $\square$

2. The next steps were made by M. Deuring [33] and L. J. Mordell [34]. The first proved that the existence of a non-trivial zero of the Riemann zeta-function implies that the number of negative discriminants d with h(d) = 1 is finite, and the second established Gauss's conjecture under the same assumption. The final step was made by H. Heilbronn [34].

We do not reproduce the proofs of the three authors mentioned above (the main idea of Heilbronn's approach will reappear in the analytical part of the proof of Theorem 5.6), and go directly to Siegel's theorem, which gives the rate of growth of h(d).

THEOREM 5.5 (C. L. Siegel [36]). *If X is a real primitive character (mod D), then for every positive ε we have*

$$L(1, X) \geqslant C(\varepsilon) D^{-\varepsilon}$$

with a positive constant C(ε).

(Unfortunately the constant C(ε) is not effective.)

Proof. We give a simple and transparent proof found by M. Goldfeld [74].

LEMMA 5.5. *For any given positive ε < 1/2 one can find an integer q ⩾ 3, a real primitive character χ(mod q) and a real number a∈[1−ε, 1] such that for every Q > 1 and every real primitive character X(mod Q) the function*

$$f(s) = \zeta(s) L(s, \chi) L(s, X) L(s, \chi X)$$

satisfies f(a) ⩽ 0.

Proof. If there is no L-function associated with a real primitive character which vanishes at some point from $[1-\varepsilon, 1]$, then we can take for a any number from this interval and $q = 3$ (since under this assumption all L-functions are positive at a and $\zeta(a) < 0$). However, if there is such a function L then we take for χ the character corresponding to it and for a any zero of L in $[1-\varepsilon, 1]$. Then obviously for any choice of X we have $f(a) = 0$. $\square$

Now let $f(s)$ be the function occurring in the last lemma. For $\mathrm{Re}\, s > 1$ we can write it in the form

$$f(s) = \sum_{n=1}^{\infty} a_n n^{-s}.$$

Note that $a_1 = 1$ and $a_n \geq 0$. In fact, since a_n is a multiplicative function of n, it suffices to establish $a_{p^k} \geq 0$ for prime p and $k = 1, 2, \ldots$; this, however, follows by elementary transformations from the identity

$$a_{p^k} = \sum_{\alpha_1 + \alpha_2 + \alpha_3 \leq k} \chi(p)^{\alpha_1 + \alpha_3} X(p)^{\alpha_2 + \alpha_3},$$

which results by multiplying the Dirichlet series occurring as factors in the definition of f.

Writing

$$g(s) = f(s+a) \prod_{j=0}^{4} (s+j)^{-1}$$

(with a given by Lemma 5.5), we get for $x \geq 2$

$$I(x) = \frac{1}{2\pi i} \int_{2-i\infty}^{2+i\infty} g(s) x^s \, ds = \frac{1}{24} \sum_{n \leq x} a_n n^{-a} (1 - n/x)^4 \geq \frac{1 - 1/x}{24} \geq \frac{1}{48}.$$

We now approach the integral $I(x)$ in another way. Using the bounds for the zeta-function and L-functions given in Proposition A.4, we obtain for $s = \sigma + it$, $|t| \geq 1$ and $2 \geq \sigma \geq a/2$ the evaluation

$$|f(s)| \ll ((qQ)^2 |t|^4)^{(1 - a/2)};$$

thus for $2 \geq \sigma \geq -a/2$ and $|t| \geq 1$ the bound

(5.20) $$|g(s)| \ll (qQ)^{3/2} t^{-3/2}$$

follows. This shows that both integrals

$$\int_{-a/2+iT}^{2+iT} g(s) x^s \, ds, \qquad \int_{-a/2-iT}^{2-iT} g(s) x^s \, ds$$

are $\ll x^2 (qQ)^{3/2} T^{-3/2}$ and so tend to zero as T approaches infinity; hence we are allowed to shift the line of integration in $I(x)$ to $\operatorname{Re} s = -a/2$. Taking into account the residues of $g(s)\, x^s$ in the strip $-a/2 \leqslant \operatorname{Re} s \leqslant 2$, we arrive at

$$(5.21) \qquad I(x) = f(a)/4! + x^{1-a} L(1, \chi) L(1, X) L(1, \chi X) \prod_{j=1}^{5} (j-a)^{-1} +$$

$$+ \int_{-a/2+i}^{-a/2+i\infty} g(s)\, x^s\, dx + \int_{-a/2-i}^{-a/2+i} g(s)\, x^s\, ds + \int_{-a/2-i\infty}^{-a/2-i} g(s)\, x^s\, ds.$$

Since on the segment joining $-a/2+i$ with $-a/2-i$ the function $\zeta(s)$ is bounded and $|x^s| = x^{-a/2}$, we have

$$|g(s)\, x^s| \ll (qQ)^{3/2}\, x^{-a/2}$$

and with the use of (5.20) we find that the three integrals in (5.21) are $O\big((qQ)^{3/2}\, x^{-a/2}\big)$.

Now recall that by Lemma 5.3 we have $f(a) \leqslant 0$ and moreover Lemma 5.4 implies

$$L(1, \chi) L(1, \chi X) \leqslant M \log(qQ) \log q$$

for a suitable M; thus

$$1/48 \leqslant I(x) \leqslant M x^{1-a}(1-a)^{-1} L(1, X) \log(qQ) \log q + O\big((qQ)^{3/2}\, x^{-a/2}\big).$$

If we take x larger than $M_1 (qQ)^{3/a}$ with a sufficiently large M_1, then the last term will be smaller than 0.01, and thus with such choice of x we get

$$L(1, X) \gg \frac{1-a}{\log(qQ) \log q}\, x^{a-1} \gg \frac{1-a}{\log q}\, M_1^{a-1}\, Q^{3(a-1)a^{-1}} \gg Q^{-6\varepsilon}. \quad \square$$

COROLLARY 1.

$$\lim_{d \to -\infty} (\log h(d))/(\log |d|) = 1/2.$$

This follows from Theorem 5.5 and formula (5.7). $\square$

COROLLARY 2. *There are only finitely many fundamental negative discriminants with a given class number.* $\square$

COROLLARY 3 (S. Chowla [34]). *There are only finitely many negative fundamental discriminants d such that every genus of forms with discriminant d contains only one class.*

Proof. Let $d = -D < 0$ be such a discriminant. Theorem 5.2 implies the equality $h(d) = 2^{\omega(D)-1}$ and, since Corollary 1 shows that for D sufficiently large one has $h(d) \geqslant D^{1/4}$, we obtain in view of $\log D \gg \omega(D) \log \omega(D)$ the inequalities

$$\tfrac{1}{4} \log D \leqslant \log h(d) \ll \omega(D) \ll \log D / \log \omega(D),$$

which imply $\log \omega(D) \ll 1$ and $\omega(D) \ll 1$. Thus $h(d)$ is bounded and Corollary 1 shows that there are only finitely many possibilities for d. $\square$

3. Shortly after Gauss's conjecture was established H. Heilbronn and E. Linfoot [34] proved that there can be at most ten negative discriminants with class number one. Since only nine such discriminants were known, viz. $d = -3, -4, -7, -8, -11, -19, -43, -67$ and -163 (all found by C. F. Gauss [01], art. 303) and the numerical search made by L. E. Dickson [10] and D. H. Lehmer [33] indicated that the possible tenth discriminant d must satisfy $|d| \geqslant 5 \cdot 10^9$, it became common belief that the tenth discriminant does not exist. This belief was confirmed by H. M. Stark [67a], who obtained earlier, in his thesis (H. M. Stark [66]), the bound $|d| \geqslant \exp(2.2 \cdot 10^7)$. At the same time A. Baker developed a method which made it possible in principle to obtain an upper bound for $|d|$. As early as 1948 A. O. Gelfond and Yu. V. Linnik [48] showed that such a bound would follow from an effective lower bound for a linear form in logarithms of algebraic numbers and Baker's method provided such a bound.

It should be noted that a proof of the non-existence of the tenth discriminant using the theory of modular functions was published by K. Heegner [52]; however, it was not regarded as fully adequate, due to certain obscure arguments in Weber [08], on which Heegner based his idea. This opinion changed when owing to the work of M. Deuring [68], B. J. Birch [69] and H. M. Stark [69a] it became clear that Heegner's approach was sound and the minor inaccuracies attributed to Weber can be rectified.

We shall now present the proof of this result based on Baker's method and obtained by P. Bundschuh and P. Hock [69]. It gives for the possible tenth discriminant d the bound $|d| \leqslant 10^{2759}$; hence, to show that it does not exist one has to appeal to the main result of H. M. Stark's thesis [66], which is applicable here since $\exp(2.2 \cdot 10^7) > 10^{2759}$.

So we are going to prove

THEOREM 5.6. *If d is a fundamental negative discriminant with $h(d) = 1$ then $|d| \leqslant 10^{2759}$.*

Proof. We start with a lemma determining the residue of $d \pmod 8$.

LEMMA 5.6. *If d is a fundamental negative discriminant where $h(d) = 1$, then either $d = -4, -7, -8$ or $-d$ is a prime congruent to $3 \pmod 8$.*

Proof. Theorem 5.2 implies that $-d$ is a prime power, whence either $d = -4, -8$ or $-d$ is a prime. Thus it remains to rule out the possibility of $-d \equiv 7 \pmod 8$, $-d \neq 7$. Assuming that this congruence does hold, we conclude that $(1-d)/4$ is an even integer $\neq 2$ and so we can write it as a product ac of two factors larger than 1. The form $f(x, y) = ax^2 + xy + cy^2$ is of discriminant d, and to obtain a contradiction it suffices to show that f does not represent 1, and so cannot be equivalent to the form

$x^2 + ((1-d)/4) y^2$. However, for integral x we have $f(x, 0) = ax^2 \neq 1$ since $a \neq 1$, and for integral x, y with $y \neq 0$ we get, in view of $8a \leqslant 4ac = 1 - d$, the inequality

$$f(x, y) \geqslant -dy^2/4a \geqslant (-2d)/(1-d) > 1. \quad \square$$

In the sequel we may and shall assume that $|d| > 163$. Let $Q(x, y)$ denote the form $x^2 + xy + ((1-d)/4) y^2$ of discriminant d, let $X(n)$ be the quadratic character $\left(\dfrac{d}{n}\right)$ and for any odd prime p denote by X_p the primitive quadratic character (mod p). We obtain an expansion of the product $L(s, X_p) L(s, XX_p)$ on which our argument will be based.

LEMMA 5.7. *If d is a negative fundamental discriminant where $h(d) = 1$ and $p \equiv 1 \pmod{4}$ is a prime not dividing d, then for $\mathrm{Re}\, s > 1$ the following identity holds*:

(5.22) $\quad L(s, X_p) L(s, XX_p)$

$$= \zeta(2s)(1 - p^{-2s}) + (|d|/4)^{1/2-s} \pi^{1/2} p^{-1} \frac{\Gamma(s-\tfrac{1}{2})}{\Gamma(s)} (p^{2-2s} - 1) \zeta(2s-1) + R_p(s)$$

where

$$R_p(s) = \frac{1}{p} \left(\frac{|d|^{1/2}}{2}\right)^{1-2s} \sum_{y=1}^{\infty} y^{1-2s} \sum_{m=0}^{p-1} X_p(Q(m, y)) \times$$

$$\times \sum_{k \neq 0} \exp\left\{\frac{2\pi i k}{p} (m + y/2)\right\} \cdot J_2(ky, s)$$

and

$$J_2(N, s) = \int_{-\infty}^{\infty} \exp\left\{-\frac{\pi i N |d|^{1/2} u}{p}\right\} (1 + u^2)^{-s} \, du.$$

(It can be shown that $R_p(s)$ is entire, but this would not be of any use for us.)

Proof. For $\mathrm{Re}\, s > 1$ we have

$$L(s, X_p) L(s, XX_p) = \sum_{n=1}^{\infty} \sum_{m=1}^{\infty} X_p(n) X(m) X_p(m) (mn)^{-s}$$

$$= \sum_{r=1}^{\infty} X_p(r) r^{-s} \sum_{\delta|r} X(\delta).$$

Observe now that in view of $h(d) = 1$ we have

(5.23) $$\sum_{\delta|r} X(\delta) = N_Q(r)/2$$

where $N_Q(r)$ denotes the number of representation of r by the form Q. Indeed, the Dedekind zeta-function $\zeta_K(s)$ of the field $K = Q(\sqrt{d})$ equals $\zeta(s)L(s, X)$ and by comparing coefficients in the corresponding Dirichlet series we find that the left-hand side of (5.23) gives the number of ideals in the ring of integers of K with norm r. Since the only units in K are ± 1, Proposition 5.2 and its corollary imply (5.23).

Thus

$$L(s, X_p)L(s, XX_p) = \frac{1}{2}\sum_{r=1}^{\infty} N_Q(r)X_p(r)r^{-s}$$

$$= \frac{1}{2}\sum_{x\neq 0}\frac{X_p(Q(x, 0))}{Q(x, 0)^s} + \frac{1}{2}\sum_{y\neq 0}\sum_{x\neq 0}\frac{X_p(Q(x, y))}{Q(x, y)^s} = S_1 + S_2.$$

The first summand equals

$$\frac{1}{2}\sum_{x\neq 0}\frac{X_p(x^2)}{x^{2s}} = \sum_{\substack{n\geq 1 \\ p\nmid n}} n^{-2s} = \zeta(2s)(1 - p^{-2s})$$

and so gives the first term in (5.22).

The second summand can be written

$$\sum_{y=1}^{\infty}\sum_{x=-\infty}^{\infty} X_p(Q(x, y))Q(x, y)^{-s} = \sum_{y=1}^{\infty}\sum_{m=0}^{p-1} X_p(Q(m, y))\sum_{x=-\infty}^{\infty} Q(px+m, y)^{-s}$$

and, since the Poisson formula gives

$$\sum_{x=-\infty}^{\infty} Q(px+m, y)^{-s} = \sum_{k=-\infty}^{\infty}\int_{-\infty}^{\infty} Q(pt+m, y)^{-s}\exp\{-2\pi ikt\}\,dt,$$

we have

(5.24) $$S_2 = \sum_{y=1}^{\infty}\sum_{m=0}^{p-1} X_p(Q(m, y))\sum_{k=-\infty}^{\infty}\int_{-\infty}^{\infty} Q(pt+m, y)^{-s}\exp\{-2\pi ikt\}\,dt.$$

Obviously $Q(x, y) = (x + y/2)^2 + |d|y^2/4$; hence, if we substitute in the inner integral $m + pt + y/2 = |d|^{1/2}yu/2$, it will be equal to

$$\frac{|d|^{1/2}y}{2p}\left(\frac{|d|}{4}y^2\right)^{-s}\int_{-\infty}^{\infty} (1+u^2)^{-s}\exp\left\{-\frac{2\pi ik}{p}\left(\frac{1}{2}y(|d|^{1/2}u - 1) - m\right)\right\}\,du$$

$$= (|d|^{1/2}y/2)^{1-2s}p^{-1}\exp\left\{\frac{2\pi ik}{p}\left(m + \frac{y}{2}\right)\right\}\int_{-\infty}^{\infty}\exp\left\{-\frac{2\pi i}{p}ky\frac{|d|^{1/2}}{2}u\right\}\times$$

$$\times(1+u^2)^{-s}\,du,$$

and thus

$$(5.25) \quad S_2 = \frac{1}{p}(|d|^{1/2}/2)^{1-2s} \sum_{y=1}^{\infty} y^{1-2s} \sum_{m=0}^{p-1} X_p(Q(m, y)) \times$$

$$\times \sum_{k=-\infty}^{\infty} \exp\left\{\frac{2\pi i k}{p}\left(m+\frac{y}{2}\right)\right\} \int_{-\infty}^{\infty} \exp\left\{-\frac{2\pi i k y|d|^{1/2} u}{2p}\right\}(1+u^2)^{-s} du.$$

Now put $z = ky$, so that

$$S_2 = \frac{1}{p}(|d|^{1/2}/2)^{1-2s} \sum_{z=-\infty}^{\infty} \exp\left\{\frac{2\pi i z}{2p}\right\} \int_{-\infty}^{\infty} \frac{\exp\{-(2\pi i/2p)|d|^{1/2} zu\}}{(1+u^2)^s} du \times$$

$$\times \sum_{\substack{y|z \\ y>0}} y^{1-2s} \sum_{m=0}^{p-1} X_p(Q(m, y))\exp\left\{\frac{2\pi i m z}{py}\right\}.$$

The term corresponding to $z = 0$ equals

$$\frac{1}{p}(|d|^{1/2}/2)^{1-2s}\left(\int_{-\infty}^{\infty} du/(1+u^2)^s\right) \sum_{y=1}^{\infty} y^{1-2s} \sum_{m=0}^{p-1} X_p(Q(m, y))$$

and, since

$$\int_{-\infty}^{\infty}(1+u^2)^s du = \pi^{1/2}\Gamma(s-\tfrac{1}{2})\Gamma^{-1}(s),$$

we can write this term in the form

$$p^{-1}(|d|/4)^{1/2-s}\pi^{1/2}\Gamma(s-\tfrac{1}{2})\Gamma^{-1}(s) \sum_{y=1}^{\infty} y^{1-2s} \sum_{m=0}^{p-1} X_p(Q(m, y)).$$

To recognize here the second summand in (5.22) we need the equality

$$(5.26) \qquad \sum_{y=1}^{\infty} y^{1-2s} \sum_{m=0}^{p-1} X_p(Q(m, y)) = (p^{2-2s}-1)\zeta(2s-1),$$

which we shall now establish.

By Proposition 2.1 (i) and Theorem 2.1 we have

$$X_p(Q(m, y)) = p^{-1/2} \sum_{j=1}^{p-1} X_p(j)\exp(2\pi i j Q(m, y)/p);$$

hence

(5.27)

$$\sum_{m=0}^{p-1} X_p(Q(m, y)) = p^{-1/2} \sum_{j=1}^{p-1} X_p(j) \sum_{m=0}^{p-1} \exp\left\{\frac{2\pi i j}{p}\left(m^2+my+\frac{1-d}{4}y^2\right)\right\}.$$

Put now $M = (p+1)/2$. Then

$$Q(m, y) \equiv (m + My)^2 + |d| M^2 y^2 \pmod{p},$$

and thus the inner sum in (5.27) will be equal to

$$\exp(2\pi i j |d| M^2 y^2/p) \sum_{n=0}^{p-1} \exp(2\pi i j n^2/p).$$

Since in view of Theorem 2.1 and Proposition 2.1 (i) for $p \nmid j$

$$\sum_{n=0}^{p-1} \exp\left\{\frac{2\pi i j}{p} n^2\right\} = 1 + \sum_{x=1}^{p-1}\left(1 + \left(\frac{x}{p}\right)\right)\exp\left\{\frac{2\pi i j x}{p}\right\}$$

$$= \sum_{x=1}^{p}\left(\frac{x}{p}\right)\exp\left\{\frac{2\pi i j x}{p}\right\} = \left(\frac{j}{p}\right)p^{1/2}$$

and also (in view of $p \equiv 1 \pmod 4$) $X_p(j) - \left(\dfrac{p}{j}\right) = \left(\dfrac{j}{p}\right)$, we have

$$\sum_{m=0}^{p-1} X_p(Q(m, y)) = \sum_{j=1}^{p-1} X_p(j)\left(\frac{j}{p}\right)\exp\left\{\frac{2\pi i}{p}(|d| M^2 y^2)j\right\}$$

$$= \sum_{j=1}^{p-1} \exp\left\{\frac{2\pi i}{p}(|d| M^2 y^2)j\right\} = \begin{cases} p-1 & \text{if} & p\,|\,y, \\ -1 & \text{if} & p\nmid y \end{cases}$$

and so finally

$$\sum_{y=1}^{\infty} y^{1-2s} \sum_{m=0}^{p-1} X_p(Q(m, y)) = \sum_{\substack{p\,|\,y \\ y>0}} (p-1) y^{1-2s} - \sum_{\substack{p\nmid y \\ y>0}} y^{1-2s}$$

$$= \sum_{n=1}^{\infty} p(pn)^{1-2s} - \zeta(2s-1)$$

$$= (p^{2-2s} - 1)\zeta(2s-1),$$

proving (5.26). Formula (5.22) follows immediately, $R_p(s)$ being the sum of terms in (5.25) corresponding to $y \neq 0$. ◻

Our next lemma gives a bound for the value of $R_p(s)$ at $s = 1$.

LEMMA 5.8. *Under the conditions of the preceding lemma we have for* $|d| \geqslant 163$ *and* $p \leqslant 13$ *the inequality*

$$|R_p(1)| \leqslant 23 |d|^{-1/2} \exp(-\pi |d|^{1/2} p^{-1}).$$

Proof. From the definition it follows that

$$|R_p(1)| \leqslant \frac{2}{p|d|^{1/2}} \sum_{y=1}^{\infty} \sum_{m=0}^{p-1} \left| \sum_{k\neq 0} \exp\left\{\frac{2\pi i k}{p}\left(m + \frac{y}{2}\right)\right\} J_2(ky, 1)\right|.$$

Integrating the function $\exp(iAz)(1+z^2)^{-1}$ over the boundary of the upper half of the circle $|z| = R$ in the case $A > 0$ and the lower half in the case $A < 0$ we easily get the equality

$$J_2(ky, 1) = \pi q^{|ky|},$$

where we put $q = \exp(-\pi|d|^{1/2}p^{-1}) < 1$, which leads to

$$|R_p(1)| \leqslant \frac{4\pi}{p|d|^{1/2}} \sum_{m=0}^{p-1} \sum_{y=1}^{\infty} \sum_{k=1}^{\infty} q^{ky} = 4\pi|d|^{-1/2} \sum_{y=1}^{\infty} q^y(1-q^y)^{-1}$$

$$\leqslant 4\pi|d|^{-1/2} q(1-q)^{-2}.$$

Finally, $(1-q)^{-2} \leqslant (1+p\pi^{-1}|d|^{-1/2})^2$ and, since $p \leqslant 13$ and $|d|^{1/2} \geqslant 12$, we arrive at

$$R_p(1) \leqslant 4\pi|d|^{-1/2}\left(1+\frac{13}{12\pi}\right)^2 q \leqslant 23|d|^{-1/2}\exp\left\{-\frac{\pi|d|^{1/2}}{p}\right\}. \quad \square$$

We shall use these two lemmas to pave the way for the application of Baker's method. In identity (5.22) of Lemma 5.7 let s tend to unity. In view of $\Gamma(\tfrac{1}{2}) = \sqrt{\pi}$ we obtain

$$L(1, X_p)L(1, XX_p) = \frac{\pi^2}{6}(1-p^{-2})+2\pi|d|^{-1/2}\frac{\log p}{p}+R_p(1).$$

In this equality first put $p = 5$ and multiply it by $1-13^{-2}$ and then put $p = 13$ and multiply the resulting equality by $1-5^{-2}$. The resulting two equalities give after subtraction

$$\tfrac{168}{169}L(1, X_5)L(1, XX_5)-\tfrac{24}{25}L(1, X_{13})L(1, XX_{13})+$$

$$+2\pi|d|^{-1/2}(\tfrac{168}{845}\log 5 - \tfrac{24}{325}\log 13) = \tfrac{168}{169}R_5(1)-\tfrac{24}{25}R_{13}(1).$$

Using Lemma 5.1, we obtain after a short computation

$$L(1, X_5) = \frac{\log \alpha}{\sqrt{5}} \quad \text{where} \quad \alpha = (1+\sqrt{5})/2$$

and

$$L(1, X_{13}) = \frac{\log \beta}{\sqrt{13}} \quad \text{where} \quad \beta = (3+\sqrt{13})/2,$$

and, since by Theorem 5.3

$$L(1, XX_5) = h(5d)/(5|d|)^{1/2}, \quad L(1, XX_{13}) = h(13d)/(13|d|)^{1/2},$$

we get

$$840\, h(5d)\log\alpha - 312\, h(13d)\log\beta + 1680\log 5 - 624\log 13$$
$$= |d|^{1/2}\,\pi^{-1}\,(4200\, R_5(1) - 4056\, R_{13}(1)).$$

Invoking Corollary 1 to Proposition 5.1, we obtain the inequalities

$$h(5d) \leqslant 10\,|d|/3, \qquad h(13d) \leqslant 26\,|d|/3,$$

and thus the left-hand side of the last equality can be written in the form

$$L = x_1 \log\alpha + x_2 \log\beta + \log a$$

with rational integers x_1, x_2 satisfying $|x_i| \leqslant 2800\,|d|$ ($i = 1, 2$) and $a = 5^{1680}\, 13^{-624}$. Now observe that the field generated by α, β and a is quartic, the height of α equals 1, the height of β equals 3, the height of a equals $\max(5^{1680}, 13^{624}) \leqslant e^{2704}$ and finally $L \neq 0$ since otherwise we would have

$$\alpha^{x_1}\beta^{x_2} a = 1$$

and so β^{x_2} would lie in the field $Q(5^{1/2})$, which is clearly impossible. We are thus in a position to apply Theorem A.8 with $A_1 = A_2 = 4$, $A_3 = \exp(2704)$, $C_1 = 192^{600} \leqslant \exp(3155)$, $M = 2800\,|d|$, $D = \log^2 4 \cdot 2704 < 5197$, $D' = \log^2 4 < 2$. Assuming $|d| > 10^{2500}$, we obtain

$$|L| \geqslant \exp(-e^{3167}\log|d|).$$

On the other hand, the application of Lemma 5.8 yields

$$|L| \leqslant |d|^{1/2}\frac{4225}{\pi}\left(23\,|d|^{-1/2}\exp\left\{\frac{-\pi\,|d|^{1/2}}{\sqrt 5}\right\} + 23\,|d|^{-1/2}\exp\left\{-\frac{\pi\,|d|^{1/2}}{\sqrt{13}}\right\}\right)$$
$$\leqslant \exp\left\{12 - \frac{\pi\,|d|^{1/2}}{\sqrt{13}}\right\};$$

hence

$$e^{3167}\log|d| \geqslant \frac{\pi}{\sqrt{13}}\,|d|^{1/2} - 12 \geqslant 0.87\,|d|^{1/2},$$

which is possible only for $|d| \leqslant \exp(6352) < 10^{2759}$. □

Notes and comments

1. There are many variants of Theorem 5.4, which was first proved by E. Hecke; its proof was published by E. Landau [18] in the following form:

If the L-function $L(s, X)$ corresponding to the character $X(n) = \left(\dfrac{d}{n}\right)$ where *d is a fundamental negative discriminant does not vanish in the interval* $[1 - a/\log|d|, 1]$, *then we have*

$$h(d) > c(a)|d|^{1/2} \log^{-1}|d|$$

for a certain positive $c(a)$.

The proof we give is that of J. Pintz [76a]. There are many proofs available leading to various values of the constant $c(a)$. S. Chowla, J. B. Friedlander [76] gave a very simple proof based on the method of Goldfeld, which we used in the proof of Siegel's theorem. J. Hoffstein [80] applied the same method. See also E. Landau [27b], E. Grosswald [62], J. Pintz [77b].

K. Mahler [34b] generalized Hecke's theorem, replacing the class number $h(d)$ by $h'(d)$ defined as the ratio of $h(d)$ to the sum $\sum_C a_C^{-1}$ in which C runs over all classes of positive definite forms of discriminant d and a_C denotes the minimal positive integer represented by a form from the class C.

That part of Corollary 3 to Theorem 5.4 which concerns the case $h(d) = 1$ can also be obtained from the theory of Epstein's zeta-function (A. Selberg, S. Chowla [49], [67]).

2. The first proof of Siegel's Theorem 5.5 (C. L. Siegel [36]) was based on an integral formula involving the Dedekind zeta-function of a suitable quartic field, due to E. Hecke. H. Heilbronn [38] provided another proof, which was later modified by N. G. Chudakov [42]. It is again based on an integral formula. Yu. V. Linnik gave three proofs of Siegel's theorem. The first was sketched in [43c] and involved heavy machinery, whereas the second ([50]) has the advantage of being elementary although by no means easy. The same paper contains also a short analytical proof. It is worth noting that in the last proof one of the lemmas concerns a partial sum of the series

$$\sum_{(x,y) \neq (0,0)} \chi(Q(x, y))Q(x, y)^{-s}$$

(where χ is a Dirichlet character), which plays an important role in the determination of discriminants with class number one.

A simplification of Linnik's elementary proof was given by J. Pintz [74a].

One of the simplest proofs of Siegel's theorem is that found by T. Estermann [48b], which uses only Taylor expansions and Cauchy's bounds for power series coefficients. His proof is presented in Chandrasekharan [70]. Other proofs were given by S. Chowla [50], T. Tatuzawa [51], K. A. Rodosskii [56], S. Knapowski [68] and K. Ramachandra [75], [80]. The proof presented in this book is due to M. Goldfeld [74] and its idea may be also applied to other problems. (See e.g. S. Chowla and J. Friedlander [76], J. Hoffstein [80].)

Siegel's theorem is equivalent, as noted first by A. Walfisz [36], to the non-vanishing of $L(s, X)$ in the interval $[1 - c(\varepsilon)D^{-\varepsilon}, 1]$ for a certain positive

$c(\varepsilon)$. A simple deduction of this fact was given by J. Pintz [74a], [77b]. Previously the non-vanishing of $L(s, X)$ was known for the interval $[1 - ck^{-1/2} \log^{-1} k, 1]$ (A. Page [35]).

Corollary 1 to Theorem 5.5 has its analogue for the class number of algebraic number fields. In the case of imaginary quadratic fields this analogue follows from the Corollary to Proposition 5.2 and for real quadratic fields the formula

$$\lim_{d \to \infty} \frac{\log \left(h(d) \log \varepsilon \right)}{\log d} = \frac{1}{2}$$

(with ε being the fundamental unit > 1 of the field $Q(d^{1/2})$) follows from Siegel's theorem and Dirichlet's formula expressing $h(d)$ for positive discriminants by the value at 1 of the corresponding L-function.

A generalization to other algebraic number fields was given by R. Brauer [47]. Other proofs can be found in Lang [64] and Pintz [74b].

Unfortunately Siegel's theorem is not effective, since one does not know how to evaluate the value of $C(\varepsilon)$ occurring in its formulation for a value of ε less than $1/2$. (The same applies to Brauer's generalization; however, as proved by H. M. Stark [74], the Siegel–Brauer theorem can be made effective for certain classes of fields.) In the case $\varepsilon = 1/2$ one can compute $C(\varepsilon)$. This was done by W. Haneke [73] (see also J. Pintz [76b], D. M. Goldfeld, A. Schinzel [75]). However, as demonstrated by T. Tatuzawa [51], one can make Siegel's theorem "almost" effective in the following sense: for every $\varepsilon > 0$ and every primitive real character $X (\mathrm{mod}\, k)$ we have

$$L(1, X) > 0.1\, \varepsilon k^{-\varepsilon}$$

with the exception of at most one value of k.

Other proofs of similar inequalities were given by K. A. Rodosskii [56], J. Pintz [76b], [76c], [77b] and J. Hoffstein [80].

3. The same argument as that given in the proof of Corollary 3 to Theorem 5.5 shows that the ratio of the number $h(d)$ of classes of forms of a negative discriminant d to the number $g(d)$ of genera tends to infinity (S. Chowla [34]). Already C. F. Gauss [01] (art. 252) noted that this ratio equals the number of classes in the principal genus, since in fact every genus contains the same number of classes, which is obvious from the interpretation of the genera in the group of ideal classes of $Q(d^{1/2})$. For an analytical proof of this fact see G. Dirichlet [39b] and L. Kronecker [64].

As we already noted in the preceding chapter, positive integers N with the property $g(-4N) = h(-4N)$ were considered by L. Euler in 1778, who called them *idoneal numbers*. Corollary 3 to Theorem 5.5 shows that there are only finitely many square-free idoneal numbers, but it is possible to show that the number of all idoneal numbers is finite (cf. F. Grube [74],

N. A. Hall [39], E. Grosswald [62]). The largest known idoneal number equals 1848 and it is conjectured that there exists no larger one. S. Chowla and W. E. Briggs [54] proved that there can be only one idoneal square-free number larger than 10^{65} and later P. J. Weinberger [73] reduced this bound to 1365 and showed that under the Extended Riemann Hypothesis there are no other solutions of $h(d) = g(d)$ for negative d than those known by Gauss. As to idoneal numbers $N > 1365$ that are not square-free they are of the form $4k$ where k is idoneal square-free and even. For earlier numerical results see J. D. Swift [48].

A. Baker and A. Schinzel [71] proved that the minimal integer prime to the discriminant $d < 0$ and represented by a form of this discriminant from a given genus is bounded by $c(\varepsilon)|d|^{3/8+\varepsilon}$ for every positive ε, where $c(\varepsilon)$ is a constant. Unfortunately, this constant is non-effective and if it could be effectivized we could use this fact for a complete determination of idoneal numbers. D. R. Heath-Brown [79] improved the bound in question to $c_1(\varepsilon)|d|^{1/4+\varepsilon}$ but again $c_1(\varepsilon)$ is non-effective, being dependent, just as $c(\varepsilon)$, on the constant appearing in Siegel's theorem.

4. Let $m(d)$ be the exponent of the class group of $Q(d^{1/2})$. Corollary 3 to Theorem 5.5 may also be stated in the form

$$\liminf_{d \to -\infty} m(d) \geqslant 3,$$

and P. J. Weinberger [73] and D. W. Boyd and H. Kisilevsky [72] proved

$$\liminf_{d \to -\infty} m(d) \geqslant 4$$

and showed that under the Extended Riemann Hypothesis (or even under certain weaker assumptions) we have for negative d

$$m(d) \gg \log |d| (\log \log |d|)^{-1}.$$

For $0 > d > -4 \cdot 10^6$ the value of $m(d)$ can be obtained from the tables of the group structure of the ideal classes in $Q(d^{1/2})$ prepared by D. A. Buell [76].

For negative discriminants d with $g(d) = h(d)$ the reduced forms were explicitly determined by H. Möller [76a] in terms of the divisors of the discriminant.

For a generalization of idoneal numbers to the case of forms with a larger number of variables see M. Peters [80].

5. As already said, the first important step after Hecke's Theorem 5.4 towards the establishment of Gauss's conjecture was made by M. Deuring [33], who showed that the assumption of the existence of infinitely many negative discriminants with class number one implies the truth of Riemann's conjecture. The idea of the proof was to consider an expansion for the product $\zeta(s) L(s, X_d)$, where $X_d(n) = \left(\dfrac{d}{n}\right)$, leading in the case of $h(d) = 1$ to

$$\zeta(s) L(s, X_d)$$
$$= \zeta(2s) + |d|^{1/2-s} \pi^{1/2} \zeta(2s-1) \Gamma(s-\tfrac{1}{2}) \Gamma^{-1}(s) + O(\exp\{-2|d|^{1/2} t_1^{-1}\})$$

with

$$t_1 = \begin{cases} |\operatorname{Im} s| & \text{if} \quad |\operatorname{Im} s| \geqslant 1, \\ 1 & \text{if} \quad |\operatorname{Im} s| \leqslant 1 \end{cases}$$

provided $|t_1| = \tfrac{1}{9} \pi |d|^{1/2}$. Since for a fixed s with $1/2 < \operatorname{Re} s$ the right-hand side of this equality tends to $\zeta(2s)$ as $|d| \to \infty$, the existence of a zero ϱ of $\zeta(s)$ in the critical strip would imply $\zeta(2\varrho) = 0$, which is impossible in view of $\operatorname{Re}(2\varrho) > 1$, and so Riemann's conjecture follows.

Shortly afterwards, by using a similar expansion of $\zeta(s) L(s, X_d)$ for arbitrary discriminants $d < 0$ L. J. Mordell [34] was able to prove that if $h(d)$ does not tend to infinity for negative d then Riemann's conjecture must hold.

The final step in proving Gauss's conjecture (Corollary 2 to Theorem 5.5) was made by H. Heilbronn [34]. He was the first to consider an equality similar to that used by Deuring and Mordell in the case of a product of two L-functions with non-principal characters, which he obtained by using the summation formula of Maclaurin:

$$L(s, X_k) L(s, X_k X_d) = \zeta(2s) \prod_{p|k} (1 - p^{-2s}) \sum_a X_d(a) a^{-s} + o(|s| + |s-1|^{-1})$$

where the summation is taken over all reduced inequivalent forms $ax^2 + bxy + cy^2$ of discriminant d. Assuming the falsity of the Extended Riemann Conjecture for real primitive characters, he chose for X_k a character with the property that for a certain ϱ ($\operatorname{Re} \varrho > \tfrac{1}{2}$) we have $L(\varrho, X_k) = 0$, which led to

$$\lim_{d \to -\infty} \sum_a X_d(a) a^{-\varrho} = 0,$$

but a simple argument gave for $\operatorname{Re} s > \tfrac{1}{2}$

$$\left| \sum_a X_d(a) a^{-s} \right| \geqslant 0.25 h(d)^{-2} + o(1)$$

and thus $h(d) \to \infty$.

In the same year H. Heilbronn and E. Linfoot [34] proved that there can be at most ten negative discriminants with class number one. This was generalized by E. Landau [35], who showed that if $d < 0$ and $h(d) = h$, then with the exception of at most one discriminant we have $|d| \leqslant B h^8 \log^6(3h)$ with a certain constant B. This was later made more explicit in the case of

$h = 2$ by K. Iseki [51], who showed that in this case we have $|d| \leqslant 9 \cdot 10^4$ with at most one exception. Finally, T. Tatuzawa [51] improved considerably Landau's estimate by showing

$$|d| \leqslant 2100 \, h^2 \log^2 (13 \, h)$$

with at most one exception. (Clearly, Corollary 3 to Theorem 5.4 implies that if the Extended Riemann Hypothesis holds, then for $h \geqslant 2$ we have $|d| \leqslant 20\,706\,000 \, h^2 \log^2 h$ without any exception.)

A new proof of the Heilbronn–Linfoot theorem was given by R. G. Ayoub [67], and J. Pintz [76b] proved Tatuzawa's result with an unspecified constant in place of 2100.

6. In 1948 A. O. Gelfond and Yu. V. Linnik [48] observed that in the case of $h(d) = 1$ one can apply to the product $L(s, X_k) L(s, X_{kd})$ (with k, $-d$ prime) the method used previously by M. Deuring [37] in the case of $k = 1$ to obtain an expansion of form (5.22), the remainder term being equal to a quickly convergent series. By choosing two suitable values of k we get two such expansions and taking a linear combination of them one arrives at a linear form in three logarithms of algebraic numbers with algebraic coefficients which has a very small absolute value and is non-zero. It is of the same type as that appearing in our proof of Theorem 5.6.

Unfortunately at that time the method of Baker was not yet available and so Gelfond and Linnik could not deduce an upper bound for $|d|$. It was later observed by H. M. Stark [69b] and A. Baker [71b] that by applying the same approach to a similar expansion with k composite we get a linear form in two logarithms, and a lower bound for it is provided by an old result of A. O. Gelfond (see A. O. Gelfond [52]). Although such an expansion in the general form was then unknown, there is no principal difficulty in obtaining it for particular values of k.

7. In 1967 H. M. Stark [67a] found in the case of $h(d) = 1$ an expansion of $L(s, X_k) L(s, X_{kd})$ for $k = 8$ and $k = 12$ of the same type as that considered by Gelfond and Linnik, and by using it was able to derive a set of diophantine equations of which at least one should have a solution. In the final step he proved that in fact for $|d| \geqslant 200$ those equations do not have solutions, and this settled the problem of the existence of the tenth discriminant with class number one in the negative. Stark's proof involved rather messy computations but, as shown later (H. M. Stark [67b], [68], [69c], E. Brown [74]), most of them can be avoided.

Shortly afterwards H. M. Stark [68] studied the series

$$L_Q(s, X) = \sum_{(x,y) \neq (0,0)} X\big(Q(x, y)\big) Q(x, y)^{-s}$$

(where Q is a positive definite quadratic form and X a Dirichlet character), providing a general framework for the theory of products $L(s, X_k) L(s, X_{kd})$ which are, as can be inferred from the proof of Lemma 5.7, linear combinations of suitable functions $L_Q(s, X)$. The expansions obtained are similar to that given in (5.22) in the case of prime k, the only real difficulty in obtaining them lying in the necessity of finding a formula for the sum of the series occurring in (5.26). This was done explicitly in Stark [68], and S. Chowla [67] expressed the sum in question by Kloosterman sums.

In the case of $X = 1$ Stark's L-functions coincide with Epstein's zeta-functions, which were extensively studied earlier (see e.g. L. J. Mordell [29], M. Deuring [37], A. Selberg, S. Chowla [49], [67]).

8. Baker's method was first applied to prove Theorem 5.6 by P. Bundschuh and A. Hock [69], which possibility had been pointed out by A. Baker [66]. The proof given in this book is due to them.

A proof using Gelfond's lower bounds for a linear combination of two logarithms was given in Chudakov [69] and Feldman, Chudakov [72]. It leads to the bound $|d| \leqslant 10^{42}$.

Other proofs were given by C. L. Siegel [68] and S. Chowla [70]. (Siegel used modular functions and Chowla based his approach on Kronecker's limit formula.) We already quoted the proofs of M. Deuring [68], B. J. Birch [69] and H. M. Stark [69b], justifying Heegner's approach.

9. One can apply similar methods to deal with discriminants of class number two. For square-free negative d satisfying $d \not\equiv 5 \pmod 8$ A. Baker [69b] showed by a combination of Gelfond's bounds for linear forms in logarithms and Stark's expansions that $h(d) = 2$ implies the inequality $|d| \leqslant 10^{500}$. This allowed W. J. Ellison, J. Pesek, D. S. Stall and W. F. Lunnon [71] to determine all such discriminants, and the same result was obtained by M. A. Kenku [71], who used an analogue of Stark's approach.

A strengthening of Baker's method led independently A. Baker [71a] and H. M. Stark [71], [72] to an effective upper bound for discriminants with $h = 2$. (Stark had $|d| \leqslant 10^{1030}$ and Baker did not estimate his bound.) This bound enabled H. M. Stark [75] to obtain a complete list of all such determinants, which turned out to be eighteen numbers $-d$ where $d = 15$, 20, 24, 35, 40, 51, 52, 88, 91, 115, 123, 148, 187, 232, 235, 267, 403 and 427, all known for a long time. The same result was obtained independently by H. L. Montgomery and P. J. Weinberger [74] (cf. also L. J. Goldstein [72]).

In 1975 D. M. Goldfeld [77] proved an effective lower bound for $h(-d)$ under the assumption of an unproved hypothesis concerning elliptic curves. This conjecture was proved in 1983 by B. Gross and D. Zagier [83] so that the class number problem can be now regarded as solved.

The form of the estimate obtained is much weaker than Siegel's theorem, namely:

$$h(-d) \geqslant C(\varepsilon)(\log d)^{1-\varepsilon}$$

for every positive ε, with an effective constant $C(\varepsilon)$, and for d prime

$$h(-d) \geqslant c_0 (\log d)/(\log \log d)$$

where c_0 is an effective constant (for d large enough one can take $c_0 = 1/8$).

Exercises

1 (T. Tatuzawa [51]). Let X be a real primitive character mod k. Prove that

$$L(1, X) \geqslant 2 \log \varepsilon / k^{1/2}$$

(where $\varepsilon = (1 + 5^{1/2})/2$) and show that the equality sign holds here if and only if X is the primitive real character (mod 5).

2 (S. Chowla [34]). Prove that if $g(d)$ denotes the number of genera of discriminant d, then

$$\lim_{d \to -\infty} g(d)/h(d) = 0.$$

3. Using Tatuzawa's bound ($L(1, X) > 0.1 \varepsilon k^{-\varepsilon}$ for all k except at most one), deduce an explicit bound for all negative discriminants d except at most one with $g(d) = h(d)$.

OPEN PROBLEMS

1. Obtain analogues of the Frobenius–Rabinowitsch theorem for the case of the class number $h(d) \geqslant 3$.

2. Effectivize Siegel's theorem.

3. Determine all negative discriminants d with $g(d) = h(d)$.

4. Find an upper bound for the largest absolute value of a negative discriminant d with a given ratio $h(d)/g(d)$.

5. Obtain a proof of Theorem 5.6 by Baker's method with the upper bound for $|d|$ of lower order, so that one could dispose of the remaining cases without the aid of a computer.

6. Determine whether there exist infinitely many positive discriminants with $h(d) = 1$.

7. Prove that the exponent $m(d)$ of the ideal class group of the field $Q(d^{1/2})$ tends to infinity as $d \to -\infty$.

In this appendix we shall present, mostly without proof, various results from number theory which are used in the main text.

1. Arithmetical functions

In the chapter on Waring's problem the following proposition, permitting a convenient replacement of finite sums by integrals was used:

PROPOSITION A.0 (H. Heilbronn [36]). *If f is a real non-negative function defined on an interval $I = [a, b]$ belonging to $C^2(I)$ and satisfying on I the conditions*:

(i) $|f(x)| \leqslant B_0$,

(ii) $|f'(x)| \leqslant B_1$,

(iii) $f'(x) f''(x)$ *does not vanish on I,*

where B_0, B_1 are given constants, then

$$\sum_{n \in I} \exp \{2\pi i f(n)\} = \int_a^b \exp \{2\pi i f(x)\} \, dx + R,$$

where $|R| \leqslant 2 + 8B_1 + 40 B_0 B_1$.

Proof. We need a lemma.

LEMMA A.1. *If F is a real function defined on an interval $I = [a, b]$ (with $a \in Z$) and belonging to $C^2(I)$, then we have*

$$\sum_{n \in I} F(n) = \int_a^b F(x) \, dx + (\tfrac{1}{2} - \{b\}) F(b) + \tfrac{1}{2} F(a) - F'(b) \, \Phi(b) + \int_a^b F''(x) \, \Phi(x) \, dx$$

where $\{x\}$ denotes the fractional part of x and

$$\Phi(x) = \int_0^x (\tfrac{1}{2} - \{t\}) \, dt.$$

Proof. The function $a(x) = \tfrac{1}{2} - \{x\}$ has its derivative equal to -1

at every point not belonging to Z; hence, for every $n \in Z$ and $n < x_1 < x_2 < n+1$, we have

(A.1)
$$\int_{x_1}^{x_2} F(t)\,dt = -\int_{x_1}^{x_2} a'(t)\,F(t)\,dt$$

$$= -\int_{x_1}^{x_2} \Phi(t)\,F''(t)\,dt + a(x_1)\,F(x_1) - a(x_2)\,F(x_2) +$$

$$+ \Phi(x_2)\,F'(x_2) - \Phi(x_1)\,F'(x_1),$$

which implies (by letting x_1 tend to n and x_2 to $n+1$)

$$\int_{n}^{n+1} F(t)\,dt = -\int_{n}^{n+1} \Phi(t)\,F''(t)\,dt + \frac{F(n)+F(n+1)}{2}.$$

Hence, for $N = [b]$, we obtain

$$\sum_{n \in I} F(n) = \sum_{n=a}^{N} F(n) = F(a) + F(N) + \sum_{n=1+a}^{N-1} F(n)$$

$$= \frac{1}{2} \sum_{n=a}^{N-1} (F(n)+F(n+1)) + \frac{F(a)+F(N)}{2}$$

$$= \sum_{n=a}^{N-1} \int_{n}^{n+1} F(t)\,dt + \sum_{n=a}^{N-1} \int_{n}^{n+1} \Phi(t)\,F''(t)\,dt + \frac{F(a)+F(N)}{2}$$

$$= \int_{a}^{N} F(t)\,dt + \int_{a}^{N} \Phi(t)\,F''(t)\,dt + \frac{F(A)+F(N)}{2}.$$

The resulting expression differs from the right-hand side of the asserted equality by

$$\int_{N}^{b} F(t)\,dt + \int_{N}^{a} F''(t)\,\Phi(t)\,dt - F'(b)\,\Phi(b) + F(b)\,a(b) - \tfrac{1}{2} F(N),$$

which vanishes if we let in (A.1) x_1 tend to N. $\square$

To prove the proposition it suffices to obtain its assertion in the case where a is an integer, provided we get for R a slightly stronger evaluation $|R| \leqslant 8B_1 + 40B_0 B_1 + 1$. We apply the lemma to $F(t) = \exp(2\pi i f(x))$ and obtain

$$R = (\tfrac{1}{2} - \{b\})\,F(b) + F(a)/2 - F'(b)\,\Phi(b) + \int_{a}^{b} F''(t)\,\Phi(t)\,dt.$$

As $|\Phi(x)| \leqslant \frac{1}{4}$ we majorize the first three terms by

$$|F(b)|/2 + |F(a)|/2 + |F'(b)|/4 \leqslant 1 + \pi B_1/2.$$

To deal with the last term we write it in the form

$$2\pi i \int_a^b \cos\{2\pi f(t)\} f''(t) \Phi(t) - 4\pi^2 i \int_a^b \sin\{2\pi f(t)\} f'(t)^2 \Phi(t) dt +$$

$$+ (-2\pi) \int_a^b \sin\{2\pi f(t)\} f''(t) \Phi(t) dt - 4\pi^2 \int_a^b \cos\{2\pi f(t)\} f'(t)^2 \Phi(t) dt$$

$$= I_1 + I_2 + I_3 + I_4,$$

and apply the mean value theorem.

This gives, for suitable ξ, η,

$$|I_1| = 2\pi \left|\cos(2\pi f(\xi)) \Phi(\xi)\right| |f'(b) - f'(a)| \leqslant \pi B_1$$

and similarly $|I_3| \leqslant \pi B_1$. Moreover,

$$|I_2| \leqslant 4\pi^2 \left|\sin(2\pi f(\eta)) f'(\eta) \Phi(\eta)\right| |f(b) - f(a)| \leqslant 2\pi^2 B_0 B_1$$

and the same bound holds for I_4. Thus finally

$$|R| \leqslant 1 + 5\pi B_1/2 + 4\pi^2 B_0 B_1 \leqslant 1 + 8B_1 + 40 B_0 B_1. \quad \square$$

The next proposition puts together certain elementary facts about Euler's function $\varphi(n)$ and the divisor function $d(n)$:

PROPOSITION A.1 (see e.g. [H–W], Theorem 320 for (i) and Theorem 328 for (iii); (ii) follows from (i) by partial summation).

(i) $\sum_{m \leqslant x} d(m) = x \log x + O(x)$ $(x \geqslant 2)$,

(ii) $\sum_{m \leqslant x} d(m) m^{-1} = (\frac{1}{2} + o(1)) \log^2 x$ $(x \geqslant 2)$,

(iii) $\varphi(m) \gg m/\log\log m$ $(m \geqslant 3)$.

COROLLARY. For integral $k \geqslant 1$ we have

$$\sum_{m \leqslant x} d^k(m) \ll x \log^{2^k - 1} x.$$

Proof. For $k = 1$ this follows from (i) and, assuming its truth for a certain $k \geqslant 1$ and using the obvious inequality $d(mn) \leqslant d(m) d(n)$ we obtain:

$$\sum_{n \leqslant x} d^{1+k}(n) = \sum_{n \leqslant x} d^k(n) \sum_{\delta | n} 1 = \sum_{\delta \leqslant x} \sum_{m \leqslant x/\delta} d^k(\delta m)$$

$$\leqslant \sum_{\delta \leqslant x} d^k(\delta) \sum_{m \leqslant x/\delta} d^k(m) \ll x \log^{2^k - 1} x \sum_{\delta \leqslant x} d^k(\delta) \delta^{-1};$$

since partial summation gives

$$\sum_{\delta \leqslant x} d^k(\delta) \delta^{-1} \ll \log^{2^k} x,$$

our assertion follows. $\square$

2. The large sieve

· Here we shall state and prove the large sieve inequality and obtain some evaluations of expressions often occurring in the application of that inequality; finally we shall apply it to the proof of the Brun–Titchmarsh theorem and Gallagher's theorem on character sums.

THEOREM A.1. *Let A be a finite set of integers contained in an interval of length N and denote its cardinality by Z. Assume that for every prime $p \leqslant Q$ (where $Q \geqslant 2$ is a given integer) there are $\omega(p)$ residue classes not containing any element of A. Assume that $\omega(p) < p$. Then*

$$Z \leqslant (Q^2 + \pi N)/L$$

where

$$L = \sum_{q \leqslant Q} \mu^2(q) \prod_{p|q} \frac{\omega(p)}{p - \omega(p)}.$$

Proof. Let $S(x) = \sum_{n \in A} a_n \exp(2\pi i n x)$ where a_n $(n \in A)$ are given complex numbers.

LEMMA A.2. *For all $q \geqslant 1$ we have*

$$|S(0)|^2 \mu^2(q) \prod_{p|q} \frac{\omega(p)}{p - \omega(p)} \leqslant \sum_{\substack{1 \leqslant a \leqslant q \\ (a,q)=1}} |S(a/q)|^2.$$

Proof. We shall first consider the case where q is a prime. Our assertion takes the form

$$|S(0)|^2 \frac{q}{q - \omega(q)} \leqslant \sum_{a=1}^{q} |S(a/q)|^2$$

because $S(0) = S(1)$.

Since

$$\sum_{a=1}^{q} |S(a/q)|^2 = \sum_{a=1}^{q} \sum_{n,n_1 \in A} a_n \bar{a}_{n_1} \exp\left\{ \frac{2\pi i(n - n_1)a}{q} \right\}$$

$$= \sum_{h=1}^{q} \sum_{\substack{n \equiv h \pmod q \\ n \in A}} a_n \sum_{n_1 \in A} \bar{a}_{n_1} \sum_{a=1}^{q} \exp\left\{ \frac{2\pi i(n - n_1)a}{q} \right\}$$

$$= q \sum_{h=1}^{q} \sum_{\substack{n \equiv h \pmod q \\ n \in A}} a_n \sum_{\substack{n_1 \equiv h \pmod q \\ n_1 \in A}} \bar{a}_{n_1} = q \sum_{h=1}^{q} \left| \sum_{\substack{n \in A \\ n \equiv h \pmod q}} a_n \right|^2$$

and the sum $\sum_{\substack{n \in A \\ n \equiv h \pmod q}} a_n$ vanishes for $\omega(q)$ values of h, by using Cauchy's inequality we get

$$|S(0)|^2 = \left|\sum_{n \in A} a_n\right|^2 = \left|\sum_{h=1}^{q} \sum_{\substack{n \in A \\ n \equiv h \,(\text{mod}\, q)}} a_n\right|^2$$

$$\leqslant (q - \omega(q)) \sum_{h=1}^{q} \left|\sum_{\substack{n \in A \\ n \equiv h \,(\text{mod}\, q)}} a_n\right|^2$$

and thus

$$q \frac{|S(0)|^2}{q - \omega(q)} \leqslant \frac{1}{q} \sum_{h=1}^{q} \left|\sum_{\substack{n \in A \\ n \equiv h \,(\text{mod}\, q)}} a_n\right|^2 = \sum_{a=1}^{q} |S(a/q)|^2.$$

In the case of q composite we may obviously assume that q is square-free as otherwise the assertion becomes evident. We use induction on the number k of prime factors of q. The case $k = 1$ has already been treated, and so write $q = rs$ with $(r, s) = 1$, r, $s \geqslant 2$, and $\omega(r)$, $\omega(s) \leqslant k-1$. By the inductive assumption applied to the sequence $a_n \exp(2\pi i n t)$ with a real t we obtain

$$|S(t)|^2 \prod_{p|s} \frac{\omega(p)}{p - \omega(p)} \leqslant \sum_{\substack{1 \leqslant k \leqslant s \\ (k,s) = 1}} \left|S\left(\frac{k}{s} + t\right)\right|^2 ;$$

thus

$$\sum_{\substack{1 \leqslant a \leqslant q \\ (a,q) = 1}} |S(a/q)|^2 = \sum_{\substack{1 \leqslant b \leqslant r \\ (b,r) = 1}} \sum_{\substack{1 \leqslant c \leqslant s \\ (c,s) = 1}} \left|S\left(\frac{b}{r} + \frac{c}{s}\right)\right|^2$$

$$\geqslant \sum_{\substack{1 \leqslant b \leqslant r \\ (b,r) = 1}} \left|S\left(\frac{b}{r}\right)\right|^2 \prod_{p|s} \frac{\omega(p)}{p - \omega(p)}$$

$$\geqslant |S(0)|^2 \prod_{p|r} \frac{\omega(p)}{p - \omega(p)} \cdot \prod_{p|s} \frac{\omega(p)}{p - \omega(p)}. \quad \square$$

LEMMA A.3. *For all $Q \geqslant 2$ we have*

$$\sum_{q \leqslant Q} \sum_{\substack{1 \leqslant a \leqslant q \\ (a,q) = 1}} |S(a/q)|^2 \leqslant (Q^2 + \pi N) \sum_{n \in A} |a_n|^2.$$

Proof. Let $F(x)$ be an arbitrary complex-valued function defined on the real line, having period 1 and a continuous derivative. Since for any x, y we have

$$F(x) = F(y) - \int_{x}^{y} F'(t)\, dt,$$

it follows that

$$|F(x)| \leqslant |F(y)| + \left|\int_x^y |F'(t)|\,dt\right|.$$

Let Q be a fixed positive integer and, for an arbitrary rational number a/q $((a, q) = 1, q \leqslant Q)$, let $I_{a,q}$ denote the interval $(a/q - 1/2Q^2, a/q + 1/2Q^2)$.

Integrating the last inequality over $I_{a,q}$ we obtain

$$Q^{-2}|F(a/q)| \leqslant \int_{I_{a,q}} |F(y)|\,dy + \int_{I_{a,q}} dy \left|\int_{a/q}^y |F'(t)|\,dt\right|$$

and, using the inequality

$$\int_{I_{a,q}} dy \left|\int_{a/q}^y |F'(t)|\,dt\right| = \int_{a/q}^{a/q+Q^{-2}/2} \left\{\left|\int_{a/q}^y |F'(t)|\,dt\right| + \left|\int_{2a/q-y}^{a/q} |F'(t)|\,dt\right|\right\} dy$$

$$\leqslant \int_{a/q}^{a/q+Q^{-2}/2} dy \int_{I_{a,q}} |F'(t)|\,dt = \tfrac{1}{2}Q^{-2} \int_{I_{a,q}} |F'(t)|\,dt,$$

we arrive at

$$|F(a/q)| \leqslant Q^2 \int_{I_{a,q}} |F(y)|\,dy + \tfrac{1}{2} \int_{I_{a,q}} |F'(t)|\,dt.$$

This can be written in the form

(A.2) $$|F(a/q)| \leqslant Q^2 \int_{J_{a,q}} |F(y)|\,dy + \tfrac{1}{2} \int_{J_{a,q}} |F'(t)|\,dt$$

where $J_{a,q}$ denotes the set of all fractional parts of the numbers belonging to the interval $I_{a,q}$.

Observe now that the sets $J_{a,q}$ are pairwise disjoint. Indeed, assume that $J_{a,q}$ and $J_{b,r}$ have a point x in common, i.e., there exist a $y \in I_{a,q}$ and a $z \in I_{b,r}$ whose difference is an integer. If $y = z$, then from

$$|y - a/q| < (2Q^2)^{-1} \quad \text{and} \quad |z - b/r| < (2Q^2)^{-1}$$

we get

$$1/Q^2 \leqslant |ar - bq|/rq < 1/Q^2,$$

a contradiction.

However, if $|y - z| \geqslant 1$ then

$$1 \leqslant |y - z| \leqslant |y - a/q| + |z - b/r| + |a/q - b/r| < 1/Q^2 + |ar - bq|/qr;$$

hence

$$1/Q^2 > 1 - |ar - bq|/qr.$$

On the other hand $|ar - bq|/qr < 1$; thus $1 - |ar - bq|/qr$ is positive and hence exceeds Q^{-2}, again a contradiction.

Adding inequalities (A.2), we finally obtain

$$\sum_{q \leqslant Q} \sum_{\substack{1 \leqslant a \leqslant q \\ (a,q)=1}} |F(a/q)| \leqslant Q^2 \int_0^1 |F(t)| \, dt + \tfrac{1}{2} \int_0^1 |F'(t)| \, dt.$$

We apply this inequality to the function $F(x) = T^2(x)$, where $T(x) = S(x) \exp(-2\pi x i m)$ and m equals $N/2 + M$ for even N and $(N+1)/2 + M$ for N odd. Since

$$|S(x)| = |T(x)|,$$

$$\int_0^1 |F(t)| \, dt = \int_0^1 |S(t)|^2 \, dt = \sum_{n=1+N}^{M+N} |a_n|^2 = Z,$$

$$\int_0^1 |F'(t)| \, dt \leqslant 2 \left(\int_0^1 |S(t)|^2 \, dt \right)^{1/2} \left(\int_0^1 |T'(t)|^2 \, dt \right)^{1/2}$$

and

$$\int_0^1 |T'(t)|^2 \, dt = 4\pi^2 \sum_{|k| \leqslant N/2} k^2 |a_{m+k}|^2 \leqslant \pi^2 N^2 Z,$$

we obtain

$$\sum_{q \leqslant Q} \sum_{\substack{1 \leqslant a \leqslant q \\ (a,q)=1}} |S(a/q)|^2 \leqslant (Q^2 + \pi N) Z$$

as asserted. $\square$

To prove the theorem put $a_n = 1$ for n in A and $a_n = 0$ otherwise. Then $S(0) = Z$ and $\sum_{n \in A} |a_n|^2 = Z$; hence, using both previous lemmas, we get

$$Z^2 L = Z^2 \sum_{q \leqslant Q} \mu^2(q) \prod_{p|q} \frac{\omega(p)}{p - \omega(p)} \leqslant \sum_{q \leqslant Q} \sum_{\substack{1 \leqslant a \leqslant q \\ (a,q)=1}} |S(a/q)|^2 \leqslant (Q^2 + \pi N) Z;$$

thus

$$Z \leqslant (Q^2 + \pi N)/L$$

as asserted. $\square$

As a corollary we shall now deduce a result of P. X. Gallagher [67] giving an upper bound for a certain mean value of character sums:

C오ROLLARY. *Let M, N be given integers and a_{1+M}, a_{2+M}, ..., a_{N+M} given complex numbers. For every $q \geqslant 1$ and for every primitive character $\chi \pmod q$ put*

$$T(\chi) = \sum_{n=1+M}^{N+M} a_n \chi(n).$$

Then

$$\sum_{q \leqslant Q} \frac{q}{\varphi(q)} {\sum_{\chi}}^* |T(\chi)|^2 \leqslant (Q^2 + \pi N) \sum_{n=1+M}^{N+M} |a_n|^2$$

where the asterisk indicates that the sum has to be taken over all primitive characters $(\mathrm{mod}\, q)$.

Proof. If we put

$$S(x) = \sum_{n=1+M}^{N+M} a_n \exp(2\pi i n x),$$

then by using Proposition 2.1 (i) we get for primitive characters χ

$$T(\chi) = \sum_{n=1+M}^{N+M} a_n \chi(n) = \tau(\bar{\chi})^{-1} \sum_{(b,q)=1} \overline{\chi(b)}\, S(b/q)$$

$$= \tau(\bar{\chi})^{-1} \sum_{b=1}^{q} \overline{\chi(b)}\, S(b/q);$$

thus, in view of Proposition 2.1 (iii),

$${\sum_{\chi}}^* |T(\chi)|^2 = q^{-1} {\sum_{\chi}}^* \left| \sum_{b=1}^{q} \overline{\chi(b)}\, S(b/q) \right|^2$$

$$\leqslant q^{-1} \sum_{\chi} \left| \sum_{b=1}^{q} \overline{\chi(b)}\, S(b/q) \right|^2 \leqslant \varphi(q)\, q^{-1} \sum_{(b,q)=1} |S(b/q)|^2,$$

and it remains to apply Lemma A.3. $\square$

As an application of the large sieve we now prove the Brun–Titchmarsh theorem:

THEOREM A.2. *There exists an absolute constant C such that for all k and l satisfying $(k, l) = 1$ we have for $x \geqslant 2$ the inequality*

$$\pi(x, k, l) \leqslant \frac{Cx}{\varphi(k) \log(x/k)}.$$

Moreover, if $k \leqslant x^{1-\varepsilon}$ with a positive ε, then with a constant $C(\varepsilon)$ we have

$$\pi(x, k, l) \leqslant \frac{C(\varepsilon)}{\varphi(k)}\, x/\log x.$$

Proof. Let A be the set of those integers $(\sqrt{x} - l)/k \leqslant n \leqslant x/k - 1$ for which the number $kn + l$ is prime. Obviously $\pi(x, k, l) \leqslant |A| + 1 + \sqrt{x/k}$. If $n \in A$ then $kn + l$ cannot have prime factors $\leqslant x^{1/2}$; hence for $p \nmid k$, $p \leqslant x^{1/2}$ no element of A can lie in the residue class $-l/k \,(\mathrm{mod}\, p)$. We may thus apply Theorem A.1 with $Q = (x/k)^{1/2}$, $N = x/k$ and

$$\omega(p) = \begin{cases} 1 & \text{if} \quad x^{1/2} \geqslant p,\ p \nmid k, \\ 0 & \text{if} \quad x^{1/2} \leqslant p \ \text{or} \ p \mid k, \end{cases}$$

which leads to

$$\pi(x, k, l) \leqslant x^{1/2}/k + (x + \pi x/k)/L$$

where

$$L = \sum_{\substack{q \leqslant Q \\ (k,q)=1}} \mu^2(q) \prod_{p \leqslant x^{1/2}} \frac{1}{p-1} = \sum_{\substack{q \leqslant Q \\ (k,q)=1}} \mu^2(q) \varphi^{-1}(q).$$

But

$$\frac{k}{\varphi(k)} \sum_{\substack{q \leqslant Q \\ (k,q)=1}} \mu^2(q) \varphi^{-1}(q) = \sum_{d|k} \mu^2(d) \varphi^{-1}(d) \sum_{\substack{q \leqslant Q \\ (q,k)=1}} \mu^2(q) \varphi^{-1}(q)$$

$$= \sum_{\substack{q \leqslant Q \\ (q,k)=1}} \sum_{d|k} \mu^2(dq) \varphi^{-1}(dq)$$

$$\geqslant \sum_{q_1 \leqslant Q} \mu^2(q_1) \varphi^{-1}(q_1) \gg \log Q$$

since every integer $q_1 \leqslant Q$ can be written in the form $q_1 = dq$ with d dividing k and $(q, k) = 1$. Thus

$$L \gg \varphi(k) k^{-1} \log Q$$

and we arrive at

$$\pi(x, k, l) \ll \frac{x^{1/2}}{k} + (1+\pi) \frac{x}{\varphi(k) \log(x/k)} \ll \frac{x}{\varphi(k) \log(x/k)},$$

implying the first assertion. The second follows immediately since $k \leqslant x^{1-\varepsilon}$ implies the evaluation

$$\log(x/k) \geqslant \varepsilon \log x. \quad \square$$

To apply the large sieve to a particular problem it is necessary to obtain a lower bound for the sum L appearing in Theorem A.1. We now give such a bound in the special case which is used in the main text. We follow R. C. Vaughan [73].

PROPOSITION A.2. *If* $0 \leqslant f(p) < p$ *is a function defined on the set of all primes and for all sufficiently large Q we have*

$$\sum_{p \leqslant Q} f(p) p^{-1} > C \log^a Q$$

with certain positive constants C and a, then for large Q

$$L = \sum_{q \leqslant Q} \mu^2(q) \prod_{p|q} \frac{f(p)}{p - f(p)} \geqslant \exp\{C_1 \log^b Q\}$$

with $b = a/(a+1)$ and a positive constant C_1.

Proof. Extend f to a completely multiplicative function and observe that due to the identity

$$\frac{f(p)}{p-f(p)} = \sum_{k=1}^{\infty} (f(p)p^{-1})^k$$

we can write

$$L = \sum_{q \leqslant Q} \mu^2(q) \prod_{p|q} \sum_{k=1}^{\infty} (f(p)p^{-1})^k = \sum_{q \leqslant Q} \mu^2(q) \sum_{\substack{r \\ \prod_{p|r} p = q}} f(r)r^{-1}$$

$$= \sum_{\substack{r \\ \prod_{p|r} p \leqslant Q}} f(r)r^{-1} = \sum_m \sum_{\substack{\Omega(r)=m \\ \prod_{p|r} p \leqslant Q}} f(r)r^{-1}.$$

Observe now that the inner sum is at least equal to

$$\frac{1}{m!} \Big(\sum_{p \leqslant Q^{1/m}} f(p)p^{-1} \Big)^m \geqslant \Big(\sum_{p \leqslant Q^{1/m}} f(p)(pm)^{-1} \Big)^m,$$

which implies that, if we denote by $m_0 = m_0(Q)$ the largest integer with the property that there is a prime $p \leqslant Q^{1/m_0}$ with $f(p) \neq 0$, then

$$L \geqslant \sum_{m=1}^{m_0} \exp\Big(m \log \sum_{p \leqslant Q^{1/m}} f(p)(mp)^{-1}\Big).$$

It follows that for any $m \leqslant m_0$

$$L \geqslant \exp\Big(m \log \sum_{p \leqslant Q^{1/m}} f(p)(mp)^{-1}\Big).$$

If we now choose

$$m = [(Ce^{-1} \log^a Q)^{1/(a+1)}]$$

then for large Q we get $m \leqslant m_0$ since from $f(p_0) \neq 0$ for a certain prime p_0 it follows that $m_0 \geqslant (\log Q)/(\log p_0) - 1$ and $m = o(\log Q)$.

Thus

$$L \geqslant \exp(m \log Cm^{-1-a} \log^a Q) \geqslant \exp m \geqslant \exp(C_1 \log^b Q)$$

as asserted. $\square$

3. Prime numbers

In this section we put together the principal results concerning the theory of prime numbers which are used in the main text.

We begin with two bounds concerning the primes due to J. B. Rosser and L. Schoenfeld [62]:

PROPOSITION A.3. (a) *For* $x \geqslant 2$ *we have*

$$\theta(x) = \sum_{p \leqslant x} \log p \leqslant 1.01\, x,$$

and for $x \geqslant 41$, $\theta(x) > x(1 - 1/\log x)$.

(b) *For* $x \geqslant 2$ *we have* $\pi(x) \leqslant 1.256(x/\log x) < 2x/\log x$.

COROLLARY (Bertrand's postulate). *For* $x \geqslant 1$ *there is a prime in* $(x, 2x]$.

Proof. By (a) we have for $x \geqslant 41$

$$\sum_{x < p \leqslant 2x} \log p \geqslant 2x\left(1 - \frac{1}{\log x}\right) - 1.01x$$

$$= x\left(0.99 - \frac{2}{\log 2x}\right) \geqslant x\left(0.99 - \frac{2}{\log 82}\right) > \frac{x}{2} > 0.$$

The proof of (a) involves certain numerical work, connected with zeros of the zeta-function. Proposition 3.2 implies the bound

$$\sum_{p \leqslant x} \log p \leqslant 1.1\, x$$

for $x \geqslant 2$, and this suffices for the proof of Theorems 4.6 and 4.7 for large values of k.

Now we state two results concerning the distribution of prime numbers in arithmetical progressions.

THEOREM A.3 (The Siegel–Walfisz theorem). (A. Walfisz [36]. For a proof cf. K. Prachar [57] or H. Davenport [67].) *Let* $B > 0$ *be fixed. If* $k \ll \log^B x$, *then for* $(k, l) = 1$

$$\pi(x, k, l) = \frac{\operatorname{li} x}{\varphi(k)} + O(x \exp\{-C \log^{1/2} x\})$$

with C *and the implied constant in* $O(\cdot)$ *depending only on* B. *For* $k = 1$ *we can take* $C = 1$.

COROLLARY (Prime Number Theorem). *For* $x \geqslant 2$

$$\pi(x) = \operatorname{li} x + O(x \exp(-\log^{1/2} x)).$$

THEOREM A.4 (E. Bombieri [65], A. I. Vinogradov [65]. For a proof see also H. Davenport [67], Chapter 24, Theorem 1.) *To every positive constant* A *there corresponds a positive constant* B *such that*

$$\sum_{q \leqslant x^{1/2}\log^{-B} x} \max_{y \leqslant x} \max_{\substack{r \\ (r,q)=1}} |A(y, q, r) - y\varphi^{-1}(q)| \ll x \log^{-A} x,$$

where

$$A(y, q, r) = \sum_{\substack{p \leqslant y \\ p \equiv r \,(\mathrm{mod}\, q)}} \log p$$

and

$$\sum_{q \leqslant x^{1/2}\log^{-B}x} \max_{y \leqslant x} \max_{\substack{r \\ (r,q)=1}} \left| \pi(y, q, r) - \frac{\operatorname{li} y}{\varphi(q)} \right| \ll x \log^{-A} x.$$

COROLLARY (Yu. V. Linnik [61]). *We have*

$$\sum_{p \leqslant x} d(p-1) = (C + o(1)) x \quad \text{with a positive constant } C.$$

Proof (G. Rodriguez [65], H. Halberstam [67]). Since

$$d(n) = 2 \sum_{\substack{d|n \\ d < \sqrt{n}}} 1 + \theta(n)$$

where $\theta(n) = 1$ if n is a square and $\theta(n) = 0$ otherwise, we get

$$\sum_{p \leqslant x} d(p-1) = 2 \sum_{p \leqslant x} \sum_{\substack{d|p-1 \\ d < \sqrt{p-1}}} 1 + O(x^{1/2})$$

$$= 2 \sum_{d < \sqrt{x}} \left(\pi(x, d, 1) - \pi(1+d^2, d, 1) \right) + O(x^{1/2})$$

$$= 2 \sum_{d < \sqrt{x}} \pi(x, d, 1) + O(x \log^{-1} x)$$

by the Brun–Titchmarsh theorem. By using Theorem A.4 we obtain

$$\sum_{p \leqslant x} d(p-1) = 2 \operatorname{li} x \sum_{d \leqslant \sqrt{x} \log^{-B}x} \varphi^{-1}(d) +$$

$$+ \sum_{\sqrt{x} \log^{-B}x < d < \sqrt{x}} \pi(x, d, 1) + O(x \log^{-1} x)$$

$$= 2 \operatorname{li} x \sum_{d \leqslant x} \varphi^{-1}(d) + O\left(x \log^{-1} x \left(1 + \sum_{\sqrt{x} \log^{-B}x < d < x^{1/2}} \varphi^{-1}(d) \right) \right)$$

$$= 2 \operatorname{li} x \left(C_1 \log x + O(1) \right) + O\left(\frac{x \log \log x}{\log x} \right) = (C + o(1)) x$$

because $\sum_{d \leqslant x} \varphi^{-1}(d) = C_1 \log x + O(1)$ with a positive C_1. $\square$

Finally we state here two evaluations used in the proof of Theorem 5.5, simple proofs of which can be found e.g. in K. Chandrasekharan [70] (p. 43 and p. 180):

PROPOSITION A.4. *If* $0 < \varepsilon < 1$, $s = \sigma + it$ *then in the region* $\sigma \geqslant \varepsilon$, $|t| \geqslant 1$, *we have*

$$|\zeta(s)| \ll |t|^{1-\varepsilon}$$

with the implied constant depending only on ε. *Moreover, if* $q \geqslant 3$ *and* χ *is a primitive character* (mod q), *then in the region* $\sigma \geqslant \varepsilon$ (*where* $0 < \varepsilon < 1$ *is a fixed positive number) we have*

$$|L(s, \chi)| \ll q^{1-\varepsilon}|s|,$$

where again the implied constant depends only on ε.

4. Geometry of numbers

From this branch of number theory we use only the following two classical results:

THEOREM A.5 (H. Minkowski. For a proof see e.g. [H–W] or J. W. S. Cassels [59], Chapter III, § 2, Theorem 2.) *Let X be a convex set in the n-dimensional real space, symmetrical with respect to the origin with volume exceeding 2^n. Then X contains at least one point with integral coordinates distinct from the origin.*

THEOREM A.6′ (C. Carathéodory. A proof can be found in H. G. Eggleston [58].) *If X is a subset of the n-dimensional real space and* Conv X *is its convex hull, then for every element x of that hull one can find $n+1$ elements in X whose convex hull contains x.*

5. Ternary quadratic forms

We use in the main text the following result, which derives from the classical reduction theory:

PROPOSITION A.5. *Every ternary positive definite quadratic form with integral coefficients of discriminant 1 is equivalent to $x^2+y^2+z^2$.*

Proof. We shall need the following result, a proof of which may be found in J. W. S. Cassels [59] (Chapter II, § 3, Theorem 3) or C. F. Gauss [31]:

LEMMA A.4. *If $f(\bar{x}) = \sum\limits_{1 \leqslant i \leqslant j \leqslant 3} a_{ij} x_i x_j \ (a_{ij} = a_{ji})$ is a ternary positive definite quadratic form of discriminant D over the field of real numbers, then f is equivalent (over Z) to a form $\sum\limits_{1 \leqslant i \leqslant j \leqslant 3} A_{ij} x_i x_j$ satisfying $A_{11} A_{22} A_{33} \leqslant 2D$ and equality holds here only for multiples of the form*

$$f_0 = x_1^2 + x_2^2 + x_3^2 + x_1 x_2 + x_1 x_3 + x_2 x_3.$$

Since an integral form f with discriminant 1 cannot be a multiple of f_0 because the discriminant of cf_0 equals $c^3/2 \neq 1$, it must be equivalent to a form g with $A_{11} A_{22} A_{33} = 1$, i.e.,

$$g(x, y, z) = x^2 + y^2 + z^2 + 2axy + 2bxz + 2cyz$$

with suitable integral a, b, c. The discriminant of g equals $1 + 2abc - a^2 -$

$-b^2-c^2$ and thus we must have $a^2+b^2+c^2 = 2abc$. Since g is positive definite, $\det\begin{bmatrix} 1 & a \\ a & 1 \end{bmatrix} = 1-a^2$ is non-negative; hence $a = \pm 1$ or 0. If $a \neq 0$ then $1+b^2+c^2 = \pm 2bc$, which is impossible; thus $a = 0$, $b^2+c^2 = 0$ and $b = 0 = c$, showing that $g(x, y, z) = x^2+y^2+z^2$, as asserted. □

6. Diophantine approximations

We use Dirichlet's classical theorem and two extensions of Roth's theorem.

PROPOSITION A.6 (G. Dirichlet). *If x is any real number and $N \geqslant 1$ an integer, then we can find integers $1 \leqslant q \leqslant N$ and $0 \leqslant p < q$ such that*

$$|x - p/q| < 1/q^N.$$

The proof is so simple that we give it here: the set of fractional parts $\{x\}, \{2x\}, \ldots, \{(N+1)x\}$ has $N+1$ elements and since there are N intervals $[j/N, (j+1)/N)$ $(j = 0, 1, \ldots, N-1)$, two of those fractional parts must belong to the same interval, i.e., there exist integers $1 \leqslant r < s \leqslant N+1$ such that with a suitable integer p one has $|sa-ra-p| < N^{-1}$. If we put $q = s-r$ we obtain our assertion. □

Now we turn to extensions of Roth's theorems.

To state the first of them we need the notion of *height*. Let a be an element of an algebraic number field K, let N be the degree of K/Q and let n be the degree of a over Q. Then obviously n is a divisor of N. Let $F(x) \in Z[x]$ be the minimal polynomial for a, determined uniquely up to a sign by the condition that its coefficients do not have a non-trivial common divisor, and put $G(x) = F^{N/n}(x)$. Then the *height of a over K*, $H_K(a)$, is defined as the largest absolute value of the coefficients of $G(x)$. Of course, if a generates K, then $H_K(a)$ is the maximal absolute value of the coefficients of its minimal polynomial.

THEOREM A.6. (For $K = Q$ proved by K. F. Roth [55] and in the general case by W. J. Leveque [56], vol. II, Ch. 4.) *If x is an algebraic number and K an algebraic number field, then for every positive ε the inequality*

$$|x - a| < H_K(a)^{-2-\varepsilon}$$

can have only finitely many solutions $a \in K$.

The second extension is due to D. Ridout. We need only a very special case of this extension and to state it we introduce certain simple definitions: Let $A = \{p_1, \ldots, p_m\}$ be a finite set of primes, and for given constants $C_1 > 0$ and $0 < C_2 < 1$ denote by $S(A, C_1, C_2)$ the set of all integers n of the form

$$n = n_1 p_1^{a_1} \ldots p_m^{a_m}$$

with $a_i \geqslant 0$ and $|n_1| \leqslant C_1 n^{C_2}$, $n_1 \in Z$.

THEOREM A.7 (D. Ridout [57]). *If A_1, A_2 are two finite sets of primes, and $0 < a < 1$, $0 < b < 1$, $c < a+b$ and $C > 0$ are given, then there exists a constant $M = M(a, b, c, C) > 0$ such that for $m \in S(A_1, C, a)$ and $n \in S(A_2, C, b)$ with $m \neq n$ we have*

$$|1 - m/n| > Mn^{-c}.$$

7. Baker's method

There are many variants of the method of Baker but in this book it is used only via the following theorem:

THEOREM A.8 (A. Baker [77]). *If $L(X_1, \ldots, X_n) = \sum_{j=1}^{n} X_j \log \alpha_j$ where α_j are rational numbers, and the numbers $A_1, \ldots, A_n$ are so chosen that $A_j \geqslant 4$ and the height of α_j does not exceed A_j for $j = 1, 2, \ldots, n$, then for all integers $x_1, \ldots, x_n$ with $|x_j| \leqslant M$ ($j = 1, 2, \ldots, n$) where $M \geqslant 4$ is a constant we have either*

$$L(x_1, \ldots, x_n) = 0$$

or

$$|L(x_1, \ldots, x_n)| \geqslant \exp(-CD(\log D')(\log M))$$

where C is a constant depending only on n (we may take $C = (16n)^{200n}$), $D = \prod_{j=1}^{n} \log A_j$ and $D' = D/\log A_n$.

If the numbers α_j are algebraic with heights not exceeding A_j ($j = 1, 2, \ldots, n$) and x_j's are also algebraic with heights less than M, then either $L(x_1, \ldots, x_n) = 0$ or

$$|L(x_1, \ldots, x_n)| \geqslant \exp(-C_1 D(\log D)(\log D')(\log M))$$

where D and D' are as above and $C_1 = (16nd)^{200n}$ where d is the degree of the field generated by $\alpha_1, \ldots, \alpha_n, x_1, \ldots, x_n$.

8. Weil's bound

The result we need is a corollary to an analogue of the Riemann hypothesis for curves established by A. Weil [48]. An elementary proof is given in W. M. Schmidt [76] (Ch. II, th. 2C', p. 43).

THEOREM A.9. *If X is a non-principal character (mod p) with a prime p, and $P(x) \in Z[x]$ is not congruent (mod p) to a polynomial of the form $cV^d(x)$ where*

$\cdot c$ is a constant, $V \in Z[x]$ and $d > 1$ is a divisor of the order of X, then

$$\left| \sum_{x (\mathrm{mod}\, p)} X(P(x)) \right| \leqslant (k-1) p^{1/2}$$

where k is the number of distinct roots of $P(x) (\mathrm{mod}\, p)$ in an algebraic closure of $\mathrm{GF}(p)$.

9. Primitive real characters

We list here for quick reference fundamental facts concerning real primitive Dirichlet characters which are used in our work.

First we recall that a character $X (\mathrm{mod}\, N)$ is called *primitive* if there is no proper divisor n of N such that we have the equality $X(m) = 1$ for all those integers m which satisfy $(m, N) = 1$ and $m \equiv 1 (\mathrm{mod}\, n)$. Obviously every non-principal character $(\mathrm{mod}\, p)$ for prime p is primitive and among them there is one real character, namely the character $\chi_p(x) = \left(\dfrac{x}{p}\right)$. One also sees immediately that there is one real primitive character $(\mathrm{mod}\, 4)$, namely

$$\chi_4(x) = \begin{cases} 1 & \text{if} \quad x \equiv 1 (\mathrm{mod}\, 4), \\ -1 & \text{if} \quad x \equiv 3 (\mathrm{mod}\, 4), \end{cases}$$

and there are two primitive real characters $(\mathrm{mod}\, 8)$, namely

$$\chi_8(x) = (-1)^{(x^2-1)/8} \qquad (\text{for odd } x)$$

and $\chi_8(x) \chi_4(x)$.

If $N = p_1^{a_1} \ldots p_r^{a_r}$ then every character $(\mathrm{mod}\, N)$ can be factorized into a product of characters $(\mathrm{mod}\, p_i^{a_i})$, say

$$\chi = \chi_1 \ldots \chi_r,$$

and one easily sees that χ is primitive if and only if each factor χ_i is primitive. This observation permits us to construct all primitive real characters.

PROPOSITION A.7. *A primitive real character* $(\mathrm{mod}\, N)$ *exists if and only if* $N = 2^a p_1 \ldots p_r$, *where* $a = 0, 2$ *or* 3 *and* $p_1, \ldots, p_r$ *are distinct odd primes. If N satisfies this condition then there is exactly one primitive character* $(\mathrm{mod}\, N)$ *except where N is divisible by* 8, *in which case there are two such characters. In the first case the only real primitive character* $(\mathrm{mod}\, N)$ *is defined by*

$$X(n) = \begin{cases} \displaystyle\prod_{i=1}^{r} \left(\dfrac{n}{p_i}\right) & \text{if} \quad a = 0, \\[3ex] \displaystyle\chi_4(n) \prod_{i=1}^{r} \left(\dfrac{n}{p_i}\right) & \text{if} \quad a = 2, \end{cases}$$

and in the second case the primitive real characters (mod N) *are equal to*

$$\chi_8(n) \prod_{i=1}^{r} \left(\frac{n}{p_i}\right) \quad and \quad \chi_4(n)\chi_8(n) \prod_{i=1}^{r} \left(\frac{n}{p_i}\right).$$

Proof. The previous observation implies that the characters written above are primitive and that for those N's there are no more such real characters. To show that for other N's there are no primitive real characters it suffices to prove that there are no such characters (mod p^a) (where p is an odd prime and $a \geqslant 2$), (mod 2) and (mod 2^k) (for $k \geqslant 4$). In the first case observe that the multiplicative group $G(p^a)$ of residue classes (mod p^a) prime to p is cyclic of order $p^a(p-1)$ and thus has only one character of order two. Since the real primitive character (mod p) can be lifted to a (non-primitive) character (mod p^a), this shows that there is no other real character (mod p^a). The case of modulus 2 is trivial and, since $G(2^k)$ is a product of a cyclic group of two elements and a cyclic group of 2^{k-2} elements, we see that there are four real characters (mod 2^k). One of them is principal and the remaining ones are lifted from primitive characters (mod 4) and (mod 8). Hence there is no place for a primitive character. $\square$

Now we define the *Kronecker symbol* $\left(\dfrac{d}{x}\right)$ in the case where the integer d has one of the following forms:

(a) $d = \varepsilon p_1 \ldots p_r \equiv 1 \,(\text{mod } 4)$ $(r \geqslant 1)$,
(b) $d = 4\varepsilon p_1 \ldots p_r$ $(\varepsilon p_1 \ldots p_r \equiv 3 \,(\text{mod } 4)$, $r \geqslant 0)$,
(c) $d = 8\varepsilon p_1 \ldots p_r$ $(r \geqslant 0)$.

In all cases $\varepsilon = 1$ or $\varepsilon = -1$ and $p_1, \ldots, p_r$ are odd primes.
The Kronecker symbol is defined by

$$X(x) = \left(\frac{d}{x}\right) = \chi(x) \prod_{i=1}^{r} \chi_{p_i}(x)$$

where $\chi = 1$ in case (a), $\chi = \chi_4$ in case (b), and in case (c) the character is chosen in the following way: if the product $\prod_{i=1}^{r} \left(\dfrac{-1}{p_i}\right)$ equals sign d, then $\chi = \chi_8$ and otherwise $\chi = \chi_4 \cdot \chi_8$. From the definition we obtain the following important property of the Kronecker symbol:

PROPOSITION A.8. *The character X is a primitive real character* (mod $|d|$) *and its value at* -1 *coincides with the sign of d.* $\square$

10. Algebraic numbers

In many places we used the principal results of the theory of algebraic numbers which may be found in a suitable text-book on this subject (see e.g.

S. Lang [64], H. B. Mann [55], W. Narkiewicz [74]) and which we state below for convenient reference:

THEOREM A.10 (Dirichlet's theorem, W. Narkiewicz [74], th. 3.6). *If the field K has r real and 2s non-real embeddings in the field of complex numbers, then there exists a system $\varepsilon_1, \ldots, \varepsilon_t$ of units with $t = r + s - 1$ such that every unit of K can be uniquely written in the form*

$$\zeta \varepsilon_1^{n_1} \ldots \varepsilon_t^{n_t}$$

where $n_i \in Z$ and ζ is a root of unity.

PROPOSITION A.9 (The Kummer–Dedekind theorem, W. Narkiewicz [74], th. 4.10). *If a is an algebraic integer, $f(x) \in Z[x]$ its minimal polynomial, p a prime not dividing the discriminant of f and finally*

$$f(x) \equiv f_i^{a_i}(x) \ldots f_m^{a_m}(x) \pmod{p}$$

a factorization of f into polynomials irreducible (mod p), then in the extension $Q(a)/Q$ the ideal generated by p has a factorization into prime ideals of the form

$$(p) = P_1^{a_1} \ldots P_m^{a_m}.$$

PROPOSITION A.10 (W. Narkiewicz [74], th. 4.13 and 4.14). (i) *If d is the discriminant of the quadratic field K, then the prime ideals generated by rational primes factorize in K according to the following law:*

$$(p) = \begin{cases} P_1 P_2 & \text{if} \quad \left(\dfrac{d}{p}\right) = +1, \\[2mm] P & \text{if} \quad \left(\dfrac{d}{p}\right) = -1, \\[2mm] P^2 & \text{if} \quad p \mid d. \end{cases}$$

(ii) *In the n-th cyclotomic field $Q(\exp(2\pi i/n))$ the prime ideals generated by rational primes factorize according to the following law:*

$$(p) = (P_1 \ldots P_g)^e$$

where $n = p^a m$, $(p \nmid m)$, $e = \varphi(p^a)$, $g = \varphi(m)/\mathrm{ord}_p(m)$, where $\mathrm{ord}_p(m)$ denotes the multiplicative order of $m \pmod p$.

THEOREM A.11 (The prime ideal theorem of E. Landau, W. Narkiewicz [74], Corollary to th. 7.7). *If $\pi_K(x)$ denotes the number of prime ideals of K with norms not exceeding x, then*

$$\pi_K(x) = x/\log x + O(x/\log^2 x).$$

PROPOSITION A.11 (W. Narkiewicz [74], th. 4.16). *Every finite extension K of the rationals can be embedded in a larger extension L/Q in which all ideals of K become principal and the degree of L/K does not exceed the class number of K.*

Bibliography

Albis González, V. S.

[75] *The equations of Fermat and Catalan in $K[t]$* (Spanish), Bol. Mat. 9 (1975), 217–220.

Alpár, L.

[55] *Un problème de la théorie des nombres* (Hungarian), Mat. Lapok 6 (1955), 309–322.

Alter, R., Kubota, K. K.

[73] *The diophantine equation $x^2 + D = p^n$*, Pacific J. Math. 46 (1973), 11–16.

[75] *The diophantine equation $x^2 + 11 = 3^n$ and a related sequence*, J. Number Theory 7 (1975), 5–10.

André, D.

[71] *Théorèmes d'arithmètique*, Nouv. Annales Math., (2), 10 (1871), 207–208.

Andree, R. V.

[62] *A table of indices and power residues for all primes and prime powers below* 2000, New York 1962.

Ankeny, N. C.

[52] *The least quadratic non-residue*, Ann. of Math., (2), 55 (1952), 65–71.

[57] *Sums of three squares*, Proc. Amer. Math. Soc. 8 (1957), 316–319.

Apéry, R.

[60a] *Sur une équation diophantienne*, C. R. Acad. Sci. Paris 251 (1960), 1263–1264.

[60b] *Sur une équation diophantienne*, C. R. Acad. Sci. Paris 251 (1960), 1451–1452.

Apostol, T. M.

[70] *Euler's φ-function and separable Gauss sums*, Proc. Amer. Math. Soc. 24 (1970), 482–485.

Archibald, R. C., Chace, A. B., Manning, H. P. (see A. B. Chace, H. P. Manning, R. C. Archibald)

Arndt, F.

[59] *Über die Anzahl der Genera der quadratischen Formen*, J. Reine Angew. Math. 56 (1859), 72–78.

Artin, E., Whaples, G.

[45] *Axiomatic characterization of fields by the product formula for valuations*, Bull. Amer. Math. Soc. 51 (1945), 469–492.

Artyukhov, M. M.

[73] *On the problem of odd h-fold perfect numbers*, Acta Arith. 23 (1973), 249–255.

Aubry, L.

[13] Sphinx-Oedipe, 8 (1913), 136.

Auluck, F. C.

[40] *On Waring's problem for biquadrates*, Proc. Nat. Acad. Sci. India, Sect. A, 11 (1940), 437–450.

Auluck, F. C., Chowla, S.

[37] *The representation of a large number as a sum of "almost equal" squares*, Proc. Nat. Acad. Sci. India, Sect. A, 6 (1937), 81–82.

Ayoub, R. G.

[63] *An introduction to the analytic theory of numbers*, Providence 1963.

[67] *A note on the class number of imaginary quadratic fields*, Math. Comp. 21 (1967), 442–445.

Bachmann, P.

[94] *Analytische Zahlentheorie*, Leipzig 1894.

[10] *Niedere Zahlentheorie*, II Teil, Leipzig 1910.

Baer, W. S.

[13a] *Beiträge zum Waringschen Problem*, Dissertation, Göttingen 1913.

[13b] *Über die Zerlegung der ganzen Zahlen in sieben Kuben*, Math. Ann. 74 (1913), 511–514.

Baines, M. J., Daykin, D. E. (see D. E. Daykin, M. J. Baines)

Baker, A.

[66] *Linear forms in the logarithms of algebraic numbers*, Mathematika 13 (1966), 204–216.

[68] *Contributions to the theory of Diophantine equations, II. The Diophantine equation* $y^2 = x^3 + k$, Philos. Trans. Roy. Soc. London, Ser. A, 263 (1967/68), 193–208.

[69a] *Bounds for the solution of the hyperelliptic equation*, Proc. Cambridge Philos. Soc. 65 (1969), 439–444.

[69b] *A remark on the class number of quadratic fields*, Bull. London Math. Soc. 1 (1969), 98–102.

[71a] *Imaginary quadratic fields with class number 2*, Ann. of Math., (2), 94 (1971), 139–152.

[71b] *On the class number of imaginary quadratic fields*, Bull. Amer. Math. Soc. 77 (1971), 678–684.

[77] *The theory of linear forms in logarithms*. In: *Transcendence Theory*, Academic Press, 1977, pp. 1–27.

Baker, A., Coates, J.

[75] *Fractional parts of powers of rationals*, Math. Proc. Cambridge Philos. Soc. 77 (1975), 269–279.

Baker, A., Schinzel, A.

[71] *On the least integers represented by the genera of binary quadratic forms*, Acta Arith. 18 (1971), 137–144.

Balasubramanian, R.

[79] *On Warings problem:* $g(4) \leqslant 21$, Hardy-Ramanujan J. 2 (1979), 31 pp.

Baltes, H. P., Draxl, P. K. J., Hilf, E. R.

[74] *Quadratsummen und gewisse Randwertprobleme der mathematischen Physik*, J. Reine Angew. Math. 268/9 (1974), 410–417.

Bambah, R. P., Chowla, S.

[47] *On the sign of the Gaussian sum*, Proc. Nat. Acad. Sci. India 13 (1947), 175–176.

Banerjee, D. P.

[42] *On the solution of the "easier" Waring problem*, Bull. Calcutta Math. Soc. 34 (1942), 197–199.

Bang, A. S.

[86] *Taltheoritiske undersøgelser*, Tidsskr. Mat. 4 (1886), 70–80, 130–137.

Bang, T.

[54] *Congruence properties of Tchebycheff polynomials*, Math. Scand. 2 (1954), 327–333.

Barbilian, D.

[46] *Modernisierung des Beweises des Dirichlet–Jacobischen Satzes*, Mathematica (Timişoara) 22 (1946), 159–169.

Bateman, P. T.

[51] *On the representation of a number as the sum of three squares*, Trans. Amer. Math. Soc. 71 (1951), 70–101.

[69] *A multiplicative function*, Problem E 2051, Amer. Math. Monthly 76 (1969), 190–191.

[72] *The distribution of values of the Euler function*, Acta Arith. 21 (1972), 329–345.

Bateman, P. T., Chowla, S.

[50] *Averages of character sums*, Proc. Amer. Math. Soc. 1 (1950), 781–787.

Baum, J. D.

[65] Math. Magazine 38 (1965), 146.

Beck, A., Bleicher, M. N., Crowe, D. W.

[69] *Excursions in mathematics*, New York 1969.

Beeger, N. G. W. H.

[19] *Über die Teilkörper des Kreiskörpers $K(\zeta_n)$*, Proc. Akad. Wetensch. Amsterdam 21 (1919), 454–465, 758–773, 774–779.

[22a] *On a new case of the congruence $2^{p-1} \equiv 1 \pmod{p^2}$*, Messenger of Math. 51 (1922), 149–150.

[22b] *Bestimmung der Klassenzahl der Ideale aller Unterkörper des Kreiskörpers der ζ_m wo m durch mehr als eine Primzahl teilbar ist*, Proc. Akad. Wetensch. Amsterdam 22 (1922), 331–350, 395–414; corr. ibidem 23 (1922), 1399–1401.

Bennett, A. A.

[25] *On sets of three consecutive integers which are quadratic residues of primes*, Bull. Amer. Math. Soc. 31 (1925), 411–412.

[26a] *Large primes have four consecutive quadratic residues*, Tôhoku Math. J. 27 (1926), 53–57.

[26b] *Consecutive quadratic residues*, Bull. Amer. Math. Soc. 32 (1926), 283–284.

Beresin, M., Levine, E.

[72] *Primitive numbers for a class of multiplicative functions*, Duke Math. J. 39 (1972), 529–537.

Berg, M., Kravitz, S. (see S. Kravitz, M. Berg)

Berndt, B., Evans, R.

[79] *Sums of Gauss, Jacobi and Jacobsthal*, J. Number Theory 11 (1979), 349–398.

[81] *The determination of Gauss sums*, Bull. Amer. Math. Soc. 5 (1981), 107–129.

Bernstein, L.

[62] *Zur Lösung der diophantischen Gleichung $m/n = 1/x + 1/y + 1/z$ insbesondere im Fall m = 4*, J. Reine Angew. Math. 211 (1962), 1–10.

Bessel-Hagen, E.

[29] *Bemerkungen zur Behandlung des major arc bei der Anwendung der Hardy–Littlewoodschen Methode auf das Waringsche Problem*, Proc. London Math. Soc., (2), 29 (1929), 382–400.

Beukers, F.

[79] *The generalized Ramanujan–Nagell equation*, Proefschrift, Leiden 1979.

[81a] *Fractional parts of powers of rationals*, Math. Proc. Cambridge Philos. Soc. 90 (1981), 13–20.

[81b] *On the generalized Ramanujan–Nagell equation, I*, Acta Arith. 38 (1981), 389–410; *II*, ibidem 39 (1981), 113–123.

Bilharz, H.

    [37] *Primdivisoren mit vorgegebener Primitivwurzel*, Math. Ann. 114 (1937), 476–492.

Birch, B. J.

    [64] *Waring's problem for p-adic number fields*, Acta Arith. 9 (1964), 169–176.

    [69] *Weber's class invariants*, Mathematika 16 (1969), 283–294.

Birch, B. J., Chowla, S., Hall, M., Jr., Schinzel, A.

    [65] *On the difference* $x^3 - y^2$, Norske Vid. Selsk. Forh. Trondheim 38 (1965), 65–69.

Birkhoff, G. D., Vandiver, H. S.

    [04] *On the integral divisors of* $a^n - b^n$, Ann. of Math., (2), 5 (1904), 173–180.

Bleicher, M. N.

    [72] *A new algorithm for the expansion of Egyptian fractions*, J. Number Theory 4 (1972), 342–382.

Bleicher, M. N., Beck, A., Crowe, D. W. (see A. Beck, M. N. Bleicher, D. W. Crowe)

Bleicher, M. N., Erdös, P.

    [75] *The number of distinct subsums of* $\sum_1^N \frac{1}{i}$, Math. Comp. 29 (1975), 29–42.

    [76a] *Denominators of Egyptian fractions*, J. Number Theory 8 (1976), 157–168.

    [76b] *Denominators of Egyptian fractions, II*, Illinois J. Math. 20 (1976), 598–613.

Blundon, W. J., Lal, M., Jones, M. F. (see M. Lal, M. F. Jones, W. J. Blundon)

Bombieri, E.

    [65] *On the large sieve*, Mathematika 12 (1965), 201–225.

Borevich Z. I., Shafarevich, I. R.

    [72] *Theory of Numbers* (Russian), 2nd ed., Moskva 1972.

Bovey, J. D.

    [76] *A note on Waring's problem in p-adic fields*, Acta Arith. 29 (1976), 343–351.

    [77] *A new upper bound for Waring's problem* (mod p), Acta Arith. 32 (1977), 157–162.

Boyd, D. W., Kisilevsky, H.

    [72] *On the exponent of the ideal class groups of complex quadratic fields*, Proc. Amer. Math. Soc. 31 (1972), 433–436.

Brauer, A.

    [28] *Über Sequenzen von Potenzresten*, S.-Ber. Preuss. Akad. Wiss. 1928, 9–16.

    [31] *Über den kleinsten quadratischen Nichtrest*, Math. Zeitschr. 33 (1931), 161–176.

    [32] *Über die Verteilung der Potenzreste*, Math. Zeitschr. 35 (1932), 39–50.

    [41] *On a property of k consecutive integers*, Bull. Amer. Math. Soc. 47 (1941), 328–331.

    [43] *On the non-existence of odd perfect numbers of the form* $p^\alpha q_1^2 \ldots q_{t-1}^2 q_t^4$, Bull. Amer. Math. Soc. 49 (1943), 712–718.

    [54] *Elementary estimates for the least primitive root*, In: *Studies in mathematics and mechanics presented to Richard von Mises*, Academic Press, 1954, pp. 20–29.

Brauer, A., Reynolds, T. L.

    [51] *On a theorem of Aubry–Thue*, Canad. J. Math. 3 (1951), 367–374.

Brauer, R.

    [47] *On the Zeta-functions of algebraic number fields*, Amer. J. Math. 69 (1947), 243–250.

Bray, H. G., Warren, L. R. J. (see Le Roy J. Warren, H. G. Bray)

Bredikhin, B. M., Grishina, T. I.

    [78] *Elementary bound for G(n) in Waring problem* (Russian), Mat. Zametki 24 (1978), 7–18.

Brenner, C., Brenner, J. L.

    [62] *The popularity of small integers as primitive roots*, Number. Math. 4 (1962), 336–342.

Brent, R. P.

[73] *The first occurrence of large gaps between successive primes*, Math. Comp. 27 (1973), 959–963.

[80] *The first occurrence of certain large prime gaps*, Math. Comp. 35 (1980), 1435–1436.

Bressoud, D. M.

[81] *On the value of Gaussian sums*, J. Number Theory 13 (1981), 88–94.

Bretschneider, C. A.

[53] *Tafeln zur Zerlegung der Zahlen bis* 4100 *in Biquadrate*, J. Reine Angew. Mat. 46 (1853), 1–23.

Breusch, R.

[54] *Solution of problem A 4512*, Amer. Math. Monthly 61 (1954), 200–201.

Brewer, B. W.

[51] *Tests for primality*, Duke Math. J. 18 (1951), 757–763.

Briggs, W. E., Chowla, S. (see S. Chowla, W. E. Briggs)

Brillhart, J.

[64] *On the factors of certain Mersenne numbers, II*, Math. Comp. 18 (1964), 87–92.

Brillhart, J., Johnson, G. D.

[60] *On the factors of certain Mersenne numbers*, Math. Comp. 14 (1960), 365–369.

Brillhart, J., Lehmer, D. H., Selfridge, J. L.

[75] *New primality criteria and factorizations of* $2^n \pm 1$, Math. Comp. 29 (1975), 620–647.

Brillhart, J., Lehmer, D. H., Selfridge, J. L., Tuckerman, B., Wagstaff, S. S., Jr.

[83] *Factorizations of* $b^n \pm 1$, $b = 2, 3, 5, 6, 7, 10, 11, 12$ *up to high powers*, Providence 1983.

Brillhart, J., Selfridge, J. L.

[67] *Some factorizations of* $2^n \pm 1$ *and related results*, Math. Comp. 21 (1967), 87–96.

Brillhart, J., Tonascia, J., Weinberger, P.

[71] *On the Fermat quotient*, In: *Computers in number theory*, London 1971, pp. 213–222.

Browkin, J., Schinzel, A.

[56] *Sur les nombres de Mersenne qui sont triangulaires*, C. R. Acad. Sci. Paris 242 (1956), 1780–1781.

[60] *On the equation* $2^n - D = y^2$, Bull. Acad. Sci. Polonaise, Sér. Sci. Math. Astr. Phys. 8 (1960), 311–318.

Brown, E.

[74] *A lemma of Stark*, J. Reine Angew. Math. 265 (1974), 201.

[75] *Diophantine equations of the form* $x^2 + D = y^n$, J. Reine Angew. Math. 274/5 (1975), 385–389.

[76] *The diophantine equation* $x^2 + 3 = 7^n$, J. Reine Angew. Math. 288 (1976), 74–76.

Brown, J. L., Jr.

[76] *Generalization of Richert's theorem*, Amer. Math. Monthly 83 (1976), 631–634.

Brun, V.

[20] *Le crible d'Erathosthène et le théorème de Goldbach*, Vid. selsk. Skr. Kristiania, I Math. Nat. Kl., 1920, no. 3, 36 pp.

Buell, D. A.

[76] *Class groups of quadratic fields*, Math. Comp. 30 (1976), 610–623.

Buell, D. A., Williams, K. S.

[78] *Maximal residue difference sets modulo p*, Proc. Amer. Math. Soc. 69 (1978), 205–209.

Bundschuh, P., Hock, A.

[69] *Bestimmung aller imaginär-quadratischen Zahlkörper der Klassenzahl Eins mit Hilfe eines Satzes von Baker*, Math. Zeitschr. 111 (1969), 191–204.

Burgess, D. A.

[57] *The distribution of quadratic residues and non-residues*, Mathematika 4 (1957), 106–112.

[62a] *On character sums and primitive roots*, Proc. London Math. Soc., (3), 12 (1962), 179–192.

[62b] *On character sums and L-series*, Proc. London Math. Soc., (3), 12 (1962), 193–206.

[63a] *On character sums and L-series, II*, Proc. London Math. Soc., (3), 13 (1963), 524–536.

[63b] *A note on the distribution of residues and non-residues*, J. London Math. Soc. 38 (1963), 253–256.

[71] *The average of the least primitive root modulo p^2*, Acta Arith. 18 (1971), 263–271.

Burgess, D. A., Elliott, P. D. T. A.

[68] *The average of the least primitive root*, Mathematika 15 (1968), 39–50.

Butts, H. S., Dulin, B. J. (see B. J. Dulin, H. S. Butts)

Butts, H. S., Estes, D.

[68] *Modules and binary quadratic forms over integral domains*, Linear Algebra Appl. 1 (1968), 153–180.

Butts, H. S., Pall, G.

[68] *Modules and binary quadratic forms*, Acta Arith. 15 (1968), 23–44.

Buxton, M., Elmore, S.

[76] *An extension of lower bounds for odd perfect numbers*, Notices Amer. Math. Soc. 23 (1976), A-55.

Calloway, A., Calloway, J., Grosswald, E. (see E. Grosswald, A. Colloway, J. Calloway)

Car, M.

[71] *Le problème de Waring pour l'anneau des pôlynomes sur un corps fini*, C. R. Acad. Sci. Paris 273 (1971), A 141–144.

Carlitz, L.

[56a] *A note on Gauss's sums*, Proc. Amer. Math. Soc. 7 (1956), 910–911.

[56b] *Sets of primitive roots*, Compositio Math. 13 (1956), 65–70.

[60] *A note on exponential sums*, Acta Sci. Math. (Szeged) 21 (1960), 135–143.

[68] *A note on Gauss's sum*, Matematiche 23 (1968), 147–150.

Carlitz, L., Uchiyama, S.

[57] *Bounds for exponential sums*, Duke Math. J. 24 (1957), 37–41.

Carmichael, R. D.

[06] *Multiply perfect numbers of four different primes*, Ann. of Math., (2), 8 (1906–07), 149–158.

[07] *On Euler's φ-function*, Bull. Amer. Math. Soc. 13 (1907), 241–243.

[08] *A table of the values of m corresponding to given values of $\varphi(m)$*, Amer. J. Math. 30 (1908), 394–400.

[09] *On the numerical factors of certain arithmetic forms*, Amer. Math. Monthly 16 (1909), 153–159.

[12] *On composite numbers P, which satisfy the Fermat congruence $a^{P-1} \equiv 1 \pmod{P}$*, Amer. Math. Monthly 19 (1912), 22–27.

[13] *On the numerical factors of the arithmetic forms $\alpha^n \pm \beta^n$*, Ann. of Math., (2), 15 (1913), 30–70.

[14] *The Theory of Numbers*, New York 1914.

[22] *Note on Euler's φ-function*, Bull. Amer. Math. Soc. 28 (1922), 109–110.

Caro, Y.

[79] *On a division property of consecutive integers*, Israel J. Math. 33 (1979), 32–36.

Cassels, J. W. S.

[50] *The rational solutions of the diophantine equation* $Y^2 = X^3 - D$, Acta Math. 82 (1950), 243–273; corr. ibidem 84 (1951), 299.

[53] *On the equation* $a^x - b^y = 1$, Amer. J. Math. 75 (1953), 159–162.

[59] *Geometry of Numbers*, Springer 1959.

[60] *On the equation* $a^x - b^y = 1$, II, Proc. Cambridge Philos. Soc. 56 (1960), 97–103; corr. ibidem 57 (1961), 187.

[69] *On the determination of generalized Gauss sums*, Arch. Math. (Brno) 5 (1969), 79–84.

[70] *On Kummer sums*, Proc. London Math. Soc., (3), 21 (1970), 19–27.

[78] *Rational quadratic forms*, Academic Press, 1978.

Cassels, J. W. S., Fröhlich, A. (editors)

[67] *Algebraic number theory*, Academic Press, 1967.

Cattaneo, P.

[51] *Sui numeri quasiperfetti*, Boll. Un. Mat. Ital., (3), 6 (1951), 59–62.

Cauchy, A.

[13] *Dèmonstration du théorème général de Fermat sur les nombres polygones*, Mèmoires de l'Institut, 14 (1813/15), 177 et suiv. = *Oeuvres* (2), VI, 320–353, Paris 1887.

[40a] *Mèmoire sur la théorie des nombres*, Mèmoires de l'Acad. des Sciences 17 (1840), 249 et suiv. = *Oeuvres* (1), III, 5–450, Paris 1911.

[40b] *Méthode simple et nouvelle por la dètermination des sommes alternées formées avec les racines primitives des èquations binômes*, C. R. Acad. Sci. Paris 10 (1840), 560 et suiv. = *Oeuvres* (1), V, 152–166, Paris, 1885.

Cavior, S. R.

[64] *Exponential sums related to polynomials over* $\mathrm{GF}(p)$, Proc. Amer. Math. Soc. 15 (1964), 175–178.

Cayley, A.

[62] *Tables des formes quadratiques binaires pour les determinants négatifs depuis* $D = -1$ *jusqu'a* $D = -100...$, J. Reine Angew. Math. 60 (1862), 357–372 = *Collected Mathematical Papers*, V, 141–156, Cambridge 1892.

Chace, A. B., Manning, H. P., Archibald, R. C.

[27] *The Rhind Mathematical Papyrus*, vol. I, Oberlin 1927.

Chakrabarti, M. C.

[40] *On the limit points of a function connected with the three-square problem*, Bull. Calcutta Math. Soc. 32 (1940), 1–6.

Chandler, E.

[33] *Warings theorem for fourth powers*, Chicago 1933.

Chandrasekharan, K.

[70] *Arithmetical functions*, Springer, 1970.

Chang, K. L.

[48] *On some Diophantine equations* $y^2 = x^3 + k$ *with no rational solutions*, Quart. J. Math. (Oxford) 19 (1948), 181–188.

Chao Ko

[36] *Decomposition into four cubes*, J. London Math. Soc. 11 (1936), 218–219.

[65] *On the Diophantine equation* $x^2 = y^n + 1$, $xy \neq 0$, Sci. Sinica 14 (1965), 457–460.

Chebyshev, P. L.

[50] *Mémoire sur nombres premiers*, Mémoires des savants ètrangers de l'Academie Imperiale Sci. de St. Pètersbourg, 7 (1850), 17–33 = J. de math. p. et appl. 17 (1852), 366–390 = *Collected Works*, I (Russian), Moskva 1946, pp. 191–207.

Chein, E. Z.
- [76]   *A note on the equation* $x^2 = y^q + 1$, Proc. Amer. Math. Soc. 56 (1976), 83–84.
- [79a] *An odd perfect number has at least 8 prime factors*, Ph. D. thesis, Pennsylvania State University 1979.
- [79b] *Remark on the binomial coefficients*, Notices Amer. Math. Soc. 26 (1979), A 506.

Chen, J. J. (Chen J. R.)
- [58]   *On Waring's problem for n-th powers* (Chinese), Acta Math. Sinica 8 (1958), 253–257.
- [59a] *Waring's problem for* $g(5)$, Science Record 3 (1959), 327–330.
- [59b] *On the representation of a natural number as a sum of terms of the form* $\dfrac{x(x+1)\ldots(x+k-1)}{k!}$ *(Chinese)*, Acta Math. Sinica 9 (1959), 264–270.
- [64]   *Waring's problem for* $g(5)$, Sci. Sinica 12 (1964), 1547–1568.
- [67]   *On Waring's problem for n-th powers*, Chinese Math., Acta, 8 (1967), 849–853. (English translation of [58].)
- [74]   *An estimate for* $g(4)$ *in Waring's problem* (Chinese), Acta Math. Sinica 17 (1974), 131–142.
- [75]   *On the distribution of almost primes in an interval*, Sci. Sinica 18 (1975), 611–627.
- [77]   *On Professors Hua's estimate of exponential sums*, Sci. Sinica 20 (1977), 711–719.
- [79a] *On the distribution of almost primes in an interval, II*, Sci. Sinica 22 (1979), 253–275.
- [79b] *On the least prime in an arithmetical progression and theorems concerning the zeros of Dirichlet's L-functions, II*, Sci. Sinica 22 (1979), 859–889.

Chernick, J.
- [39]   *On Fermat's simple theorem*, Bull. Amer. Math. Soc. 45 (1939), 269–274.

Chinburg, T.
- [79]   *'Easier' Waring problems for commutative rings*, Acta Arith. 35 (1979), 303–331.

Chowla, I.
- [37a] *On* $\Gamma(k)$ *in Waring's problem and an analogous function*, Proc. Nat. Acad. Sci. India, Sect. A, 5 (1937), 269–276.
- [37b] *A new evaluation of the number* $\Gamma(k)$ *in Waring's problem*, Proc. Nat. Acad. Sci. India, Sect. A, 6 (1937), 97–103.
- [43]   *On Waring's problem* (mod p), Proc. Nat. Acad. Sci. India, Sect. A, 12 (1943), 195–220.

Chowla, S.
- [30]   *Remarks on Waring's theorem*, J. London Math. Soc. 5 (1930), 155–158.
- [33]   *Contributions to the analytic theory of numbers II*, J. Indian Math. Soc. 20 (1933), 120–128.
- [34]   *An extension of Heilbronn's theorem*, Quart. J. Math. (Oxford) 5 (1934), 304–307.
- [35a] *An easier Waring's problem*, Indian Phys.-Math. J. 6 (1935), 5–7.
- [35b] *A theorem on sums of powers with applications to the additive theory of numbers*, Proc. Nat. Acad. Sci. India, Sect. A, 1 (1935), 698–700.
- [35c] *A theorem on sums of powers with applications to the additive theory of numbers, II*, Proc. Nat. Acad. Sci. India, Sect. A, 1 (1935), 701–706.
- [35d] *The representation of a large number as a sum of "almost equal" cubes*, Quart. J. Math. (Oxford) 6 (1935), 146–148.
- [35e] *A remarkable property of the "singular series" in Waring's problem and its relation to hypothesis K of Hardy and Littlewood*, Proc. Nat. Acad. Sci. India, Sect. A, 2 (1935), 397–401.
- [35f] *The number of representations of a large number as a sum of n nonnegative n-th powers*, Indian Phys.-Math. J. 6 (1935), 65–68.
- [35g] *The greatest prime factor of* $x^2 + 1$, J. London Math. Soc. 10 (1935), 117–120.

[36a] *Pillai's exact formula for the number g(k) in Waring's problem*, Proc. Nat. Acad. Sci. India, Sect. A, 3 (1936), 339–340.

[36b] *Note on Waring's problem*, Proc. Nat. Acad. Sci. India, Sect. A, 4 (1936), 173.

[39] *A remark on g(n)*, Proc. Nat. Acad. Sci. India, Sect. A, 9 (1939), 20–21.

[44] *On g(k) in Waring's problem*, Proc. Lahore Philos. Soc. 6 (1944), 16–17.

[50] *A new proof of a theorem of Siegel*, Ann. of Math., (2), 51 (1950), 120–122.

[62a] *On Gaussian sums*, Proc. Nat. Acad. Sci. USA 48 (1962), 1127–1128.

[62b] *On Gaussian sums*, Norske Vid. Selsk. Forh. 35 (1962), 66–67.

[67] *Observation on a theorem of Stark*, Norske Vid. Selsk. Forh. 40 (1967), 34–36.

[70] *The Heegner–Stark–Baker–Deuring–Siegel theorem*, J. Reine Angew. Math. 241 (1970), 47–48.

Chowla, S., Auluck, F. C. (see F. C. Auluck, S. Chowla)

Chowla, S., Bambah, R. P. (see R. P. Bambah, S. Chowla)

Chowla, S., Bateman, P. T. (see P. T. Bateman, S. Chowla)

Chowla, S., Birch, B. J., Hall., M., Jr., Schinzel, A. (see B. J. Birch et al.)

Chowla, S., Briggs, W. E.

[54] *On discriminants of binary quadratic forms with a single class in each genus*, Canad. J. Math. 6 (1954), 463–470.

Chowla, S., Dunton, M., Lewis, D. J.

[60] *All integral solutions of $2^n - 7 = x^2$ are given by n = 3, 4, 5, 7, 15*, Norske Vid. Selsk. Forh. 33 (1960), 37–38.

Chowla, S., Friedlander, J. B.

[76] *Some remarks on L-functions and class numbers*, Acta Arith. 28 (1976), 413–417.

Chowla, S., Lewis, D. J., Skolem, Th. (see Th. Skolem, S. Chowla, D. J. Lewis)

Chowla, S., Pillai, S. S. (see also S. S. Pillai, S. D. Chowla)

[36] *The number of representations of a number as a sum of n nonnegative n-th powers*, Quart. J. Math. (Oxford) 7 (1936), 56–59.

Chowla, S., Selberg, A. (see A. Selberg, S. Chowla)

Chudakov, N. G. (Tchudakoff, N.)

[36] *On the difference between two neighbouring prime numbers*, Mat. Sbornik 1 (43) (1936), 799–814.

[42] *On Siegel's theorem* (Russian), Izv. Akad. Nauk SSSR, ser. mat. 6 (1942), 135–142.

[69] *Upper bound for the discriminant of the tenth imaginary quadratic field with class number one* (Russian), Issledov. po teorii čisel, Saratov, 3 (1969), 75–77.

Chudakov, N. G., Feldman, N. I. (see N. I. Feldman, N. G. Chudakov)

Chvátal, V.

[71] *A remark on Newman's conjecture*, Proc. Washington State Univ. Conf. on Number Theory, Pullman 1971, pp. 113–129.

Cijsouw, P. L., Tijdeman, R.

[72] *Distinct prime factors of consecutive integers*, Proc. Conference Diophantine Approximations, Washington, D. C., 1972, pp. 59–76.

Coates, J.

[70a] *An effective p-adic analogue of a theorem of Thue, II. The greatest prime factor of a binary form*, Acta Arith. 16 (1970), 399–412.

[70b] *An effective p-adic analogue of a theorem of Thue, III. The diophantine equation $y^2 = x^3 + k$*, Acta Arith. 16 (1970), 425–435.

Coates, J., Baker, A. (see A. Baker, J. Coates)

Coghlan, F. B., Stephens, N. M. (see N. M. Stephens, F. B. Coghlan)

Cohen, E. L.

[72a]   *Sur certaines équations diophantiennes quadratiques,* C. R. Acad. Sci. Paris 274 (1972), 139–140.

[72b]   *Sur l'équation diophantienne $x^2 + 11 = 3^k$,* C. R. Acad. Sci. Paris 275 (1972), 5–7.

[74]   *On diophantine equations of the form $x^2 + D = p^k$,* L'Enseign. Math., (2), 20 (1974), 235–241.

[76]   *The Diophantine equation $x^2 + 11 = 3^k$ and related questions,* Math. Scand. 38 (1976), 240–246.

[78]   *Sur une équation diophantienne de Ljunggren,* Annal. Sci. Math. Québec 2 (1978), 109–112.

Cohen, S. D., Odoni, R. W. K., Stothers, W. W.

[74]   *On the least primitive root modulo p^2,* Bull. London Math. Soc. 6 (1974), 42–46.

Cole, F. N.

[03]   *On the factoring of large numbers,* Bull. Amer. Math. Soc. 10 (1903–04), 134–137.

Condict, J. T.

[78]   *Senior Thesis,* Middleburgh College, 1978.

Cook, R. J.

[73]   *A note on Waring's problem,* Bull. London Math. Soc. 5 (1973), 11–12.

Cooke, G., Weinberger, P. J.

[75]   *On the construction of division chains in algebraic number fields with applications to SL_2,* Commun. Algebra 3 (1975), 481–524.

Cooper, A. E.

[25]   *Tables of quadratic forms,* Ann. of Math., (2), 26 (1925), 309–316.

Corput, J. G. van der

[21]   *Zahlentheoretische Abschätzungen,* Math. Ann. 84 (1921), 53–79.

Cramer, G. F.

[41]   *On "almost perfect" numbers,* Amer. Math. Monthly 48 (1941), 17–20.

Cramér, H.

[21]   *Some theorems concerning prime numbers,* Arkiv Mat. Astr. Fys. 15 (1921), nr. 5.

[37]   *On the order of magnitude of the difference between consecutive prime numbers,* Acta Arith. 2 (1937), 23–46.

Crowe, D. W., Beck, A., Bleicher, M. N. (see A. Beck M. N. Bleicher, D. W. Crowe)

Curtiss, D. R.

[22]   *On Kellogg's diophantine problem,* Amer. Math. Monthly 29 (1922), 380–387.

D*., Mlle Adolphine**

[57]   *Solution de la question 386,* Nouv. Annales Math. 16 (1857), 288–290.

Danilov, L. V.

[82]   *The diophantine equation $x^3 - y^2 = k$ and the conjecture of M. Hall* (Russian), Mat. Zam. 32 (1982), 273–275.

Davenport, H.

[33]   *On certain exponential sums,* J. Reine Angew. Math. 169 (1933), 158–176.

[38]   *Sur les sommes de puissances entières,* C. R. Acad. Sci. Paris 207 (1938), 1366–1368.

[39a]   *On character sums in finite fields,* Acta Math. 71 (1939), 99–121.

[39b]   *On Waring's problem for cubes,* Acta Math. 71 (1939), 123–143.

[39c]   *On Waring's problem for fourth powers,* Ann. of Math., (2), 40 (1939), 731–747.

[41]   *Note on sums of fourth powers,* J. London Math. Soc. 16 (1941), 3–4.

[42a]   *On sums of positive integral k-th powers,* Amer. J. Math. 64 (1942), 189–198.

[42b] *On Waring's problem for fifth and sixth powers*, Amer. J. Math. 64 (1942), 199–207.

[50] *Sums of three positive cubes*, J. London Math. Soc. 25 (1950), 339–343.

[62] *Analytic Methods for Diophantine Equations and Diophantine Inequalities*, Ann Arbor 1962.

[67] *Multiplicative number theory*, Chicago 1967, 2nd. ed. Springer 1980.

Davenport, H., Erdős, P.

[39] *On sums of positive integral k-th powers*, Ann. of Math., (2), 40 (1939), 533–536.

Davenport, H., Heilbronn, H.

[36] *On Waring's problem for fourth powers*, Proc. London Math. Soc., (2), 41 (1936), 143–150.

[37a] *On Waring's problem: two cubes and a square*, Proc. London Math. Soc., (2), 43 (1937), 73–104.

[37b] *Note on a result in the additive theory of numbers*, Proc. London Math. Soc., (2), 43 (1937), 142–151.

Davenport, H., Landau, E.

[69] *On the representation of positive integers as sums of three cubes of positive rational numbers*, In: Number Theory and Analysis, New York 1969, pp. 49–53.

Davenport, H., Lewis, D. J., Schinzel, A.

[61] *Equations of the form $f(x) = g(y)$*, Quart. J. Math. (Oxford), (2), 12 (1961), 304–312.

Davis, R. W.

[76] *Class number formulae for imaginary quadratic fields*, J. Reine Angew. Math. 286/7 (1976), 369–379; II, ibidem 299/300 (1978), 247–255.

Daykin, D. E., Baines, M. J.

[63] *Coprime mappings between sets of consecutive integers*, Mathematika 10 (1963), 132–139.

Dedekind, R.

[71] *Über die Theorie der ganzen algebraischen Zahlen*, XI Supplement to Dirichlet's lectures, II ed. 1871, III ed. 1879, IV ed. 1894 = Ges. math. Werke, III, Braunschweig, 1932, 1–222.

Deleon, M. J.

[78] *Solution of E 2631*, Amer. Math. Monthly 85 (1978), 279.

Demyanenko, V. A.

[66] *On sums of four cubes* (Russian), Izvestia VUZ, Mat., 1966, no 5 (54), 63–69.

Descartes, R.

[38] *Letter to Mersenne*, 15 Nov. 1638 = Oeuvres, II, 429, Paris 1898.

Deshouillers, J.-M.

[70a] *Sur la fonction de répartition de certaines fonctions arithmétiques définies sur l'ensemble des nombres premiers moins un*, C. R. Acad. Sci. Paris 271 (1970), A 1141–1143.

[70b] *Sur la fonction de répartition de certaines fonctions arithmétiques définies sur l'ensemble des nombres premiers moins un*, Séminaire Delange—Pisot—Poitou, 11, 1969/70, exp. 17, 13 pp.

[76] *A remark on a question of E. Lieuwens: "Do there exist composite numbers M for which $k\varphi(M) = M - 1$ holds?"*, Delft Progress Rep. 2 (1976/7), 32–33.

Desq, R.

[78] *Sur une classe de solutions de l'équation d'Euler $\varphi(x) = 2^a 3^b$*, C. R. Acad. Sci. Paris 287 (1978), A1–A3.

Deuring, M.

[33] *Imaginäre quadratische Zahlkörper mit der Klassenzahl 1*, Math. Zeitschr. 37 (1933), 405–415.

[37] *On Epstein's zeta function*, Ann. of Math., (2), 38 (1937), 584–593.

[68] *Imaginäre quadratische Zahlkörper mit der Klassenzahl Eins*, Invent. math. 6 (1968), 169–179.

Dickson, L. E.

[HTN] *History of the theory of numbers*, reprinted by Chelsea 1952.

[04] *A new extension of Dirichlet's theorem on prime numbers*, Messenger Math. 33 (1904), 155–161.

[10] *On the negative discriminants for which there is a unique class of positive primitive binary quadratic forms*, Bull. Amer. Math. Soc. 17 (1910-11), 534–537.

[11] *Notes on the theory of numbers*, Amer. Math. Monthly 18 (1911), 109–111.

[13] *Finiteness of the odd perfect and primitive abundant numbers with n distinct prime factors*, Amer. J. Math. 35 (1913), 413–422.

[24a] *On the theory of numbers and generalized quaternions*, Amer. J. Math. 46 (1924), 1–16.

[24b] *Quadratic fields in which factorization is always unique*, Bull. Amer. Math. Soc. 30 (1924), 328–334.

[27a] *Generalizations of Waring's theorem on fourth, sixth and eighth powers*, Amer. J. Math. 49 (1927), 241–250.

[27b] *All positive integers are sums of values of a quadratic functions of x*, Bull. Amer. Math. Soc. 33 (1927), 713–720.

[28a] *Generalizations of the theorem of Fermat and Cauchy on polygonal numbers*, Bull. Amer. Math. Soc. 34 (1928), 63–72.

[28b] *Extended polygonal numbers*, Bull. Amer. Math. Soc. 34 (1928), 205–217.

[28c] *Additive number theory for all quadratic functions*, Amer. J. Math. 50 (1928), 1–48.

[31] *Proof of a Waring theorem on fifth powers*, Bull. Amer. Math. Soc. 37 (1931), 549–553.

[33] *Recent progress on Waring's theorem and its generalizations*, Bull. Amer. Math. Soc. 39 (1933), 701–727.

[34a] *Waring's problem for cubic functions*, Trans. Amer. Math. Soc. 36 (1934), 1–12.

[34b] *Waring's problem for ninth powers*, Bull. Amer. Math. Soc. 40 (1934), 487–493.

[34c] *Universal Waring theorem for eleventh powers*, J. London Math. Soc. 9 (1934), 201–206.

[34d] *A new method for universal Waring theorems with details for seventh powers*, Amer. Math. Monthly 41 (1934), 547–555.

[34e] *Polygonal numbers and related Waring problems*, Quart. J. Math. (Oxford) 5 (1934), 283–290.

[34f] *A new method for Waring theorems with polynomial summands*, Trans. Amer. Math. Soc. 36 (1934), 731–748.

[35] *Cyclotomy, higher congruences and Waring's problem*, I, II, Amer. J. Math. 57 (1935), 391–424, 463–474.

[36a] *The ideal Waring theorem for twelfth powers*, Duke Math. J. 2 (1936), 192–204.

[36b] *On Waring's problem and its generalization*, Ann. of Math., (2), 37 (1936), 293–316.

[36c] *Proof of the ideal Waring theorem for exponents 7–180*, Amer. J. Math. 58 (1936), 521–529.

[36d] *Universal Waring theorems with cubic summands*, Acta Arith. 1 (1936), 184–196.

[36e] *Solution of Waring's problem*, Amer. J. Math. 58 (1936), 530–535.

[36f] *A generalization of Waring's problem*, Bull. Amer. Math. Soc. 42 (1936), 525–529.

[37] *New Waring theorems for polygonal numbers*, Quart. J. Math. (Oxford) 8 (1937), 62–65.

[39] *All integers except 23 and 239 are sums of eight cubes*, Bull. Amer. Math. Soc. 45 (1939), 588–591.

Dirichlet, G. (P. G. Lejeune-Dirichlet)

[37a] *Sur l'usage des intègrales définies dans la sommation des sèries finies ou infinies*, J. Reine Angew. Math. 17 (1837), 57–67 = Werke, I, 257–270, Berlin, 1889.

[37b] *Beweis des Satzes, dass jede unbegrenzte arithmetische Progression, deren erstes Glied und Differenz ganze Zahlen ohne gemeinschaftlichen Factor sind, unendlich viele Primzahlen enthält*, Abhandl. Kgl. Preuss. Akad. Wiss., 1837, 45–81 = Werke, I, 313–342, Berlin, 1889.

[38] *Sur l'usage des sèries infinies dans la théorie des nombres*, J. Reine Angew. Math. 18 (1838), 259–274 = Werke, I, 357–374, Berlin, 1889.

[39a] *Über eine neue Methode zur Bestimmung vielfacher Integrale*, Abhandl. Kgl. Preuss. Akad. Wiss., 1839, 61–79 = Werke, I, 391–410, Berlin, 1889.

[39b] *Recherches sur diverses applications de l'analyse infinitésimale a la théorie des nombres*, J. Reine Angew. Math. 19 (1839), 324–369; 21 (1840), 1–12, 134–155 = Werke, I, 411–496, Berlin, 1889.

[50] *Über die Zerlegbarkeit der Zahlen in drei Quadrate*, J. Reine Angew. Math. 40 (1850), 228–232 = Werke, II, 91–96, Berlin, 1897.

[56] *Sur l'équation $t^2 + u^2 + v^2 + w^2 = 4m$*, J. de math. p. et appl. (2), 1 (1856), 210–214 = Werke, II, 203–208, Berlin, 1897.

[63] *Vorlesungen über Zahlentheorie*, Braunschweig 1863. (II Aufl. 1871, III Aufl. 1879-80, IV Aufl. 1894, reprinted by Chelsea 1968.)

Dixon, J. D.

[64] *Another proof of Lagrange's four square theorem*, Amer. Math. Monthly 71 (1964), 286–288.

Dodson, M. M.

[69] *The average order of two arithmetical functions*, Acta Arith. 16 (1969-70), 71–84.

[71] *On Waring's problem in GF[p]*, Acta Arith. 19 (1971), 147–173.

[73] *On Waring's problem in p-adic fields*, Acta Arith. 22 (1972-73), 315–327.

Dodson, M. M., Tietäväinen, A.

[76] *A note on Waring's problem in GF(p)*, Acta Arith. 30 (1976), 159–167.

Donnelly, M.

[73] *On a problem concerning Euler's phi-function*, Amer. Math. Monthly 80 (1973), 1029–1031.

Draxl, P. K. J., Baltes, H. P., Hilf, E. R. (see H. P. Baltes, P. K. J. Draxl, E. R. Hilf)

Dress, F.

[71a] *Sur le problème de Waring pour les puissances quatrièmes*, C. R. Acad. Sci. Paris 272 (1971), A 457–459.

[71b] *Méthodes elementaires dans le problème de Waring pour les entiers*, Journèes Arithmètiques, Marseille 1971.

[72] *Théorie additive des nombres, problème de Waring et théorème de Hilbert*, L'Enseign. Math., (2), 18 (1972), 175–190; corr. ibidem 301–302.

[73] *Amélioration de la majoration de $g(4)$ dans le problème de Waring: $g(4) \leqslant 30$*, Acta Arith. 22 (1973), 137–147.

Dressler, R. E.

[70] *A density which counts multiplicity*, Pacific J. Math. 34 (1970), 371–378.

Dressler, R. E., Parker, T.

[74] *12758*, Math. Comput. 28 (1974), 313–314.

Dulin, B. J., Butts, H. S.

[72] *Composition of binary quadratic forms over integral domains*, Acta Arith. 20 (1972), 223–251.

Dunton, M., Chowla, S., Lewis, D. J. (see S. Chowla, M. Dunton, D. J. Lewis)

Durst, L. K.

    [59]   *Exceptional real Lehmer sequences*, Pacific J. Math. 9 (1959), 437–441.

    [61]   *Exceptional real Lucas sequences*, Pacific J. Math. 11 (1961), 489–494.

    [62]   *The growth of Sylvester's cyclotomic numbers*, Duke Math. J. 29 (1962), 447–454.

Ecklund, E. F., Jr.

    [67]   *On prime divisors of the binomial coefficient*, Pacific J. Math. 29 (1967), 267–270.

Ecklund, E. F., Jr., Eggleton, R. B.

    [72]   *Prime factors of consecutive integers*, Amer. Math. Monthly 79 (1972), 1082–1089.

    [75]   *A note on consecutive composite integers*, Math. Magazine 48 (1975), 277–281.

Ecklund, E. F., Jr., Eggleton, R. B., Selfridge, J. L.

    [74]   *Consecutive integers all of whose factors belong to a given set*, Proc. III Manitoba Conf. Numerical Math., Winnipeg 1973, pp. 161–162.

Edgar, H. M.

    [66]   *Classes of equations of the type $y^2 = x^3 + k$ having no rational solutions*, Nagoya Math. J. 28 (1966), 49–58.

Eggleston, H. G.

    [58]   *Convexity*, Cambridge 1958.

Eggleton, R. B., Ecklund, E. F., Jr. (see E. F. Ecklund, Jr., R. B. Eggleton)

Eggleton, R. B., Ecklund, E. F., Jr., Selfridge, J. L. (see E. F. Ecklund Jr., R. B. Eggleton, J. L. Selfridge)

Eggleton, R. B., Selfridge, J. L.

    [76]   *Consecutive integers with no large prime factors*, J. Austral. Math. Soc. 22 (1976), 1–11.

Ehlich, H.

    [65]   *Zur Pillaischen Vermutung*, Archiv Math. 16 (1965), 223–226.

Ehrmann, J. R.

    [67]   *The number of prime divisors of certain Mersenne numbers*, Math. Comput. 21 (1967), 700–704.

Eisenstein, G.

    [47]   *Note sur la représentation d'un nombre par la somme de cinq carrés*, J. Reine Angew. Math. 35 (1847), 368.

Elliott, P. D. T. A.

    [67a] *A note on a recent paper of U. V. Linnik and A. I. Vinogradov*, Acta Arith. 13 (1967/68), 103–105.

    [67b] *A problem of Erdös concerning power residue sums*, Acta Arith. 13 (1967/68), 131–149; corr. ibidem 14 (1968), 437.

    [68]   *Some notes on k-th power residues*, Acta Arith. 14 (1968), 153–162.

    [69a] *The distribution of primitive roots*, Canad. J. Math. 21 (1969), 822–841.

    [69b] *On the size of $L(1, \chi)$*, J. Reine Angew. Math. 236 (1969), 26–36.

    [70a] *The distribution of power residues and certain related results*, Acta Arith. 17 (1970), 141–159.

    [70b] *On the mean value of $f(p)$*, Proc. London Math. Soc., (3), 21 (1970), 28–96.

    [72]   *On the least pair of consecutive quadratic non-residues (mod p)*, Proc. Number Theory Conference Boulder 1972, pp. 75–79.

Elliott, P. D. T. A., Burgess, D. A. (see D. A. Burgess, P. D. T. A. Elliott)

Ellison, W. J.

    [70]   *On a theorem of S. Srivasankanarayama Pillai*, Sem. Th. des Nombres Bordeaux, 1970-71, Nr. 12, pp. 1–10.

[71]   *Waring's problem*, Amer. Math. Monthly 78 (1971), 10–36.

[75]   *Les nombres premiers*, Paris 1975.

Ellison, W. J., Ellison, F., Pesek, J., Stahl, C. F., Stall, D. S.

[72]   *The diophantine equation* $y^2 + k = x^3$, J. Number Theory 4 (1972), 107–117.

Ellison, W. J., Pesek, J., Stall, D. S., Lunnon, W. F.

[71]   *A postscript to a paper of A. Baker*, Bull. London Math. Soc. 3 (1971), 75–78.

Elmore, S., Buxton, M. (see M. Buxton, S. Elmore)

Erdös, P.

[34]   *A theorem of Sylvester and Schur*, J. London Math. Soc. 9 (1934), 282–288.

[35]   *On the normal number of prime factors of $p-1$ and some related problems concerning Euler's φ-function*, Quart. J. Math. (Oxford) 6 (1935), 205–213.

[36a] *On the integers which are the totient of a product of three primes*, Quart. J. Math. (Oxford) 7 (1936), 16–19.

[36b] *On the representation of an integer as the sum of k k-th powers*, J. London Math. Soc. 11 (1936), 133–136.

[39a] *Note on products of consecutive integers*, J. London Math. Soc. 14 (1939), 194–198.

[39b] *Note on the product of consecutive integers*, J. London Math. Soc. 14 (1939), 245–249.

[39c] *On the integers of the form $x^k + y^k$*, J. London Math. Soc. 14 (1939), 250–254.

[45a] *On the least primitive root of a prime p*, Bull. Amer. Math. Soc. 51 (1945), 131–132.

[45b] *Some remarks on Euler's φ function and some related problems*, Bull. Amer. Math. Soc. 51 (1945), 540–544.

[46]   *Problem E 4220*, Amer. Math. Monthly 53 (1946), 537.

[48]   *Some asymptotical formulas in number theory*, J. Indian Math. Soc. 12 (1948), 75–78.

[50]   *On a diophantine equation* (Hungarian), Mat. Lapok 1 (1950), 192–210.

[51]   *On a diophantine equation*, J. London Math. Soc. 26 (1951), 176–178.

[55a] *On the products of consecutive integers*, III, Indag. Math. 17 (1955), 85–90.

[55b] *On consecutive integers*, Nieuw Arch. Wiskunde, (3), 3 (1955), 124–128.

[56a] *On perfect and multiply perfect numbers*, Annali Mat. Pura Appl., (4), 42 (1956), 253–258.

[56b] *On pseudoprimes and Carmichael numbers*, Publicat. Math. (Debrecen) 4 (1956), 201–206.

[58]   *Some remarks on Euler's φ function*, Acta Arith. 4 (1958), 10–19.

[61]   *Remarks on number theory, I* (Hungarian), Mat. Lapok 12 (1961), 10–17.

[62]   *On the integers relatively prime to n and a number theoretic function considered by Jacobsthal*, Math. Scand. 10 (1962), 163–170.

[65]   *Some recent advances and current problems in number theory*, In: Lectures in Modern Mathematics 3 (1965), 196–244.

[71]   *On the sum* $\sum\limits_{d \mid 2^n - 1} d^{-1}$, Israel J. Math. 9 (1971), 43–48.

[73]   *Über die Anzahl der Primfaktoren von* $\binom{n}{k}$, Archiv Math. 24 (1973), 53–56.

[76a] *Bemerkungen zu einer Aufgabe in den Elementen*, Archiv Math. 27 (1976), 159–163.

[76b] *Problems and results on consecutive integers*, Publicat. Math. (Debrecen) 23 (1976), 271–282.

Erdös, P., Bleicher, M. N. (see M. N. Bleicher, P. Erdös)

Erdös, P., Davenport, H. (see H. Davenport, P. Erdös)

Erdös, P., Gupta, H., Khare, S. P.

[76]   *On the number of distinct prime divisors of* $\binom{n}{k}$, Utilitas Math. 10 (1976), 51–60.

Erdös, P., Hall, R. R.

[73]   *On the values of Euler's φ-function*, Acta Arith. 22 (1973), 201–206.

[76]   *Distinct values of Euler's φ-function*, Mathematika 23 (1976), 1–3.

[77]   *Euler's φ-function and its iterates*, Mathematika 24 (1977), 173–177.

Erdös, P., Mahler, K.

[38]   *On the number of integers which can be represented by a binary form*, J. London Math. Soc. 13 (1938), 134–139.

Erdös, P., Sárközy, A.

[79]   *On the prime factors of* $\binom{n}{k}$ *and of consecutive integers*, Utilitas Math. 16 (1979), 197–215.

Erdös, P., Selfridge, J. L.

[67]   *Some problems of the prime factors of consecutive integers*, Illinois J. Math. 11 (1967), 428–430.

[71]   *Some problems on the prime factors of consecutive integers*, Proc. Washington State Univ. Conf. on Number Theory, Pullman 1971, pp. 13–21.

[75]   *The product of consecutive integers is never a power*, Illinois J. Math. 19 (1975), 292–301.

Erdös, P., Shapiro, H. N.

[51]   *On the changes of sign of a certain error function*, Canad. J. Math. 3 (1951), 375–385.

[57]   *On the least primitive root of a prime*, Pacific J. Math. 7 (1977), 861–865.

Erdös, P., Shorey, T. N.

[76]   *On the greatest prime factor of* $2^p - 1$ *for a prime p and other expressions*, Acta Arith. 30 (1976), 257–265.

Erdös, P., Straus, E. G.

[77]   *On products of consecutive integers*, In: *Number Theory and Algebra*, Academic Press, 1977, pp. 63–70.

Estermann, Th.

[36]   *Proof that every large integer is a sum of seventeen biquadrates*, Proc. London Math. Soc., (2), 41 (1936), 126–142.

[37a] *On the representation of a number as a sum of squares*, Acta Arith. 2 (1937), 47–79.

[37b] *On Waring's problem for fourth and higher powers*, Acta Arith. 2 (1937), 197–211.

[45]   *On the sign of the Gaussian sum*, J. London Math. Soc. 20 (1945), 66–67.

[48a] *On Waring's problem: a simple proof of a theorem of Hua*, Sci. Rep. Nat. Tsing Hua Univ. 5 (1948), 226–239.

[48b] *On Dirichlet's L-functions*, J. London Math. Soc. 23 (1948), 275–279.

[59]   *On the representation of a number as a sum of three squares*, Proc. London Math. Soc., (3), 9 (1959), 575–594.

Estes, D., Butts, H. S. (see H. S. Butts, D. Estes)

Euler, L.

[32]   *Observationes de theoremate quodam Fermatiano aliisque ad numeros primos spectantibus*, Comment. Acad. Petropoli 6 (1732), 103 = Comment. Arith. I, Petropoli, 1849, pp. 1–3.

[38]   *Theorematum quorundam arithmeticorum demonstrationes*, Comment. Acad. Petropoli 10 (1738), 125 = Comment. Arith. I, Petropoli, 1849, pp. 24–34.

[54]   *Demonstratio theorematis Fermatiani, omnem numerum primum formae* $4n+1$ *esse summam duorum quadratorum*, N. Comment. Acad. Petropoli, 5 (1754/55), 3 = Comment. Arith., I, Petropoli, 1849, pp. 210–233.

[70]   *Vollständige Anleitung zur Algebra*, St. Petersburg 1770 = Opera Omnia, I, Lipsiae et Berolini 1911.

[72]   *Lettre a M. Bernoulli (Extrait de)*, Mémoires de Berlin 1772, 35 = Comment. Arith. I, Petropoli, 1849, p. 584.

[73]   *Novae demonstrationes circa resolutionem numerorum in quadrata*, Acta Eruditorum
       1773, 193 = Comment. Arith., II, Petropoli, 1849, pp. 538–548.

[95]   *De variis modis numeros praegrandes examinandi, utrum sint primi nec ne?* Nova
       Acta Acad. Petropoli, 13 (1795/96), 14 = Comment. Arith., II, Petropoli, 1849, pp.
       198–214.

[49a] *Tractatus de numerorum doctrina*, Comment. Arith., II, Petropoli, 1849, pp. 503–575.

[49b] *De numeribus amicabilibus*, Comment. Arith., II, Petropoli, 1849, pp. 627–636.

Evans, R. J. (Evans, R.)

[69]   *On blocks of consecutive integers*, Amer. Math. Monthly 76 (1969), 48–49.

[72]   *On N consecutive integers in an arithmetic progression*, Acta Sci. Math. (Szeged) 33
       (1972), 295–296.

[77]   *Generalizations of a theorem of Chowla on Gaussian sums*, Houston J. Math. 3
       (1977), 343–349.

[80]   *Bioctic Gauss sums and sixteenth power residue difference sets*, Acta Arith. 38 (1980),
       37–46.

Evans, R., Berndt, B. (see B. Berndt, R. Evans)

Faulkner, M.

[66]   *On a theorem of Sylvester and Schur*, J. London Math. Soc. 41 (1966), 107–110.

Fauquembergue, E.

[94]   *Question 266*, L'intermédiaire des math. 1 (1894), 448.

Fein, B., Gordon, B., Smith, J. H.

[71]   *On the representation of* -1 *as a sum of two squares in an algebraic number field*,
       J. Number Theory 3 (1971), 310–315.

Feldman, N. I., Chudakov, N. G.

[72]   *On a theorem of Stark* (Russian), Matem. Zametki 11 (1972), 329–340.

Fermat, P.

[57]   *Letter to K. Digby, 15 August 1657*; Oeuvres, II, Paris, 1894, pp. 342–346.

[58]   *Letter to K. Digby, June 1658*; Oeuvres, II, Paris, 1894, pp. 402–408.

[70]   *Observationes Domini Petri de Fermat*, In: *Diophanti Alexandrini Arithmeticorum
       libri sex et de numeris multangulis liber unus cum commentariis C. G. Bacheti V. C. et
       observationibus D. P. de Fermat Senatoris Tolosani*, Tolosae 1670 = Oeuvres, I,
       Paris, 1891, pp. 289–342.

Finkelstein, R., London, H. (see also H. London, R. Finkelstein)

[70]   *On Mordell's equation* $y^2 - k = x^3$: *an interesting case of Sierpiński*, J. Number
       Theory 2 (1970), 310–321.

[71]   *Completion of a table of O. Hemer*, Proc. Washington State Univ. Conf. on Number
       Theory, Pullman 1971, pp. 148–159.

Fisher, J., Hauptmann, H., Vegh, E. (see H. Hauptmann, E. Vegh, J. Fisher)

Fleck, A.

[06]   *Über die Darstellung ganzer Zahlen als Summen von positiven Kuben und als Summen
       von Biquadraten ganzer Zahlen*, S-Ber. Berliner Math. Gesellsch. 5 (1906), 2–9.

[07]   *Über die Darstellung ganzer Zahlen als Summen von sechster Potenzen ganzer
       Zahlen*, Math. Ann. 64 (1907), 561–566.

Flikop, E. L., Stepanova, L. L. (see L. L. Stepanova, E. L. Flikop)

Fraser, O., Gordon, B.

[69]   *On representing a square as the sum of three squares*, Amer. Math. Monthly 76
       (1969), 922–923.

Frei, G.

[79]   *On the development of the genus of quadratic forms*, Annal. Sci. Math. Québec 3
       (1979), 5–62.

Freiman, G. A.
[49] *Solution of Waring's problem in a new version* (Russian), Uspehi Mat. Nauk 4 (1) (1949), 193.

Frenicle (Bernard Frenicle de Bassy)
[57] *Solutio duorum problematum circa numeros cubos et quadratos...*, 1657.

Fridlender, V. R.
[49] *On the least power non-residues* (Russian), Doklady AN SSSR 66 (1949), 351–352.

Friedlander, J. B., Chowla, S. (see S. Chowla, J. B. Friedlander)

Frobenius, G.
[12a] *Über den Stridsbergschen Beweis des Waringschen Satzes*, S. Ber. Preuss. Akad. Wissensch., 1912, pp. 666–670, = Ges. Abh., III, Springer 1968, pp. 568–572.
[12b] *Über quadratische Formen, die viele Primzahlen darstellen*, S. Ber. Preuss. Akad. Wissensch., 1912, pp. 966–980, = Ges. Abh., III, Springer 1968, pp. 573–587.

Fröberg, C.-E.
[74] *New results on the Kummer conjecture*, Nordisk Tidskr. Inform. 14 (1974), 117–119.

Fröhlich, A., Cassels, J. W. S. (see J. W. S. Cassels, A. Fröhlich)

Fuchs, W. H. J., Wright, E. M.
[39] *The "easier" Waring problem*, Quart. J. Math. (Oxford) 10 (1939), 190–209.

Fueter, R.
[30] *Über kubische diophantische Gleichungen*, Comment. Math. Helvet. 2 (1930), 69–89.
[46] *Über primitive Wurzeln von Primzahlen*, Comment. Math. Helvet. 18 (1946), 217–223.

Fujii, A.
[73] *A note on character sums*, Proc. Japan Acad. 49 (1973), 723–726.

Fujii, A., Gallagher, P. X., Montgomery, H. L.
[74] *Some hybrid bounds for character sums and Dirichlet L-series*, Coll. Math. J. Bólyai, Number Theory, Debrecen 1974, pp. 41–57, North-Holland, 1976.

Gallagher, P. X.
[67] *The large sieve*, Mathematika 14 (1967), 14–20.

Gallagher, P. X., Fujii, A., Montgomery, H. L. (see A. Fujii, P. X. Gallagher, H. L. Montgomery)

Gauss, C. F.
[01] *Disquisitiones Arithmeticae*, Lipsiae 1801, (German translation: Springer 1889, reprinted by Chelsea 1965; English translation: Yale Univ. Press 1966).
[11] *Summatio quarumdam serierum singularium*, Comment. Soc. reg. sc. Götting. rec., 1, 1811, = Werke II, Göttingen, 1863, pp. 9–45.
[31] *Besprechung des Buches von L. A. Seeber: Untersuchungen über die Eigenschaften der positiven ternären quadratischen Formen...*, Götting. Gelehrte Anzeigen, 1831 = Werke, II, Göttingen, 1863, pp. 188–196.

Gelbcke, M.
[31] *Zum Waringschen Problem*, Math. Ann. 105 (1931), 637–652.
[33] *À propos de g(k) dans le problème de Waring* (Russian), Doklady AN SSSR 7 (1933), 631–640.

Gelfond, A. O.
[52] *Transcendental and algebraic numbers* (Russian), Moskva 1952. English translation, Dover 1960.

Gelfond, A. O., Linnik, Yu. V.
[48] *On Thue's method and the problem of effectivization in quadratic fields* (Russian), Doklady AN SSSR 61 (1948), 773–776 = Linnik, *Izbrannye Trudy, II*, Leningrad 1980, pp. 40–44.

Gerono, G. C.

[60]   *Solution de question* 416, Nouv. Annales Math. 19 (1860), 38–42.

[70]   *Note sur la résolution en nombres entiers et positifs de l'équation* $x^m = y^n + 1$, Nouv. Annales Math., (2), 9 (1870), 469–471; 10 (1871), 204–296.

Gillies, D. B.

[64]   *Three new Mersenne primes and a statistical theory*, Math. Comput. 18 (1964), 93–97.

Goldfeld, D. M.

[68]   *Artin's conjecture on the average*, Mathematika 15 (1968), 223–226.

[74]   *A simple proof of Siegel's theorem*, Proc. Nat. Acad. Sci. USA 71 (1974), 1055.

[77]   *The conjectures of Birch and Swinnerton-Dyer and the class numbers of quadratic fields*, Astérisque 41–42 (1977), 219–227.

Goldfeld, D. M., Schinzel, A.

[75]   *On Siegel's zero*, Annali Scuola Norm. Sup. Pisa, (4), 2 (1975), 571–583.

Goldstein, L. J.

[68]   *Analogues of Artin's conjecture*, Bull. Amer. Math. Soc. 74 (1968), 517–519.

[70]   *Analogues of Artin's conjecture*, Trans. Amer. Math. Soc. 149 (1970), 431–442.

[71]   *Density questions in algebraic number theory*, Amer. Math. Monthly 78 (1971), 342–351.

[72]   *Imaginary quadratic fields of class number 2*, J. Number Theory 4 (1972), 286–301.

[73]   *Some remarks on arithmetic density questions*, Proc. Symposia Pure Math. 24 (1973), 103–110.

Goldstine, H. H., Neumann, J. v. (see J. v. Neumann, H. H. Goldstine)

Golomb, S. W.

[62]   *An algebraic algorithm for the representation problems of the Ahmes papyrus*, Amer. Math. Monthly 69 (1962), 785–786.

Golubev, V. A.

[58]   *Nombres de Mersenne et caractères du nombre 2*, Mathesis 67 (1958), 257–262.

Gordon, B., Fein, B., Smith, J. H. (see B. Fein, B. Gordon, J. H. Smith)

Gordon, B., Fraser, O. (see O. Fraser, B. Gordon)

Grace, J. H.

[27]   *The four square theorem*, J. London Math. Soc. 2 (1927), 3–8.

Gradshtein, I. S.

[25]   *On odd perfect numbers* (Russian), Matem. Sbornik 32 (1925), 476–510.

Grimm, C. A.

[69]   *A conjecture on consecutive composite integers*, Amer. Math. Monthly 76 (1969), 1126–1128.

Grimson, W. E. L., Hanson, D.

[78]   *Estimates for the product of the primes not exceeding x*, Proc. VII Manitoba Conf. Numerical Math., Winnipeg 1978, pp. 407–416.

Grishina, T. I., Bredikhin, B. M. (see B. M. Bredikhin, T. I. Grishina)

Gronwall, T. H.

[13]   *Sur les séries de Dirichlet correspondant à des caractéres complexes*, Rendiconti Circ. Mat. Palermo 35 (1913), 145–159.

Gross, B., Zagier, D.

[83]   *Points de Heegner et dérivées de fonctions L*, C. R. Acad. Sci. Paris, sér. I, 297 (1983), 85–87.

Grossman, E. H.

[74]   *On the prime ideal divisors of* $a^n - b^n$, Pacific J. Math. 54 (1974), 73–83.

Grosswald, E.

[62]   *Negative discriminants of binary quadratic forms with one class in each genus*, Acta Arith. 8 (1962/63), 295–306.

[73]   *Contributions to the theory of Euler's function* $\varphi(x)$, Bull. Amer. Math. Soc. 79 (1973), 337–341.

Grosswald, E., Calloway, A., Calloway, J.

[59]   *The representation of integers by three positive squares*, Proc. Amer. Math. Soc. 10 (1959), 451–455.

Grube, F.

[74]   *Über einige Eulersche Sätze aus der Theorie der quadratischen Formen*, Zeitschrift Math. Phys., (5), 19 (1874), 492–519.

Grün, O.

[52]   *Über ungerade vollkommene Zahlen*, Math. Zeitschr. 55 (1952), 353–354.

Guibert, M. D. A.

[60]   *Remarques sur quelques produits dont les facteurs sont en progression arithmétique*, Nouv. Annales Math. 19 (1860), 213–215.

[62]   *Sur quatre produits d'entiers consecutifs*, Nouv. Annales Math., (2), 1 (1862), 102–109.

Gupta, H.

[41]   *On numbers of the form* $4^a(8b+7)$, J. Indian Math. Soc., (N. S.), 5 (1941), 192–202.

Gupta, H., Erdös, P., Khare, S. P. (see P. Erdös, H. Gupta, S. P. Khare)

Gut, M.

[29]   *Die Zeta-Funktion, die Klassenzahl und die Kroneckersche Grenzformel eines beliebigen Kreiskörpers*, Comment. Math. Helvet. 1 (1929), 160–226.

Haberzetle, M.

[39]   *The Waring problem with summands* x^m, $m \geqslant n$, Duke Math. J. 5 (1939), 49–57.

Hagis, P., Jr.

[73]   *A lower bound for the set of odd perfect numbers*, Math. Comput. 27 (1973), 951–953.

[80]   *Outline of a proof that every odd perfect number has at least eight prime factors*, Math. Comput. 35 (1980), 1027–1031.

[81]   *On the second largest prime divisor of an odd perfect number, Analytic number theory*, Proc. Conf. Temple Univ., Philadelphia 1980, pp. 254–263; Lecture Notes in Math. 899, Springer, 1981.

Hagis, P., Jr., McDaniel, W.

[72]   *A new result concerning the structure of odd perfect numbers*, Proc. Amer. Math. Soc. 32 (1972), 13–15.

[73]   *On the largest prime divisor of an odd perfect number*, Math. Comput. 27 (1973), 955–957.

[75a] *On the largest prime divisor of an odd perfect number*, Math. Comput. 29 (1975), 922–924.

[75b] *Some results concerning the non-existence of odd perfect numbers of the form* $p^z M^{2\beta}$, Fibonacci Quart. 13 (1975), 25–28.

Halberstam, H.

[67]   *Footnote to the Titchmarsh–Linnik divisor problem*, Proc. Amer. Math. Soc. 18 (1967), 187–188.

Hall, M., Jr.

[53]   *Some equations* $y^2 = x^3 - k$ *without integer solutions*, J. London Math. Soc. 28 (1953), 379–383.

[71]   *The diophantine equation* $x^3 - y^2 = k$, In: *Computers in Number Theory*, Academic Press, 1971, pp. 173–198.

Hall, M., Jr., Birch, B. J., Chowla, S., Schinzel, A. (see B. J. Birch et al.)

Hall, N. A.

[39] *Binary quadratic discriminants with a single class in each genus*, Math. Zeitschr. 44 (1939), 85–90.

Hall, Ph.

[35] *On representatives of subsets*, J. London Math. Soc. 10 (1935), 26–30.

Hall, R. R., Erdös, P. (see P. Erdös, R. R. Hall)

Hampel, R.

[56] *On the solution in natural numbers of the equation* $x^m - y^n = 1$, Ann. Polon. Math. 3 (1956), 14.

Haneke, W.

[63] *Verschärfung der Abschätzung von* $\zeta(1/2+it)$, Acta Arith. 8 (1963), 357–430.

[73] *Über die reellen Nullstellen der Dirichletschen L-Reihen*, Acta Arith. 22 (1973), 391–421, corr. ibidem 31 (1976), 99–100.

Hanson, D.

[72] *On the product of the primes*, Canad. Math. Bull. 15 (1972), 33–37.

[73] *On a theorem of Sylvester and Schur*, Canad. Math. Bull. 16 (1973), 195–199.

Hanson, D., Grimson, W. E. L. (see W. E. L. Grimson, D. Hanson)

Harborth, H.

[65] *Eine untere Grenze für* $g(n)$, Dissertation, Braunschweig 1965.

Hardy, G. H.

[16] *Asymptotic formulae in combinatory analysis*, Quatrième Congrès de Math., Scand., Stockholm 1916, pp. 46–53 = *Collected Papers*, I, Oxford 1966, pp. 265–273.

[20] *On the representation of a number as the sum of any number of squares, and in particular of five*, Trans. Amer. Math. Soc. 21 (1920), 255–284 = *Collected Papers*, I, Oxford 1966, pp. 345–374.

Hardy, G. H., Littlewood, J. E.

[20] *Some problems of "Partitio Numerorum", I, A new solution of Waring's problem*, Nachr. Ges. Wiss. Göttingen 1920, pp. 33–54 = G. H. Hardy, *Collected Papers*, I, Oxford 1966, pp. 405–426.

[21] *Some problems of "Partitio Numerorum", II, Proof that every large number is a sum of at most 21 biquadrates*, Math. Zeitschr. 9 (1921), 14–27 = G. H. Hardy, *Collected Papers*, I, Oxford 1966, pp. 427–440.

[22] *Some problems of "Partitio Numerorum", IV, The singular series in Waring's problem and the value of the number* $G(k)$, Math. Zeitschr. 12 (1922), 161–188 = G. H. Hardy, *Collected Papers*, I, Oxford 1966, pp. 441–468.

[25] *Some problems of "Partitio Numerorum", VI, Further research in Waring's problem*, Math. Zeitschr. 23 (1925), 1–37 = G. H. Hardy, *Collected Papers*, I, Oxford 1966, pp. 469–505.

[28] *Some problems of "Partitio Numerorum", VIII, The number* $\Gamma(k)$ *in Waring's problem*, Proc. London Math. Soc. 28 (1928), 518–524 = G. H. Hardy, *Collected Papers*, I, Oxford 1966, pp. 506–542.

Hardy, G. H., Ramanujan, S.

[18] *Asymptotic formulae in combinatory analysis*, Proc. London Math. Soc., (2), 17 (1918), 75–115 = G. H. Hardy, *Collected Papers*, I, Oxford 1966, pp. 306–339.

Hardy, G. H., Wright, E. M.

[H–W] *An introduction to the theory of numbers*, 3 ed., Oxford 1954.

Hasse, H.

[50] *Vorlesungen über Zahlentheorie*, Berlin 1950, 2 Aufl. 1964.

[51] *Allgemeine Theorie der Gaussschen Summen in algebraischen Zahlkörpern*, Abhandl. DAW, Math.-Natur. Kl., 1951, nr. 1, pp. 1–23 = Math. Abh., III, Berlin, New York 1975, pp. 15–34.

[52a] *Über die Artinsche Vermutung und verwandte Dichtefragen*, Annales Acad. Fennicae, ser. AI, 116 (1952), 17 pp.

[52b] *Gausssche Summen zu Normalkörpern über endlich-algebraischen Zahlkörpern*, Abhandl. DAW, Math. Natur. Kl., 1952, nr. 1, pp. 1–19.

[52c] *Über die Klassenzahl Abelscher Zahlkörper*, Berlin 1952.

[65] *Über die Dichte der Primzahlen p, für die eine vorgegebene ganzrationale Zahl $\alpha \neq 0$ von durch eine vorgegebene Primzahl $l \neq 2$ teilbarer bzw. unteilbarer Ordnung mod p ist*, Math. Ann. 162 (1965), 74–76.

[66a] *Über die Dichte der Primzahlen p, für die eine vorgegebene ganzrationale Zahl $a \neq 0$ von gerader bzw. ungerader Ordnung mod p ist*, Math. Ann. 166 (1966), 19–23.

[66b] *Über eine diophantische Gleichung von Ramanujan–Nagell und seine Verallgemeinerung*, Nagoya Math. J. 27 (1966), 77–102.

Hauptmann, H., Vegh, E., Fisher, J.

[70] *Table of all primitive roots for primes less than 5000*, Math. Research Center, Naval Res. Lab. Report 7070, Washington 1970.

Hausdorff, F.

[09] *Zur Hilbertschen Lösung des Waringschen Problems*, Math. Ann. 67 (1909), 301–302.

Hausman, M.

[76] *Primitive roots satisfying a coprime condition*, Amer. Math. Monthly 83 (1976), 720–723.

Hausman, M., Shapiro, H. N,

[76] *Perfect ideals over the Gaussian integers*, Communic. Pure Appl. Math. 29 (1976), 323–341.

Heaslett, M. A., Uspensky, J. V. (see J. V. Uspensky, M. A. Heaslett)

Heath-Brown, D. R.

[79] *On a paper of Baker and Schinzel*, Acta Arith. 35 (1979), 203–207.

Heath-Brown, D. R., Iwaniec, H.

[79] *On the difference between consecutive prime numbers*, Invent. Math. 55 (1979), 49–69.

Heath-Brown, D. R., Patterson, S. J.

[79] *The distribution of Kummer sums at prime arguments*, J. Reine Angew. Math. 310 (1979), 111–130.

Hecke, E.

[19] *Reziprozitätsgesetz und Gausssche Summen in quadratischen Zahlkörpern*, Nachr. Ges. Wiss. Göttingen, 1919, pp. 265–278 = Math. Werke, Göttingen 1959, pp. 235–248.

[23] *Vorlesungen über die Theorie der algebraischen Zahlen*, Leipzig 1923.

Heegner, K.

[52] *Diophantische Analysis und Modulfunktionen*, Math. Zeitschr. 56 (1952), 227–253.

Heilbronn, H.

[33] *Über den Primzahlsatz von Herrn Hoheisel*, Math. Zeitschr. 36 (1933), 394–423.

[34] *On the class-number in imaginary quadratic fields*, Quart. J. Math. (Oxford) 5 (1934), 150–160.

[36] *Über das Waringsche Problem*, Acta Arith. 1 (1936), 212–221.

[38] *On Dirichlet series which satisfy certain functional equation*, Quart. J. Math. (Oxford) 9 (1938), 194–195.

[64] *Lecture Notes on Additive Number Theory mod p*, California Inst. Technology, 1964.

Heilbronn, H., Davenport, H. (see H. Davenport, H. Heilbronn)

Heilbronn, H., Linfoot, E.

[34] *On the imaginary quadratic corpora of class number one*, Quart. J. Math. (Oxford) 5 (1934), 293–301.

Hemer, O.

[52] *On the Diophantine equation $y^2 - k = x^3$*, Ph.D. thesis, Uppsala 1952.

[54] *Notes on the Diophantine equation $y^2 - k = x^3$*, Arkiv Mat. 3 (1954), 67–77.

[56] *On some diophantine equations of the type $y^2 - f^2 = x^3$*, Math. Scand. 4 (1956), 95–107.

Hendy, M. D.

[74] *Prime quadratics associated with complex quadratic fields of class number two*, Proc. Amer. Math. Soc. 43 (1974), 253–260.

Hering, G. F.

[68] *Eine Beziehung zwischen Binomialkoeffizienten und Primzahlexponenten*, Archiv Math. 19 (1968), 411–412.

Hermite, C.

[53] *Sur la décomposition d'un nombre en quatre carrés*, C. R. Acad. Sci. Paris 37 (1853), 133–134 = *Oeuvres I*, Paris 1905, pp. 288–289.

Herschfeld, A.

[36] *The equation $2^x - 3^y = d$*, Bull. Amer. Math. Soc. 42 (1936), 231–234.

Herzberg, N. P.

[75] *Integer solutions of $by^2 + p^n = x^3$*, J. Number Theory 7 (1975), 221–234.

Herzog, E.

[38] *Note zum Wieferichschen Beweis der Darstellbarkeit der ganzen Zahlen durch neun Kuben*, Acta Arith. 3 (1938), 86–88.

Hilbert, D.

[97] *Die Theorie der algebraischen Zahlkörper*, Jahresbericht DMV 4 (1897) = Ges. Abh., I, pp. 63–363, Berlin 1932, reprinted by Chelsea 1965.

[09a] *Beweis für die Darstellbarkeit der ganzen Zahlen durch eine feste Anzahl n-ter Potenzen (Waringsches Problem)*, Nachr. Ges. Wiss. Göttingen, 1909, pp. 17–36.

[09b] *Beweis für die Darstellbarkeit der ganzen Zahlen durch eine feste Anzahl n-ter Potenzen (Waringsches Problem)*, Math. Ann. 67 (1909), 281–300, = Ges. Abh., I, Berlin 1932, pp. 510–535; reprinted by Chelsea 1965.

Hilf, E. R., Baltes, H. P., Draxl, P. K. J. (see H. P. Baltes, P. K. J. Draxl, E. R. Hilf)

Hock, A., Bundschuh, P. (see P. Bundschuh, A. Hock)

Hoffstein, J.

[80] *On the Siegel–Tatuzawa theorem*, Acta Arith. 38 (1980), 167–174.

Hoheisel, G.

[30] *Primzahlprobleme in der Analysis*, Sitz.-Ber. Preuss. Akad. Wissensch. 33 (1930), 580–588.

Hooley, C.

[63] *On the representation of a number as the sum of two cubes*, Math. Zeitschr. 82 (1963), 259–266.

[64] *On the representation of a number as the sum of two h-th powers*, Math. Zeitschr. 84 (1964), 126–136.

[67] *On Artin's conjecture*, J. Reine Angew. Math. 225 (1967), 209–220.

[76] *Application of sieve methods to the theory of numbers*, Cambridge 1976.

[77] *On the representation of a number as the sum of four cubes, II*, J. London Math. Soc. 16 (1977), 424–428.

[78] *On the representation of a number as the sum of four cubes*, I, Proc. London Math.
      Soc., (3), 36 (1978), 117–140.
[80] *On the numbers that are representable as the sum of two cubes*, J. Reine Angew.
      Math. 314 (1980), 146–173.
[81] *On another sieve method and the numbers that are a sum of two h-th powers*, Proc.
      London Math. Soc., (3), 43 (1981), 73–109.

Hornfeck, B.
[55] *Zur Dichte der Menge der vollkommenen Zahlen*, Archiv Math. 6 (1955), 442–443.

Hornfeck, B., Wirsing, E.
[57] *Über die Häufigkeit vollkommener Zahlen*, Math. Ann. 133 (1957), 431–438.

Hua, L. K.
[35a] *The representation of integers as sums of the cubic function* $(x^3 + 5x)/6$, Tôhoku
      Math. J. 41 (1935/36), 356–360.
[35b] *On Waring theorem with cubic polynomial summands*, Math. Ann. 111 (1935), 622–
      628.
[35c] *On the representation of integers by the sum of seven cubic functions*, Tôhoku Math.
      J. 41 (1935/36), 361–366.
[35d] *The representation of integers as sums of the cubic function* $(x^3 + 2x)/6$, Tôhoku
      Math. J. 41 (1935/36), 367–370.
[35e] *Waring's problem for cubes*, Bull. Calcutta Math. Soc. 26 (1935), 139–140.
[35f] *On an easier Waring–Kamke problem*, Sci. Rep. Tsing Hua Univ. 3 (1935), 247–260.
[36a] *An easier Waring–Kamke problem*, J. London Math. Soc. 11 (1936), 4–5.
[36b] *On Waring problem with polynomial summands*, Amer. J. Math. 58 (1936), 553–562.
[37a] *On a generalized Waring problem*, Proc. London Math. Soc., (2), 43 (1937), 161–182.
[37b] *On Waring's problem for fifth powers*, Proc. London Math. Soc., (2), 45 (1937), 144–
      160.
[38a] *On Waring's problem*, Quart. J. Math. (Oxford) 9 (1938), 199–202.
[38b] *On an exponential sum*, J. London Math. Soc. 13 (1938), 54–61.
[40a] *Sur une somme exponentielle*, C. R. Acad. Sci. Paris 210 (1940), 520–523.
[40b] *On an exponential sum*, J. Chinese Math. Soc. 2 (1940), 301–312.
[40c] *Sur le problème de Waring relatif à un polynome du troisième degré*, C. R. Acad. Sci.
      Paris 210 (1940), 650–652.
[40d] *On Waring problem with cubic polynomial summands*, J. Indian Math. Soc., (N. S.), 4
      (1940), 127–135.
[42a] *On character sums*, Sci. Record 1 (1942), 21–23.
[42b] *On the least primitive root of a prime*, Bull. Amer. Math. Soc. 48 (1942), 726–730.
[47] *Some results on additive theory of numbers*, Proc. Nat. Acad. Sci. USA 33 (1947),
      136–137.
[49] *An improvement of Vinogradov's mean-value theorem and several applications*, Quart.
      J. Math. (Oxford) 20 (1949), 48–61.
[51] *On exponential sums over an algebraic number field*, Canad. J. Math. 3 (1951), 44–51.
[57] *On the major arcs of Waring problem*, Sci. Record 1 (1957), 17–18.

Hudson, R. H.
[71] *On sequences of consecutive quadratic nonresidues*, J. Number Theory 3 (1971), 178–
      181.
[72] *On the distribution of k-th power nonresidues*, Duke Math. J. 39 (1972), 85–88.
[73a] *A note on Dirichlet characters*, Math. Comput. 27 (1973), 973–975.
[73b] *A bound for the first occurrence of three consecutive integers with equal quadratic
      character*, Duke Math. J. 40 (1973), 33–39.
[77] *On a conjecture of Issai Schur*, J. Reine Angew. Math. 289 (1977), 215–220.

Hudson, R. H., Williams, K. S.

[80] *On the least quadratic nonresidue of a prime $p \equiv 3 \pmod 4$*, J. Reine Angew. Math. 318 (1980), 106–109.

Hull, R.

[32] *The numbers of solutions of congruences involving only k-th powers*, Trans. Amer. Math. Soc. 34 (1932), 908–937.

Hunter, W.

[41] *The representation of numbers by sums of fourth powers*, J. London Math. Soc. 16 (1941), 177–179.

Hurwitz, A.

[84] *Sur la décomposition des nombres en cinq carrés*, C. R. Acad. Sci. Paris, 98 (1884), 504–507, = Math. Werke, II, Basel 1933, pp. 5–7.

[95] *Zur Theorie der algebraischer Zahlen*, Nachr. Ges. Wiss. Göttingen, 1895, pp. 324–331, = Math. Werke, II, Basel 1933, pp. 236–243.

[07] *Somme de trois carrés*, Intérmédiaire des Recherches Math. 14 (1907), 106–107, = Math. Werke, II, Basel 1933, pp. 751.

[08] *Über die Darstellung der ganzen Zahlen als Summen von n-ten Potenzen ganzer Zahlen*, Math. Ann. 65 (1908), 424–427, = Math. Werke, II, Basel 1933, pp. 422–426.

Huxley, M. N.

[72] *On the difference between consecutive primes*, Invent. Math. 15 (1972), 164–170.

Hyyrö, S.

[63] *On the Catalan problem* (Finnish), Arkhimedes 1963, nr. 1, 53–54.

[64] *Über das Catalansche Problem*, Ann. Univ. Turku 79 (1964), 10 pp.

Ingham, A. E.

[37] *On the difference between consecutive primes*, Quart. J. Math. (Oxford) 8 (1937), 255–266.

Inkeri, K.

[60] *Tests for primality*, Annales Acad. Fennicae 279 (1960), 19 pp.

[64] *On Catalan's problem*, Acta Arith. 9 (1964), 285–290.

[79] *On the diophantine equations $2y^2 = 7^k + 1$ and $x^2 + 11 = 3^n$*, Elemente Math. 34 (1979), 119–121.

Inkeri, K., Sirkesalo, J.

[59] *Factorization of certain numbers of the form $h2^m + k$*, Ann. Univ. Turku 138 (1959), 15 pp.

Iseki, K.

[51] *On the imaginary quadratic fields of class number one or two*, Japanese J. Math. 21 (1951), 145–162.

Iwaniec, H.

[71] *On the error term in the linear sieve*, Acta Arith. 19 (1971), 1–30.

[78] *On the problem of Jacobsthal*, Demonstratio Math. 11 (1978), 225–231.

Iwaniec, H., Heath-Brown, D. R. (see D. R. Heath-Brown, H. Iwaniec)

Iwaniec, H., Jutila, M.

[79] *Primes in short intervals*, Arkiv Mat. 17 (1979), 167–176.

Iwaniec, H., Laborde, M.

[81] *P_2 in short intervals*, Ann. Inst. Fourier 31 (1981), 37–56.

Jackson, T. H., Rehman, F.

[74] *Note on difference covers that are not k-sum covers*, Mathematika 21 (1974), 107–109.

Jacobi, C. G. J.

[28]   *Lettre à Legendre, 9 sept. 1828*, Werke, I, Berlin 1881, pp. 422–425.

[29]   *Fundamenta nova theoriae functionum ellipticorum*, Regiomonti 1829 = Werke, I, Berlin 1881, pp. 49–239.

[34]   *De compositione numerorum e quator quadratis*, J. Reine Angew. Math. 12 (1834), 167–172 = Werke, VI, Berlin 1891, pp. 245–251.

[39]   *Canon Arithmeticus*, Berolini 1839, new reworked edition Berlin 1956.

[51]   *Über die Zusammensetzung der Zahlen aus ganzen positiven Cuben; nebst einer Tabelle für die kleinste Cubenanzahl, aus welcher jede Zahl bis* 12 000 *zusammengesetzt werden kann*, J. Reine Angew. Math. 42 (1851), 41–69 = Werke, VI, Berlin 1891, pp. 322–354.

Jacobsthal, E.

[60]   *Über Sequenzen ganzer Zahlen, von denen keine zu n teilerfremd ist, I–V*, Norske Vid. Selsk. Forh. 33 (1960), 117–124, 125–131, 132–139; 34 (1961), 1–7, 110–115.

Jakóbczyk, F.

[51]   *Les applications de la fonction $\lambda_g(n)$ à l'étude des fractions pèriodiques et de la congruence chinoise $2^n - 2 \equiv 0 \pmod{n}$*, Annales Univ. MCS, A5 (1951), 97–138.

James, R. D.

[33]   *The representation of integers as sum of pyramidal numbers*, Math. Ann. 109 (1933), 196–199.

[34a] *The value of the number $g(k)$ in Waring's problem*, Trans. Amer. Math. Soc. 35 (1934), 395–444.

[34b] *On Waring's problem for odd powers*, Proc. London Math. Soc., (2), 37 (1934), 257–291.

[34c] *The representation of integers as sums of values of cubic polynomials*, Amer. J. Math. 56 (1934), 303–315.

[35]   *The constants in Waring's problem for odd powers*, Bull. Amer. Math. Soc. 41 (1935), 689–694.

[37]   *The representation of integers as sums of values of cubic polynomials*, II, Amer. J. Math. 59 (1937), 393–398.

[38]   *On a diophantine equation of the fourth degree*, Proc. London Math. Soc., (2), 44 (1938), 140–148.

Johnsen, J.

[71]   *On the distribution of powers in finite fields*, J. Reine Angew. Math. 251 (1971), 10–19.

Johnson, G. D., Brillhart, J. (see J. Brillhart, G. D. Johnson)

Johnson, L. L.

[40]   *On the diophantine equation $x(x+1)\ldots(x+n-1) = y^k$*, Amer. Math. Monthly 47 (1940), 280–289.

Johnson, W.

[77]   *On the nonvanishing of Fermat quotients* (mod p), J. Reine Angew. Math. 292 (1977), 196–200.

[78]   *On the p-divisibility of the Fermat quotients*, Math. Comput. 32 (1978), 297–301.

Jollensten, R. W.

[76]   *A note on the Egyptian problem*, Proc. Conf. Combinatorics, Group Theory and Computation, Baton Rouge 1976, pp. 351–364.

Joly, J. R.

[70]   *Sommes de puissances d-ièmes dans un anneau commutatif*, Acta Arith. 17 (1970), 37–114.

Jones, B. W.

[49] *The composition of quadratic binary forms*, Amer. Math. Monthly 56 (1949), 380–391.

[50] *The arithmetic theory of quadratic forms*, Buffalo 1950.

Jones, J. P.

[79] *Diophantine representation of Mersenne and Fermat primes*, Acta Arith. 35 (1979), 209–221.

Jones, M. F., Lal, M., Blundon, W. J. (see M. Lal, M. F. Jones, W. J. Blundon)

Joris, H.

[77] *On the evaluation of Gaussian sums for non-primitive Dirichlet characters*, L'Enseign. Math., (2), 23 (1977), 13–18.

Jurkat, W. B., Richert, H. J.

[65] *An improvement of Selberg's sieve method*, I, Acta Arith. 11 (1965), 216–240.

Jutila, M.

[73] *On numbers with a large prime factors*, I, II, J. Indian Math. Soc., (N. S.), 37 (1973), 43–53; 38 (1974), 125–130.

[75] *Prime factors of consecutive integers*, Séminaire Th. des Nombres, Bordeaux, 1975-76, exp. 5, 6 pp.

Jutila, M., Iwaniec, H. (see H. Iwaniec, M. Jutila)

Kamke, E.

[21] *Verallgemeinerungen des Waring–Hilbertschen Satzes*, Math. Ann. 83 (1921), 85–112.

[22] *Bemerkung zum allgemeinen Waringschen Problem*, Math. Zeitschr. 15 (1922), 188–194.

[24] *Zur Arithmetik der Polynome*, Math. Zeitschr. 19 (1924), 247–264.

Kanold, H. J.

[39] *Über eine notwendige Bedingung für die Existenz einer ungeraden vollkommenen Zahl*, Deutsche Math. 4 (1939), 53–57.

[41] *Untersuchungen über ungerade vollkommene Zahlen*, J. Reine Angew. Math. 183 (1941), 98–101.

[42] *Verschärfung einer notwendigen Bedingung für die Existenz einer ungeraden vollkommener Zahl*, J. Reine Angew. Math. 184 (1942), 116–123.

[49] *Folgerungen aus dem Vorkommen einer Gaussschen Primzahl in der Primfaktorzerlegung einer ungerader vollkommenen Zahl*, J. Reine Angew. Math. 186 (1949), 25–29.

[50a] *Sätze über Kreisteilungspolynome und ihre Anwendung auf einige zahlentheoretische Probleme*, J. Reine Angew. Math. 187 (1950), 169–172.

[50b] *Eine Bemerkung zur Verteilung der r-ten Potenznichtreste einer ungeraden Primzahl*, J. Reine Angew. Math. 188 (1950), 74–77.

[50c] *Sätze über Kreisteilungspolynome und ihre Anwendungen auf einige zahlentheoretische Probleme, II*, J. Reine Angew. Math. 188 (1950), 129–146.

[53] *Einige neuere Bedingungen für die Existenz ungerader vollkommener Zahlen*, J. Reine Angew. Math. 192 (1953), 24–34.

[56a] *Über einem Satz von L. E. Dickson*, Math. Ann. 131 (1956), 167–169; *II*, ibidem, 132 (1956), 246–255; *III*, ibidem 137 (1959), 263–268.

[56b] *Eine Bemerkung über die Menge der vollkommenen Zahlen*, Math. Ann. 131 (1956), 390–392.

[57] *Über die Verteilung der vollkommenen Zahlen und allgemeiner Zahlenmengen*, Math. Ann. 132 (1957), 442–450.

[64] *Über Primzahlen in arithmetischen Folgen*, Math. Ann. 156 (1964), 393–395.

[65] *Über Primzahlen in arithmetischen Folgen*, II, Math. Ann. 157 (1965), 358–362.

[67] *Über eine zahlentheoretische Funktion von Jacobsthal*, Math. Ann. 170 (1967), 314–326.

[69] *Über "super perfect numbers"*, Elemente Math. 24 (1969), 61–62.

[75] *Über eine zahlentheoretische Funktion von E. Jacobsthal*, Abhandl. Braunschweig. Wiss. Gesellsch. 25 (1975), 7–10.

[77a] *Über einige Abschätzungen von g(n)*, J. Reine Angew. Math. 290 (1977), 142–153.

[77b] *Neuere Untersuchungen über die Jacobsthal-Funktion g(n)*, Monatsh. Math. 84 (1977), 109–124.

[77c] *Abschätzungen der zahlentheoretischer Funktion g(n)*, Abhandl. Braunschweig. Wiss. Gesellsch. 28 (1977), 65–68.

Kaplansky, I.

[45] *Lucas's test for Mersenne numbers*, Amer. Math. Monthly 52 (1945), 188–190.

[68] *Composition of binary quadratic forms*, Studia Math. 35 (1968), 523–530.

Keates, M.

[68] *On the greatest prime factor of a polynomial*, Proc. Edinburgh Math. Soc., (2), 16 (1968/69). 301–303.

Keller, O. H.

[64] *Darstellungen von Restklassen (mod n) als Summen von zwei Quadraten*, Acta Sci. Math. (Szeged) 26 (1964), 191–192.

Kellogg, O. D.

[21] *On a diophantine problem*, Amer. Math. Monthly 28 (1921), 300–303.

Kempner, A.

[12] *Bemerkungen zum Waringschen Problem*, Math. Ann. 72 (1912), 387–399.

Kenku, M. A.

[71] *Determination of the even discriminants of complex quadratic fields with class number 2*, Proc. London Math. Soc., (3), 22 (1971), 734–746.

Kestelman, H.

[37] *An integral connected with Waring's problem*, J. London Math. Soc. 12 (1937), 232–240.

Khare, S. P., Erdös, P., Gupta, H. (see P. Erdös, H. Gupta, S. P. Khare)

Kishore, M.

[77] *On the number of distinct prime factors of n for which $\varphi(n)|n-1$*, Nieuw Arch. Wisk., (3), 25 (1977), 48–53.

Kisilevsky, H., Boyd, D. W. (see D. W. Boyd, H. Kisilevsky)

Kiss, E.

[59] *Quelques remarques sur une équation diophantienne*, Stud. Cerc. Mat. Acad. RPR 10 (1959), 59–62.

Klee, V. L., Jr.

[46] *On the equation $\varphi(x) = 2m$*, Amer. Math. Monthly 53 (1946), 327–328.

[47] *On a conjecture of Carmichael*, Bull. Amer. Math. Soc. 53 (1947), 1183–1186.

Kloosterman, H. D.

[39] *On the singular series in Waring's problem and in the problem of the representation of integers as a sum of powers of primes*, Indag. Math. 1 (1939), 51–56.

Kloss, K. E.

[65] *Some number-theoretic calculations*, J. Research Nat. Bureau Standards 69 B (1965), 335–336.

Kløve, T.

[72] *Representation of integers as sums of powers with increasing exponents*, Nord. Tidskr. Inform. 12 (1972), 342–346.

Knapowski, S.

[68] *On Siegel's theorem*, Acta Arith. 14 (1968), 417–424.

Knizhnerman, L. A., Sokolinskij, V. Z.

[79] *Certain evaluations of rational trigonometrical sums and sums of Legendre symbols* (Russian), Uspehi Mat. Nauk, 34 (3) (1979), 199–200.

Knobloch, H. W.

[54] *Über Primzahlreihen nebst Anwendung auf ein elementares Dichteproblem*, Abhandl. Math. Seminar Univ. Hamburg 19 (1954), 1–13.

Knödel, W.

[53a] *Carmichaelsche Zahlen*, Math. Nachrichten 9 (1953), 343–350.

[53b] *Eine obere Schranke für die Anzahl der Carmichaelschen Zahlen kleiner als x*, Archiv Math. 4 (1953), 282–284.

Koch, H., Pieper, H.

[76] *Zahlentheorie*, Berlin 1976.

König, R.

[13] *Über quadratische Formen und Zahlkörper, sowie zwei Gruppensätze*, Jahresber. DMV 22 (1913), 239–254.

Körner, O., Stähle, H.

[79] *Remarks on Hua's estimate of complete trigonometrical sums*, Acta Arith. 35 (1979), 353–359.

Korobov, N. M.

[53] *Distribution of non-residues and primitive roots in recurrent series* (Russian), Doklady AN SSSR 88 (1953), 603–606.

Kotov, S. V.

[73] *The greatest prime factor of a polynomial* (Russian), Mat. Zametki 13 (1973), 515–522.

[76] *Über die maximale Norm der Idealteiler des Polynoms $\alpha x^m + \beta y^n$ mit den algebraischen Koeffizienten*, Acta Arith. 31 (1976), 219–230.

Kravitz, S.

[66] *Distribution of Mersenne divisors*, Math. Comput. 20 (1966), 448–449.

[70] *The Lucas–Lehmer test for Mersenne numbers*, Fibonacci Quart. 8 (1970), 1–3.

Kravitz, S., Berg, M.

[64] *Lucas' test for Mersenne numbers*, Math. Comput. 18 (1964), 148–149.

Kravitz, S., Shanks, D. (see D. Shanks, S. Kravitz)

Kronecker, L.

[56] *Sur une formule de Gauss*, J. de math. p. et appl., (2), 1 (1856), 392–395 = *Werke, IV*, Leipzig 1929, pp. 171–175.

[60] *Über die Anzahl der verschiedenen Classen quadratischer Formen von negativer Determinante*, J. Reine Angew. Math. 57 (1860), 248–255 = *Werke, IV*, Leipzig 1929, pp. 185–196.

[64] *Über den Gebrauch der Dirichletschen Methoden in der Theorie der quadratischen Formen*, Monatsber. Kgl. Preuss. Akad. Wissensch., 1864, 285–303 = *Werke, IV*, Leipzig 1929, pp. 227–244.

[80] *Über den vierten Gauss'schen Beweis des Reziprozitätsgesetzes für die quadratische Reste*, Monatsber. Kgl. Preuss. Akad. Wissensch., 1880, 683–698 = *Werke, IV*, Leipzig 1929, pp. 275–294.

[82] *Grundzüge einer arithmetischer Theorie der algebraischen Grössen*, J. Reine Angew. Math. 92 (1882), 1–122 = *Werke, II*, Leipzig 1897, pp. 237–281.

[83] *Über bilineare Formen mit vier Variabeln*, Abhandl. Kgl. Preuss, Akad. Wissensch., 1883, 1–60 = *Werke, II*, Leipzig 1897, pp. 425–495.

[85] *Zur Theorie der elliptischen Functionen*, III, Sitzungsber. Kgl. Preuss. Akad. Wissensch., 1885, 761–784 = *Werke, IV*, Leipzig 1929, pp. 347–495.

[89] *Summirung der Gaussischen Reihen* $\sum_{h=0}^{h=n-1} e^{\frac{2h^2\pi i}{n}}$, J. Reine Angew. Math. 105 (1889), 267–268 = *Werke, IV*, Leipzig 1929, pp. 295–300.

Krubeck, E.

[53] *Über Zerfällung in paarweise ungleiche Polynomwerte*, Math. Zeitschr. 59 (1953), 255–257.

Kubota, K. K., Alter, R. (see R. Alter, K. K. Kubota)

Kubota, R. M.

[74] *Waring's problem for* $F_q[X]$, Dissertationes Math. 117 (1974), 1–60.

Kühnel, U.

[49] *Verschärfung der notwendigen Bedingungen für die Existenz von ungeraden vollkommenen Zahlen*, Math. Zeitschr. 52 (1949), 202–211.

Kummer, E. E.

[42] *Eine Aufgabe, bettreffend die Theorie der cubischen Reste*, J. Reine Angew. Math. 23 (1842), 285–286 = *Collected papers, I*, Springer 1975, pp. 143–144.

[46] *De residuis cubicis disquisitionis nonnullae analyticae*, J. Reine Angew. Math. 32 (1846), 341–359 = *Collected papers, I*, Springer 1975, pp. 145–163.

[47] *Über die Zerlegung der aus Wurzeln der Einheit gebildeten complexen Zahlen in ihre Primfaktoren*, J. Reine Angew. Math. 35 (1847), 327–367 = *Collected papers, I*, Springer 1975, pp. 211–251.

[50] *Bestimmung der Anzahl nicht äquivalenter Classen für die aus λ-ten Wurzeln der Einheit gebildeten complexen Zahlen und die ideale Faktoren derselben*, J. Reine Angew. Math. 40 (1850), 93–116 = *Collected papers, I*, Springer 1975, pp. 298–322.

Kuzel', A. V.

[56] *Elementary solution of Waring's problem for polynomials with Yu. V. Linnik's method* (Russian), Uspehi Mat. Nauk 11 (3) (1956), 165–168.

Laborde, M.

[76] *Équirépartition des solutions du probléme de Waring*, Séminaire Delange–Pisot–Poitou 18 (1976/77), f. 2, exp. 20, 16 pp.

Laborde, M., Iwaniec, H. (see H. Iwaniec, M. Laborde)

Lagrange, J.

[72] *Décomposition d'un entier en somme de carrés et fonction multiplicative*, Séminaire Delange–Pisot–Poitou 14 (1972/73), exp. 1.

Lagrange, J. L.

[70] *Démonstration d'un théorème d'arithmétique*, Nouveaux Mémoires de l'Acad. Royale des Sciences et Belles-Lettres de Berlin, 1770 = *Oeuvres, III*, Paris 1869, pp. 189–201.

[73] *Recherches d'arithmétique, I, II*, Nouveaux Mémoires de l'Acad. Royale des Sciences et Belles-Lettres de Berlin, 1773, 1775 = *Oeuvres, III*, Paris 1869, pp. 695–795.

Lal, M., Jones, M. F., Blundon, W. J.

[66] *Numerical solutions of the Diophantine equation* $y^3 - x^2 = k$, Math. Comput. 20 (1966), 322–325.

Lamprecht, E.

[53] *Allgemeine Theorie der Gaussschen Summen in endlichen kommutativen Ringen*, Math. Nachr. 9 (1953), 149–196.

[57]   *Struktur und Relationen allgemeiner Gaussscher Summen in endlichen Ringen*, J. Reine Angew. Math. 197 (1957), 1–26, 27–48.

Landau, E.

[02]   *Über die Klassenzahl der binären quadratischen Formen von negativer Discriminante*, Math. Ann. 56 (1902), 671–676.

[07]   *Über die Darstellung einer ganzen Zahl als Summe von Biquadraten*, Rendiconti Circ. Mat. Palermo 23 (1907), 91–96.

[09]   *Über eine Anwendung der Primzahltheorie auf das Waringsche Problem in der elementaren Zahlentheorie*, Math. Ann. 66 (1909), 102–105.

[12]   *Über die Anzahl der Gitterpunkte in gewisser Bereichen*, Nachr. Ges. Wiss. Göttingen, 1912, 687–771.

[18]   *Über die Klassenzahl imaginär-quadratischer Zahlkörper*, Nachr. Ges. Wiss. Göttingen, 1918, 285–295.

[21]   *Zur Hardy–Littlewoodschen Lösung des Waringschen Problems*, Nachr. Ges. Wiss. Göttingen, 1921, 88–92.

[22]   *Zum Waringschen Problem*, Math. Zeitschr. 12 (1922), 219–247.

[26a] *Zum Waringschen Problem*, Proc. London Math. Soc., (2), 25 (1926), 484–486.

[26b] *Die Winogradovsche Methode zum Beweise des Waring–Kamkeschen Satzes*, Acta Math. 48 (1926), 217–253.

[26c] *On the representation of a number as the sum of two k-th powers*, J. London Math. Soc. 1 (1926), 72–74.

[27a] *Vorlesungen über Zahlentheorie, I*, Leipzig 1927.

[27b] *Über Dirichletsche Reihen mit komplexen Charakteren*, J. Reine Angew. Math. 157 (1927), 26–31.

[30a] *Zum Waringschen Problem, II*, Math. Zeitschr. 31 (1930), 149–150.

[30b] *Über die neue Winogradoffsche Behandlung des Waringschen Problems*, Math. Zeitschr. 31 (1930), 319–338.

[30c] *Zum Waringschen Problem, III*, Math. Zeitschr. 32 (1930), 699–702.

[35]   *Bemerkungen zum Heilbronnschen Satz*, Acta Arith. 1 (1935), 1–18.

Landau, E., Davenport, H. (see H. Davenport, E. Landau)

Landau, E., Ostrowski, A.

[20]   *On the diophantine equation $ay^2 + by + c = dx^n$*, Proc. London Math. Soc., (2), 19 (1920), 276–280.

Lander, L. J., Parkin, T. R.

[67]   *On first appearance of prime differences*, Math. Comput. 21 (1967), 483–488.

Lang, S.

[64]   *Algebraic numbers*, Reading 1964.

Langevin, M.

[75a] *Plus grand facteur premier d'entiers consécutifs*, C. R. Acad. Sci. Paris 280 (1975), A 1567–1570.

[75b] *Plus grand facteur premier d'entiers voisins*, C. R. Acad. Sci. Paris 281 (1975), A 491–493.

[76a] *Quelques applications de nouveaux resultats de van der Poorten*, Séminaire Delange–Pisot–Poitou 17 (1975/76), nr. G12, 11 pp.

[76b] *Plus grand facteur premier d'entiers en progression arithmétique*, Séminaire Delange–Pisot–Poitou 18 (1976/77), f. 1, exp. 3, 7 pp.

Lebesgue, V. A.

[44]   *Note sur les nombres parfaites*, Nouv. Annales Math. 3 (1844), 552–553.

[50]   *Sur l'impossibilité en nombres entiers de l'équation $x^m = y^2 + 1$*, Nouv. Annales Math. 9 (1850), 178–181.

[59] *Exercises d'analyse numérique*, Paris 1859.
[60a] *Théorème sur cinq nombres consecutifs*, Nouv. Annales Math. 19 (1860), 112–115.
[60b] *Remarque sur l'article de la page 112*, Nouv. Annales Math. 19 (1860), 135–136.
[67] C. R. Acad. Sci. Paris 64 (1867), 1268–1269.

Legendre, A. M.
[98] *Essai sur la théorie des nombres*, Paris 1798. (III ed. *Théorie des nombres*, Paris 1830).

Lehmer, D. H.
[30] *An extended theory of Lucas' functions*, Annals of Math., (2), 31 (1930), 419–448.
[32] *On Euler's totient function*, Bull. Amer. Math. Soc. 38 (1932), 745–751.
[33] *On imaginary quadratic fields whose class-number is unity*, Bull. Amer. Math. Soc. 39 (1933), 360.
[35] *On Lucas's test for the primality of Mersenne's numbers*, J. London Math. Soc. 10 (1935), 162–165.
[64] *On a problem of Størmer*, Illinois J. Math. 8 (1964), 57–79.
[65] *The prime factors of consecutive integers*, Amer. Math. Monthly 72 (1965), nr. 2, part II, 19–20.
[76] *Strong Carmichael numbers*, J. Austral. Math. Soc. 21 (1976), 508–510.
[81] *On Fermat's quotient, base 2*, Math. Comput. 36 (1981), 289–290.

Lehmer, D. H., Brillhart, J., Selfridge, J. L. (see J. Brillhart, D. H. Lehmer, J. L. Selfridge)

Lehmer, D. H., Brillhart, J., Selfridge, J. L., Tuckerman, B., Wagstaff, S. S., Jr. (see J. Brillhart et al.)

Lehmer, D. H., Lehmer, E.
[62] *Heuristics, anyone?* In: *Studies in mathematical analysis and related topics*, Stanford 1962, 202–210.

Lehmer, E.
[51] *The quintic character of 2 and 3*, Duke Math. J. 18 (1951), 11–18.
[56] *On the location of Gauss sums*, Math. Tables Aids Comput. 10 (1956), 194–202.

Lehmer, E., Lehmer, D. H. (see D. H. Lehmer, E. Lehmer).
Lekkerkerker, C. G.
[53] *Prime factors of the elements of certain sequences of integers, I, II*, Indagat. Math. 15 (1953), 265–276, 277–280.

Lenstra, H. W., Jr.
[77] *On Artin's conjecture and Euclid's algorithm in global fields*, Invent. Math. 42 (1977), 201–224.

Leopoldt, H. W.
[59] *Über die Hauptordnung der ganzen Elemente eines abelschen Zahlkörpers*, J. Reine Angew. Math. 201 (1959), 119–149.
[62] *Zur Arithmetik in abelschen Zahlkörpern*, J. Reine Angew. Math. 209 (1962), 54–71.
[66] *Lösung einer Aufgabe von Kostrikhin*, J. Reine Angew. Math. 221 (1966), 160–161.

Lerch, M.
[03] *Über die arithmetische Gleichung* $Cl(-\Delta) = 1$, Math. Ann. 57 (1903), 569–570.

Leveque, W. J.
[52] *On the equation* $a^x - b^y = 1$, Amer. J. Math. 74 (1952), 325–331.
[56] *Topics in number theory*, Reading 1956.
[64] *On the equation* $y^m = f(x)$, Acta Arith. 9 (1964), 209–219.
[74] (editor) *Reviews in Number Theory*, Providence 1974.

Levine, E., Beresin, M. (see M. Beresin, E. Levine)

Lewis, D. J.

[61]   *Two classes of Diophantine equations*, Pacific J. Math. 11 (1961), 1063–1067.

Lewis, D. J., Chowla, S., Dunton, M. (see S. Chowla, M. Dunton, D. J. Lewis)

Lewis, D. J., Chowla, S., Skolem, Th. (see Th. Skolem, S. Chowla, D. J. Lewis)

Lewis, D. J., Davenport, H., Schinzel, A. (see H. Davenport, D. J. Lewis, A. Schinzel)

Lieuwens, E.

[70]   *Do there exist composite numbers M for which $k\varphi(M) = M - 1$ holds?* Nieuw Arch. Wisk., (3), 18 (1970), 165–169.

Linfoot, E., Heilbronn, H. (see H. Heilbronn, E. Linfoot)

Linnik, Yu. V. (Linnik, U. V.)

[42]   *A remark on the least quadratic non-residue* (Russian), Doklady AN SSSR 36 (1942), 119–120 = Izbr. Trudy I, Leningrad 1979, pp. 296–297.

[43a] *On the decomposition of large integers into seven cubes* (Russian), Matem. Sbornik. 12 (1943), 218–224 = Izbr. Trudy I, Leningrad 1979, pp. 122–131.

[43b] *Elementary solution of Waring's problem by Schnirelman's method* (Russian), Matem. Sbornik 12 (1943), 225–230 = Izbr. Trudy I, Leningrad 1979, pp. 297–303.

[43c] *The analogy property of L-series and Siegel's theorem* (Russian), Doklady AN SSSR 38 (1943), 115–117 = Izbr. Trudy I, Leningrad 1979, pp. 314–316.

[50]   *Elementary proof of Siegel's theorem based on the method of I. M. Vinigradov* (Russian), Izvestia AN SSSR, ser. mat., 14 (1950), 327–342 = Izbr. Trudy II, Leningrad 1980. pp. 44–59.

[61]   *The dispersion method in binary additive problems* (Russian), Leningrad 1961.

Linnik, Yu. V., Gelfond, A. O. (see A. O. Gelfond, Yu. V. Linnik)

Linnik, Yu. V., Vinogradov, A. I.

[66]   *Hyperelliptical curves and the smallest prime quadratic residue* (Russian), Doklady AN SSSR 168 (1966), 259–261 = Linnik, Izbr. Tr. II, Leningrad 1980, pp. 166–169.

Liouville, J.

[57]   *Sur le produit $m(m+1)(m+2)\ldots(m+n-1)$*, J. de math. p. et appl. (2), 2 (1857), 277–278.

Littlewood, J. E., Hardy, G. H. (see G. H. Hardy, J. E. Littlewood)

Litver, E. L., Yudina, G. E.

[71]   *Primitive roots for prime numbers of the first million and their powers* (Russian), In: *Matematičeskij analiz i ego priloženija*, III, Rostov 1971, pp. 106–109.

Ljunggren, W.

[63]   *On the diophantine equation $y^2 - k = x^3$*, Acta Arith. 8 (1962/63), 451–463.

London, H.

[68]   *On the diophantine equation $y^2 + p^2 = x^3$*, Amer. Math. Monthly 75 (1968), 56.

London, H., Finkelstein, R. (see also R. Finkelstein, H. London)

[73]   *On Mordell's equation $y^2 - k = x^3$*, Bowling Green State University 1973.

Lord, G.

[75]   *Even perfect and super perfect numbers*, Elemente Math. 30 (1975), 87–88.

Loxton, J. H.

[74]   *Products related to Gauss sums*, J. Reine Angew. Math. 268/9 (1974), 53–67.

[76]   *On the determination of Gauss sums*, Séminaire Delange–Pisot–Poitou 18 (1976/77), f. 2, exp. 27, 12 pp.

[78]   *Some conjectures concerning Gauss sums*, J. Reine Angew. Math. 297 (1978), 153–158.

Lucas, É.

  [77]   *On the interpretation of a passage in Mersenne's works,* Messenger of Mathematics 7 (1877/78), 185–187.

  [78a]   *Sur la décomposition des nombres en bicarrés,* Nouv. Corresp. Math. 4 (1878), 323–325.

  [78b]   *Sur un théorème de M. Liouville, concernant la décomposition des nombres en bicarrés,* Nouv. Annales Math., (2), 17 (1878), 536–537.

  [78c]   *Théorie des fonctions numériques simplement périodiques,* Amer. J. Math. 1 (1878), 184–240, 289–321.

Lunnon, W. F., Ellison, W. J., Pesek, J., Stall, D. S. (see W. J. Ellison et al.)

Maass, H.

  [38]   *Konstruktion ganzer Modulformen halbzahliger Dimension mit θ-Multiplikatoren in einer und zweier Variabeln,* Abh. Math. Seminar Univ. Hamburg 12 (1938), 133–162.

Mahler, K.

  [33]   *Zur Approximation algebraischer Zahlen I: Über den grössten Primteiler binärer Formen,* Math. Ann. 107 (1933), 691–730.

  [34a]   *Über die Darstellung einer Zahl als Summe von drei Biquadraten,* Mathematica (Leiden) 3 (1934), 69–72.

  [34b]   *On Hecke's theorem on the real zeros of the L-functions and the class number of quadratic fields,* J. London Math. Soc. 9 (1934), 298–302.

  [35a]   *Über den grössten Primteiler der Polynome $X^2 \mp 1$,* Arch. Math. og Naturvid. 41 (1) (1935), 1–8.

  [35b]   *Über den grössten Primteiler spezieller Polynome zweiten Grades,* Arch. Math. og Naturvid. 41 (6) (1935), 1–26.

  [36]   *Note on hypothesis K of Hardy and Littlewood,* J. London Math. Soc. 11 (1936), 136–138.

  [53]   *On the greatest prime factor of $ax^m + by^n$,* Nieuw Arch. Wisk., (2), 1 (1953), 113–122.

  [57]   *On the fractional parts of the powers of a rational number, II,* Mathematika 4 (1957), 122–124.

  [64]   *Inequalities for ideal bases in algebraic number fields,* J. Austral. Math. Soc. 4 (1964), 425–448.

Mahler, K., Erdös, P. (see P. Erdös, K. Mahler)

Maillet, E.

  [95]   *Sur la décomposition d'un nombre entier en une somme de cubes d'entiers positifs,* C. R. II session Assoc. Francaise pour l'avancement des sciences, II, Bordeaux 1895, pp. 242–247.

  [96]   *Quelques extensions du théorème de Fermat sur les nombres polygones,* J. de math. p. et appl., (5), 2 (1896), 363–380.

  [08]   *Sur la décomposition d'un entier en une somme de puissances huitièmes d'entiers,* Bull. Soc. Math. France 36 (1908), 69–77.

Mąkowski, A.

  [62]   *Three consecutive integers cannot be powers,* Colloq. Math. 9 (1962), 297.

Mann, H. B.

  [55]   *Introduction to Algebraic Number Theory,* Columbus 1955.

Manning, H. P., Chace, A. B., Archibald, A. R. (see A. B. Chace, H. P. Manning, A. R. Archibald)

Marsh, D. C. B.

  [57]   *Solution of E 1221,* Amer. Math. Monthly 64 (1957), 110.

Matthews, C. R.

  [79a]   *Gauss sums and elliptic functions, I,* Invent. Math. 52 (1979), 163–185.

  [79b]   *Gauss sums and elliptic functions, II,* Invent. Math. 53 (1979), 23–52.

Matthews, K. R.

[76]   *A generalisation of Artin's conjecture for primitive roots*, Acta Arith. 29 (1976), 113–146.

McDaniel, W. L.

[70]   *The non-existence of odd perfect numbers of a certain form*, Archiv Math. 21 (1970), 52–53.

McDaniel, W. L., Hagis, P., Jr. (see P. Hagis, Jr., W. L. McDaniel)

McGettrick, A. D.

[72]   *On the biquadratic Gauss sum*, Proc. Cambridge Philos. Soc. 71 (1972), 79–83.

Meffroy, J.

[72]   *Sur les solutions paires de l'équation d'Euler $\varphi(x) = 2^a 3^b$*, C. R. Acad. Sci. Paris 275 (1972), A 1277–1280.

[75]   *Sur une classe de solutions paires de l'équation d'Euler $\varphi(x) = 2^a 3^b$*, C. R. Acad. Sci. Paris 280 (1975), A 611–614.

[77]   *Sur une classe de solutions impaires de l'équation de Euler $\varphi(x) = 2^a 3^b$*, C. R. Acad. Sci. Paris 284 (1977), 1097–1100.

Meissner, W.

[13]   *Über die Teilbarkeit von $2^p - 2$ durch das Quadrat der Primzahl $p = 1093$*, Sitz.-Ber. Preuss. Akad. Wissensch., 1913, pp. 663–667.

Mendelsohn, N. S.

[76]   *The equation $\varphi(x) = k$*, Mathematical Magazine 49 (1976), 37–39.

Mertens, F.

[05]   *Ein Beweis des Satzes, dass jede Klasse von ganzzahligen primitiven binären quadratischen Formen des Hauptgeschlechts durch Duplikation entsteht*, J. Reine Angew. Math. 129 (1905), 181–186.

Mientka, W.

[61]   *An application of the Selberg sieve method*, J. Indian Math. Soc., (N. S.), 25 (1961), 129–138.

Mignotte, M.

[73]   *Sur les coefficients du binôme*, Archiv Math. 24 (1973), 162–163.

Miller, J. C. P.

[51]   *Large primes*, Eureka 1951, nr. 14, 10–11.

Miller, J. C. P., Western, A. E. (see A. E. Western, J. C. P. Miller)

Min, S. H.

[49]   *On the order of $\zeta(\frac{1}{2}+it)$*, Trans. Amer. Math. Soc. 65 (1949), 448–472.

Minkowski, H.

[87]   *Mèmoire sur la théorie des formes quadratiques à coefficients entières*, Mèmoires pres. par divers savants à l'Acadèmie, 29, 1887, nr. 2, 1–178 = Gesamm. Math. Abhandl., I, Leipzig, Berlin 1911, pp. 3–144.

[91]   *Über die positiven quadratischen Formen und über kettenbruchähnliche Algorithmen*, J. Reine Angew. Math. 107 (1891), 278–297 = Gesamm. Math. Abhandl., I, Leipzig, Berlin 1911, pp. 244–260.

Mirsky, L.

[49]   *The number of representations of an integer as the sum of a prime and a k-free integer*, Amer. Math. Monthly 56 (1949), 17–19.

Mitchell, H. H.

[25]   *On classes of ideals in a quadratic field*, Ann. of Math., (2), 27 (1925), 297–314.

Mit'kin, D. A.

[75]   *On estimates of rational trigonometrical sums of a special form* (Russian), Doklady AN SSSR 224 (1975), 760–763.

Mohanty, S. P.

[73] *A note on Mordell's equation $y^2 = x^3 + k$,* Proc. Amer. Math. Soc. 39 (1973), 645–646.

[75] *On consecutive integer solutions for $y^2 - k = x^3$,* Proc. Amer. Math. Soc. 48 (1975), 281–285.

Möller, H.

[72] *Zur Verteilung der Restindizes ganzer Zahlen,* Peschl-Festband, 1972, Bonn 1972, pp. 83–98.

[76a] *Imaginär-quadratische Zahlkörper mit einklassigen Geschlechtern,* Acta Arith. 30 (1976), 179–186.

[76b] *Verallgemeinerung eines Satzes von Rabinowitsch über imaginär-quadratische Zahlkörper,* J. Reine Angew. Math. 285 (1976), 100–113.

Montgomery, H. L.

[69] *Zeros of L-functions,* Invent. Math. 8 (1969), 346–354.

[71] *Topics in multiplicative number theory,* Lecture Notes in Math. 227, Springer, 1971.

Montgomery, H. L., Fujii, A., Gallagher, P. X. (see A. Fujii, P. X. Gallagher, H. L. Montgomery)

Montgomery, H. L., Vaughan, R. C.

[77] *Exponential sums with multiplicative coefficients,* Invent. Math. 43 (1977), 69–82.

[79] *Mean values of character sums,* Canad. J. Math. 31 (1979), 476–487.

Montgomery, H. L., Weinberger, P. J.

[74] *Notes on small class numbers,* Acta Arith. 24 (1974), 529–542.

Monzingo, M. G.

[76] *On consecutive primitive roots,* Fibonacci Quart. 14 (1976), 391–394.

Mordell, L. J.

[14] *The diophantine equation $y^2 - k = x^3$,* Proc. London Math. Soc., (2), 13 (1914), 60–80.

[18a] *The class number for definite binary quadratics,* Messenger of Mathematics 47 (1918), 138–142.

[18b] *On a simple summation of the series $\sum_{s=0}^{n-1} e^{2s^2 \pi i/n}$,* Messenger of Mathematics 48 (1918), 54–56.

[22] *Note on the integer solutions of the equation $Ey^2 = Ax^3 + Bx^2 + Cx + D$,* Messenger of Mathematics 51 (1922), 169–171.

[23] *On the integer solutions of the equation $ey^2 = ax^3 + bx^2 + cx + d$,* Proc. London Math. Soc. (2), 21 (1923), 415–419.

[29] *Kronecker's fundamental limit formula in the theory of numbers and elliptic functions and similar theorems,* Proc. Royal Soc. London 125 (1929), 262–276.

[32] *On a sum analogous to Gauss's sum,* Quart. J. Math. (Oxford) 3 (1932), 161–167.

[34] *On the Riemann hypothesis and imaginary quadratic fields with a given class number,* J. London Math. Soc. 9 (1934), 289–298.

[36] *On the four integer cubes problem,* J. London Math. Soc. 11 (1936), 208–218, corr. ibidem 32 (1957), 383.

[47a] *On some Diophantine equations $y^2 = x^3 + k$ with no rational solutions,* Arch. Math. og Naturvid. 49 (1947), 143–150; II. in: *Number Theory and Analysis,* New York 1969, pp. 223–232.

[47b] *A chapter in the theory of numbers,* Cambridge 1947.

[58] *On the representation of a number as a sum of three squares,* Rev. Math. Pures Appl. 3 (1958), 25–27.

[60a] *The diophantine equations $2^n = x^2 + 7$,* Arkiv Mat. 4 (1960), 455–460.

[60b] *The representation of integers by three positive squares*, Michigan Math. J. 7 (1960), 289–290.

[62a] *The sign of the Gaussian sum*, Illinois J. Math. 6 (1962), 177–180.

[62b] *On a cyclotomic resolvent*, Archiv Math. 13 (1962), 486–487.

[66] *The infinity of rational solutions of $y^2 = x^3 + k$*, J. London Math. Soc. 41 (1966), 523–525.

[71] *On the representations of positive integers as sums of three cubes of positive rational numbers*, Mathematika 18 (1971), 98–99.

Moreno, C. J.

[74] *Sur le problème de Kummer*, L'Enseign. Math., (2), 20 (1974), 45–51.

Moser, L.

[63] *Notes on number theory, V. Insolvability of $\binom{2n}{n} = \binom{2a}{a}\binom{2b}{b}$*, Canad. Math. Bull. 6 (1963), 167–169.

Motohashi, Y.

[79] *A note on almost-primes in short intervals*, Proc. Japan Acad. 55 (1979), 225–226.

Murty, M. R., Murty, V. K.

[79] *Some results in number theory, I*, Acta Arith. 35 (1979), 367–371.

Muskat, J. B.

[66] *On divisors of odd perfect numbers*, Math. Comput. 20 (1966), 141–144.

Nagell, T.

[21a] *Des équation indéterminées $x^2 + x + 1 = y^n$ et $x^2 + x + 1 = 3y^n$*, Norsk. mat. For. Skr. 2 (1921), 12–14.

[21b] *Généralisation d'un théorème de Tchebycheff*, J. de Math. p. et appl., (8), 4 (1921), 343–356.

[22] *Zur Arithmetik der Polynome*, Abhandl. Math. Seminar Univ. Hamburg 1 (1922), 180–194.

[23] *Sur l'impossibilité de quelques équations a deux indéterminées*, Norsk. Mat. Forenings Skr. I, Nr. 13, 1923.

[37] *Über den grössten Primteiler gewisser Polynome dritten Grades*, Math. Ann. 114 (1937), 284–292.

[48] *The diophantine equation $x^2 + 7 = 2^n$* (Norwegian), Nordisk Mat. Tidskr. 30 (1948), 62–64. English version: Arkiv Mat. 4 (1961), 185–187.

[50] *Sur les restes et les non-restes quadratiques suivant un module premier*, Arkiv Mat. 1 (1950), 185–193.

[52] *Sur le plus petite nonreste quadratique impair*, Arkiv Mat. 1 (1952), 573–578.

[54] *On the solvability of some congruences*, Norsk. Vid. Selsk. Forh. 27 (1954), 1–5.

[55] *Contributions to the theory of a category of Diophantine equations of the second degree with two unknowns*, Nova Acta Soc. Sci. Uppsal., (4), 16 (1955), nr. 2, 38 pp.

Nagura, J.

[52] *On the integral containing at least one prime number*, Proc. Japan Acad. 28 (1952), 177–181.

Nair, M.

[78] *A note on the equation $x^3 - y^2 = k$*, Quart. J. Math. (Oxford) 29 (1978), 483–487.

Nakayama, M.

[39] *On the decomposition of a rational number into "Stammbrüche"*, Tôhoku Math. J. 46 (1939), 1–21.

Narasimhamurti, V.

[41] *On Warings problem for 8th, 9th and 10th powers*, J. Indian Math. Soc., (N. S.), 5 (1941), 122.

Narkiewicz, W.

[74] *Elementary and analytic theory of algebraic numbers*, Warszawa 1974.

Narumi, S.

[17] *An extension of a theorem of Liouville's*, Tôhoku Math. J. 11 (1917), 128–142.

Nathanson, M. B.

[74] *Catalan's equation in $K(t)$*, Amer. Math. Monthly 81 (1974), 371–373.

Nechaev, V. I.

[51] *Waring's problem for polynomials* (Russian), Trudy Mat. Inst. im. Steklova 38 (1951), 190–243.

[53] *On the representation of natural numbers as sums of summands of the form $\dfrac{x(x+1)\dots(x+k-1)}{k!}$* (Russian), Izvestia AN SSSR, ser. mat., 17 (1953), 485–498.

[75] *Estimate of the complete rational trigonometric sum* (Russian), Matem. Zametki 17 (1975), 839–843.

Nechaev, V. I., Polosuev, A. M.

[64] *On the distribution of non-residues and primitive roots in sequences satisfying a finite-difference equation with polynomial coefficients* (Russian), Vestnik Moskovsk. Gos. Univ. 19 (1964), nr. 6, 75–84.

Nechaev, V. I., Stepanova, L. L.

[65] *Distribution of non-residues and primitive roots in recurrence sequences over an algebraic number field* (Russian), Uspehi Mat. Nauk 20 (1965), nr. 3, 197–203.

Neumann, J. v., Goldstine, H. H.

[53] *A numerical study of a conjecture of Kummer*, Math. Tables Aids Comput. 7 (1953), 133–134.

Newman, D. J.

[60] *A simplified proof of Waring's conjecture*, Michigan Math. J. 7 (1960), 291–295.

Nickel, L., Noll, C. (see C. Noll, L. Nickel)

Nikishin, E. M.

[79] *On logarithms of natural numbers* (Russian), Izvestia AN SSSR, ser. mat., 43 (1979), 1319–1327.

Niven, I.

[44] *An unsolved case of the Waring problem*, Amer. J. Math. 66 (1944), 137–143.

Noll, C., Nickel, L.

[80] *The 25th and 26th Mersenne primes*, Math. Comput. 35 (1980), 1387–1390.

Norton, K. K.

[61] *Remarks on the number of factors of an odd perfect number*, Acta Arith. 6 (1960/61), 365–374.

[71] *Numbers with small prime factors, and the least k-th power non-residue*, Memoirs Amer. Math. Soc. 106 (1971), 1–106.

Obláth, R.

[33] *Über Produkte aufeinanderfolgenden Zahlen*, Tôhoku J. Math. 38 (1933), 73–92.

[49] *Sur l'équation diophantienne $\dfrac{4}{n} = \dfrac{1}{x_1} + \dfrac{1}{x_2} + \dfrac{1}{x_3}$*, Mathesis 59 (1949), 308–316.

[51] *Eine Bemerkung über Produkte aufeinanderfolgender Zahlen*, J. Indian Math. Soc., (N. S.), 15 (1951), 135–139.

Odoni, R. W. K.

[73] *On Gauss sums (mod p^n)*, Bull. London Math. Soc. 5 (1973), 325–327.

[81] *A conjecture of Krishnamurthy on decimal periods and some allied problems,* J. Number Theory 13 (1981), 303–319.

Odoni, R. W. K., Cohen, S. D., Stothers, W. W. (see S. D. Cohen, R. W. K. Odoni, W. W. Stothers)

Orde, H. L. S.
[78] *On Dirichlet's class number formula,* J. London Math. Soc. 18 (1978), 409–420.

Osborn, R.
[61] *Tables of all primitive roots of odd primes less than 1000,* Austin 1961.

Osgood, C. F., Wisner, R. J.
[61] *New proof of a theorem on decimal periodicity,* Publicat. Math. (Debrecen) 8 (1961), 360–367.

Ostrowski, A.
[21] *Bemerkung zur Hardy–Littlewoodschen Lösung des Waringschen Problems,* Math. Zeitschr. 9 (1921), 28–34.

Ostrowski, A., Landau, E. (see E. Landau, A. Ostrowski)

Otramare, G.
[94] Intérmédiaire des math. 1 (1894), 25.

Page, A.
[35] *On the number of primes in an arithmetic progression,* Proc. London Math. Soc., (2), 39 (1935), 116–141.

Palamá, G.
[59] *Su di una congettura di Schinzel,* Boll. Un. Mat. Ital., (3), 14 (1959), 82–94.

Paley, R. E. A. C.
[32] *A theorem on characters,* J. London Math. Soc. 7 (1932), 28–32.
[33] *Theorems on polynomials in a Galois field,* Quart. J. Math. (Oxford) 4 (1933), 52–63.

Pall, G.
[30] *On the number of representations of a square, or a constant times a square, as the sum of an odd number of squares,* J. London Math. Soc. 5 (1930), 102–105.
[31] *Sums of four and more values of $ux^2 + vx$ for integers x,* Bull. Amer. Math. Soc. 37 (1931), 267–270.
[32a] *Large positive integers are sums of four and five values of a quadratic function,* Amer. J. Math. 54 (1932), 66–78.
[32b] *On sums of two or four values of a quadratic function of x,* Trans. Amer. Math. Soc. 34 (1932), 98–125.
[73] *Some aspects of Gaussian composition,* Acta Arith. 24 (1973), 405–409.

Pall, G., Butts, H. S. (see H. S. Butts, G. Pall)
Parker, T., Dressler, R. E. (see R. E. Dressler, T. Parker)
Parkin, T. R., Lander, L. J. (see L. J. Lander, T. R. Parkin)
Parthasarathy, M.
[53] *On the representation of an integer as the sum of three fourth powers,* Proc. Amer. Math. Soc. 4 (1953), 523–527.

Patterson, S. J.
[78] *On the distribution of Kummer sums,* J. Reine Angew. Math. 303/304 (1978), 126–143.

Patterson, S. J., Heath-Brown D. R. (see D. R. Heath-Brown, S. J. Patterson)
Pearson, E. H.
[63] *On the congruences $(p-1)! \equiv -1$ and $2^{p-1} \equiv 1 \pmod{p^2}$,* Math. Comput. 17 (1963), 194–195.

Peirce, B.
[32] The Mathematical Diary 2 (1832), 267–277.

Pepin, T.

[92] *Démonstration du théorème de Fermat sur les nombres polygones*, Atti dei Lincei 46 (1892/3), 119–131.

[98] *Étude sur les nombres parfaits*, Memorie Acad. Pontif. Nuovi Lincei 13 (1898), 345–420.

Pervushin, I. M.

[87] Bull. Acad. Sci. St. Petersbourg 31 (1887), 532.

Pesek, J., Ellison, W. J., Ellison, F., Stahl, C. E., Stall, D. S. (see W. J. Ellison et al.)

Pesek, J., Ellison, W. J., Stall, D. S., Lunnon, W. F. (see W. J. Ellison et al.)

Peters, M.

[80] *Definite binary quadratic forms with class number one*, Acta Arith. 36 (1980), 271–272.

Pieper, H., Koch, H. (see H. Koch, H. Pieper)

Pillai, S. S.

[28] *On the representation of a number as the sum of two positive k-th powers*, J. London Math. Soc. 3 (1928), 56–61, corr. 83.

[29] *On some functions connected with $\varphi(n)$*, Bull. Amer. Math. Soc. 35 (1929), 832–836.

[31] *On the inequality "$0 < a^x - b^y \leqslant n$"*, J. Indian Math. Soc. 19 (1931), 1–11.

[36a] *On Waring's problem*, J. Indian Math. Soc., (N. S.), 2 (1936), 16–44.

[36b] *On Waring's problem, II*, J. Annamalai Univ. 5 (1936), 145–166.

[36c] *On $a^x - b^y = c$*, J. Indian Math. Soc., (N. S.), 2 (1936), 119–122.

[36d] *On Waring's problem, III*, J. Annamalai Univ. 6 (1936), 50–53.

[36e] *On Waring's problem, IV*, J. Annamalai Univ. 6 (1936), 54–64.

[37a] *On Waring's problem, V*, J. Indian Math. Soc., (N. S.), 2 (1937), 213–214.

[37b] *On Waring's problem, VI, Polynomial summands*, J. Annam. Univ. 6 (1937), 171–197.

[40a] *On m consecutive integers, I*, Proc. Nat. Acad. Sci. India, Sect. A., 11 (1940), 6–12.

[40b] *On m consecutive integers, II*, Proc. Nat. Acad. Sci. India, Sect. A., 11 (1940), 73–80.

[40c] *On Waring's problem $g(6) = 73$*, Proc. Nat. Acad. Sci. India. Sect. A, 12 (1940), 30–40.

[40d] *Waring's problem with indices $\geqslant n$*, Proc. Nat. Acad. Sci. India, Sect. A, 12 (1940), 41–45.

[41] *On m consecutive integers, III*, Proc. Nat. Acad. Sci. India, Sect. A, 13 (1941), 530–533.

[44a] *On m consecutive integers, IV*, Bull. Calcutta Math. Soc. 36 (1944), 99–101.

[44b] *On the smallest primitive root of a prime*, J. Indian Math. Soc. 8 (1944), 14–17.

[45] *On the equation $2^x - 3^y = 2^X + 3^Y$*, Bull. Calcutta Math. Soc. 37 (1945), 15–20.

Pillai, S. S., Chowla, S. D. (see also S. Chowla, S. S. Pillai)

[30] *On the error terms in some asymptotic formulae in the theory of numbers, I*, J. London Math. Soc. 5 (1930), 95–101.

Pintz, J.

[74a] *On Siegel's theorem*, Acta Arith. 24 (1973-74), 543–551.

[74b] *On the Brauer–Siegel theorem*, Coll. Math. J. Bólyai, Number Theory, Debrécen 1974, North-Holland 1976, pp. 259–265.

[76a] *Elementary methods in the theory of L-functions, I, Hecke's theorem*, Acta Arith. 31 (1976), 53–60.

[76b] *Elementary methods in the theory of L-functions, II, On the greatest zero of a real L-function*, Acta Arith. 31 (1976), 273–289.

[76c] *Elementary methods in the theory of L-functions, IV, The Heilbronn phenomenon*, Acta Arith. 31 (1976), 419–429.

[77a] *Elementary methods in the theory of L-functions, VI, On the least prime quadratic residue (mod p)*, Acta Arith. 32 (1977), 173–178.

[77b] *Elementary methods in the theory of L-functions, VII, Upper bound for $L(1, \chi)$*, Acta Arith. 32 (1977), 397–406.

[77c] *Elementary methods in the theory of L-functions, VIII, Real zeros of real L-functions*, Acta Arith. 33 (1977), 89–98.

Polosuev, A. M., Nechaev, V. I. (see V. I. Nechaev, A. M. Polosuev)

Pólya, G.

[18a] *Über die Verteilung der quadratischer Reste und Nichtreste*, Nachr. Ges. Wissensch. Göttingen 1918, pp. 21–29.

[18b] *Zur arithmetischer Untersuchung der Polynome*, Math. Zeitschr. 1 (1918), 143–148.

Pomerance, C.

[74a] *Odd perfect numbers are divisible by at least seven distinct primes*, Acta Arith. 25 (1974), 265–300.

[74b] *On Carmichaels conjecture*, Proc. Amer. Math. Soc. 43 (1974), 297–298.

[75a] *The second largest prime factor of an odd perfect number*, Math. Comput. 29 (1975), 914–921.

[75b] *On the congruences $\sigma(n) \equiv a(\bmod n)$ and $n \equiv a(\bmod \varphi(n))$*, Acta Arith. 26 (1975), 265–272.

[76] *On composite n for which $\varphi(n)|n-1$*, Acta Arith. 28 (1976), 387–388.

[77a] *Multiply perfect numbers, Mersenne primes and effective computability*, Math. Ann. 226 (1977), 195–206.

[77b] *On composite n for which $\varphi(n)|n-1$, II*, Pacific J. Math. 69 (1977), 177–186.

[80] *Popular values of Euler's function*, Mathematika 27 (1980), 84–89.

[81] *On the distribution of pseudoprimes*, Math. Comput. 37 (1981), 587–593.

Pomerance, C., Selfridge, J. L.

[80] *Proof of D. J. Newman's coprime mapping conjecture*, Mathematika 27 (1980), 69–83.

van der Poorten, A. J.

[77] *Effectively computable bounds for the solutions of certain diophantine equations*, Acta Arith. 33 (1977), 195–207.

Posse, C.

[10] *Deux erreurs dans la table des racines primitives de Wertheim*, Acta Math. 33 (1910), 405–406.

[11a] *Exposé succinct des résultats principaux du mémoire posthume de Korkine, avec une table des racines primitives et des caractères, qui s'y rapportent, calculée par lui pour les nombres premiers inférieurs a 4000 et prolongée jusqu'a 5000*, Acta Math. 35 (1911-12), 193–231.

[11b] *Table des racines primitives et des caractères qui s'y rapportent pour les nombres premiers entre 5000 et 10 000*, Acta Math. 35 (1911-12), 233–252.

Postnikova, L. P., Shincel, A. (Schinzel, A.)

[68] *On primitive divisors of $a^n - b^n$ in algebraic number fields* (Russian), Mat. Sbornik 75 (1968), 171–177.

Powers, R. E.

[11] Bull. Amer. Math. Soc. 18 (1911-12), 160.

[14] *On Mersenne numbers*, Proc. London Math. Soc., (2), 13 (1914), xxxix.

Prachar, K.

[57] *Primzahlverteilung*, Springer 1957.

Rabinowitsch, G.

[13] *Eindeutigkeit der Zerlegung in Primzahlfaktoren in quadratischen Zahlkörpern*, J. Reine Angew. Math. 142 (1913), 153–164.

Rademacher, H.

[37] *On the partition function $p(n)$*, Proc. London Math. Soc., (2), 43 (1937), 241–254.

Raghavachari, M.

[66] *On the form of odd perfect numbers*, Math. Student 34 (1966), 85–86.

Rai, T.

[50] *Easier Waring problem*, J. Sci. Research Benares Hindu Univ. 1 (1950-51), 5–12.

Rajwade, A. R.

[76] *Note sur le théorème des trois carrés*, L'Enseign. Math., (2), 22 (1976), 171–173.

Ramachandra, K.

[69] *A note on numbers with a large prime factor*, J. London Math. Soc. 1 (1969), 303–306.

[70] *A note on numbers with a large prime factor, II*, J. Indian Math. Soc., (N. S.), 34 (1970), 39–48.

[71] *A note on numbers with a large prime factor, III*, Acta Arith. 19 (1971), 49–62.

[73a] *Application of Baker's theory to two problems considered by Erdös and Selfridge*, J. Indian Math. Soc., (N. S.), 37 (1973), 25–34.

[73b] *Largest prime factor of the product of k consecutive integers*, Tr. Mat. Inst. im. Steklova 132 (1973), 77–81.

[75] *On a theorem of Siegel*, Nachr. Akad. Wissensch. Göttingen, 1975, nr. 5, 43–47.

[80] *One more proof of Siegel's theorem*, Hardy–Ramanujan J. 3 (1980), 25–40.

Ramachandra, K., Shorey, T. N.

[73] *On gaps between numbers with a large prime factor*, Acta Arith. 24 (1973), 99–111.

Ramachandra, K., Shorey, T. N., Tijdeman, R.

[75] *On Grimm's problem relating to factorisation of a block of consecutive integers*, J. Reine Angew. Math. 273 (1975), 109–124.

[76] *On Grimm's problem relating to factorisation of a block of consecutive integers, II*, J. Reine Angew. Math. 288 (1976), 192–201.

Ramanujam, C. P.

[63] *Sums of m-th powers in p-adic rings*, Mathematika 10 (1963), 137–146.

Ramanujan, S. S.

[13] *Question 464*, J. Indian Math. Soc. 5 (1913), 120 = *Collected Papers*, Cambridge 1927, p. 327.

Ramanujan, S., Hardy, G. H. (see G. H. Hardy, S. Ramanujan)

Rameswar Rao, D.

[72] *Note on odd perfect numbers*, Proc. Nat. Acad. Sci. India, A 42 (1972), 170.

Rankin, R. A.

[38] *The difference between consecutive primes*, J. London Math. Soc. 13 (1938), 242–244.

[62] *The difference between consecutive primes, II*, Proc. Edinburgh Math. Soc., (2), 13 (1962/63), 331–332.

Réalis, S.

[78] *Note sur un théorème d'arithmétique*, Nouv. Correspond. Math. 4 (1878), 209–210.

Rédei, L.

[47] *Zwei Lückensätze über Polynome in endlichen Primkörpern mit Anwendung auf die endlichen Abelschen Gruppen und die Gaussische Summen*, Acta Math. 79 (1947), 273–290.

[53] *Die Existenz eines ungeraden quadratischen Nichtrestes* mod p *im Intervall* 1, $\sqrt{p}$, Acta Sci. Math. (Szeged) 15 (1953), 12–19.

[58] *Über die algebraischzahlentheoretische Verallgemeinerung eines elementarzahlentheoretischen Satzes von Zsigmondy*, Acta Sci. Math. (Szeged) 19 (1958), 98–126.

Rehman, F., Jackson, T. H. (see T. H. Jackson, F. Rehman)

338 BIBLIOGRAPHY

Reiner, I.

[45] *On genera of binary quadratic forms,* Bull. Amer. Math. Soc. 51 (1945), 909–912.

Remak, R.

[12] *Bemerkung zu Herrn Stridberg's Beweis des Waringschen Theorems,* Math. Ann. 72 (1912), 153–156.

Rényi, A.

[47] *On a new application of the method of Academician I. M. Vinogradov* (Russian), Doklady AN SSSR 56 (1947), 675–678.

Reshetukha, I. V.

[70] *A question of the theory of cubic residues* (Russian), Mat. Zametki 7 (1970), 469–476.

[75] *Analytic determination of a product of cubic character* (Russian), Ukrainskii Mat. Zh. 27 (1975), 193–201.

Reynolds, T. L., Brauer, A. (see A. Brauer, T. L. Reynolds)

Richelot, F. J.

[32] *De resolutione algebraica aequationis $X^{257} = 1$, sive de divisione circuli per bisectionem anguli septies repetitam in partes 257 inter se aequates commentatio coronata,* J. Reine Angew. Math. 9 (1832), 1–26.

Richert, H. J., Jurkat, W. B. (see W. B. Jurkat, H. J. Richert)

Richmond, H. W.

[22a] *Every positive rational number is a sum of cubes of three such numbers,* Messenger of Mathematics 51 (1922), 171–175.

[22b] *On analogues of Waring's problem for rational numbers,* Proc. London Math. Soc., (2), 21 (1922), 401–409.

[22c] *An elementary note upon Waring's problem for cubes, positive and negative,* Messenger of Mathematics 51 (1922), 177–186.

Ridout, D.

[57] *Rational approximations to algebraic numbers,* Mathematika 4 (1957), 125–131.

Rieger, G. J.

[53] *Zur Hilbertschen Lösung des Waringschen Problems: Abschätzung von $g(n)$,* Archiv Math. 4 (1953), 275–281.

[54] *Zu Linniks Lösung des Waringschen Problems: Abschätzung von $g(n)$,* Math. Zeitschr. 60 (1954), 213–234.

Riesel, H.

[56] *A note on the prime numbers of the forms $N = (6a+1)2^{2n-1}-1$ und $M = (6a-1)2^{2n}-1$,* Arkiv Mat. 3 (1956), 245–253.

[62] *All factors $q < 10^8$ in all Mersenne numbers 2^p-1, p prime, $< 10^4$,* Math. Comput. 16 (1962), 478–482.

[64] *Note on the congruence $a^{p-1} \equiv 1 \pmod{p^2}$,* Math. Comput. 18 (1964), 149–150.

[69] *Lucasian criteria for the primality of $N = h \cdot 2^n - 1$,* Math. Comput. 23 (1969), 869–875.

Rigge, O.

[39] *Über ein diophantisches Problem,* IX Congr. Math. Scandinav., 1939, pp. 155–160.

[40] *On a diophantine problem,* Arkiv Mat. Astr. Fys., 27A, nr. 3, (1940), 10 pp.

Risman, L. J.

[74] *A new proof of the three squares theorem,* J. Number Theory 6 (1974), 282–283.

Robbins, N.

[75] *Lower bounds for the largest prime factor of an odd perfect number which is divisible by a Fermat prime,* J. Reine Angew. Math. 278/9 (1975), 14–21.

Rodosskii, K. A.

[56] *On the exceptional zero* (Russian), Izvestia AN SSSR, ser. mat., 20 (1956), 667–672.

Rodriguez, G.

[65] *Sul problema dei divisori di Titchmarsh*, Boll. Un. Mat. Ital., (3), 20 (1965), 358–366.

Rohrbach, H., Weis, J.

[64] *Zum finiten Fall des Bertrandschen Postulates*, J. Reine Angew. Math. 214/5 (1964), 432–440.

Rosati, L. A.

[54] *Sull'equazione diofantea* $4/n = 1/x_1 + 1/x_2 + 1/x_3$, Boll. Unione Mat. Italiana, (3), 9 (1954), 59–63.

Rosser, J. B., Schoenfeld, L.

[62] *Approximate formulas for some functions of prime numbers*, Illinois J. Math. 6 (1962), 64–94.

[75] *Sharper bounds for the Chebyshev functions* $\theta(x)$ *and* $\psi(x)$, Math. Comput. 29 (1975), 243–269.

Roth, K. F.

[49] *Proof that almost all positive integers are sums of a square, a positive cube and a fourth power*, J. London Math. Soc. 24 (1949), 4–13.

[51] *A problem in additive number theory*, Proc. London Math. Soc., (2), 53 (1951), 381–395.

[55] *Rational approximations to algebraic numbers*, Mathematika 2 (1955), 1–20, corr. 168.

Rotkiewicz, A.

[56] *Sur l'équation* $x^z - y^t = a^t$, *où* $|x - y| = a$, Ann. Polon. Math. 3 (1956), 7–8.

[60] *Elementarny dowód istnienia dzielnika pierwszego pierwotnego liczby* $a^n - b^n$, Prace Matem. 4 (1960), 21–28.

[62] *On Lucas numbers with two intrinsic prime divisors*, Bull. Acad. Sci. Polon., Ser. Sci. Math., Astr., Phys., 10 (1962), 229–232.

[65] *Sur les nombres de Mersenne dépourvus de diviseurs carrés et sur les nombres naturels* n, *tels que* $n^2 | 2^n - 2$, Mat. Vestnik 2 (17) (1965), 78–80.

[72] *Pseudoprime numbers and their generalizations*, Novi Sad 1972.

Rubugunday, R.

[42] *On* $g(k)$ *in Waring's problem*, J. Indian Math. Soc., (N. S.), 6 (1942), 192–198.

Sachs, H.

[56] *Untersuchungen über das Problem der eigentlicher Teiler*, Wissensch. Zeitschr. Univ. Halle 6 (1956/7), 223–259.

Salié, H.

[49] *Über den kleinsten positiven quadratischen Nichtrest nach einer Primzahl*, Math. Nachr. 3 (1949), 7–8.

Saltykov, A. I.

[60] *On Euler's function* (Russian), Vestnik Moskovsk. Gosudarstv. Univ., 1960, nr. 6, 34–50.

Sambasiva Rao, K.

[41] *On Waring's problem for smaller powers*, J. Indian Math. Soc., (N. S.), 5 (1941), 117–121.

Sandham, H. F.

[53] *A square as the sum of* 7 *squares*, Quart. J. Math. (Oxford) 4 (1953), 230–236.

Sárközy, A.

[77] *Some remarks concerning irregularities of distribution of integers in arithmetical progressions*, Acta Math. Acad. Sci. Hungaricae 30 (1977), 155–162.

340 BIBLIOGRAPHY

Sárközy, A., Erdős, P. (see P. Erdős, A. Sárközy)
Savitzky, S. R., Wegner, K. W. (see K. W. Wegner, S. R. Savitzky)
Scheid, H.

[69] *Die Anzahl der Primfaktoren in* $\binom{n}{k}$, Archiv Math. 20 (1969), 581–582.

Schinzel, A.

[56a] *Sur l'équation* $x^z - y^t = 1$ *où* $|x-y| = 1$, Ann. Polon. Math. 3 (1956), 5–6.
[56b] *Sur un probléme concernant la fonction* $\varphi(n)$, Czechoslovak Math. J. 6 (1956), 164–165.
[56c] *Sur quelques propriétés des nombres* $3/n$ *et* $4/n$, *où* n *est un nombre impair*, Mathesis 65 (1956), 219–222.
[56d] *Sur l'équation* $\varphi(x) = m$, Elemente Math. 11 (1956), 75–78.
[59] *Sur les sommes de trois carrés*, Bull. Acad. Polon. Sci., Ser. Sci. Math., Astr., Phys. 7 (1959), 307–310.
[61] *Remarks on the paper "Sur certaines hypothèses concernant les nombres premiers"*, Acta Arith. 7 (1961), 1–8.
[62a] *The intrinsic divisors of Lehmer numbers in the case of negative discriminant*, Arkiv Mat. 4 (1962), 413–416.
[62b] *On primitive prime factors of Lehmer numbers, I, II*, Acta Arith. 8 (1962/63), 213–223, 251–257.
[62c] *On primitive factors of* $a^n - b^n$, Proc. Cambridge Philos. Soc. 58 (1962), 555–562.
[67] *On two theorems of Gelfond and some of their applications*, Acta Arith. 13 (1967), 177–236.
[68] *On primitive prime factors of Lehmer numbers, III*, Acta Arith. 15 (1968), 49–70; corr., ibidem 16 (1969/70), 101.
[74] *Primitive divisors of the expression* $A^n - B^n$ *in algebraic number fields*, J. Reine Angew. Math. 268/9 (1974), 27–33.
[82] *Selected topics on polynomials*, Ann Arbor 1982.

Schinzel, A., Baker, A. (see A. Baker, A. Schinzel)
Schinzel A., Birch, B. J., Chowla, S., Hall, M., Jr. (see B. J. Birch et al.)
Schinzel, A., Browkin, J. (see J. Browkin, A. Schinzel)
Schinzel, A., Davenport, H., Lewis, D. J. (see H. Davenport, D. J. Lewis, A. Schinzel)
Schinzel, A., Goldfeld, D. M. (see D. M. Goldfeld, A. Schinzel)
Schinzel, A., Postnikova, L. P. (see L. P. Postnikova, A. Schinzel)
Schinzel, A., Sierpiński, W.

[58a] *Sur les sommes de quatre cubes*, Acta Arith. 4 (1958), 20–30.
[58b] *Sur certaines hypothèses concernant les nombres premiers*, Acta Arith. 4 (1958), 185–208; corr., ibidem 5 (1959), 259.

Schinzel, A., Tijdeman, R.

[76] *On the equation* $y^m = P(x)$, Acta Arith. 31 (1976), 199–204.

Schmidt, E.

[13] *Zum Hilbertschen Beweise des Waringschen Theorems*, Math. Ann. 74 (1913), 271–274.

Schmidt, W. M.

[76] *Equations over finite fields; An elementary approach*, Lecture Notes in Math. 536, Springer 1976.

Schnirelman, L.

[33] *Über additive Eigenschaften von Zahlen*, Math. Ann. 107 (1933), 649–690.

Schoenfeld, L.

[76] *Sharper bounds for the Chebyshev functions* $\theta(x)$ *and* $\psi(x)$, *II*, Math. Comput. 30 (1976), 337–360; corr. 900.

Schoenfeld, L., Rosser, J. B. (see J. B. Rosser, L. Schoenfeld)

Scholz, B.

[55] *Bemerkung zu einem Beweis von Wieferich*, Jahresber. DMV 58 (1955), 45–48.

Schur, I.

[18] *Einige Bemerkungen zu den vorstehender Arbeit des Herrn Pólya: Über die Verteilung der quadratischen Reste und Nichtreste*, Nachricht. Ges. Wiss. Göttingen, 1918, pp. 30–36 = Gesamm. Abhandl., II, Springer 1973, pp. 239–245.

[21] *Über die Gaussschen Summen*, Nachricht. Ges. Wiss. Göttingen, 1921, pp. 147–153 = Gesamm. Abhandl., II, Springer 1973, pp. 327–333.

[29a] *Einige Sätze über Primzahlen mit Anwendungen auf Irreduzibilitätsfragen*, I, Sitz.-Ber. Preuss. Akad. Wissensch. 23 (1929), 125–136 = Gesamm. Abhandl., III, Springer 1973, pp. 140–151.

[29b] *Einige Sätze über Primzahlen mit Anwendungen auf Irreduzibilitätsfragen*, II, Sitz.-Ber. Preuss, Akad. Wissensch. 23 (1929), 370–391 = Gesamm. Abhandl., III, Springer 1973, pp. 152–173.

Schwarz, Š.

[48] *On Waring's problem for finite fields*, Quart. J. Math., (Oxford) 19 (1948), 123–128.

Scourfield, E. J.

[60] *A generalization of Waring's problem*, J. London Math. Soc. 35 (1960), 98–116.

[76] *An asymptotic formula for the property* $(n, f(n)) = 1$ *for a class of multiplicative functions*, Acta Arith. 29 (1976), 401–423.

Sédlaček, J.

[59] *On unit fractions*, (Czech.), Časopis Pest. Mat. 84 (1959), 188–197.

Seelhoff, P.

[86] *Die neunte vollkommene Zahl*, Zeitschr. Math. Phys. 31 (1886), 174–178.

Segal, B.

[41] *Character sums and their applications* (Russian), Izvestia AN SSSR, ser. mat. 5 (1941), 401–410.

Selberg, A.

[43] *On the normal density of primes in small intervals, and the difference between consecutive primes*, Arkiv Mat. Naturvid., 47 (6) (1943), 87–105.

Selberg, A., Chowla, S.

[49] *On Epstein's zeta function, I*, Proc. Nat. Acad. Sci. USA 35 (1949), 371–374.

[67] *On Epstein's zeta functions, II*, J. Reine Angew. Math. 227 (1967), 86–110.

Selfridge, J. L., Brillhart, J. (see J. Brillhart, J. L. Selfridge)

Selfridge, J. L., Brillhart, J., Lehmer, D. H. (see J. Brillhart, D. H. Lehmer, J. L. Selfridge)

Selfridge, J. L., Brillhart, J., Lehmer, D. H., Tuckerman, B., Wagstaff, S., Jr. (see J. Brillhart et al.)

Selfridge, J. L., Ecklund, E. F., Jr., Eggleton, R. B. (see E. F. Ecklund, Jr., R. B. Eggleton, J. L. Selfridge)

Selfridge, J. L., Eggleton, R. B. (see R. B. Eggleton, J. L. Selfridge)

Selfridge, J. L., Erdös, P. (see P. Erdös, J. L. Selfridge)

Selfridge, J. L., Pomerance, C. (see C. Pomerance, J. L. Selfridge)

Selmer, E. S.

[56] *The rational solutions of the Diophantine equation* $\eta^2 = \xi^3 - D$ *for* $|D| < 100$, Math. Scandinav. 4 (1956), 281–286.

[76] *On the number of prime divisors of a binomial coefficient*, Math. Scandinav. 39 (1976), 271–281.

Servais, C.

[87] *Sur les nombres parfaits*, Mathesis 7 (1887), 228–230.

[88] *Sur les nombres parfaits*, Mathesis 8 (1888), 92–93.

Shafarevich, I. R., Borevich, Z. I. (see Z. I. Borevich, I. R. Shafarevich)

Shanks, D.

[69] *On Gauss's class number problems*, Math. Comput. 23 (1969), 151–163.

[72] *Fibonacci primitive roots*, Fibonacci Quart. 10 (1972), 163–168, 181.

Shanks, D., Kravitz, S.

[67] *On the distribution of Mersenne divisors*, Math. Comput. 21 (1967), 97–101.

Shapiro, H. N.

[49] *Note on a theorem of Dickson*, Bull. Amer. Math. Soc. 55 (1949), 450–452.

Shapiro, H. N., Erdös, P. (see P. Erdös, H. N. Shapiro)

Shapiro, H. N., Hausman, M. (see M. Hausman, H. N. Shapiro)

Shorey, T. N.

[72] *On a theorem of Ramachandra*, Acta Arith. 20 (1972), 215–221.

[73] *On gaps between numbers with a large prime factor, II*, Acta Arith. 25 (1973/4), 365–373.

[80] *On the greatest prime factor of* $(ax^m + by^n)$, Acta Arith. 36 (1980), 21–25.

Shorey, T. N., Erdös, P. (see P. Erdös, T. N. Shorey)

Shorey, T. N., Ramachandra, K. (see K. Ramachandra, T. N. Shorey)

Shorey, T. N., Ramachandra, K., Tijdeman, R. (see K. Ramachandra, T. N. Shorey, R. Tijdeman)

Shorey, T. N., Tijdeman, R.

[76] *On the greatest prime factor of polynomials at integer points*, Compos. Math. 33 (1976), 187–195.

Shparlinskij, I. E.

[78] *The distribution of non-residues and primitive roots in recurrence sequences* (Russian), Matem. Zametki 24 (1978), 603–613.

Shyr, J. M.

[79] *Class numbers of binary quadratic forms over algebraic number fields*, J. Reine Angew. Math. 307/8 (1979), 353–364.

Siegel, C. L.

[21] *Approximation algebraischer Zahlen*, Math. Zeitschr. 10 (1921), 173–213 = Ges. Abh., I, Springer 1966, pp. 6–46.

[26] *The integer solutions of the equation* $y^2 = ax^n + bx^{n-1} + \ldots + k$, J. London Math. Soc. 1 (1926), 66–68 = Ges. Abh., I, Springer 1966, pp. 207–208.

[29] *Über einige Anwendungen Diophantischer Approximationen*, Abh. Preuss. Akad. Wissensch., 1929, nr. 1 = Ges. Abh., I, Springer 1966, pp. 209–266.

[35] *Über die analytische Theorie der quadratischen Formen*, Ann. of Math., (2), 36 (1935), 527–606 = Ges. Abh., I, Springer 1966, pp. 326–405.

[36] *Über die Classenzahl quadratischer Körper*, Acta Arith. 1 (1936), 83–86 = Ges. Abh., I, Springer 1966, pp. 496–409.

[37] *Die Gleichung* $ax^n - by^n = c$, Math. Ann. 114 (1937), 57–68 = Ges. Abh., II, Springer 1966, pp. 8–19.

[68] *Zum Beweise des Starkschen Satzes*, Invent. Math. 5 (1968), 180–191 = Ges. Abh., IV, Springer 1979, pp. 41–52.

Sierpiński, W.

[56] *Sur les décompositions de nombres rationnels en fractions primaires*, Mathesis 65 (1956), 16–32.

[57] *O rozkładach liczb wymiernych na ułamki proste*, Warszawa 1957.

[58] *Sur une question concernant le nombre de diviseurs premiers d'un nombre naturel*, Colloq. Math. 6 (1958), 209–210.

[64] *Elementary theory of numbers*, Warszawa 1964.

Sierpiński, W., Schinzel, A. (see A. Schinzel, W. Sierpiński)

Sirkesalo, J., Inkeri, K. (see K. Inkeri, J. Sirkesalo)

Sitaramachandra Rao, R., Suryanarayana, D. (see D. Suryanarayana, R. Sitaramachandra Rao)

Skolem, Th., Chowla, S., Lewis, D. J.

[59]   *The diophantine equation* $2^{n+2} - 7 = x^2$ *and related problems,* Proc. Amer. Math. Soc. 10 (1959), 663–669.

Slowinski, D.

[79]   *Searching for the 27th Mersenne prime,* J. Recreational Math. 11 (1978/79), 258–267.

Small, C.

[77a]   *Waring's problem* mod n, Amer. Math. Monthly 84 (1977), 12–25.

[77b]   *Solution of Waring's problem* mod n, Amer. Math. Monthly 84 (1977), 356–359.

[77c]   *Sums of powers in large finite fields,* Proc. Amer. Math. Soc. 65 (1977), 35–36.

[78]   *Sums of powers in arithmetic progressions,* Canad. Math. Bull. 21 (1978), 505–506.

Smith, H. J. S.

[87]   *Mèmoire sur la représentation des nombres par des sommes de cinq carres,* Mèmoires présentès par divers savants à l'Acadèmie, 29 (1887), nr. 1, 1–72 = *Collected Papers, II,* Oxford 1894, pp. 623–680.

Smith, J. H., Fein, B., Gordon, B. (see B. Fein, B. Gordon, J. H. Smith)

Sokolinskij, V. Z., Knizhnerman, L. A. (see L. A. Knizhnerman, V. Z. Sokolinskij)

Sprague, R.

[48a]   *Über Zerlegung in ungleiche Quadratzahlen,* Math. Zeitschr. 51 (1948), 289–290.

[48b]   *Über Zerlegung in n-te Potenzen mit lauter verschiedenen Grundzahlen,* Math. Zeitschr. 51 (1948), 466–468.

Sprindzhuk, V. G.

[63]   *On the number of solutions of the Diophantine equation* $x^3 = y^2 + A$ (Russian), Doklady AN BSSR 7 (1963), 9–11.

[71]   *On the largest prime divisor of a binary form* (Russian), Doklady AN BSSR 15 (1971), 389–391.

Stahl, C. E., Ellison, W. J., Ellison, F., Pesek, J., Stall, D. S. (see W. J. Ellison et al.)

Stahl, W.

[69]   *Bemerkung zu einer Arbeit von Hering,* Archiv Math. 20 (1969), 580.

Stähle, H., Körner, O. (see O. Körner, H. Stähle)

Stall, D. S., Ellison, W. J., Ellison, F., Pesek, J., Stahl, C. E. (see W. J. Ellison et al.)

Stall, D. S., Ellison, W. J., Pesek, J., Lunnon, W. F. (see W. J. Ellison et al.)

Stanley, G. K.

[31]   *The representation of a number as a sum of squares and cubes,* J. London Math. Soc. 6 (1931), 194–197.

Stark, H. M.

[66]   *On complex quadratic fields with class number equal to one,* Trans. Amer. Math. Soc. 122 (1966), 112–119.

[67a]   *A complete determination of the complex quadratic fields of class-number one,* Michigan Math. J. 14 (1967) 1–27.

[67b]   *On the problem of unique factorization in complex quadratic fields,* Proc. Symposia Pure Math. 12 (1967), 41–56.

[68]   *L-functions and character sums for quadratic forms, I, II,* Acta Arith. 14 (1968), 35–50; ibidem 15 (1969), 307–317.

[69a]   *On the "gap" in a theorem of Heegner,* J. Number Theory 1 (1969), 16–27.

[69b]   *A historical note on complex quadratic fields with class-number one,* Proc. Amer. Math. Soc. 21 (1969), 254–255.

[69c]   *The role of modular functions in a class-number problem,* J. Number Theory 1 (1969), 252–260.

[71]   *A transcendence theorem for class-number problems*, Ann. of Math., (2), 94 (1971), 153–173.

[72]   *A transcendence theorem for class-number problems, II*, Ann. of Math., (2), 96 (1972), 174–209.

[73]   *Effective estimates of solutions of some diophantine equations*, Acta Arith. 24 (1973), 251–259.

[74]   *Some effective cases of the Brauer–Siegel theorem*, Invent. Math. 23 (1974), 135–152.

[75]   *On complex quadratic fields with class-number two*, Math. Comput. 29 (1975), 289–302.

Stechkin, S. B.

[75]   *A bound for Gauss' sums* (Russian), Mat. Zametki 17 (1975), 579–588.

[77]   *Estimate of a complete rational trigonometrical sum* (Russian), Trudy Mat. Inst. im. Steklova 143 (1977), 188–207.

Steinig, J.

[66]   *On Euler's idoneal numbers*, Elemente Math. 21 (1966), 73–88.

Stemmler, R. M.

[64]   *The ideal Waring theorem for exponents 401–200 000*, Math. Comput. 18 (1964), 144–146.

Stepanova, L. L., Flikop, E. L.

[72]   *On the question of the number of solutions of the equation $\varphi(x) = m$* (Russian), Issled. po teorii čisel (Saratov) 4 (1972), 89–93.

Stepanova, L. L., Nechaev, V. I. (see V. I. Nechaev, L. L. Stepanova)

Stephens, N. M.

[75]   *On the number of coprime solutions of $y^2 = x^3 + k$*, Proc. Amer. Math. Soc. 48 (1975), 325–327.

Stephens, N. M., Coghlan, F. B.

[71]   *The diophantine equation $x^3 - y^2 = k$*, In: *Computers in Number Theory*, Academic Press 1971, pp. 199–205.

Stephens, P. J.

[69]   *An average result for Artin's conjecture*, Mathematika 16 (1969), 178–188.

Stern, M. A.

[30]   *Bemerkungen über höhere Arithmetik*, J. Reine Angew. Math. 6 (1830), 147–153.

Sterneck, R. D. v.

[03]   *Über die kleinste Anzahl von Kuben, aus welche jede Zahl bis 40 000 zusammengesetzt werden kann*, Sitz.-Ber., Kaiserl. Akad. Wiss. Wien, Math.-Nat. Kl., 112, IIa, (1903), 1627–1666.

Steuerwald, R.

[37]   *Verschärfung einer notwendigen Bedingung für die Existenz einer ungeraden vollkommenen Zahl*, Sitz.-Ber. Bayer. Akad. Wiss., Math.-Nat. Kl., 1937, pp. 69–72.

Stevens, H.

[77]   *On Jacobsthal's $g(n)$-function*, Math. Ann. 226 (1977), 95–97.

Stewart, B. M.

[54]   *Sums of distinct divisors*, Amer. J. Math. 76 (1954), 779–785.

Stewart, B. M., Webb, W. A.

[66]   *Sums of fractions with bounded numerators*, Canad. J. Math. 18 (1966), 999–1003.

Stewart, C. L.

[75]   *The greatest prime factor of $a^n - b^n$*, Acta Arith. 26 (1974/75), 427–433.

[77a] *On divisors of Fermat, Fibonacci, Lucas and Lehmer numbers*, Proc. London Math. Soc., (3), 35 (1977), 425–447.

[77b] *Primitive divisors of Lucas and Lehmer numbers,* In: *Transcendence Theory,* Academic Press 1977, pp. 79–92.

Stolt, B.
[54] *Über den kleinsten positiven quadratischen Nichtrest,* Math. Scand. 2 (1954), 187–192.

[57] *Über die diophantische Gleichung* $\binom{n}{k} = Mx^m$, Archiv Math. 7 (1957), 446–449.

Størmer, C.
[97] *Quelques théorèmes sur l'equation de Pell* $x^2 - Dy^2 = \pm 1$ *et leur applications,* Skr. Norske Vid. Akad., Oslo, I, nr. 2, 1897.

[98] *Sur une équation indéterminée,* C. R. Acad. Sci. Paris 127 (1898), 752–754.

Stothers, W. W., Cohen, S. D., Odoni, R. W. K. (see S. D. Cohen, R. W. K. Odoni, W. W. Stothers)

Straus, E. G., Subbarao, M. V.
[78] *On the representation of fractions as sums and difference of three simple fractions,* Proc. VII Manitoba Conf. Numerical Math. Comput., Winnipeg 1978, pp. 561–579.

Straus, E. G., Erdös, P. (see P. Erdös, E. G. Straus)

Stridsberg, E.
[10] *Öfver Hilberts bevis för Warings sats,* Arkiv Mat. Astr. Fys., 6, nr. 32, 1910; nr. 39, 1911.

[12] *Sur la démonstration de M. Hilbert du théorème de Waring,* Math. Ann. 72 (1912), 145–152.

[17] *Några elementära undersökningar rörande fakulteter och deras aritmetiska egenshaper,* Arkiv Mat. Astr. Fys. 11, 1916/17, nr. 25, 1 52.

[19] *Några elementära undersökningar rörande fakulteter och vissa allmännare koefficientsviter,* Arkiv Mat. Astr. Fys., 13, 1918/19, nr. 25, 1–70.

Stubblefield, B.
[73] *Greater lower bounds for odd perfect numbers,* Notices Amer. Math. Soc. 20 (1973), A-515.

Subbarao, M. V., Straus, E. G. (see E. G. Straus, M. V. Subbarao)

Sugar, A.
[35] *A new universal Waring theorem for eight powers,* Bull. Amer. Math. Soc. 41 (1935), 675–678.

[36] *A cubic analogue of the Cauchy–Fermat theorem,* Amer. J. Math. 58 (1936), 783–790.

[37] *Ideal Waring theorem for the polynomial* $m\dfrac{(x^3 - x)}{6} - m\dfrac{(x^2 - x)}{2} + x$, Amer. J. Math. 59 (1937), 43–49.

Sukthankar, N. S.
[73] *On Grimm's conjecture in algebraic number fields, I, II, III,* Indagat. Math. 35 (1973), 475–484; 37 (1975), 13–25; 39 (1977), 342–348.

Suryanarayana, D.
[66] *On a paper of Karl K. Norton concerning odd perfect numbers,* Math. Student 34 (1966), 97–101.

[69] *Super perfect numbers,* Elemente Math. 24 (1969), 16–17.

[73] *On odd perfect numbers,* Math. Student 41 (1973), 153–154.

Suryanarayana, D., Sitaramachandra Rao, R.
[72] *On the average order of the function* $E(x) = \sum\limits_{n \leqslant x} \varphi(n) - 3x^2/\pi^2$, Arkiv Mat. 10 (1972), 99–106.

Swift, J. D.

[48] *Note on discriminants of binary quadratic forms with a single class in each genus*, Bull. Amer. Math. Soc. 54 (1948), 560–561.

Sylvester, J. J.

[80a] *On a point in the theory of vulgar fractions*, Amer. J. Math. 3 (1880), 332–335, 388–389 = Math. Papers, III, Cambridge, 1909, pp. 440–445.

[80b] *Instantaneous proof of a theorem of Lagrange on the divisors of the form* $Ax^2 + By^2 + Cz^2$, *with a postscript on the divisors of the functions which multisect the primitive roots of unity*, Amer. J. Math. 3 (1880), 390–392 = Math. Papers, III, Cambridge, 1909, pp. 446–448.

[88a] *Sur les nombres parfaits*, C. R. Acad. Sci. Paris 106 (1888), 403–405 = Math. Papers, IV, Cambridge, 1912, pp. 603–606.

[88b] *Sur l'impossibilité de l'existence d'un nombre parfait impair qui ne contient pas au moins 5 diviseurs premiers distinct*, C. R. Acad. Sci. Paris, 106 (1888), 522–526 = Math. Papers, IV, Cambridge, 1912, pp. 611–614.

[92] *On Arithmetical series*, Messenger of Mathematics 21 (1892), 1–19, 87–120 = Math. Papers, IV, Cambridge, 1912, pp. 686–731.

Szalay, M.

[70] *On the distribution of primitive roots* (mod p) (Hungarian), Mat. Lapok 21 (1970), 357–362.

[75] *On the distribution of the primitive roots of a prime*, J. Number Theory 7 (1975), 184–188.

Szekeres, G.

[74] *On the number of divisors of* $x^2 + x + A$, J. Number Theory 6 (1974), 434–442.

[78] *Major arcs in the four cubes problem*, J. Austral. Math. Soc. 25 (1978), 423–437.

Szymiczek, K.

[69] *On the distribution of prime factors of Mersenne primes*, Prace Mat. 13 (1969), 33–49.

Takenouchi, T.

[21] *On an indeterminate equation*, Proc. Phys.-Math. Japan, (3), 3 (1921), 78–92.

Tatuzawa, T.

[51] *On a theorem of Siegel*, Japanese J. Math. 21 (1951), 163–178.

Tchudakoff, N. (see Chudakov, N. G.)

Thanigasalam, K.

[68] *On additive number theory*, Acta Arith. 13 (1968), 237–258.

[74] *Notes on Waring's problem*, Portugalia Math. 33 (1974), 163–165.

[80a] *On sums of powers and a related problem*, Acta Arith. 36 (1980), 125–141; corr. ibid. 42 (1983), 425.

[80b] *On Waring's problem*, Acta Arith. 38 (1980), 141–155.

[82] *Some new estimates for* $G(k)$ *in Waring's problem*, Acta Arith. 42 (1982), 73–78.

Thomas, H. E., Jr.

[74] *Waring's problem for twenty-two biquadrates*, Trans. Amer. Math. Soc. 193 (1974), 427–430.

Thue, A.

[08] *Bemerkungen über gewisse Näherungsbrüche algebraischer Zahlen*, Vid. Selsk. Skr., Mat. Nat. Kl., 1908, nr. 3, 34 pp.

[09] *Über Annäherungswerte algebraischer Zahlen*, J. Reine Angew. Math. 135 (1909), 284–305.

[17] *Über die Unlösbarkeit der Gleichung* $ax^2 + bx + c = dy^n$ *in grossen Zahlen x und y*, Arch. Math. og Naturv., Kristiania 1917.

Tietäväinen, A.

[73] *Note on Waring's problem* (mod *p*), Ann. Acad. Sci. Fennicae, AI, 554, 1973, 7 pp.

Tietäväinen, A., Dodson, M. M. (see M. M. Dodson, A. Tietäväinen)

Tijdeman, R.

[72] *On the maximal distance of numbers with a large prime factor*, J. London Math. Soc. 5 (1972), 313–320.

[73] *On integers with many small prime factors*, Compos. Math. 26 (1973), 319–330.

[76] *On the equation of Catalan*, Acta Arith. 29 (1976), 197–209.

Tijdeman, R., Cijsouw, P. L. (see P. L. Cijsouw, R. Tijdeman)

Tijdeman, R., Ramachandra, K., Shorey, T. N. (see K. Ramachandra, T. N. Shorey, R. Tijdeman)

Tijdeman, R., Schinzel, A. (see A. Schinzel, R. Tijdeman)

Tijdeman, R., Shorey, T. N. (see T. N. Shorey, R. Tijdeman)

Titchmarsh, E. C.

[42] *The order of* $\zeta(\frac{1}{2}+it)$, Quart. J. Math. (Oxford) 13 (1942), 11–17.

Tonascia, J., Brillhart, J., Weinberger, P. (see J. Brillhart, J. Tonascia, P. Weinberger)

Tong, K. C.

[57] *On Waring's problem* (Chinese), Advanc. Math. 3 (1957), 602–607.

Tornheim, L.

[38] *Sums of n-th powers in fields of prime characteristic*, Duke Math. J. 4 (1938), 359–362.

Touchard, J.

[53] *On prime numbers and perfect numbers*, Scripta Math. 19 (1953), 35–39.

Trost, E.

[58] *Eine Bemerkung zum Waringschen Problem*, Elemente Math. 13 (1958), 73–75.

Tuckerman, B.

[71] *The 24-th Mersenne prime*, Proc. Nat. Acad. Sci. USA 68 (1971), 2319–2320.

[73] *A search procedure and lower bound for odd perfect numbers*, Math. Comput. 27 (1973), 943–949, corr. 28 (1974), 887.

Tuckerman, B., Brillhart, J., Lehmer, D. H., Selfridge, J. L., Wagstaff, S. S., Jr. (see J. Brillhart et al.)

Turán, P.

[50] *Results of number-theory in the Soviet Union* (Hungarian), Math. Lapok 1 (1950), 243–266.

Turk, J. W. M.

[79] *Multiplicative properties of neighbouring integers*, Thesis, Leiden 1979.

[80] *Prime divisors of polynomials at consecutive integers*, J. Reine Angew. Math. 319 (1980), 142–152.

Uchiyama, S.

[63] *On a theorem concerning the distribution of almost primes*, J. Fac. Sci. Hokkaido Univ., s. I, 17 (1963), 152–159.

Uchiyama, S., Carlitz, L. (see L. Carlitz, S. Uchiyama)

Uspensky, J. V., Heaslett, M. A.

[39] *Elementary Number Theory*, New York 1939.

Utz, W. R.

[61] *A conjecture of Erdös concerning consecutive integers*, Amer. Math. Monthly 68 (1961), 896–897.

Vandiver, H. S.

[17] *Symmetric functions formed by systems of elements of a finite algebra and their*

connection with Fermat's quotient and Bernoulli numbers, Ann. of Math., (2), 18 (1917), 105–119.

[25] *On sets of three consecutive integers which are quadratic or cubic residues of primes*, Bull. Amer. Math. Soc. 31 (1925), 33–38.

Vandiver, H. S., Birkhoff, G. D. (see G. G. Birkhoff, H. S. Vandiver)

Vaughan, R. C.

[70a] *On a problem of Erdös, Straus and Schinzel*, Mathematika 17 (1970), 193–198.

[70b] *On the representation of numbers as sums of powers of natural numbers*, Proc. London Math. Soc., (3), 21 (1970), 160–180.

[71] *On sums of mixed powers*, J. London Math. Soc. 3 (1971), 677–688.

[73] *Some applications of Montgomery's sieve*, J. Number Theory 5 (1973), 64–79.

[76] *On the order of magnitude of Jacobsthal's function*, Proc. Edinburgh Math. Soc., (2), 20 (1976/7), 329–331.

[77] *Homogeneous additive equations and Waring's problem*, Acta Arith. 33 (1977), 231–253.

[81] *The Hardy–Littlewood method*, Cambridge 1981.

Vaughan, R. C., Montgomery, H. L. (see H. L. Montgomery, R. C. Vaughan)

Vegh, E.

[68] *Pairs of consecutive primitive roots modulo a prime*, Proc. Amer. Math. Soc. 19 (1968), 1169–1170.

[69] *Primitive roots modulo a prime as consecutive terms of an arithmetic progression*, J. Reine Angew. Math. 235 (1969), 185–188.

[70a] *Arithmetic progressions of primitive roots of a prime, II*, J. Reine Angew. Math. 244 (1970), 108–111.

[70b] *A new condition for consecutive primitive roots of a prime*, Elemente Math. 25 (1970), 113.

[71] *A note on the distribution of the primitive roots of a prime*, J. Number Theory 3 (1971), 13–18.

[72] *Arithmetic progressions of primitive roots of a prime, III*, J. Reine Angew. Math. 256 (1972), 130–137.

Vegh, E., Hauptmann, H., Fisher, J. (see H. Hauptmann, E. Vegh, J. Fisher)

Venkov, B. A.

[31] *Über die Klassenzahl positiver binären quadratischen Formen*, Math. Zeitschr. 33 (1931), 350–374.

Verner, L.

[79] *A singular series in characteristic p*, Bull. Acad. Polon. Sci., Ser. Sci. Math., Astr., Phys., 27 (1979), 147–151.

Veselý, V.

[33a] *Une démonstration élementaire de l'identité de Hurwitz* (Czech), Čas. mat. fys. 62 (1933), 117–122.

[33b] *Sur un problème analogue à celui de Waring* (Czech), Čas. mat. fys. 62 (1933), 123–127.

Vinogradov, A. I.

[65] *On the density hypothesis for Dirichlet's L-series* (Russian), Izvestia AN SSSR, ser. mat., 29 (1965), 903–934.

[71] *Artin L-series and his conjectures* (Russian), Trudy Mat. Inst. im. Steklova, 112 (1971), 123–140.

[73] *Artin's conjectures and reciprocity law* (Russian), Trudy Mat. Inst. im. Steklova 132 (1973), 35–43.

Vinogradov, A. I., Linnik Yu. V. (see Yu. V. Linnik, A. I. Vinogradov)

Vinogradov, I. M.

[18] *Sur la distribution des résidus et des nonrésidus des puissances,* Žurnal Fiz.-Mat. Obšč. Univ., Perm, 1 (1918), 94–98.

[24] *On a general Waring theorem* (Russian), Mat. Sbornik 31 (1924), 490–507.

[26] *On a bound for the smallest non-residue of n-th power* (Russian), Izvestia AN SSSR, ser. mat., 20 (1926), 47–58.

[27a] *On a general theorem concerning the distribution of the residues and non-residues of powers,* Trans. Amer. Math. Soc. 29 (1927), 209–217.

[27b] *On the bound of the least non-residue of n-th powers,* Trans. Amer. Math. Soc. 29 (1927), 218–226.

[28a] *On Waring's theorem* (Russian), Izvestia AN SSSR, ser. mat., 1928, 393–400.

[28b] *On the representation of a number by polynomial in several variables* (Russian), Izvestia AN SSSR, ser. mat., 1928, 401–414.

[30] *On the smallest primitive root* (Russian), Doklady AN SSSR, 1930, 7–11.

[34a] *New solution of Waring's problem* (Russian), Doklady AN SSSR 2 (1934), 337–341.

[34b] *On the upper bound for $G(n)$ in Waring's problem* (Russian), Izvestia AN SSSR, ser. mat., 10 (1934), 1455–1469.

[34c] *New evaluation of $G(n)$ in Waring's problem* (Russian), Doklady AN SSSR 5 (1934), 249–251.

[35a] *Une nouvelle variante de la démonstration du théorème de Waring,* C. R. Acad. Sci. Paris 200 (1935), 182–184.

[35b] *A new variant of the proof of Waring's theorem* (Russian), Trudy Mat. Inst. im. Steklova 9 (1935), 5–15.

[35c] *An asymptotic formula for the number of representations in Waring's problem,* Mat. Sbornik 42 (1935), 531–534.

[35d] *On Waring's problem,* Ann. of Math., (2), 36 (1935), 395–405.

[36a] *On the asymptotical formula in Waring's problem* (Russian), Mat. Sbornik 1 (1936), 169–174.

[36b] *New method of evaluating trigonometrical sums* (Russian), Mat. Sbornik 1 (1936), 175–188.

[36c] *Sur quelques inègalités nouvelles de la théorie des nombres,* C. R. Acad. Sci. Paris 202 (1936), 1361–1362.

[38] *Two theorems of the analytical number theory* (Russian), Trudy Tbilisskogo Mat. Inst. 5 (1938), 167–180.

[47] *The method of trigonometrical sums in number theory* (Russian), Trudy Mat. Inst. im. Steklova 23 (1947), 1–110.

[59] *On the question of an upper bound for $G(m)$,* (Russian), Izvestia AN SSSR, ser. mat., 23 (1959), 637–642.

[71] *The method of trigonometrical sums in number theory* (Russian), Moskva 1971.

Viola, C.

[73] *On the diophantine equations $\prod_{i=0}^{k} x_i - \sum_{i=0}^{k} x_i = n$ and $\sum_{i=0}^{r} 1/x_i = a/n$,* Acta Arith. 22 (1973), 339–352.

Volkmann, B.

[55] *Ein Satz über die Menge der vollkommenen Zahlen,* J. Reine Angew. Math. 195 (1955), 152–155.

van der Waall, R. W.

[75] *On some new conjectures in the theory of Artin's L-series,* Simon Stevin 49 (1975/6), 53–64.

Wagstaff, S. S., Jr., Brillhart, J., Lehmer, D. H., Selfridge, J. L., Tuckerman, B. (see J. Brillhart et al.)

Walfisz, A. (Walfisz, A. Z.)

[36]   *Zur additiven Zahlentheorie*, II, Math. Zeitschr. 40 (1936), 592–607.
[53a] *On Euler's function* (Russian), Doklady AN SSSR 90 (1953), 491–493.
[53b] *On Euler's function* (Russian), Trudy Tbilisskogo Mat. Inst. 19 (1953), 1–31.

Wall, C. T. C.

[57]   *A theorem on prime powers*, Eureka 19 (1957), 10–11.

Wang Yuan

[59a] *A note on the least primitive root of a prime*, Sc. Record 3 (1959), 174–179.
[59b] *On the least primitive root of a prime* (Chinese), Acta Math. Sinica 9 (1959), 432–441.
[61]   *On the least primitive root of a prime*, Sci. Sinica 10 (1961), 1–14. (English version of [59b]).

Ward, M.

[55]   *The intrinsic divisors of Lehmer numbers*, Ann. of Math., (2), 62 (1955), 230–236.
[59]   *Tests for primality based on Sylvester's cyclotomic numbers*, Pacific J. Math. 9 (1959), 1269–1272.

Waring, E.

[70]   *Meditationes algebraicae*, Cambridge 1770.

Warlimont, R.

[72]   *On Artin's conjecture*, J. London Math. Soc. 5 (1972), 91–94.
[78]   *Über die kleinste natürliche Zahl maximaler Ordnung* (mod m), Monatshefte Math. 85 (1978), 253–258.

Warren, Le Roy J., Bray, H. G.

[67]   *On the square-freeness of Fermat and Mersenne numbers*, Pacific J. Math. 22 (1967), 563–564.

Waterhouse, W. C.

[70]   *The sign of the Gaussian sum*, J. Number Theory 2 (1970), 363.

Watson, G. L.

[51]   *A proof of the seven cube theorem*, J. London Math. Soc. 26 (1951), 153–156.
[52]   *Sums of eight values of a cubic polynomial*, J. London Math. Soc. 27 (1952), 217–224.
[53]   *A simple proof that all large integers are sums of at most eight cubes*, Mathematical Gazette 37 (1953), 209–211.
[72]   *On sums of a square and five cubes*, J. London Math. Soc. 5 (1972), 215–218.

Webb, W. A.

[70]   *On $\frac{4}{n} = \frac{1}{x} + \frac{1}{y} + \frac{1}{z}$*, Proc. Amer. Math. Soc. 25 (1970), 578–584.
[72]   *Waring's problem in* GF $[q, x]$, Acta Arith. 22 (1972), 207–220.
[73]   *Numerical results for Waring's problem in* GF $[q, x]$, Math. Comput. 27 (1973), 193–196.
[74]   *Rationals not expressible as a sum of three unit fractions*, Elemente Math. 29 (1974), 1–6.
[76]   *On the diophantine equation $k/n = a_1/x_1 + a_2/x_2 + a_3/x_3$*, Časopis Pěstov. Mat. 101 (1976), 360–365.

Webb, W. A., Stewart, B. M. (see B. M. Stewart, W. A. Webb)

Webber, G. C.

[34]   *Waring's problem for cubic functions*, Trans. Amer. Math. Soc. 36 (1934), 493–510.
[51]   *Non existence of odd perfect numbers of the form $3^{2\beta} p^\alpha s_1^{2\beta_1} s_2^{2\beta_2} s_3^{2\beta_3}$*, Duke Math. J. 18 (1951), 741–749.

Weber, H.

[08]   *Lehrbuch der Algebra*, III, 2 Aufl., Braunschweig 1908, reprinted by Chelsea 1961.

Wegner, K. W., Savitzky, S. R.

[70] *Solutions of $\varphi(x) = n$, where φ is the Euler's φ-function,* Amer. Math. Monthly 77 (1970), 287.

Weil, A.

[48] *Sur les courbes algébriques et les variétes qui s'en deduisent,* Publ. Inst. Math. Strasbourg, 1948, pp. 1–85.

[74] *Sur les sommes de trois et quatre carrés,* L'Enseign. Math., (2), 20 (1974), 215–222.

Weinberger, P. J.

[72] *A counterexample to an analogue of Artin's conjecture,* Proc. Amer. Math. Soc. 35 (1972), 49–52.

[73] *Exponents of the class groups of complex quadratic fields,* Acta Arith. 22 (1973), 117–124.

Weinberger, P., Brillhart, J., Tonascia, J. (see J. Brillhart, J. Tonascia, P. Weinberger)

Weinberger, P. J., Cooke, G. (see G. Cooke, P. J. Weinberger)

Weinberger, P. J., Montgomery, H. L. (see H. L. Montgomery, P. J. Weinberger)

Weis, J., Rohrbach, H. (see H. Rohrbach, J. Weis)

Wertheim, G.

[93] *Tabelle der kleinsten primitiven Wurzeln g aller ungeraden Primzahlen p unter 3000,* Acta Math. 17 (1893), 315–320.

[97a] *Primitive Wurzeln der Primzahlen von der Form $2^\varkappa q^\lambda + 1$, in welcher $q = 1$ oder eine ungerade Primzahl ist,* Acta Math. 20 (1897), 143–152.

[97b] *Tabelle der kleinsten primitiven Wurzeln g aller Primzahlen p zwischen 3000 und 5000,* Acta Math. 20 (1897), 153–157; corr., ibidem 22 (1899), 200.

Western, A. E.

[26] *Computations concerning numbers representable by four or five cubes,* J. London Math. Soc. 1 (1926), 244–250.

[32] *On Lucas's and Pepin's tests for the primeness of Mersenne's numbers,* J. London Math. Soc. 7 (1932), 130–137.

Western, A. E., Miller, J. C. P.

[68] *Tables of indices and primitive roots,* London 1968.

Weyl, H.

[16] *Über die Gleichverteilung von Zahlen mod. Eins,* Math. Ann. 77 (1916), 313–352.

[21] *Bemerkung über die Hardy–Littlewoodschen Untersuchungen zum Waringschen Problem,* Nachr. Ges. Wiss. Göttingen, 1921, pp. 189–192.

[22] *Bemerkung zur Hardy–Littlewoodschen Lösung des Waringschen Problems,* Nachr. Ges. Wiss. Göttingen 1922.

Whaples, G., Artin, E. (see E. Artin, G. Whaples)

Whyburn, C. T.

[73] *Note on a method in elementary number theory,* J. Reine Angew. Math. 258 (1973), 153–160.

Wieferich, A.

[09a] *Beweis des Satzes, dass sich eine jede ganze Zahl als Summe von höchstens neun Kuben darstellen lässt,* Math. Ann. 66 (1909), 95–101.

[09b] *Über die Darstellung der Zahlen als Summen von Biquadraten,* Math. Ann. 66 (1909), 106–108.

Wiertelak, K.

[78] *On the density of some sets of primes, I, II,* Acta Arith. 34 (1978), 183–196, 197–210.

Wilansky, A.

[76] *Primitive roots without quadratic reciprocity,* Mathematical Magazine 49 (1976), 146.

Williams, H. C.

[77] *On numbers analogous to Carmichael numbers,* Canad. Math. Bull. 20 (1977), 133–143.

Williams, K. S., Buell, D. A. (see D. A. Buell, K. S. Williams)

Williams, K. S., Hudson, R. H. (see R. H. Hudson, K. S. Williams)

Wirsing, E.

[59] *Bemerkung zu der Arbeit über vollkommene Zahlen,* Math. Ann. 137 (1959), 316–318.

[61] *Das asymptotische Verhalten von Summen über multiplikative Funktionen,* Math. Ann. 143 (1961), 75–102.

Wirsing, E., Hornfeck, B. (see B. Hornfeck, E. Wirsing)

Wisner, R. J., Osgood, C. F. (see C. F. Osgood, R. J. Wisner)

Wójcik, J.

[71] *On sums of three squares,* Colloq. Math. 24 (1971), 117–119.

Wolke, D.

[69] *A note on the least prime quadratic residue* (mod p), Acta Arith. 16 (1969), 85–87.

Wooldridge, K.

[79] *Values taken many times by Euler's phi-function,* Proc. Amer. Math. Soc. 76 (1979), 229–234.

Wright, E. M.

[33a] *The representation of a number as a sum of five and more squares,* Quart. J. Math. (Oxford) 4 (1933), 37–51.

[33b] *An extension of Waring's problem,* Philos. Trans. Royal Soc. London, A 232 (1933), 1–26.

[34a] *Proportionality conditions in Waring's problem,* Math. Zeitschr. 38 (1934), 730–740.

[34b] *An easier Waring's problem,* J. London Math. Soc. 9 (1934), 267–272.

[36] *The representation of a number as a sum of four "almost proportional" squares,* Quart. J. Math. (Oxford) 7 (1936), 230–240.

[37a] *The representation of a number as a sum of four "almost equal" squares,* Quart. J. Math. (Oxford) 8 (1937), 278–279.

[37b] *The representation of a number as a sum of three or four squares,* Proc. London Math. Soc. 42 (1937), 481–500.

Wright, E. M., Fuchs, W. H. J. (see W. H. J. Fuchs, E. M. Wright)

Wright, E. M., Hardy, G. H. (see G. H. Hardy, E. M. Wright)

Yamamoto, K.

[64] *On a conjecture of Erdös,* Memoirs Fac. Sci. Kyushu Univ. 18 (1964), 166–167.

[65] *On the Diophantine equation $\dfrac{4}{n} = \dfrac{1}{x} + \dfrac{1}{y} + \dfrac{1}{z}$,* Memoirs Fac. Sci. Kyushu Univ. 19 (1965), 37–47.

[66] *On a conjecture of Hasse concerning multiplicative relations of Gaussian sums,* J. Combin. Theory 1 (1966), 476–489.

Yokoyama, A.

[64] *On the Gaussian sum and the Jacobi sum with its application,* Tôhoku Math. J. 16 (1964), 142–153.

Yudina, G. E., Litver, E. L. (see E. L. Litver, G. E. Yudina)

Zagier, D., Gross, B. (see B. Gross, D. Zagier)

Zsigmondy, K.

[92] *Zur Theorie der Potenzreste,* Monatshefte Math. Phys. 3 (1892), 265–284.

Zuckerman, H. S.

[36] *New results for the number $g(n)$ in Waring's problem,* Amer. J. Math. 58 (1936), 545–552.

Subject index

Index of names

(Not included are proper names attached to mathematical terms like Waring's problem, Cauchy–Schwarz inequality, Brun–Titchmarsh theorem etc.)